SAILING THEORY AND PRACTICE

Translated from the Polish by
L. RUSIECKI
in collaboration with
MISS S. BARKER
J. BARKER
A. Q. CHAPLEO
R. G. WOODS

Oh, who can tell, save he whose heart hath tried,
And danced in triumph o'er the waters wide,
The exulting sense—the pulse's maddening play,
That thrills the wanderer of that trackless way?

Lord Byron, "The Corsair"

SAILING THEORY AND PRACTICE

C. A. MARCHAJ

Illustrated with drawings by the author and photographs

DODD, MEAD & COMPANY NEW YORK

To Jana—
my inspiring teacher—
this work is dedicated.

Library of Congress Catalog Card Number: 64-13694
Printed in the United States of America

AUTHOR'S PREFACE

The theory and the practice of sailing are undoubtedly uneasy bedfellows.

Even when both are working to reach the same end, their relationship is full of suspicion and distrust.

In the past, this state of affairs has been due mostly to lack of scientific data on the parameters which define a yacht's behavior. Consequently, yacht design and helmsmanship are still inclined to be based on intuitive art rather than on science resulting from systematic research.

In this book, I have attempted to bridge this gap between theory and practice, as I believe that the theoretical approach can be of immediate practical use to boat designers, to sailmakers, and most of all to the men who sail.

It is not difficult for me to foresee that, in trying to wed theory and practice by means of a book called *Sailing Theory and Practice,* I am laying myself open to attack from both pure scientists and hardy practical sailors (as I have written the book in such a way that both can understand it).

One could even add that dealing with the theory of yacht behavior is risky in itself, as sailing boats naturally belong to the fair sex and are, therefore, largely unpredictable, their behavior being very difficult to analyze indeed. However, I have always found this trait particularly fascinating and attractive, and it encouraged me to take an interest in this problem.

While I was trying in some way to answer the questions how and why in order to reveal the secrets of a yacht's performance, I always bore in mind the warning of a great expert on this subject, Joseph Conrad, who said, "Of all the living creatures upon land and sea, it is ships alone that cannot be taken in by barren pretenses, that will not put up with bad art from their masters."

When I wrote this book, I was in the very fortunate position of having the encouragement of many friends in England, America, and Poland.

Leon Jensz, a gallant Polish regatta sailor, largely inspired this work, the first edition of which was published in Poland. It was based on a series of lectures I gave to yachtsmen and later to the Polish Academy of Physical Education in Warsaw. I am also very much indebted to Prof. D. Tilgner of Gdansk Polytechnic for his friendly support on many occasions.

I should like to express my utmost gratitude to Professor E. J. Richards and my supervisor, Thomas Tanner, for the excellent facilities and help they gave me while I was a research assistant in the Aeronautics Department at the University of Southampton. I have to confess that, thanks to them, I had great pleasure in initiating research on large-scale soft sails in the wind tunnel, and in this way I was able to confirm experimentally many of the ideas about sail efficiency and yacht performance which I got during my career as a regatta helmsman.

I am deeply indebted to my translator, L. Rusiecki, who in collaboration with Miss S. Barker, J. Barker, A. Q. Chapleo, and R. G. Woods prepared the English translation. I wish to express my gratitude particularly to Mr. Jeremy Barker, for the time he gave to checking, and to Miss Susan Barker, who so charmingly gave her generous and invaluable help in polishing the English typescript, and who introduced me to some of the secrets of the English language.

I should also like to thank H. M. Barkla, Col. C. E. Bowden, C. E. Dickerson, A. Farrar, B. Hayman, M. Henderson, W. G. Lucas, Gen. J. Parham, D. Phillips-Birt, J. C. Sainsbury, P. Spens, and E. G. van de Stadt of Holland for the help they gave me in their various ways; and there are many others whose names are mentioned in the list of references.

I must also acknowledge the exceptional patience with which my publishers, Dodd, Mead & Company, waited for the typescript.

Finally, I should perhaps add that although the English edition of *Sailing Theory and Practice* was prepared while I was a research assistant at the University of Southampton, and I frequently refer to experiments carried out there, the Aeronautics Department is not guilty of the ideas and opinions I express, which are my own responsibility.

C. A. MARCHAJ

Southampton University
England
October, 1962

CONTENTS

PHOTOGRAPH CREDITS

Courtesy of Morris Rosenfeld, New York: pages 81, 83, 99, 111, 134, 151, 166, 167, 176, 183, 189, 226, 238, 264, 285, 342, 344, 358, 389, 390.

Courtesy of Beken & Son, Cowes, England: pages 160, 165, 168, 175, 185, 188, 222, 223, 257, 261, 266, 304.

Courtesy of *Yachting World,* London: page 175.

Courtesy of Baker Manufacturing Company, Evansville, Wisconsin: page 306.

PART I

YACHTS AND RATING FORMULAS

1. EVOLUTION OF THE YACHT AND MEASUREMENT FORMULAS

Both men and ships live in an unstable element, are subject to subtle and powerful influences and want to have their merits understood, rather than their faults found out.

J. Conrad, *The Mirror of the Sea*

Evolution of yachts specifically for the purposes of sport and recreation developed comparatively recently, namely in the second half of the nineteenth century. The prototype yachts were small pilot boats which were adapted for the use of sailing enthusiasts.

One of the first craft built as a racing yacht was *America,* designed by G. Steers, famous for his construction of the pilot schooners *Mary Taylor* and *Cooper,* two very fast craft.

In a race in 1851 around the Isle of Wight, *America* beat fifteen of the best English yachts, and her success revolutionized current views on hull design, rigging, and sail cut. This meeting was the forerunner of the America's Cup Races, which have exerted a great influence on the over-all development of yachting.

Regattas at that time were open, without handicap for size and without time allowance. The first yacht crossing the finishing line was the winner.

In the first of the America's Cup Races, sailed over American waters, a condition of entry was that measurement of the yachts should be made according to "the Customs House Rule of the country to which the vessel belongs." This condition was the result of past experience that the speed of sailing is a consequence of a yacht's size. It was well known that the larger and longer yachts sailed faster than the smaller and shorter. There was therefore a marked tendency toward building larger yachts when the competitive element entered the sphere of pleasure sailing.

Once the significance of the size of a yacht had been realized, it was concluded that to equalize the chances of the competing crews, it was necessary either to limit entry to one size of yacht or to give a time handicap based on size. Since yachts were of different proportions, rigging, and sail area (one-designs did not exist), there arose the difficult question of how to measure and classify yachts according to their maximum possible attainable speed.

The history of the last hundred years of yachting is to a considerable extent the history of the quest for measuring formulas to classify yachts. We shall examine the evolution of several past measuring formulas so as to understand their principles and their great influence on the design of yachts.

D. Phillips-Birt, in his excellent book *An Eye for a Yacht,* says that the current "system of measurement has a more profound effect on the shape of yachts than the sea in all its moods. . . . The yacht is an artificial product, and an eye for a yacht, like an eye for the finer points of a painting, depends on a knowledge of the circumstances which produced it."

In initial attempts to apply measuring formulas it was thought that displacement (tonnage) could supply an adequate criterion of a yacht's rating. Hence the first formulas were based on the Customs House Rule defining displacement of merchant vessels by fundamental measurements of the hull.

Let us examine two British measurement formulas valid during 1854–1886, the time of formation of a traditional type of British yacht.

$$\frac{(L - B) \times B \times \frac{1}{2}B}{94} = \text{tons}$$

$$\frac{(L + B)^2 + B}{1730} = \text{tonnage, or rating}$$

The formulas were made up of the yacht's length, L, and breadth (beam), B. Their solution gave the rating of a yacht expressed in tons. Yachts of equal tonnage were supposed to have equal racing chances. If the tonnages were different, time corrections or allowances expressed in seconds per ton per mile were applied. Building yachts to be raced under such formulas, designers soon reached the conclusion that the length of the hull was the deciding factor in developing speed. It was quite easy to deduce that for two yachts of equal length, the faster, under the rules, would be the one having the greater ratio L/B, namely the finer yacht. Since the formulas highly taxed broad yachts, designers were compelled to look for something to replace the stability lost in reducing the beam. Hence the weight and draft of the hull were increased, and since they were not included in the formulas, the yacht's rating was not affected. It is apparent that a rating formula definitely inspires designers in a specific direction. In England, the general tendency was to construct yachts of small beam and large draft, very heavy, with a large sail area and a ratio $L/B \cong 6$.

Initially, American formulas were similar, but in 1882 they were radically altered by the introduction of the sail area (S_A) instead of the boat's beam (B). The sail area was becoming the second most important factor governing speed. Formulas at that time:

$$\text{Seawanhaka Yacht Club formula} = \frac{L \times S_A}{4000} \text{ “sail tons” (1882)}$$

$$\text{New York Yacht Club formula} = \frac{L \times \sqrt{S_A}}{2} \text{ R.L. (racing length)(1890)}$$

encouraged designers to construct broad and light hulls, since the dimension B, which was not included in the factors controlling the rating of a yacht, could be increased to achieve necessary transverse stability. Lighter, shallow-draft hulls could be driven by smaller sail areas. The above formulas were entirely responsible for the traditional American-constructed yacht, so different from its English counterpart, which has persisted until the present time.

A considerable part in the evolution of the yacht has been played by advances in the knowledge of hydrostatics and dynamics. This knowledge, by being in advance of the current measurement rule, has frequently inspired designers to find loopholes in the rule whereby to construct a successful yacht.

In the late 1880's, as a result of experiments carried out by the distinguished scientist W. Froude, attention was drawn to the significance of hull friction. A new school of designers endeavored to decrease the submerged area of the hull, on which depended frictional resistance. The starting point of their efforts was the English yacht *Jullanar* (Fig. 1), built in 1875 by F. M. Bentall. This yacht was a splendid example of ingenious evasion of the measurement formula. By moving the sternpost well forward, the constructor decreased the effective hull length, L, which was measured according to the requirements of the rule between the stem and stern posts. This gave him an advantage over the traditional yachts with plumb sternposts, as had *America* (Fig. 1), since the yacht had a smaller rating for the same hull waterline length.

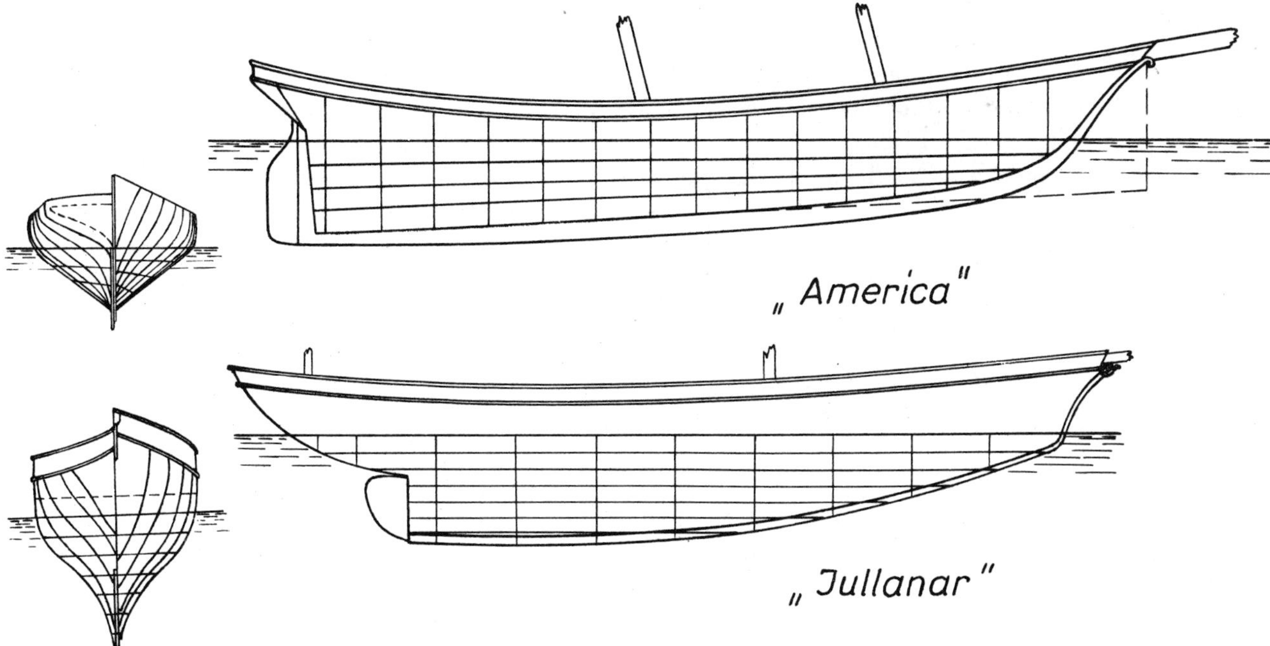

Fig. 1. *America* (G. Steers, 1850) and *Jullanar* (F. M. Bentall, 1875)

The introduction of the overhanging stern compelled the yacht designers to cut away the forefoot to preserve a balance of lateral areas.

The submerged area of the hull was considerably reduced, which gave a corresponding reduction in frictional resistance. The immersed part of a hull is a solid of a certain form, which can be described by the ratio of the surface area to its volume. It is a known fact that a ball has the least ratio of area to volume. If the form of a solid is elongated, this ratio is increased, which means that for yachts of given displacement, the friction area of the immersed hull will be greater for the longer yacht. The introduction of the overhanging stern by F. M. Bentall not only caused a radical decrease in the ratio of friction area to displacement, but also improved the shape of the hull waterline. Moreover, owing to the reduced underwater length of the hull, and the concentration of the yacht's mass about its center of gravity, its maneuverability was considerably improved. Concentration of the buoyancy midway between bow and stern increased the draft, giving more efficient generation of side force and hence smaller drift. The excellent race record of *Jullanar* is a vindication of the use of Froude's theory.

Aiming at further reductions in frictional resistance, the English designer G. L. Watson constructed in 1887 the yacht *Thistle,* with a strongly slanting sternpost (Fig. 2).

The concepts of Bentall and Watson were next improved by a Scottish designer, W. Fife, about 1888, on his famous yacht *Minerva.* Relative to her length she had considerable draft and a low center of gravity; hence she was able to carry a large sail area (Fig. 3).

Simultaneously in the United States, a similar tendency to reduce the hull's frictional area was expressed in a different way. As an example, one can take the centerboard yacht *Volunteer* by E. Burgess. He considered that a yacht should present a large side area when beating to windward, so that drift would be a minimum. On the other hand, when reaching, this large side area would not be desirable, since it would only increase friction. His solution to the problem was the introduction of an adjustable centerboard (Fig. 4). In the fifth, sixth, and seventh America's Cup races, the Burgess-constructed centerboard yachts *Puritan*, *Mayflower*, and *Volunteer* were in turn successful winners, amply justifying his concept.

In the initial stages of the evolution of the yacht, external ballast below the keel was not employed. Ballast was arranged inside the hull and was usually in the form of cast-iron blocks or chain stowed between the frames. A heavy hull could also partly fulfill this function, while shifting ballast or a numerous crew were not unknown on lighter yachts. According to the recollection of W. P. Stephens, in one race on Long Island Sound a yacht used water bags, which were filled by powerful pumps when she came on the wind and were emptied overboard on the run.

The artifice of shifting ballast, usually in the form of sand or shot bags, to the windward side considerably increased transverse stability, thus allowing a larger sail area to be carried and a greater speed developed. Nevertheless sailing opinion

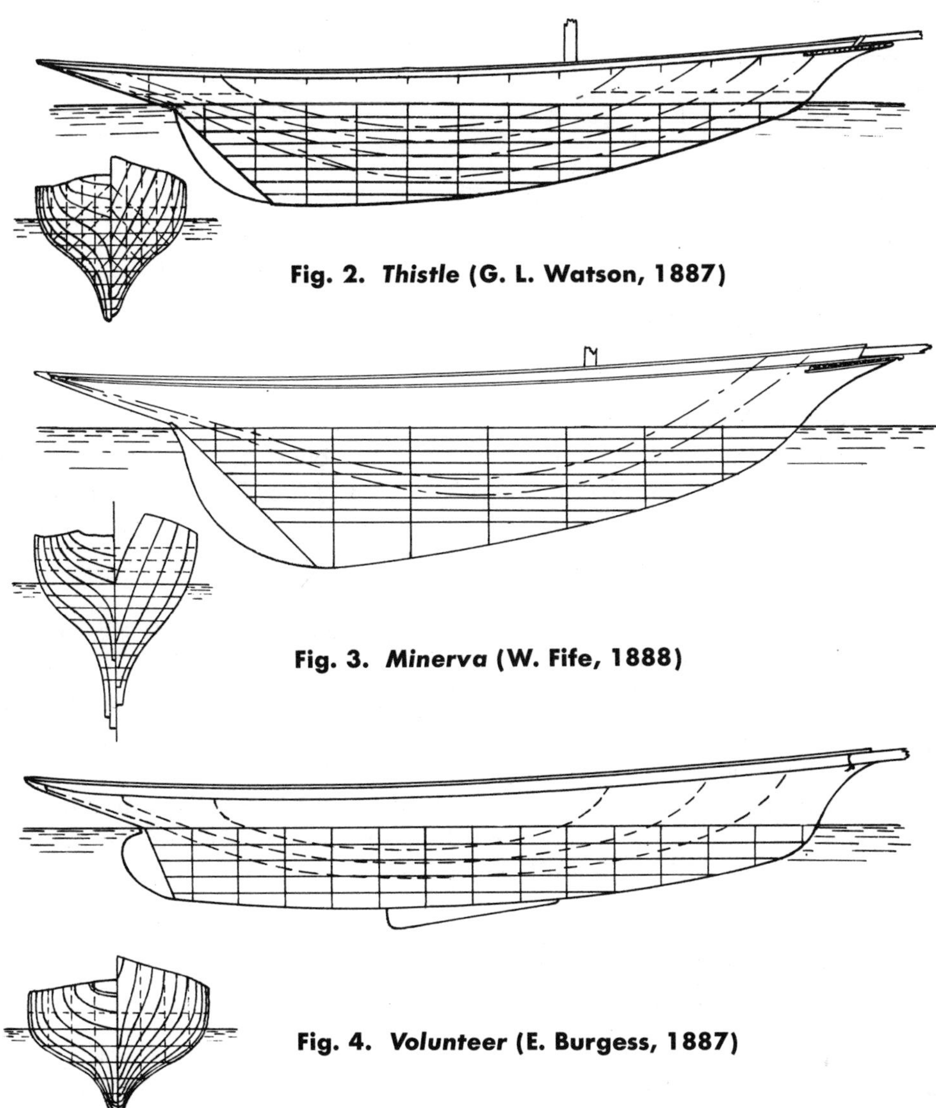

Fig. 2. *Thistle* (G. L. Watson, 1887)

Fig. 3. *Minerva* (W. Fife, 1888)

Fig. 4. *Volunteer* (E. Burgess, 1887)

declared against the use of shifting ballast. The question thus became a moral one, and to quote the same W. P. Stephens: "The possibilities for the undetected evasion of the rule against shifting ballast in the larger yachts had a detrimental effect on the ethics of the sport, and the evils of sandbag racing were accentuated by the absentee ownership of wealthy men who stood on the dock and backed their yachts by heavy wagers, while hired professionals held the stick and shifted the bags."

The prohibition of using shifting ballast, first introduced in England and later in America, compelled designers to search for different means of achieving stability. This helped, partly, the development of a new concept: the application of external ballast below the keel. The novelty was not accepted unanimously, and many experts declared against the increase of the weight suspended from the keel. On this topic we can quote two notable opinions. In 1853 Vanderdeekens wrote in

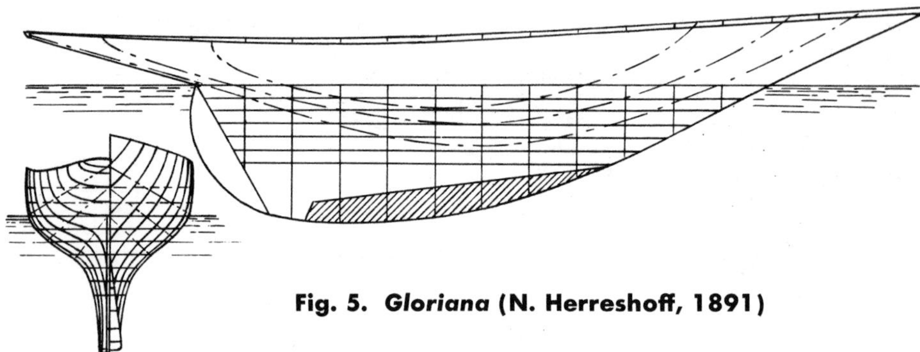

Fig. 5. *Gloriana* (N. Herreshoff, 1891)

Yachts and Yachting, "We should remember that the more metal we cram into a yacht's intestines, the more we destroy her buoyancy and elasticity in a seaway." Also, in the treatise *Yacht Architecture* by Lord Robert Montague (1850) we may find the following injunction: "Wherever the ballast is stowed, it should, above all things, be placed upon springs; in order to make it alive, and not dead weight."

Eventually external ballast was recognized as a suitable device following the successes of *Gloriana*, built in 1891 by N. Herreshoff (Fig. 5). By introducing lead ballast, suspended low down, and a full hull above the waterline, the designer achieved a relatively large transverse stability. He was, therefore, able to increase sail area and hence obtained greater speed.

The appearance of Herreshoff's yacht was the end of the search for an ideal hull, and her principles of design are still in force today. Thus designers finally reached the conclusion that the hull construction should be based on the optimum compromise between three factors:

1. Minimum resistance due to the form
2. Minimum frictional resistance
3. Maximum stability

Fig. 6. Comparison of Rigging of some America's Cup contestants. All drawn to the same scale.

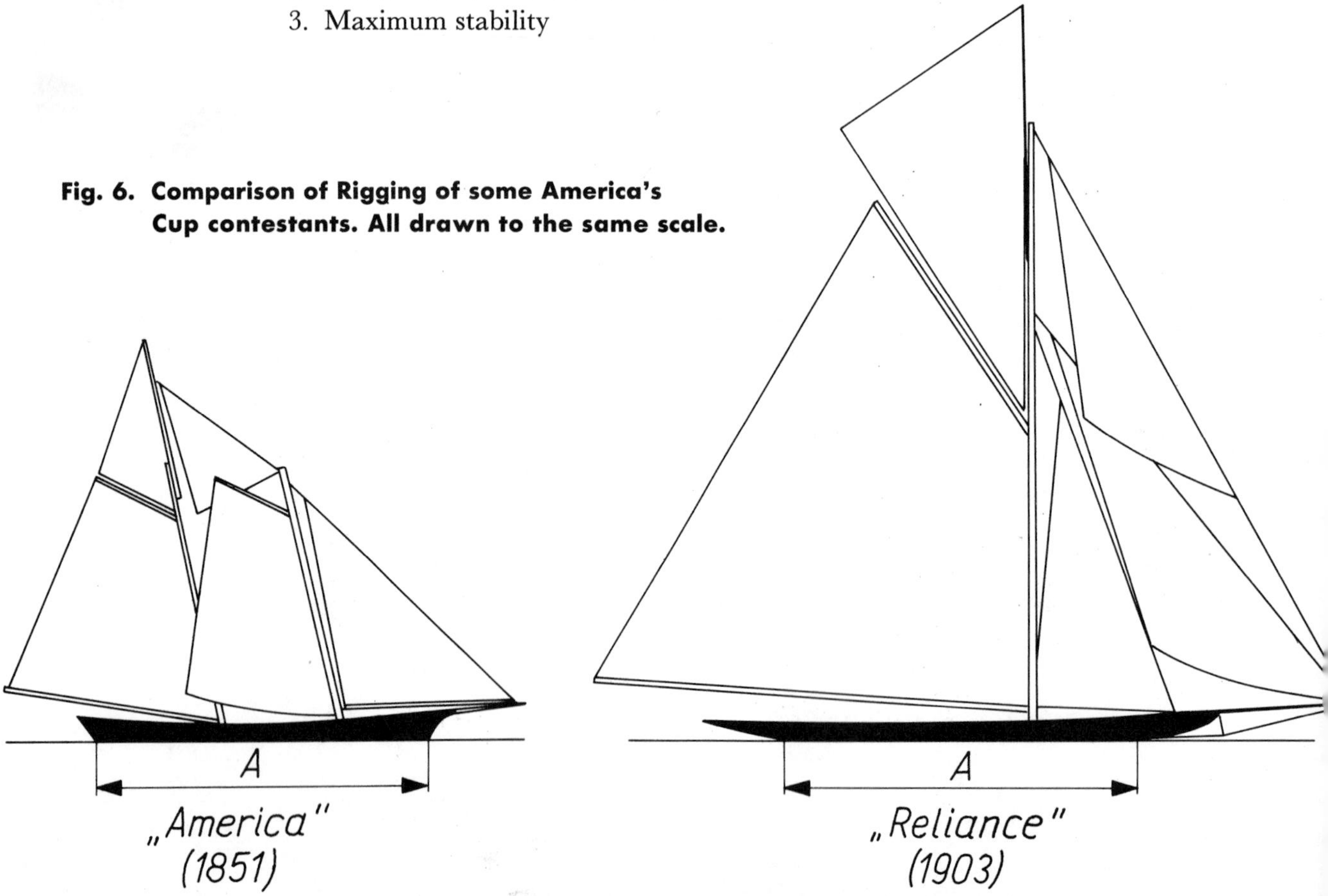

A

„America"
(1851)

A

„Reliance"
(1903)

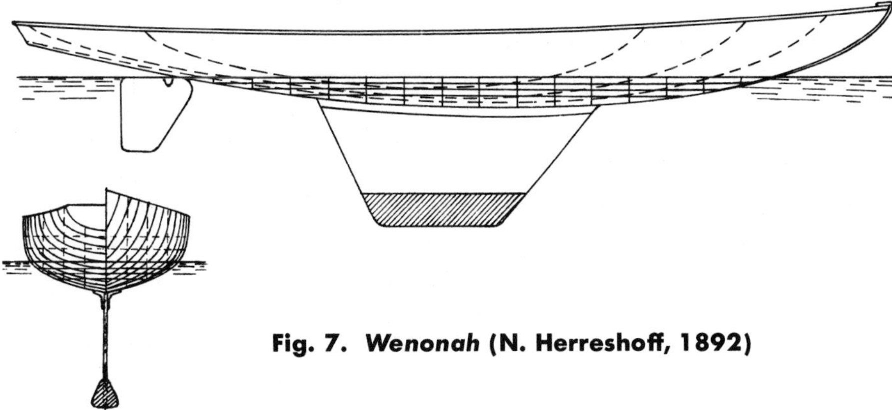

Fig. 7. *Wenonah* (N. Herreshoff, 1892)

These requirements are contradictory. A long and narrow yacht will naturally have a small form resistance, but at the same time little stability, and will not be able to carry much sail. The increase of stability through using heavy ballast will result in greater draft and a raising of frictional resistance and wavemaking. On the other hand, increasing stability by broadening the beam makes a yacht less slender, thus increasing form resistance. The task of the designer is that of the proper selection of a "golden medium" from conflicting requirements. *Gloriana's* hull form was an example of splendid intuition on the part of the designer, and contemporary designers have been able to improve very little on Herreshoff's work.

Certain progress which followed later was mainly due to improvements in the aerodynamic efficiency of the sails (see Fig. 6).

The racing success of *Gloriana's* external ballast was also responsible for a short-lived type of yacht called, in jest, "skimming dishes." A typical example of the type was *Wenonah*, built by Herreshoff in 1892 (Fig. 7). She possessed the characteristics of light-displacement, centerboard and ballast yachts, and was light and stable.

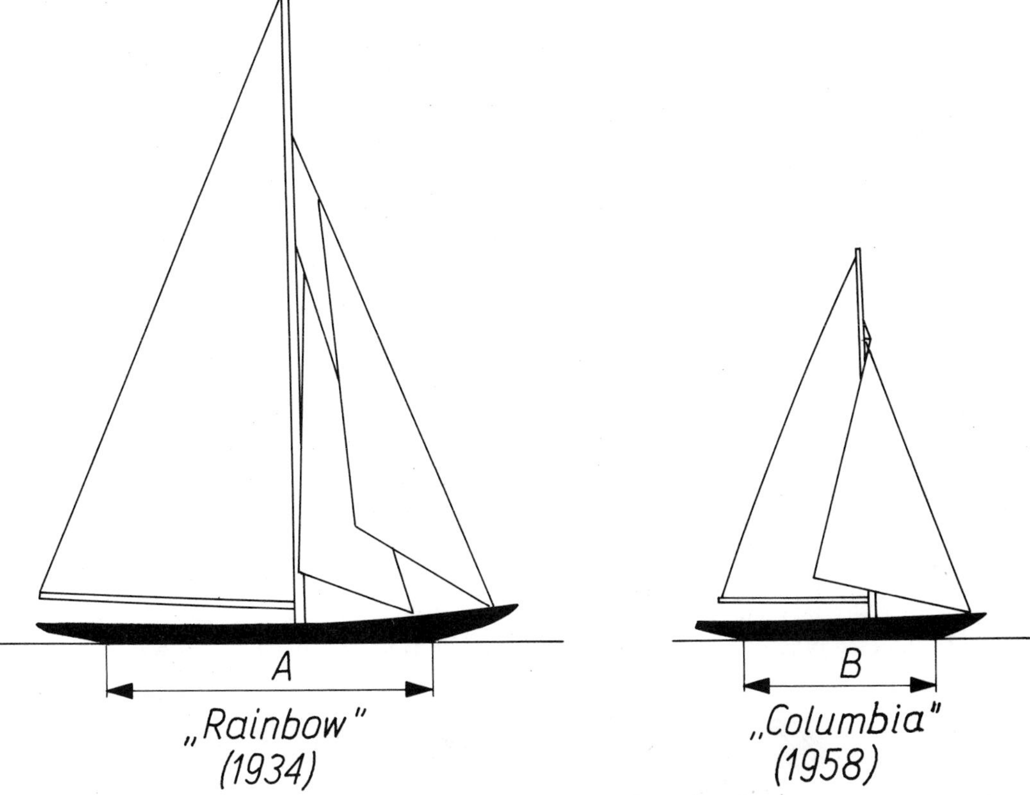

Fin-keel yachts with bulb ballast were unmatched in speed and in beating to windward. Their reputation was established mainly in short races, as they were not suitable for living aboard for any length of time. The secret of their success was attributed to the evasion of the measurement formula.

With the advent of the bulb keel, great stability was achieved by means of a profiled lead mass fixed at the bottom of a deep steel fin. In the pursuit of performance, the weight of the hull was being reduced, superstructure was removed, freeboard lowered, thin planking employed, etc. So developed the skimming dish, being light and fast, open and dangerous to sail.

Many yachtsmen were opposed to this unhealthy tendency, and in 1896 action was taken by R. F. Froude. He proposed that a good yacht should aim at comfort, be fast, habitable, and safe.

During a Y.R.A. (Yacht Racing Association) conference, a new Linear Rule for classifying yachts was accepted. Its object was to encourage fullness of the hull, with living accommodation below deck and safe sailing. The formula had the following form:

$$\text{Rating} = \frac{L + B + \tfrac{3}{4}G + \tfrac{1}{2}\sqrt{S_A}}{2}$$

where L = length at waterline
B = maximum beam
G = skin girth at midship section from waterline to waterline
S_A = sail area

The calculated rating was expressed in feet or meters.

Yet this formula failed in its purpose. It was hoped that the measurement of girth, large for a shallow hull with a bulb keel, would prevent their construction and compel designers to build yachts of full form. The factor G increased the rating of bulb-keel yachts, placing them among the faster category of yachts (Fig. 8). However, the authors of this measurement formula had underestimated the ingenuity of designers, who managed to circumvent it and preserve the superiority of the shallow-hulled yacht. By introducing fillets between the hull and keel, and by lowering freeboard, they succeeded in reducing the penalties they were supposed to suffer from the new classification.

For the above reasons, a second Linear Rating Rule was introduced in 1901, and then in 1906 its modified version under the title of International Rule:

$$\text{Rating} = \frac{L + B + \tfrac{1}{2}G + 3d + \sqrt{S_A} - F}{2.5}$$

where F = freeboard
d = $G_p - G_n$

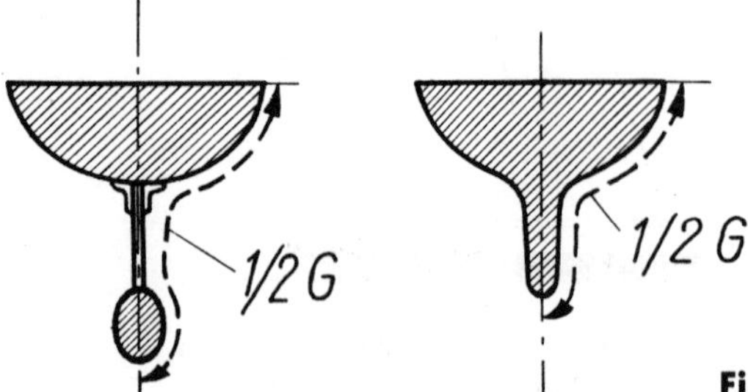

Fig. 8. Measurement of skin girth at midship section from waterline to waterline

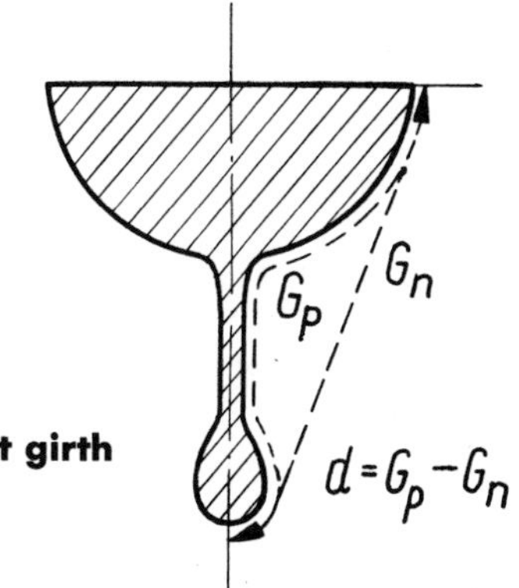

Fig. 9. Measurement of skin girth and apparent girth

The new factor d was the tax which had to be paid by the skimming dishes. It represented the difference between the girth measured on the surface of the hull, the "skin girth," and the apparent girth measured at the same section by means of a tape (Fig. 9). The measurement was taken at a distance of 6/10 waterline length from the bow. It can easily be seen that yachts having a full hull would have a smaller value of d, which, multiplied by three in the formula, would result in an advantageous rating in comparison with bulb-keel yachts of equal waterline length. Another beneficial factor was for a yacht to have a large freeboard.

After 100 years of development, measurement formulas are now very complicated as a result of two opposing aims.

1. To produce a mathematical formula based on knowledge and experience, which will indicate the racing value of a yacht, i.e., its possible speed performance, and encourage the development of seaworthy craft.
2. To construct the fastest craft, by detecting weak points in the formula and evading them even at the cost of unhealthy constructional features.

Contemporary measuring formulas by taking account of so many geometrical features of the hull and rigging limit the freedom of designers to the extent that yachts built on their basis tend to become one-design types.

Classical ballast yachts have reached certain constructional limits, strictly conditioned by their geometry, which one cannot hope to exceed. The maximum speed difference between yachts of the same rating may reach only a few per cent. In the future it will be still less. The factor that becomes more and more decisive in the outcome of a race is therefore the crew.

2. CONTEMPORARY MEASURING FORMULAS

The large yachts built at one time entirely for the purposes of racing, such as *Livonia,* the British challenger in the second America's Cup Race, carrying 18,153 sq. ft. of sail, have been replaced nowadays by relatively small cruiser/racers. As the name indicates, they are of dual purpose and can be sailed by small nonprofessional crews.

The measurement and classification of cruiser/racers are made according to one of the following, most popular rating rules:

A. International Cruiser/Racer Rule (C./R.)
B. Cruising Club of America Rule (C.C.A.)
C. Royal Ocean Racing Club Rule (R.O.R.C.)

(a) *C./R. Rule* is formulated so that the yachts are classified according to rating values of 7, 8, 9, 10.5, 12, 13.5, and 15 meters. Inshore, round-the-buoy races can be sailed within the same class without time corrections. The formulas can also be applied to offshore races with yachts of different classes by using time allowances stipulated by the R.O.R.C. Rule.

The International Cruiser/Racer Rule takes the following form:

$$\text{Rating} = \frac{L + \sqrt{S_A} - F \pm B \pm D \pm P + A \pm H + C - K}{2} \times P_f$$

in linear units, in meters or in feet, where

L = length in linear units
S_A = sail area in square units
F = freeboard in linear units
B = beam coefficient in linear units
D = draft coefficient in linear units
P = displacement coefficient in linear units
A = coefficient for overhangs at bow in linear units
H = coefficient for profile underwater
C = coefficient for abbreviated sterns in linear units
K = coefficient for iron keel in linear units
P_f = propeller factor

The rating depends primarily on $L + \sqrt{S_A}$. Each class has certain maximum and minimum values of the waterline length and associated minimum displacement. The limits to the length of waterline are as follows:

	Lower limit		*Upper limit*	
Class	*Meters*	*Feet*	*Meters*	*Feet*
7 Meter	7	22.97	7.40	24.27
8 Meter	8	26.25	8.35	27.40
9 Meter	9	29.53	9.45	31.00
10.5 Meter	10.5	34.45	11.20	36.74
etc.				

The normal or base displacement, P, shall not be less than:

Class	*In cubic meters*	*In cubic feet*
7 Meter	$(.2\ LWL + .19)^3$	$(.2\ LWL + .623)^3$
8 Meter	$(.2\ LWL + .19)^3$	$(.2\ LWL + .623)^3$
9 Meter	$(.2\ LWL + .18)^3$	$(.2\ LWL + .590)^3$
10.5 Meter	$(.2\ LWL + .16)^3$	$(.2\ LWL + .525)^3$
etc.		

For displacement greater than normal or base displacement, there shall be an allowance to be entered in the formula as $-P$. For displacement less than normal or base displacement, there shall be a penalty to be entered in the formula as $+P$.

The other factors thus ($\pm$) take their sign according to their values relative to certain basic values, in similar manner to the example given above.

The sail area is to be measured according to "instruction to measurers." The square root of the area so ascertained is to be multiplied by the rig factor (see table below) and entered in the formula as S_A. The area of the head sails is calculated from a formula for the area of the fore triangle:

$$\frac{I \times J}{2}$$

where: I is the distance from the top of deck at covering board to the point where the line of the aft side of the foremost forestay, on which a sail is set, cuts the mast

J is the distance from the fore side of the mast at main deck level to the point where the line of the aft side of the foremost forestay, on which a sail is set, cuts the deck, or bowspirit if one is fitted. (As an example see Fig. 14.)

Rig Allowance

Bermudian cutter and sloop	to sail at 100% $\sqrt{S_A}$
Bermudian yawl	to sail at 98% $\sqrt{S_A}$
Gaff cutter	to sail at 96% $\sqrt{S_A}$
Bermudian ketch and gaff yawl	to sail at 94% $\sqrt{S_A}$
Gaff schooner	to sail at 92% $\sqrt{S_A}$
Gaff ketch	to sail at 90% $\sqrt{S_A}$

(b) *C.C.A. Rule* has a structure similar to the C./R. formula.

$$\text{Rating} = 0.95(L \pm B_m \pm D_{ra} \pm D_{isp} \pm S_A \pm F - I) \times \text{Bal.R.} \times \text{Prop.}$$

The effect of the individual factors on the rating value is shown below:

Factor	*Symbol*	*Large*	*Small*
Beam	B_m	Credit	Penalty
Draft	D_{ra}	Penalty	Credit
Displacement	D_{isp}	Credit	Penalty
Sail area	S_A	Penalty	Credit
Freeboard	F	Credit	Penalty
Iron keel credit	I	Credit for boats having iron keel instead of lead keel	
Ballast ratio	Bal.R.	Penalty	Credit
Propeller factor	Prop.	More credit for large propeller, less for small	

The purpose of the C.C.A. formula is best understood by referring to the introduction in "Measurement Rule for Ocean Racing." The system developed over the years involves two major steps:

First, the creation of a table of time allowances based on the fact that, for boats of similar design, the theoretical speed increases with the length approximately in proportion to the square root of the waterline length. These time allowance tables, long ago standardized, appear in the yearbooks of the North American Yacht Racing Union, New York Yacht Club, and other organizations.

Second, the creation of a formula, or measurement rule, by which boats of differing hull form, rig, sail area, etc., may be rated in comparison with a standard design. For example, a sloop of 32-foot waterline in whose design, speed takes precedence over comfort may be rated as a 37-footer. On the other hand, a 42-foot waterline ketch, broad in beam and somewhat undercanvassed, may also be rated as a 37-footer. In giving the two boats equal ratings the expected increase in speed due to the increase in waterline length from 32 to 42 feet has been neutralized under the rule by the increased beam, decreased sail area, less efficient rig, etc., of the larger boat. The evaluation of the various factors is difficult and must be reconsidered from time to time on the basis of the actual results in ocean racing.

The Measurement Rule of the Cruising Club is concerned solely with the determination of the "rated length" of a boat. When that has been determined, then the time allowance tables are checked to determine the time allowance per mile. Knowing the rating of each boat in the race and length of the race (actual or assumed), each skipper may compute how much time he receives from, or has to give to, each of his competitors (see Table I, p. 16).

The way to use time allowance tables is illustrated in the following example:

Boat A Rating = 36.7 ft.
Boat B Rating = 42.3 ft.
Course length 675 nautical miles

As boat B allows boat A, subtract B allowance from A allowance.

Boat A allowance from table (for 36.7 ft.) = 180.19 seconds per mile
Boat B allowance from table (for 42.3 ft.) = 155.74 seconds per mile
24.45 seconds per mile

In the race 675 nautical miles,
B allows A, 675 × 24.45 seconds, or 4 hr. 35 min. 4 sec.

The tables are based upon assumption that, under average racing conditions, a yacht of rating measurement R, will sail one nautical mile in the number of seconds given by the formula:

$$\frac{2160}{\sqrt{R}} + 183.64$$

The allowance per mile between yachts of different ratings will, therefore, be given by:

$$\frac{2160}{\sqrt{r}} - \frac{2160}{\sqrt{R}}$$

in which R is the rating measurement of the larger yacht and r that of the smaller yacht.

The theoretical number of seconds required to sail one nautical mile under average conditions (as would be encountered in a triangular race) is obtained by adding 360 to the figure in the table opposite the yacht's rating measurement.

Table I

TIME ALLOWANCE TABLES

FOR ONE NAUTICAL MILE, IN SECONDS AND DECIMALS.

Rating	Allowance	Rating	Allowance	Rating	Allowance	Rating	Allowance
15.0	381.35	18.0	332.75	21.0	294.98	24.0	264.55
.1	379.49	.1	331.33	.1	293.87	.1	263.64
.2	377.65	.2	329.93	.2	292.76	.2	262.73
.3	375.83	.3	328.54	.3	291.65	.3	261.82
.4	374.03	.4	327.17	.4	290.56	.4	260.92
.5	372.26	.5	325.83	.5	289.48	.5	260.03
.6	370.50	.6	324.48	.6	288.40	.6	259.14
.7	368.76	.7	323.14	.7	287.33	.7	258.26
.8	367.03	.8	321.82	.8	286.26	.8	257.38
.9	365.31	.9	320.50	.9	285.20	.9	256.51
16.0	363.64	19.0	319.19	22.0	284.15	25.0	255.65
.1	361.97	.1	317.89	.1	238.10	.1	254.78
.2	360.31	.2	316.60	.2	282.07	.2	253.92
.3	358.66	.3	315.32	.3	281.04	.3	253.07
.4	357.02	.4	314.05	.4	280.02	.4	252.23
.5	355.39	.5	312.78	.5	279.00	.5	251.39
.6	353.79	.6	311.53	.6	277.99	.6	250.55
.7	352.21	.7	310.29	.7	276.99	.7	249.72
.8	350.64	.8	309.06	.8	276.00	.8	248.89
.9	349.08	.9	307.84	.9	275.01	.9	248.07
17.0	347.52	20.0	306.62	23.0	274.03	26.0	247.25
.1	345.99	.1	305.42	.1	273.06	.1	246.44
.2	344.47	.2	304.24	.2	272.09	.2	245.63
.3	342.96	.3	303.05	.3	271.13	.3	244.82
.4	341.46	.4	301.87	.4	270.17	.4	244.02
.5	339.97	.5	300.71	.5	269.22	.5	243.23
.6	338.50	.6	299.54	.6	268.27	.6	242.44
.7	337.04	.7	298.39	.7	267.33	.7	241.66
.8	335.60	.8	297.25	.8	266.40	.8	240.88
.9	334.17	.9	296.11	.9	265.48	.9	240.10
27.0	239.33	31.0	211.61	35.0	188.76	39.0	169.52
.1	238.56	.1	210.98	.1	188.24	.1	169.08
.2	237.79	.2	210.36	.2	187.72	.2	168.64
.3	237.03	.3	209.74	.3	187.20	.3	168.19
.4	236.27	.4	209.11	.4	186.68	.4	167.75
.5	235.52	.5	208.50	.5	186.17	.5	167.31
.6	234.78	.6	207.89	.6	185.65	.6	166.88
.7	234.04	.7	207.28	.7	185.15	.7	166.45
.8	233.30	.8	206.68	.8	184.64	.8	166.02
.9	232.57	.9	206.08	.9	184.14	.9	165.60
28.0	231.84	32.0	205.48	36.0	183.64	40.0	165.18
.1	231.11	.1	204.88	.1	183.14	.1	164.75
.2	230.39	.2	204.29	.2	182.64	.2	164.32
.3	229.67	.3	203.70	.3	182.15	.3	163.88
.4	228.95	.4	203.11	.4	181.66	.4	163.46
.5	228.24	.5	202.52	.5	181.16	.5	163.04
.6	227.53	.6	201.94	.6	180.67	.6	162.62
.7	226.82	.7	201.36	.7	180.19	.7	162.21
.8	226.12	.8	200.79	.8	179.71	.8	161.80
.9	225.43	.9	200.22	.9	179.23	.9	161.39
29.0	224.74	33.0	199.65	37.0	178.75	41.0	160.98
.1	224.05	.1	199.08	.1	178.27	.1	160.56
.2	223.37	.2	198.51	.2	177.79	.2	160.15
.3	222.68	.3	197.95	.3	177.31	.3	159.74
.4	222.00	.4	197.39	.4	176.83	.4	159.34
.5	221.33	.5	196.83	.5	176.36	.5	158.93
.6	220.66	.6	196.27	.6	175.90	.6	158.52
.7	219.99	.7	195.72	.7	175.43	.7	158.12
.8	219.32	.8	195.17	.8	174.96	.8	157.73
.9	218.66	.9	194.63	.9	174.50	.9	157.33
30.0	218.00	34.0	194.09	38.0	174.04	42.0	156.93
.1	217.34	.1	193.54	.1	173.58	.1	156.53
.2	216.70	.2	193.00	.2	173.12	.2	156.13
.3	216.05	.3	192.46	.3	172.67	.3	155.74
.4	215.40	.4	191.92	.4	172.21	.4	155.35
.5	214.75	.5	191.38	.5	171.76	.5	154.96
.6	214.11	.6	190.85	.6	171.30	.6	154.57
.7	213.48	.7	190.32	.7	170.84	.7	154.19
.8	212.85	.8	189.79	.8	170.40	.8	153.80
.9	212.23	.9	189.28	.9	169.96	.9	153.42

TIME ALLOWANCE—*Continued.*

Rating	Allowance	Rating	Allowance	Rating	Allowance	Rating	Allowance
43.0	153.04	47.0	138.71	51.0	126.10	55.0	114.90
.1	152.66	.1	138.38	.1	125.81	.1	114.64
.2	152.28	.2	138.05	.2	125.51	.2	114.37
.3	151.90	.3	137.71	.3	125.21	.3	114.11
.4	151.52	.4	137.38	.4	124.92	.4	113.84
.5	151.14	.5	137.05	.5	124.62	.5	113.58
.6	150.76	.6	136.73	.6	124.33	.6	113.32
.7	150.38	.7	136.40	.7	124.04	.7	113.05
.8	150.01	.8	136.07	.8	123.76	.8	112.79
.9	149.65	.9	135.74	.9	123.47	.9	112.53
44.0	149.28	48.0	135.41	52.0	123.18	56.0	112.27
.1	148.91	.1	135.08	.1	122.89	.1	112.01
.2	148.54	.2	134.76	.2	122.60	.2	111.75
.3	148.17	.3	134.44	.3	122.32	.3	111.49
.4	147.80	.4	134.11	.4	122.03	.4	111.24
.5	147.43	.5	133.79	.5	121.74	.5	110.99
.6	147.07	.6	133.47	.6	121.45	.6	110.74
.7	146.71	.7	133.16	.7	121.17	.7	110.49
.8	146.35	.8	132.85	.8	120.89	.8	110.24
.9	145.99	.9	132.54	.9	120.61	.9	109.99
45.0	145.64	49.0	132.22	53.0	120.33	57.0	109.74
.1	145.28	.1	131.90	.1	120.05	.1	109.49
.2	144.92	.2	131.58	.2	119.77	.2	109.24
.3	144.56	.3	131.27	.3	119.50	.3	108.99
.4	144.20	.4	130.96	.4	119.22	.4	108.74
.5	143.85	.5	130.64	.5	118.94	.5	108.49
.6	143.50	.6	130.33	.6	118.67	.6	108.24
.7	143.15	.7	130.03	.7	118.39	.7	108.00
.8	142.80	.8	129.72	.8	118.12	.8	107.76
.9	142.46	.9	129.42	.9	117.85	.9	107.52
46.0	142.12	50.0	129.12	54.0	117.58	58.0	107.28
.1	141.78	.1	128.81	.1	117.31	.1	107.03
.2	141.43	.2	128.50	.2	117.04	.2	106.78
.3	141.08	.3	128.20	.3	116.77	.3	106.52
.4	140.74	.4	127.89	.4	116.50	.4	106.28
.5	140.39	.5	127.58	.5	116.23	.5	106.04
.6	140.04	.6	127.28	.6	115.96	.6	105.80
.7	139.70	.7	126.98	.7	115.69	.7	105.56
.8	139.37	.8	126.68	.8	115.43	.8	105.32
.9	139.04	.9	126.39	.9	115.16	.9	105.08
59.0	104.84	63.0	95.78	67.0	87.52	71.0	79.99
.1	104.60	.1	95.56	.1	87.32	.1	79.80
.2	104.36	.2	95.34	.2	87.12	.2	79.62
.3	104.12	.3	95.12	.3	86.92	.3	79.44
.4	103.89	.4	94.91	.4	86.73	.4	79.26
.5	103.66	.5	94.70	.5	86.54	.5	79.08
.6	103.42	.6	94.49	.6	86.35	.6	78.90
.7	103.19	.7	94.27	.7	86.16	.7	78.72
.8	102.96	.8	94.06	.8	85.97	.8	78.54
.9	102.73	.9	93.85	.9	85.78	.9	78.37
60.0	102.50	64.0	93.64	68.0	85.59	72.0	78.20
.1	102.26	.1	93.43	.1	85.40	.1	78.02
.2	102.03	.2	93.22	.2	85.21	.2	77.84
.3	101.80	.3	93.01	.3	85.02	.3	77.66
.4	101.57	.4	92.80	.4	84.83	.4	77.48
.5	101.34	.5	92.59	.5	84.64	.5	77.30
.6	101.11	.6	92.38	.6	84.45	.6	77.13
.7	100.88	.7	92.17	.7	84.26	.7	76.96
.8	100.66	.8	91.97	.8	84.07	.8	76.79
.9	100.43	.9	91.76	.9	83.88	.9	76.62
61.0	100.21	65.0	91.55	69.0	83.69	73.0	76.45
.1	99.98	.1	91.34	.1	83.50	.1	76.27
.2	99.76	.2	91.14	.2	83.31	.2	76.10
.3	99.53	.3	90.94	.3	83.12	.3	75.93
.4	99.30	.4	90.73	.4	82.93	.4	75.76
.5	99.07	.5	90.53	.5	82.74	.5	75.59
.6	98.84	.6	90.32	.6	82.55	.6	75.42
.7	98.62	.7	90.12	.7	82.36	.7	75.25
.8	98.40	.8	89.92	.8	82.17	.8	75.08
.9	98.18	.9	89.72	.9	81.99	.9	74.91
62.0	97.96	66.0	89.52	70.0	81.82	74.0	74.74
.1	97.74	.1	89.32	.1	81.63	.1	74.57
.2	97.51	.2	89.12	.2	81.44	.2	74.39
.3	97.29	.3	88.92	.3	81.25	.3	74.22
.4	97.07	.4	88.72	.4	81.07	.4	74.05
.5	96.85	.5	88.52	.5	80.89	.5	73.88
.6	96.64	.6	88.32	.6	80.71	.6	73.72
.7	96.42	.7	88.12	.7	80.53	.7	73.55
.8	96.20	.8	87.92	.8	80.35	.8	73.39
.9	95.99	.9	87.72	.9	80.17	.9	73.23

(c) *R.O.R.C. Rule* is:

$$\text{Rating} = \frac{0.15L\sqrt{S_A}}{\sqrt{BD}} + 0.2(L + \sqrt{S_A}) \pm \text{stability allowance}$$
$$- \text{propeller allowance} + \text{draft penalty}$$

where L = rated length
B = rated beam
D = rated depth
S_A = rated sail area

Apart from beam, B, which is a straight forward measurement of the greatest breadth to outside of the normal planking, the other factors, L, D, S_A, are obtained by calculation from a number of various measurements.

R.O.R.C. formula can be used as a basis for handicapping round-the-buoy and also passage offshore races. It is usual that the races are subdivided into three classes according to rating as follows:

Class I	above 30.0 ft. (9.15 m.)
Class II	24.0–30.0 ft. (7.3–9.15 m.)
Class III	19.0–24.0 ft. (5.8–7.3 m.)

Differences between yachts can be corrected by handicaps based on time allowances. A time correction is applied to a yacht's elapsed time over any course of any distance, the formula being:

$$E \times (\text{T.C.F.}) = \text{corrected time}$$

where E = elapsed time

$$\text{T.C.F.} = \text{time correction factor} = \frac{\sqrt{R} + 2}{10}$$

Example: A yacht of rating R = 25 feet covers a course in 50 hr. 20 min. 10 sec.

$$\text{T.C.F.} = \frac{\sqrt{25} + 2}{10} = 0.7000$$

Corrected time = 50 hr. 20 min. 10 sec. × 0.7000
= 35 hr. 14 min. 7 sec.

Figure 10 shows the chart enabling rapid calculation of the time allowance for 1 hour with respect to the competing yachts. As an example, compare a yacht of 25-ft. rating, whose T.C.F. is 0.7000, with two yachts of T.C.F. 0.6500 and 0.7500 respectively.

To win the race:

1. With a yacht of T.C.F. = 0.6500, she must better her time by 4½ min. per hour of sailing

Fig. 10. R.O.R.C. time allowance

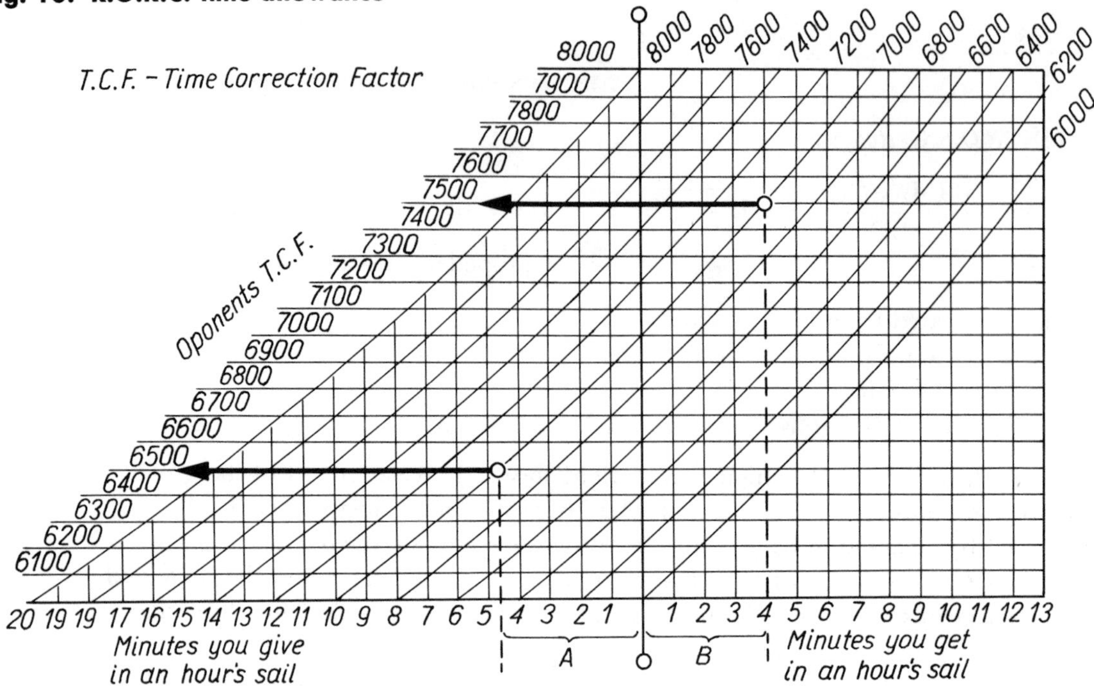

2. With a yacht of T.C.F. = 0.7500, she may lose up to 4 min. per hour of sailing.

Figures 11 and 12 show *Mouse of Malham* and *Carina,* belonging to the third and first R.O.R.C. classes respectively. *Mouse of Malham,* an oceangoing cruiser/racer yawl built in 1954–1955, is an example of a light-displacement vessel with a high ratio of sail area to displacement.

Her dimensions are:

Length over-all	LOA	32 ft. (9.75 m.)
Length waterline	LWL	24 ft. (7.3 m.)
Beam	B	8 ft. (2.43 m.)
Draft	D	5 ft. 9 in. (1.75 m.)
Displacement	Δ	2.4 tons (2440 kg.)
Ballast		0.94 tons (955 kg.)
Sail area (measured)	S_A	260 sq. ft. (29 m.^{2})

The interesting feature of the underwater part of her hull is an iron fin keel, being a compromise between a centerboard and a ballast keel. A separate fin and rudder is suspended abaft the keel.

A yacht of small displacement is considerably cheaper than a traditional keel yacht of the same length. At the same time a light yacht will not require a large sail area to maintain a satisfactory speed.

Uffa Fox said of *Carina* (Fig. 12): "One of the bravest boats to sail the Seven Seas." With a splendid racing record, having twice won the Transatlantic Race (1955 and 1957), *Carina* is considered one of the most successful cruiser/racers ever built. Designed by P. L. Rhodes, she is a yawl of similar conception to that of *Volunteer,* a keel/centerboard yacht.

Fig. 11. *Mouse of Malham* (J. H. Illingworth, 1954–1955)

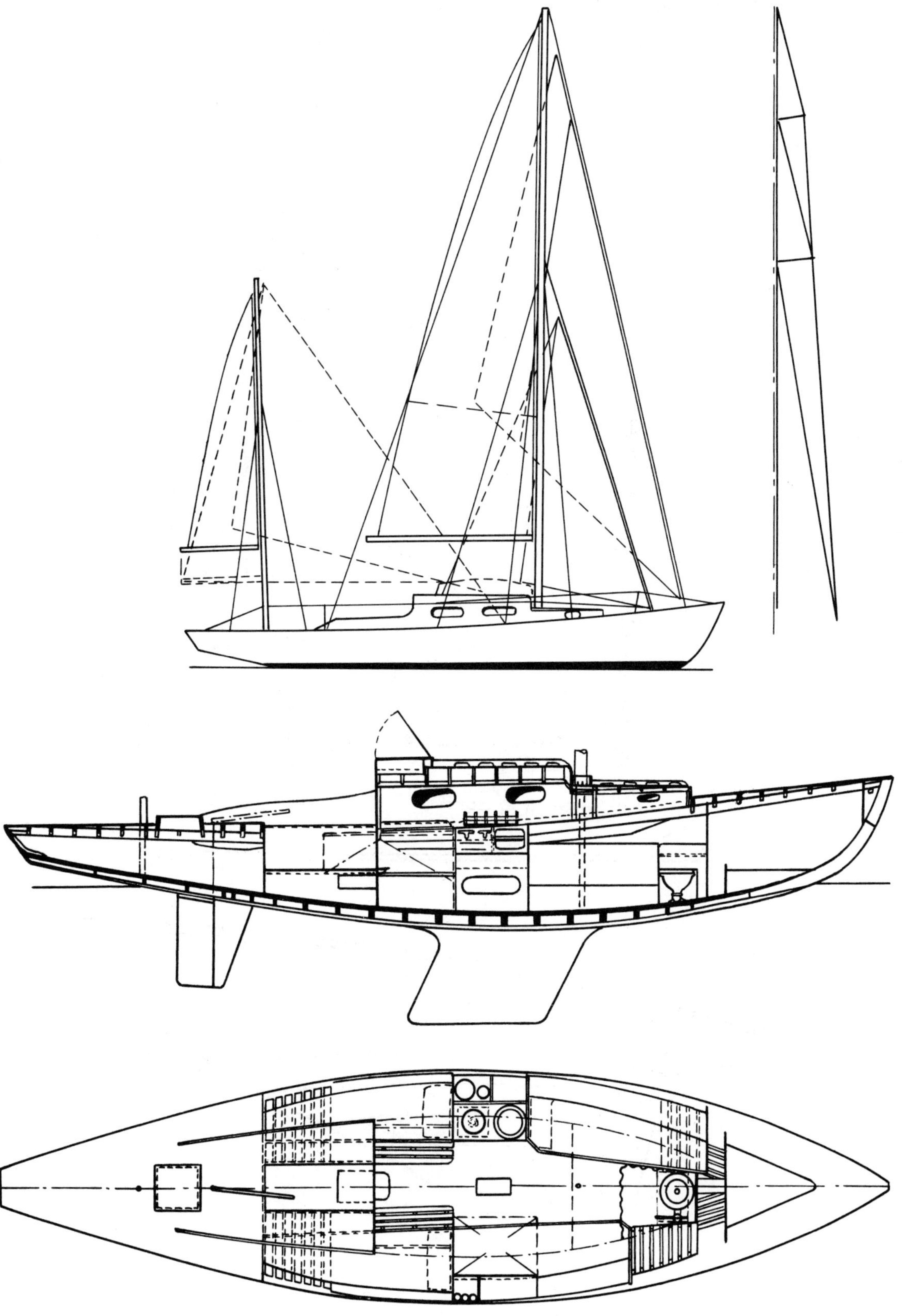

Fig. 12. *Carina* (P. L. Rhodes, 1955)

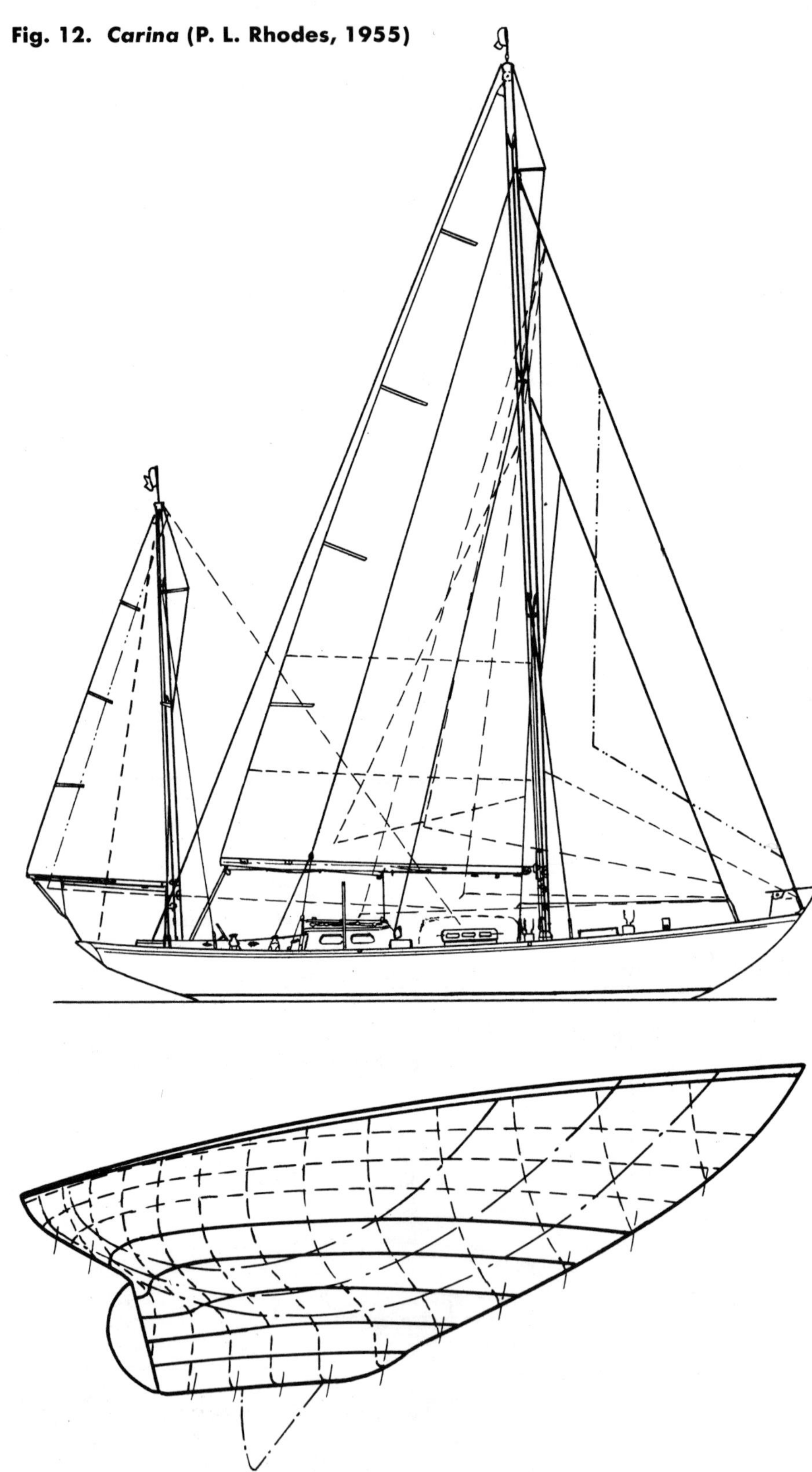

Her dimensions are:

Length over-all	LOA	53 ft. 6 in. (16.16 m.)
Length waterline	LWL	36 ft. 6 in. (11.04 m.)
Beam	B	13 ft. (3.96 m.)
Draft	D	6 ft. (1.82 m.) or 10 ft. (3.04 m.)
Displacement	Δ	14 tons (14,200 kg.)
Sail area	S_A	1,194 sq. ft. (110.92 m.^{2})

Such a solution to the problems of hull design is quite popular in the United States, where a considerable proportion of cruisers are of the centerboard type. Their consistent successes in many races forced the C.C.A. Measurement Rule Committee to introduce a correction to the formula. An amendment was made in which 1 sq. ft. of centerboard lateral plane area was to be considered equivalent to 2 sq. ft. of keel area.

In 1950, there was formed in England an association called the Junior Offshore Group (J.O.G.) whose aim was to popularize small, offshore yachts below R.O.R.C. Class III. Yachts built to the J.O.G. formula must satisfy certain safety conditions. Their LWL must be in the range 16–24 ft. and their rating 12–19 ft.

An instance of their capabilities is provided by *Sopranino* (Fig. 13), which sailed the Atlantic in 28½ days.

Measurements of *Sopranino:*

LOA	19 ft. 8 in.	(6 m.)
LWL	17 ft. 6 in.	(4.95 m.)
Beam	5 ft. 4 in.	(1.67 m.)
Draft	3 ft. 8½ in.	(1.12 m.)
Sail area	160 sq. ft.	(14.9 m.^{2})
Displacement	0.69 tons	(700 kg.)

It seems that yachts of the J.O.G. class have very bright prospects; they are inexpensive and hence within the means of many sailing enthusiasts. Their owners can enjoy the charms of long sea voyages and have the opportunity of participating in offshore races. Their seaworthiness has been demonstrated many times by racing and cruising yachtsmen.

Fig. 13. *Sopranino* (L. Giles, 1951)

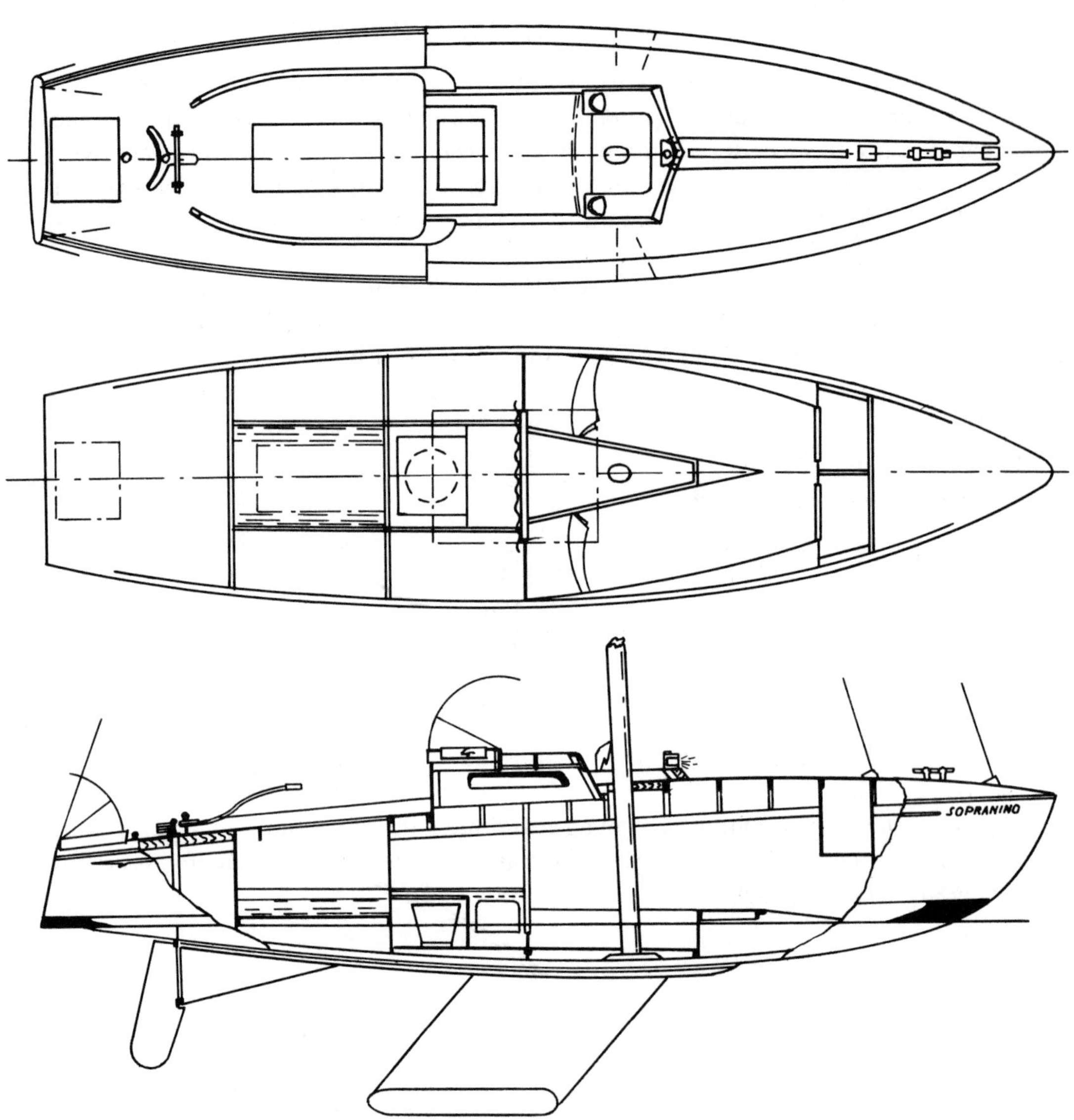

3. INTERNATIONAL RACING CLASSES

The number of different types of yachts sailing today, on inland waters and the seas over the world, is considerable, and their profusion testifies to the variation in specific water conditions in different countries and to the continuously changing needs, the traditions, and level of technical progress of their peoples. From the constructional point of view, all racing yachts can be divided into three types:

1. Free
2. Restricted
3. One-design

They differ one from another in the degree of restriction of their designs by constructional and dimensional rules and regulations. Clearly the closest limits are imposed on the one-design classes, since their prime object is to test the competing helmsmen and crews when sailing nominally identical boats. In the remaining two types some latitude, to a greater or lesser extent, is allowed the designers, builders, and even crews to improve the racing capabilities of their yachts. From the variations allowed in the rules, free and restricted classes contribute enormously toward technical progress, as has been demonstrated throughout the history of yachting.

The more successful classes are promoted by the I.Y.R.U. as International Classes. They are fostered by special institutions whose aims are to guide their development, guard the measurement and construction rules, to organize international races, etc.

It would be outside our scope to discuss the large variety of international classes,

Table II. Classes Competing in Olympic Games

Year	Class									
	R-12	R-10	R-8	R-7	R-6	R-5-5	*Star*	*Dragon*	Centerboard 2 persons	Centerboard 1 person
1900			X		X					
1908	X	X	X	X	X					
1912	X	X	X		X					
1920	X	X	X		X					X
1924		X			X					X
1928		X			X					X
1932		X			X		X			X
1936		X			X		X			X
1948					X		X	X	X	X
1952					X	X	X	X		X
1956						X	X	X	X	X
1960						X	X	X	X	X

and therefore we shall select the most important which participate in World Championships, Olympic Games, and international races.

Class R-5.5. Yachts of the R-class were introduced to the Olympic Games in 1900. From Table II we can see the tendency toward reducing the size of racing yachts. For instance, the smallest class, R-6, in the 1900 Olympics became the largest in 1952, and in 1956 was replaced by the smaller and cheaper class, R-5.5. The cost of the racing yacht R-12 in 1928 was about $125,000 (£25,000); at the same time a yacht of the R-6 class was valued at around $5,500 (£1,100). It was therefore possible to build twenty-three R-6 class yachts for the price of one R-12 yacht.

The R-5.5 (Fig. 14) is a restricted type, and the only Olympic class which is "constructional," giving designers some scope for improvements. The racing value of this yacht is expressed by the following formula:

$$0.9\left(\frac{L \times \sqrt{S_A}}{12 \times \sqrt[3]{\nabla}} + \frac{L + \sqrt{S_A}}{4}\right) = \text{not more than 5.5 m. or 18.04 ft.}$$

where L = length of the yacht, including some factors for the shape of the bow and stern, in m. or ft.

S_A = "measured" sail area in m.^{2} or sq. ft.

∇ = displacement, in m.^{3} or cu. ft.

Thus, yachts in the R-5.5 class can differ amongst one another in LWL, displacement, and sail area. The formula controls these parameters in such a way that if the LWL is increased, without any change in displacement, then the

Fig. 14. R-5-5 class

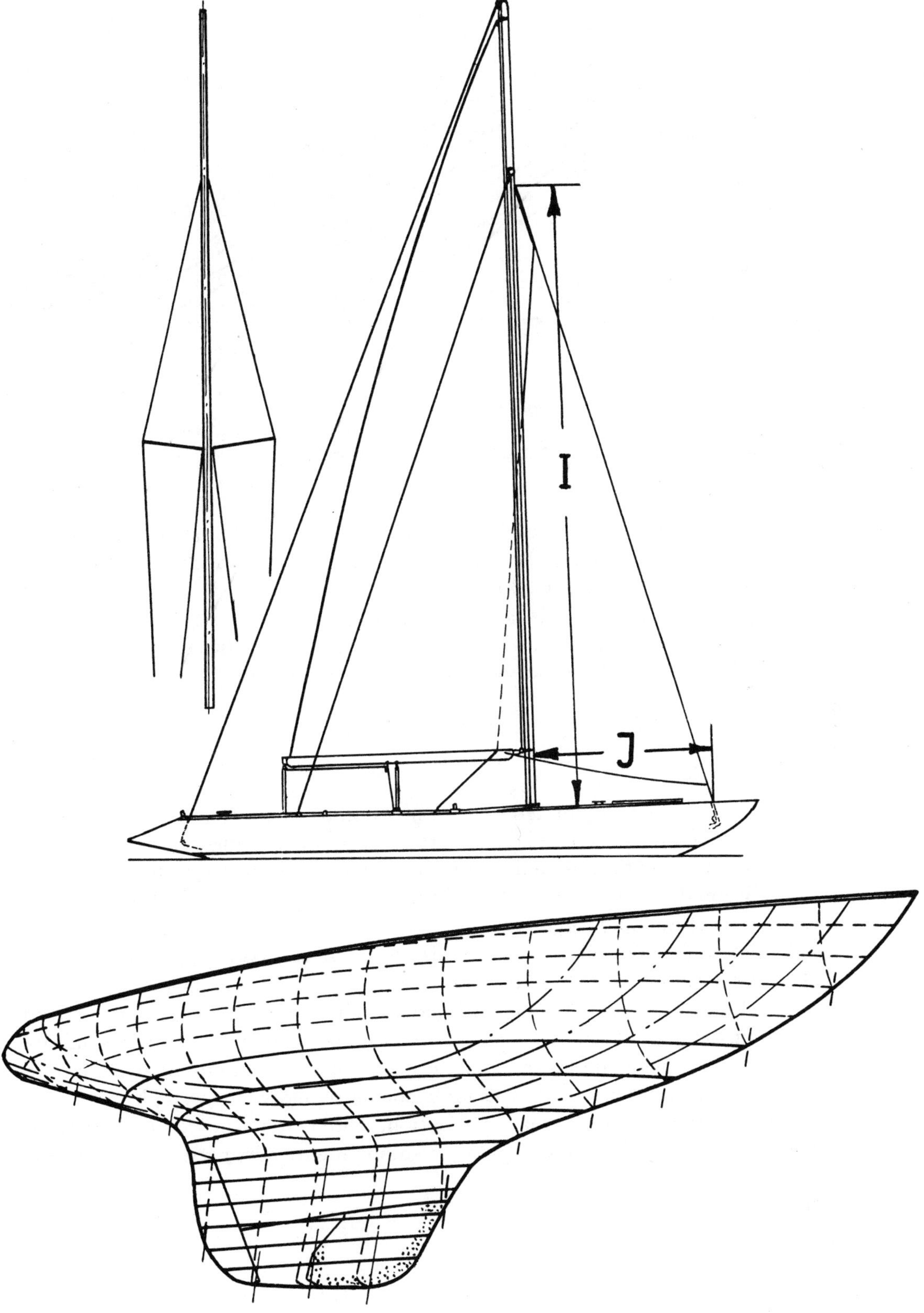

Fig. 15. Geometric restriction between sail area, length and displacement in 5.5 Meter class

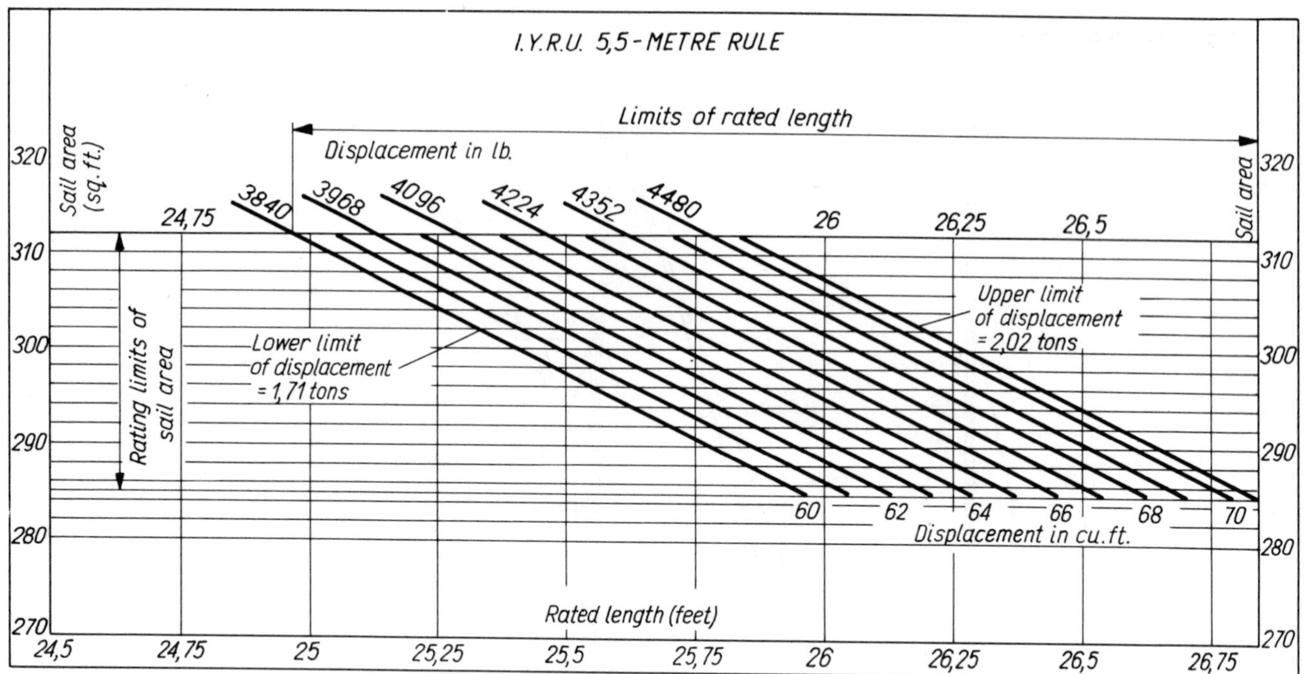

sail area must be decreased, and so on. The graph in Fig. 15 explains the geometric restrictions confronting the designers. The rules of this class also limit the minimum beam to 1.9 m. (6.23 ft.).

Within the framework of the formula, it is possible to construct yachts having very different properties. The following example demonstrates this, showing two boats of which "A" was built for heavy weather, and "B" for light.

	L(ft.)	∇(cu. ft.)	S_A(sq. ft.)
Yacht A:	26.75	70	286
Yacht B:	25.00	60	311

Star Class (Fig. 16) originated in the United States in 1911, and before becoming popular as an international class, underwent a series of changes and modifications in the twenties and thirties, mainly affecting her rigging (such as a change from gaff rig to Bermudian). Unlike the R-5.5, she is a one-design, with tightly controlled dimensions of hull and rigging.

At present, about 3500 boats of this class sail on coastal and inland waters all over the world. Since 1932 they have taken part in Olympic Games.

The Star is a classic racing yacht, demanding from the two-man crew the utmost in sailing efficiency, physical strength, and seamanship. Their adjustable rigging, within wide limits, and flexible spars allow a continuous variation of the aerodynamic properties of the sails for each course and wind strength.

Sailing in Stars gives great satisfaction, and this is the main reason why they enjoy such an immense popularity among highly advanced helmsmen. They

Fig. 16. Star class (designed by Francis Sweisguth who was working for W. Gardner)

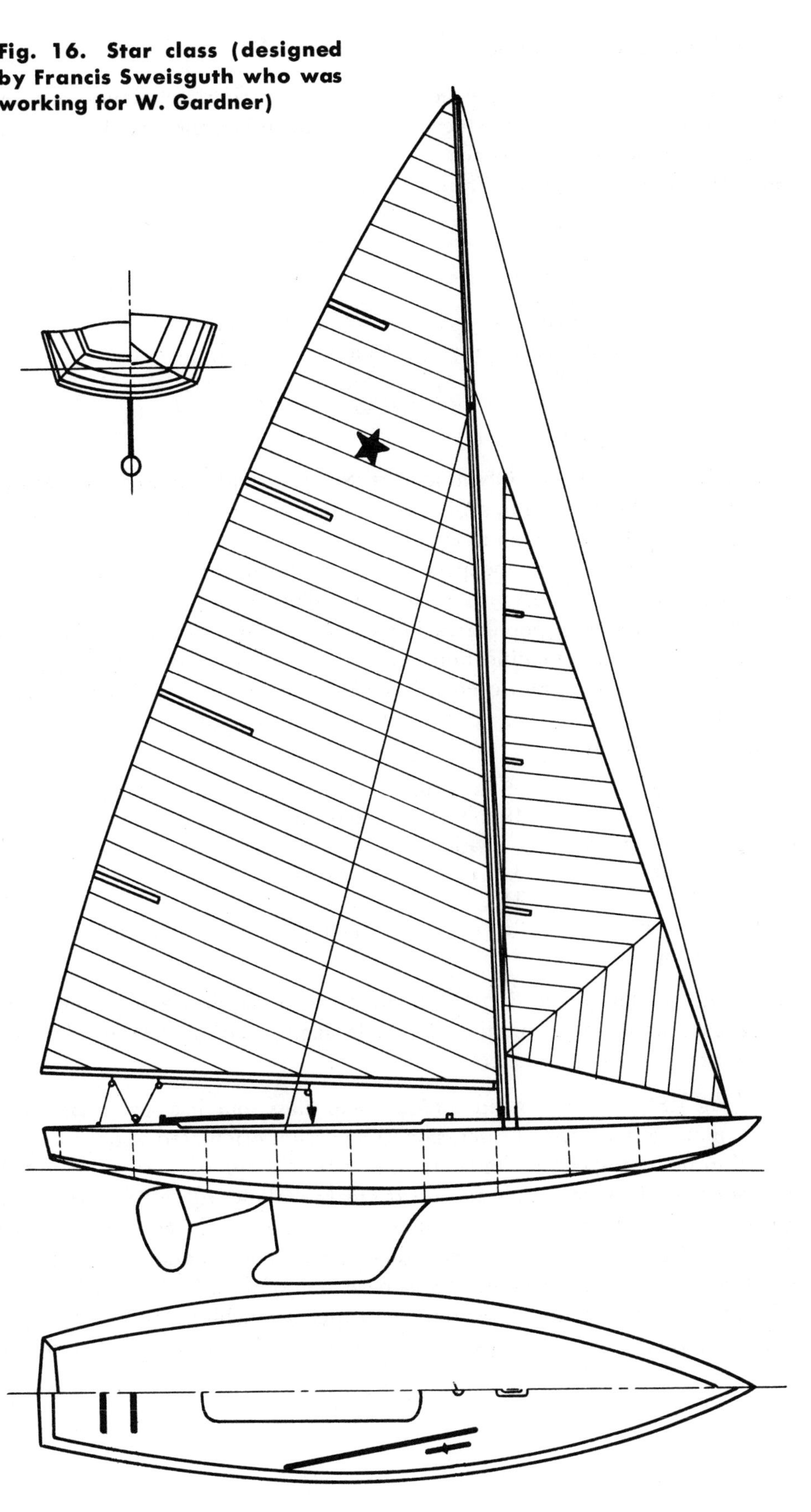

have played a great part in the advancement of racing techniques, and many progressive ideas were first introduced on Stars, including the flexible mast, which flattens out the sail in strong winds.

Star's dimensions (designer—Francis Sweisguth):

LOA	22 ft. 9 in.	6.9 m.
LWL	15 ft. 6 in.	4.8 m.
Beam (max.)	5 ft. 9 in.	1.7 m.
Draft	3 ft. 4 in.	1.05 m.
Displacement	1765 lb.	830 kg.
Ballast	900 lb.	408 kg.
Sail area	281 sq. ft.	26 m.^{2}
Crew	2	

Dragon (Fig. 17) is also an Olympic class. She is a small ballast yacht (designed by J. Anker), and evolved into an international class from a similar type used on the Great Lakes of America and Canada.

Originally considered as an inexpensive boat mainly used for cruising, the Dragon was transformed into a fairly expensive one-design racing yacht of high quality, becoming one of the most popular racing keel classes in Europe. The class regulations allow only small modifications in the arrangement of various gear and gadgets. The shape, size, and even the specific weight of the sails are all strictly controlled.

Dragon's dimensions:

LOA	29 ft. 2½ in.	8.91 m.
LWL	18 ft. 8½ in.	5.66 m.
Beam (max.)	6 ft. 4 in.	1.95 m.
Draft	3 ft. 11½ in.	1.16 m.
Displacement	4480 lb.	2032 kg.
Sail area	235½ sq. ft.	22 m.^{2} excluding spinnaker
Crew	3	

In racing, similar to the Star class, the Dragon requires a high standard of crewing to obtain the best from the adjustable rigging and the sheeting of the three sails (mainsail, jib and spinnaker).

Scow (Fig. 18). This is not an international class, but has several interesting features, making it worthy of discussion. The design originated about forty years ago, and in many respects is similar to that of the "skimming dishes." The hull is built from the lightest materials and is extremely shallow with a flat bottom. They are capable of high speed when sailing slightly heeled, in consequence of the wetted area, large when upright, becoming greatly reduced and of the increase of the waterline length with a simultaneous reduction of waterline beam.

The Scow is certainly a fine example of a racing machine, built on the idea of maximum possible speed for a specified water length. In "one-of-a-kind" races sailed by representatives of the fastest types of boats, including "catamarans," the first place in the over-all, without handicap, classification was taken by a 38 ft. Class A Scow, with speeds up to 28 knots.

Another Scow, 28 ft. long from Class E, sailing on an equilateral triangular course during the Ninth North American Sailing Championships, maintained an average speed of 8.44 knots in a 10–12 m.p.h. wind. For comparison, we can recall that the 46-ft. America's Cup defender *Columbia,* on a similar triangular course, and with a 12–17 m.p.h. wind, averaged 7.8 knots.

Boats of the Scow class are usually ballasted by the crew, whose total weight is

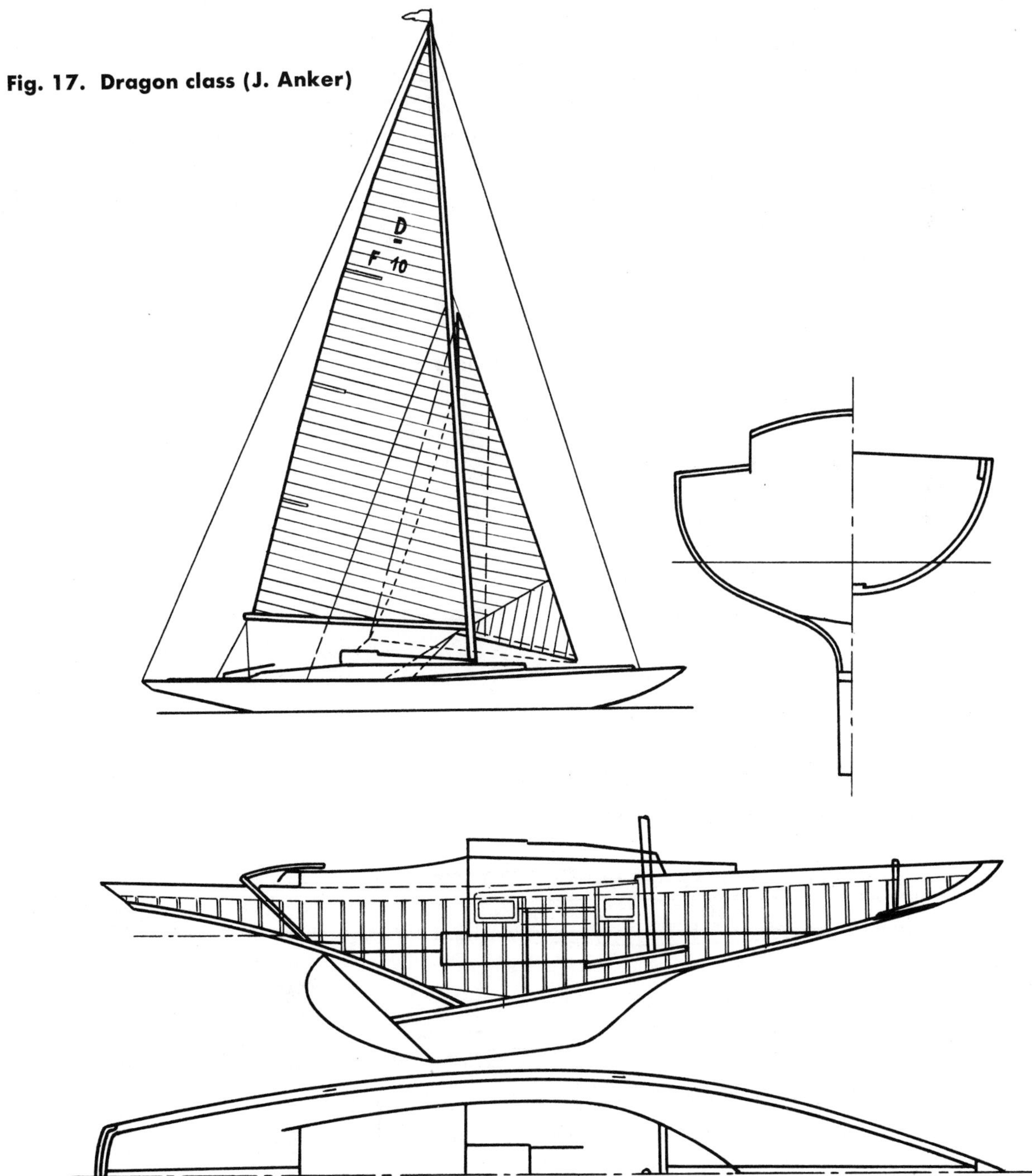

Fig. 17. Dragon class (J. Anker)

controlled by the rules of the class. The larger Scows have twin centerboards (bilge boards) and twin rudders.

Besides the A and E classes already mentioned, there are also two classes, C and D, both 28 ft. long. Class C is cat rigged and Class D sloop rigged.

Finn (Fig. 19), which is strictly a one-design boat, was designed by Rickard Sarby in 1950, and introduced as a singlehanded class into the Olympic Games of 1952 at Helsinki. Thanks to the high quality of this class, it was accepted for the Olympics of 1956 and 1960, and has been proposed for 1964.

The elongated bow, with its carefully designed profile, causes a minimal bow wave, but, on the other hand, the narrow stern poses difficulties when starting to plane.

The rigging is the most unusual feature. The sail, of 107.6 sq. ft. (10 m.^{2}) is carried by an unstayed mast, free to rotate in its step under the turning moment from the boom. Its flexibility helps to keep the sail flat when beating. The boom is rigidly attached to the mast, instead of through a gooseneck, which reduces twist in the sail, particularly when sailing off the wind. This type of rigging has the advantages of being exceptionally simple and having at the same time a high aerodynamic efficiency.

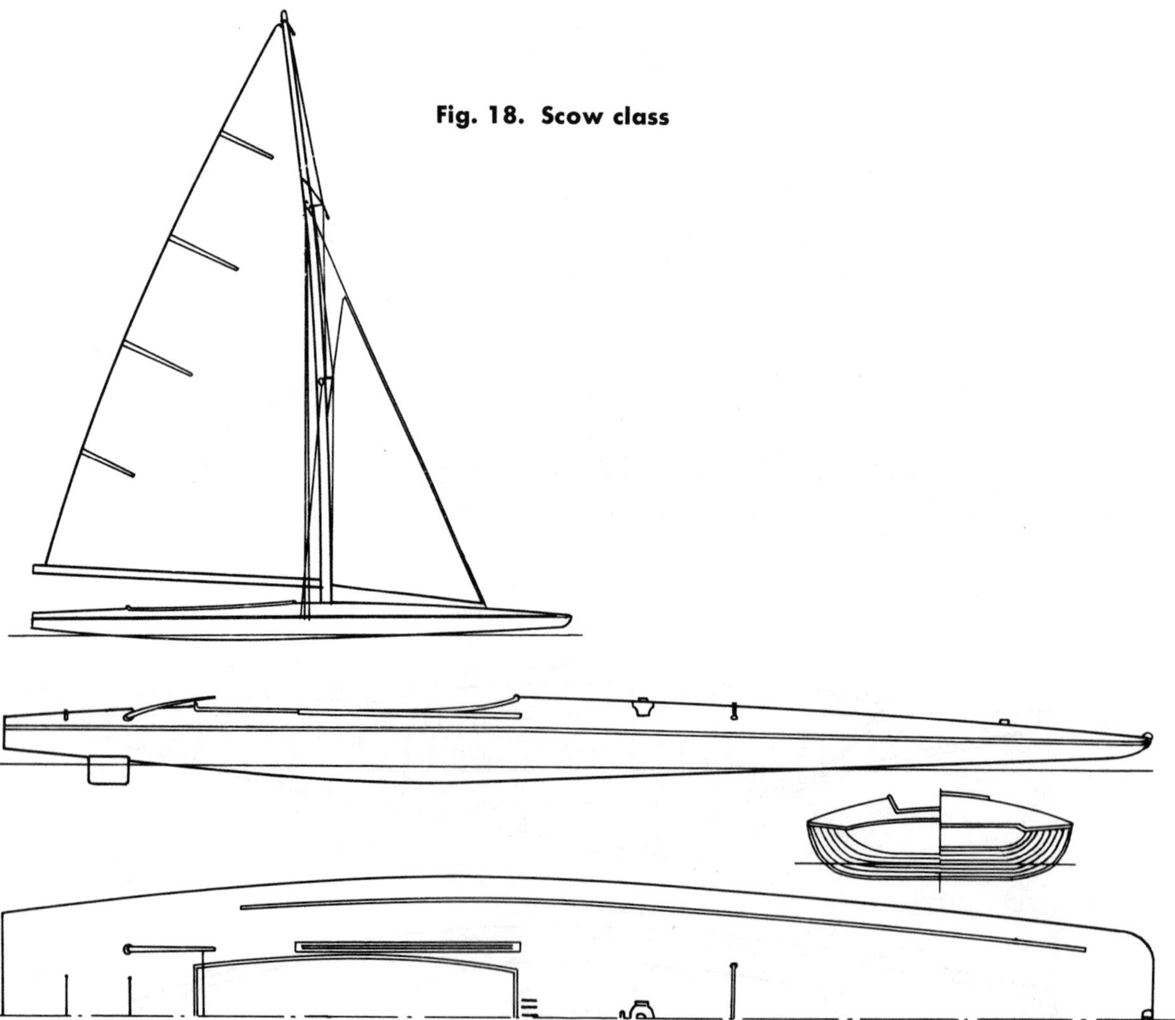

Fig. 18. Scow class

Since the Finn is a strict one-design, the most important race-winning factor is the helmsman, particularly how he uses himself as ballast. The World Champion, Paul Elvstrom, during the Helsinki Olympics, used a special fixture to hold his feet when sitting-out. With his legs and feet protected from the excessive pressure by thick woollen stockings, he could bring his whole body outboard and thus achieve considerably greater lateral stability.

Finn's dimensions:

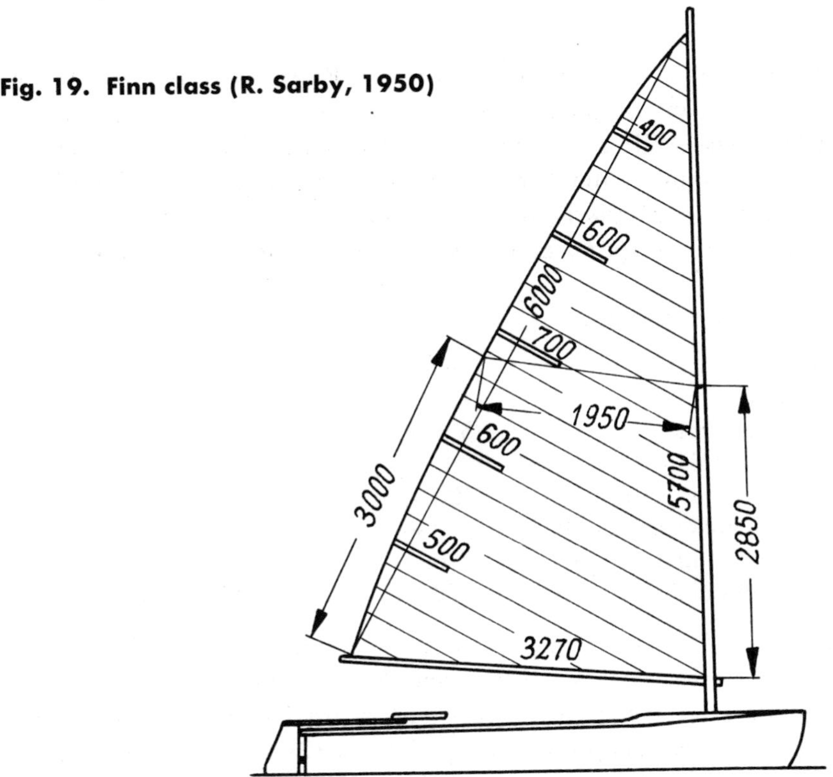

Fig. 19. Finn class (R. Sarby, 1950)

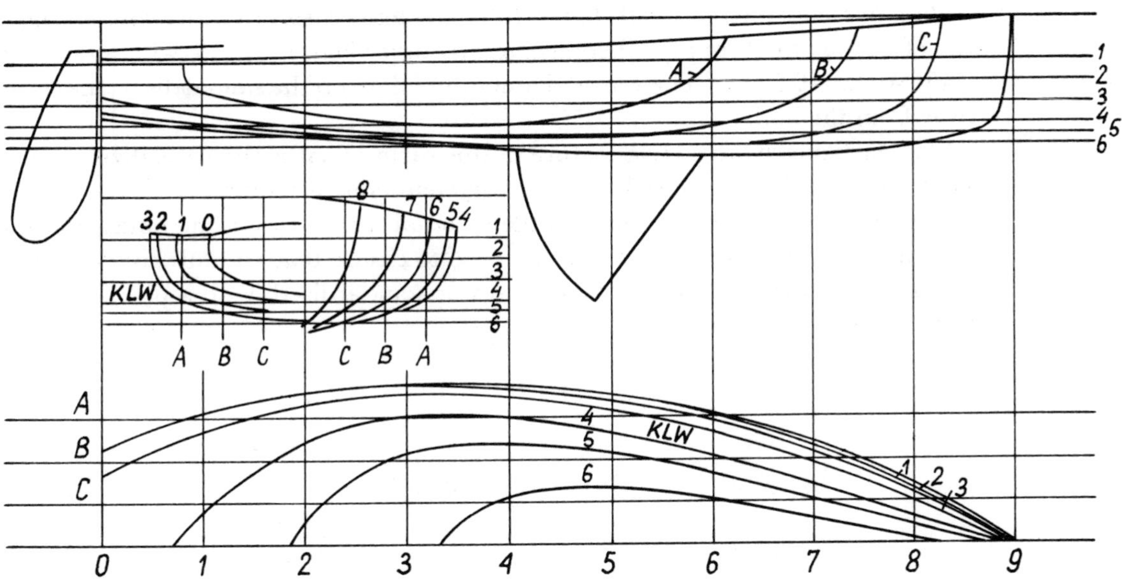

LOA	14 ft. 9 in.	4.5 m.
LWL	13 ft. 5 in.	4.1 m.
Beam (max.)	4 ft. 11½ in.	1.51 m.
Draft (plate down)	2 ft. 9 in.	0.85 m.
Draft of hull	6 in.	0.15 m.
Hull weight (empty)	232 lb.	105 kg.
Sail area	107.6 sq. ft.	10 m.^{2}

The usual hull construction is of molded ply or fiberglass, which gives a smooth, easily maintained surface.

Flying Dutchman (Fig. 20), designed by U. van Essen, is recognized by the I.Y.R.U. as a two-man international class. The hull can be manufactured from molded ply or fiberglass. With a relatively wide, flat stern, without overhang, and a fine, high bow, planing is made easy, but the class requires a skillful and well-harmonized crew, particularly in strong winds. When beating, the second crew member can use a trapeze, enabling him to transfer all his weight well outboard.

Flying Dutchman's dimensions:

LOA	19 ft. 10 in.	6.05 m.
LWL	18 ft. 0 in.	5.50 m.
Beam (max.)	5 ft. 7 in.	1.7 m.
Draft (plate down)	3 ft. 8 in.	1.1 m.
Sail area (actual)	190 sq. ft.	17.5 m.^{2}
Sail area (measured)	162 sq. ft.	15 m.^{2}
Hull weight (empty)	276 lb.	125 kg.
Hull weight (equipped)	353 lb.	160 kg.

Like the Finn, the F.D. is an Olympic "strict one-design." It is one of the longest two-man racing dinghies. Her waterline length, large sail area, low weight, and system of balancing make her a very fast boat. The planing speed in a 20-knot (10 m./sec.) breeze is approximately 15 knots (28 km./hr.). The speed to windward in a 14-knot (7 m./sec.) breeze is about 8 knots (15 km./hr.).

5-0-5 Class (Fig. 21) was designed by John Westell, and is one of the most modern two-man international classes. Its characteristic feature is an extremely light hull of 220 lb., made of ply, fiberglass, or any other light material, with a sail area of 176 sq. ft. (16.5 m.^{2}). The unusual amount of flare on the sides deflects the spray away from the hull.

One particularly attractive feature of this racing boat is the specialized equipment. In view of the large sail area, a competent crew is required.

The measurement system controls the external shape within fine limits, and the internal layout less rigidly, but sufficiently so to ensure that all hulls are essentially similar. From January 1958 the sail plan was standardized, with a jib of 50 sq. ft. and a mainsail of 100 sq. ft.

Fig. 20. Flying Dutchman class (V. von Essen)

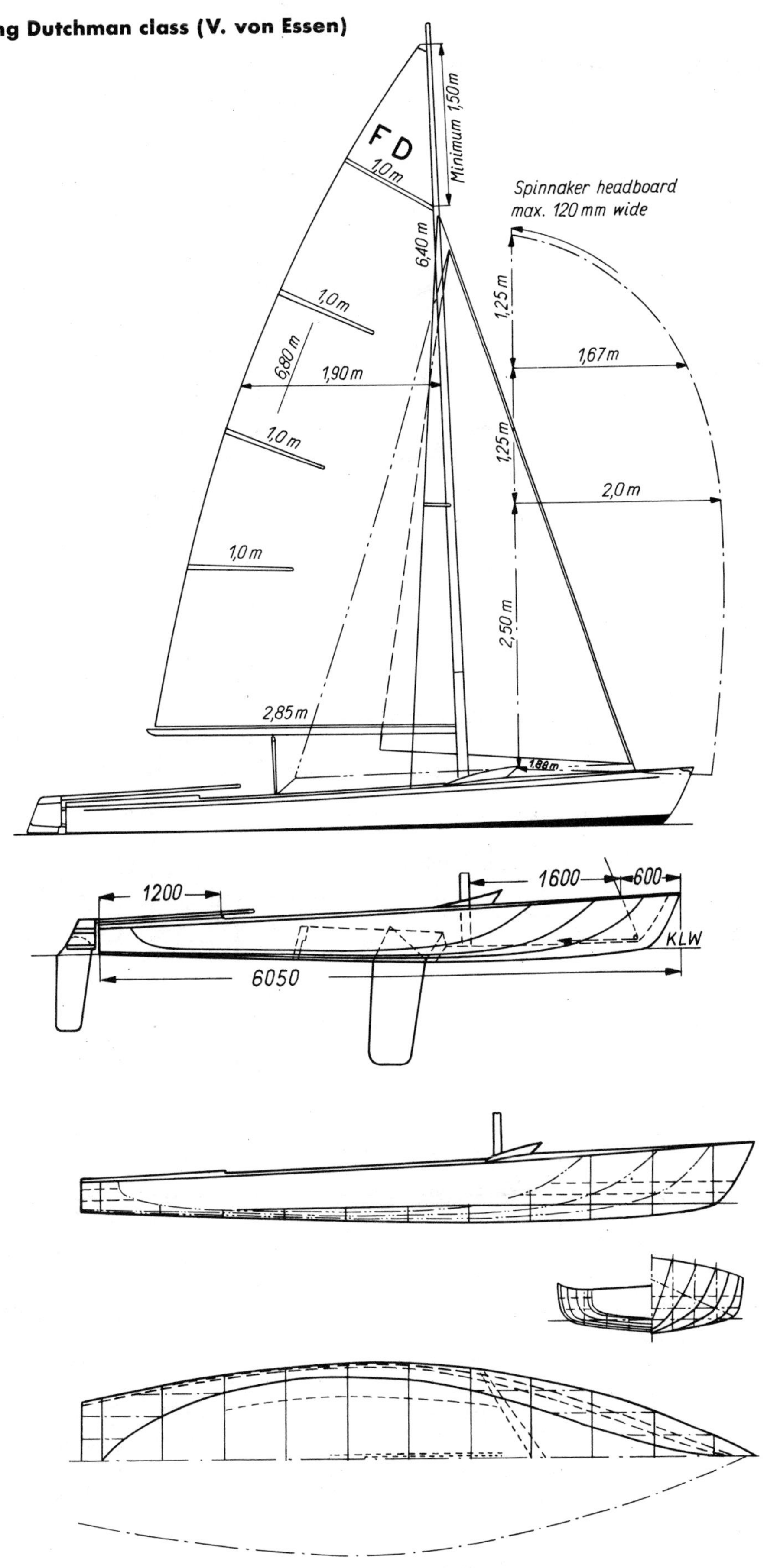

Fig. 21. 5-0-5 class (J. Westell)

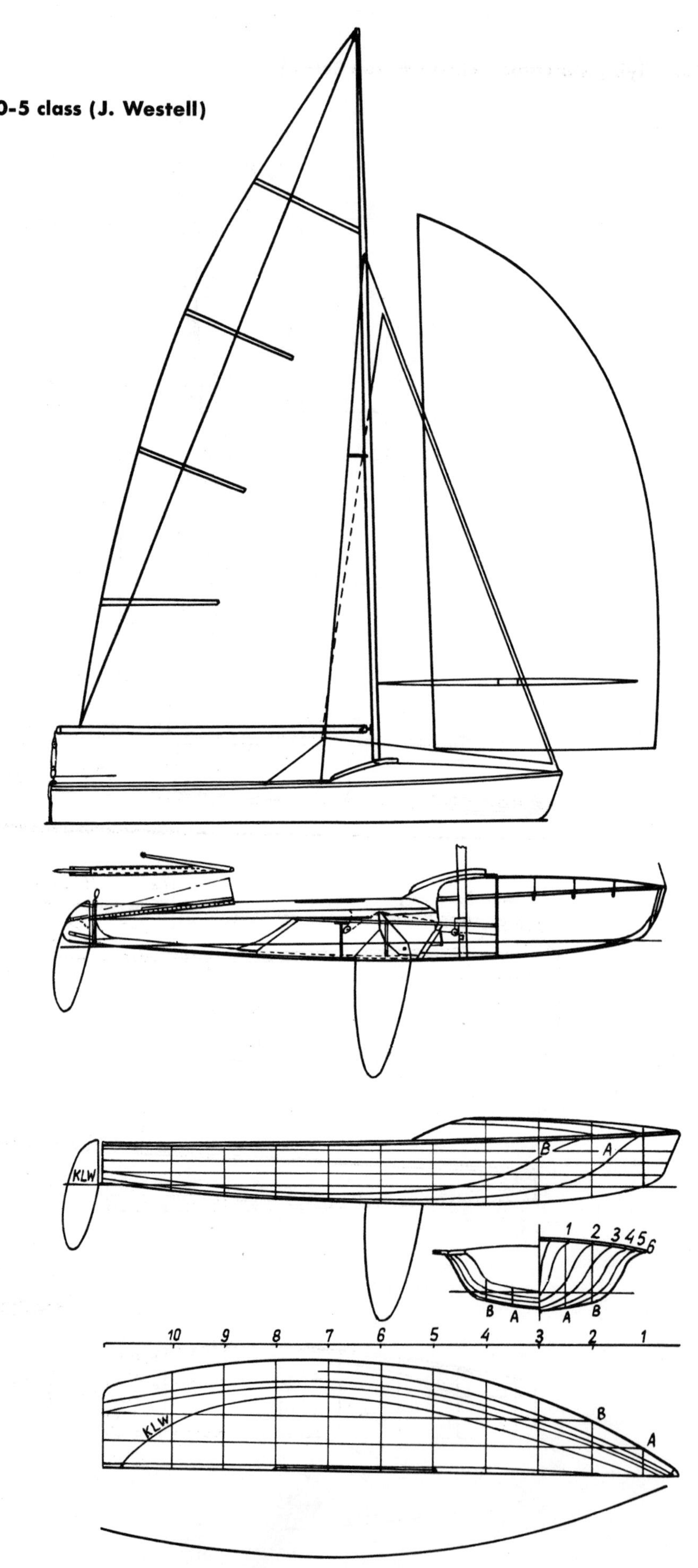

5-0-5 dimensions:

LOA	16 ft. 6 in.	5.05 m.
LWL	15 ft. 0 in.	4.57 m.
Beam (max.)	6 ft. 2 in.	1.88 m.
Draft (plate down)	3 ft. 9 in.	1.14 m.
Hull weight (min.)	220 lb.	100 kg.
Sail area (measured)	150 sq. ft.	14 m.^{2}
Sail area (actual)	176 sq. ft.	16.5 m.^{2}

Fig. 22. Snipe class (W. Crosby, 1931)

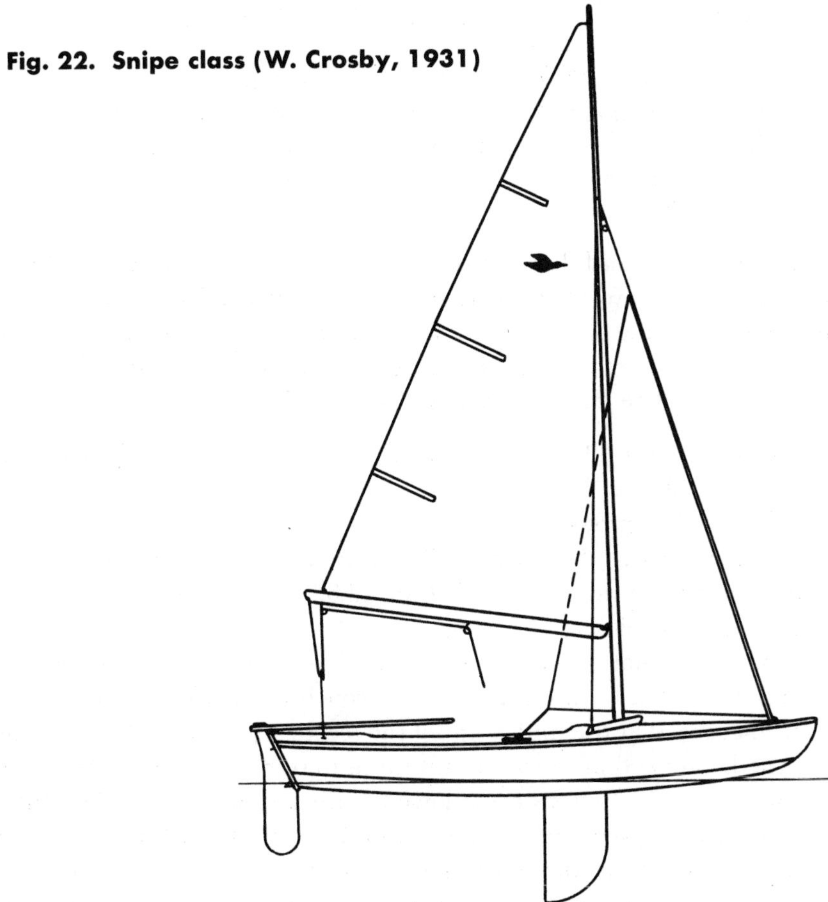

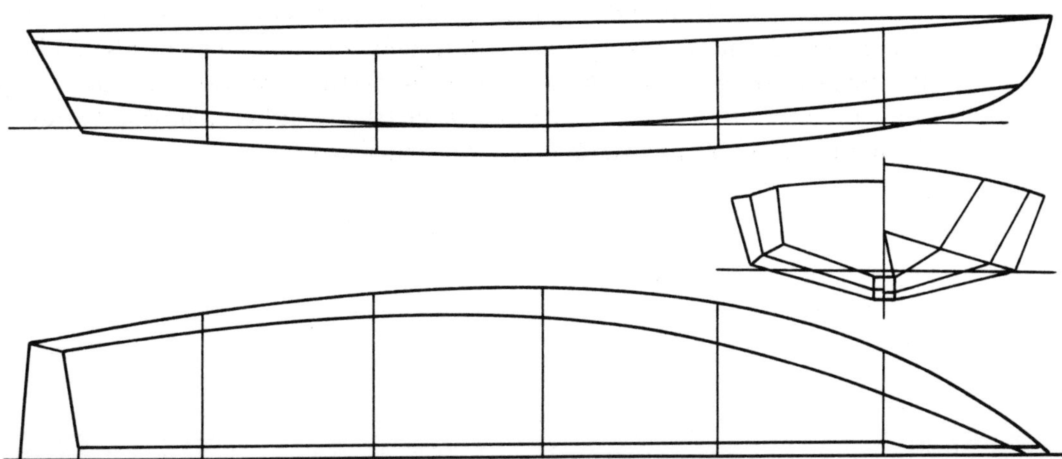

Snipe (Fig. 22), designed in 1931 by William Crosby, quickly spread all over the world. The hard chine hull can be constructed of planks, ply or fiberglass, provided its weight, including gear, is not less than 425 lb. Although it may have its disadvantages, a heavy hull, with a relatively small sail area and with a crew of two, makes it a difficult boat to capsize. As a result, the boat is safe and enjoys great popularity. After thirty years there are now about 12,000 boats of this class afloat.

The Snipe is a one-design international class, and participates in European and World Championships.

Snipe's dimensions:

LOA	15 ft. 6 in.	4.63 m.
LWL	13 ft. 7½ in.	4.15 m.
Beam (max.)	5 ft. 4 in.	1.53 m.
Draft (plate down)	3 ft. 6 in.	1.06 m.
Sail area	113 sq. ft.	10.5 $m.^2$
Hull weight (min.) including gear	425 lb.	193 kg.

International Moth (Figs. 23 and 24) originated in the United States about thirty years ago, and there are now 4000 registered in an international association. Its conception was mainly due to the desire of amateur boat builders to race their own products. The class is restricted, allowing plenty of originality of design of both the hull and sails. The main restrictions are as follows:

1. Hull—maximum length 11 ft. 0 in. (3.35 m.), with one rudder and one centerboard of any shape.
2. Construction—no restrictions.
3. Spars—must be straight; the mast to be 16 ft. 6 in. (5.03 m.) in height, and the boom of maximum length 9 ft. 6 in. (2.89 m.). There are no restrictions on the weight of spars and rigging.
4. Sails—one sail only, not higher than 15 ft. 0 in. (4.57 m.) and having a maximum foot of 9 ft. 0 in. (2.75 m.). The roach of the sail is limited to 6 in. (0.15 m.) measured at the mid-point of the leech. The foot of the sail must be fixed to the boom so that nowhere is it more than 3 in. (7.6 cm.) from the boom. A maximum of 4 battens are allowed, with a total length of less than 7 ft. 8 in. (2.39 m.). The head of the sail cannot be wider than 4 in. (10.1 cm.) measured perpendicular to the mast. The sail can be made in any manner, and there are no restrictions in the number of sails belonging to one owner.
5. Buoyancy—not less than 100 lb. of positive buoyancy must be provided.

International 10 sq. meter Canoe (Fig. 25). This singlehanded class evolved from the Eskimo kayak calls for exceptional skill in helmsmanship. The helmsman balances the boat by sitting on a plank which slides across the boat when tacking. The plank may project up to 5 ft. (1.524 m.) from the weather gunwale. Jamb cleats facilitate control of the two sails and the centerboard.

Fig. 23. International Moth class—British version

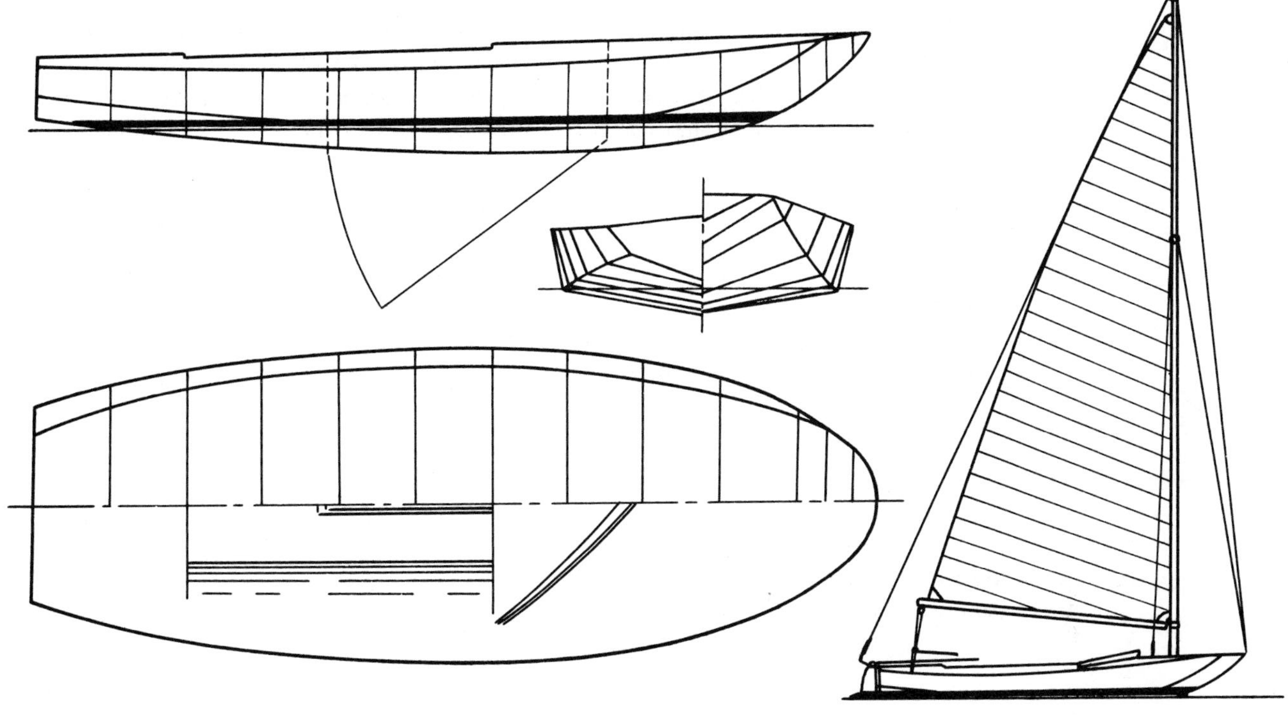

Fig. 24. International Moth class—French version

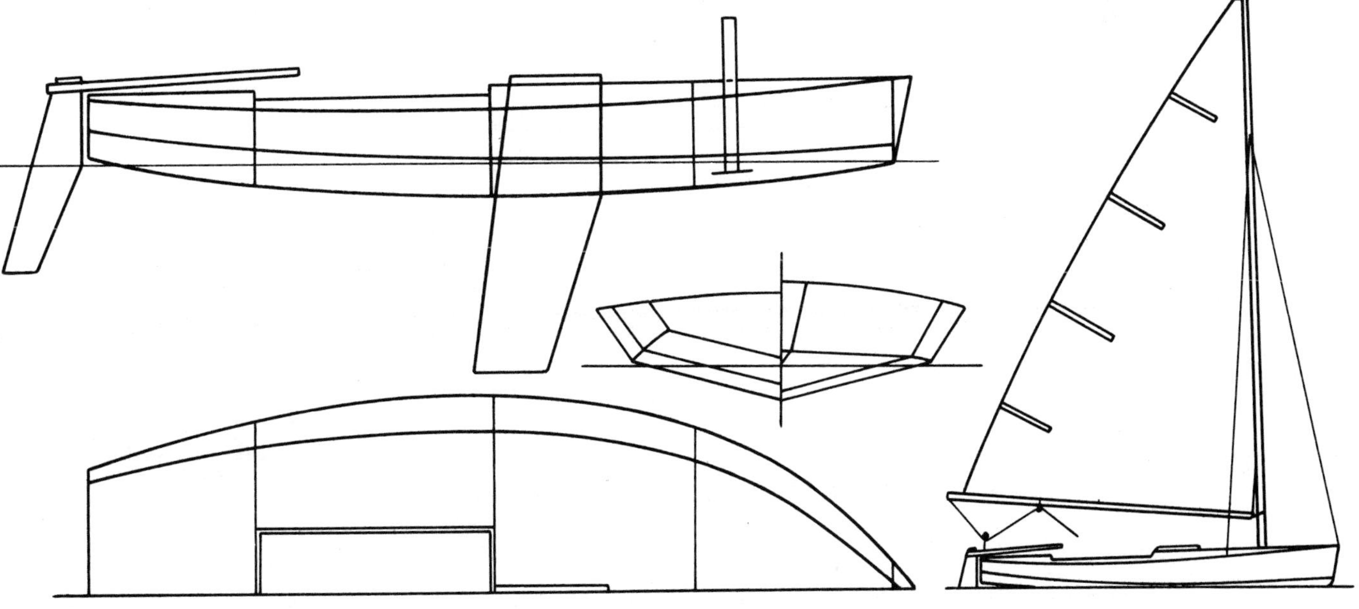

The International Canoe can reach the speed of about 16 knots and heads the Portsmouth Standard Yardstick (see Table on p. 436) for single-hulled craft. This class, popular in both Britain and the United States, is restricted and can be hard chine or round-bilged provided the dimensions are within the following limits:

LOA	17 ft. ¾ in. (5.20 m.)–16 ft. 0 in. (4.87 m.)
Beam	3 ft. 7¼ in. (1.10 m.)–3 ft. 1⅜ in. (0.95 m.)
Draft of hull not less than	11¼ in. (0.30 m.)
Draft with centerboard	3 ft. 3⅜ in. (1.0 m.)
Weight (min.)	129 lb. (60 kg.)
Sail area (actual)	107.64 sq. ft. (10 m.^{2})
Positive buoyancy not less than	100 lb. (45.36 kg.)

Fig. 25. International 10 sq. Meter canoe class

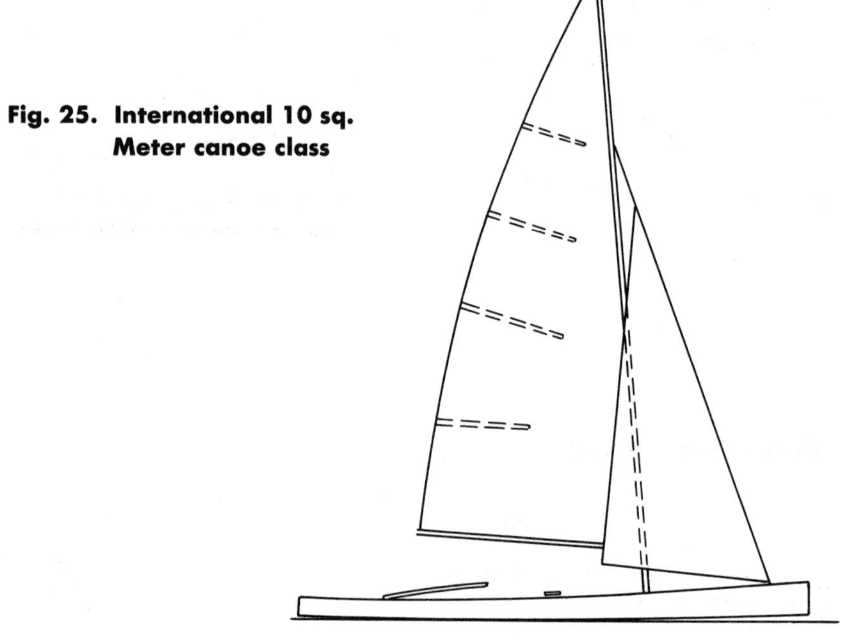

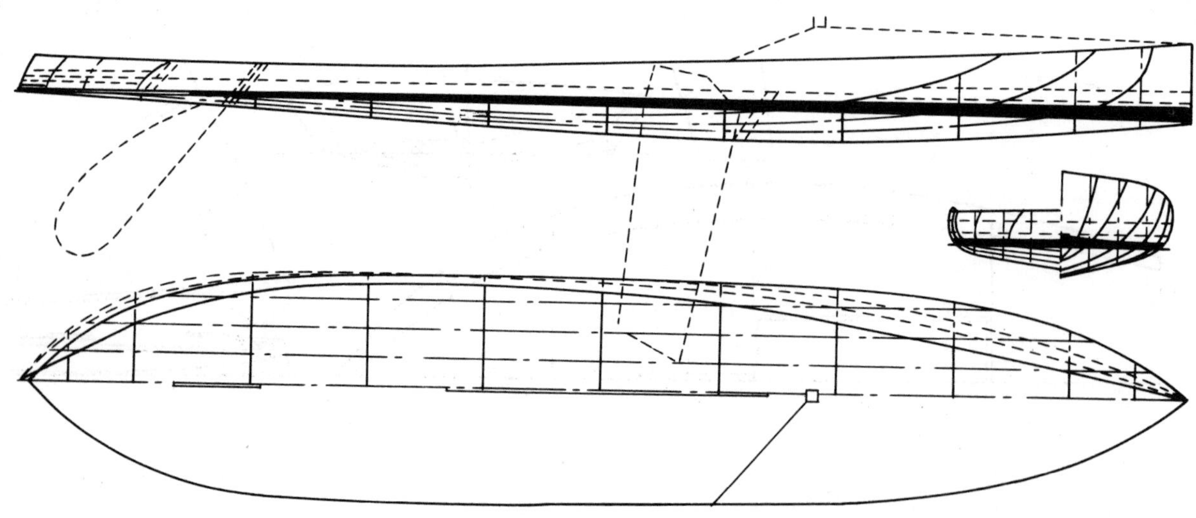

Catamarans (Figs. 26, 27). So far there is no international one-design class recognized by the I.Y.R.U. This type is still in an early stage of development, but many boats have now been built in the United States, Britain, and Australia. Races are run on a handicap, based on the boats' ratings. For this purpose, in England the Royal Yachting Association (R.Y.A.) formula is used:

$$\text{R(rating)} = \frac{L + 2B + 2\sqrt{S}}{5}$$

where L = length over-all (excluding bow sprit and rudder fittings)
B = beam (over-all)
S = actual sail area

The beam should be measured to the outside of the hulls. Should a trapeze and/or a sliding seat be used, 1 ft. shall be added to the beam measurement for each crew member using the device.

Handicapping is by "time correction factor" (T.C.F.), given by:

$$\text{T.C.F.} = \frac{4}{\sqrt{R}}$$

In the United States racing catamarans are measured on the basis of the "One-of-a-kind" Rule:

$$\text{R(rating)} = \frac{\text{Length} + 1.3\sqrt{\text{Sail area}}}{2}$$

$$\text{where length} = \frac{\text{LOA} + 0.7 \times \text{LWL}}{2}$$ (LWL measured afloat with crew and gear aboard)

sail area does not include that of the roach

Figure 26 shows *Tiger Cat,* designed by Bob Harris, one of the fastest American "sailing machines," second in absolute speed to a 38-ft. Class A Scow.

In Britain, during 1960, catamaran trials were held, in which *Thai Mk.4* was an easy over-all winner (Fig. 27). Designed by J. R. MacAlpine-Downie, *Thai Mk.4* has the following dimensions:

LOA	17 ft. 6 in.	5.35 m.
LWL	16 ft. 0 in.	4.85 m.
Beam	8 ft. 6 in.	2.60 m.
Sail area	215 sq. ft.	20 $m.^2$
Weight	275 lb.	125 kg.

The future prospects of catamarans as both cruising and racing boats are very bright. They are considered as the right answer to the "speed crisis" which is being experienced by single-hulled craft as a result of their basic conception.

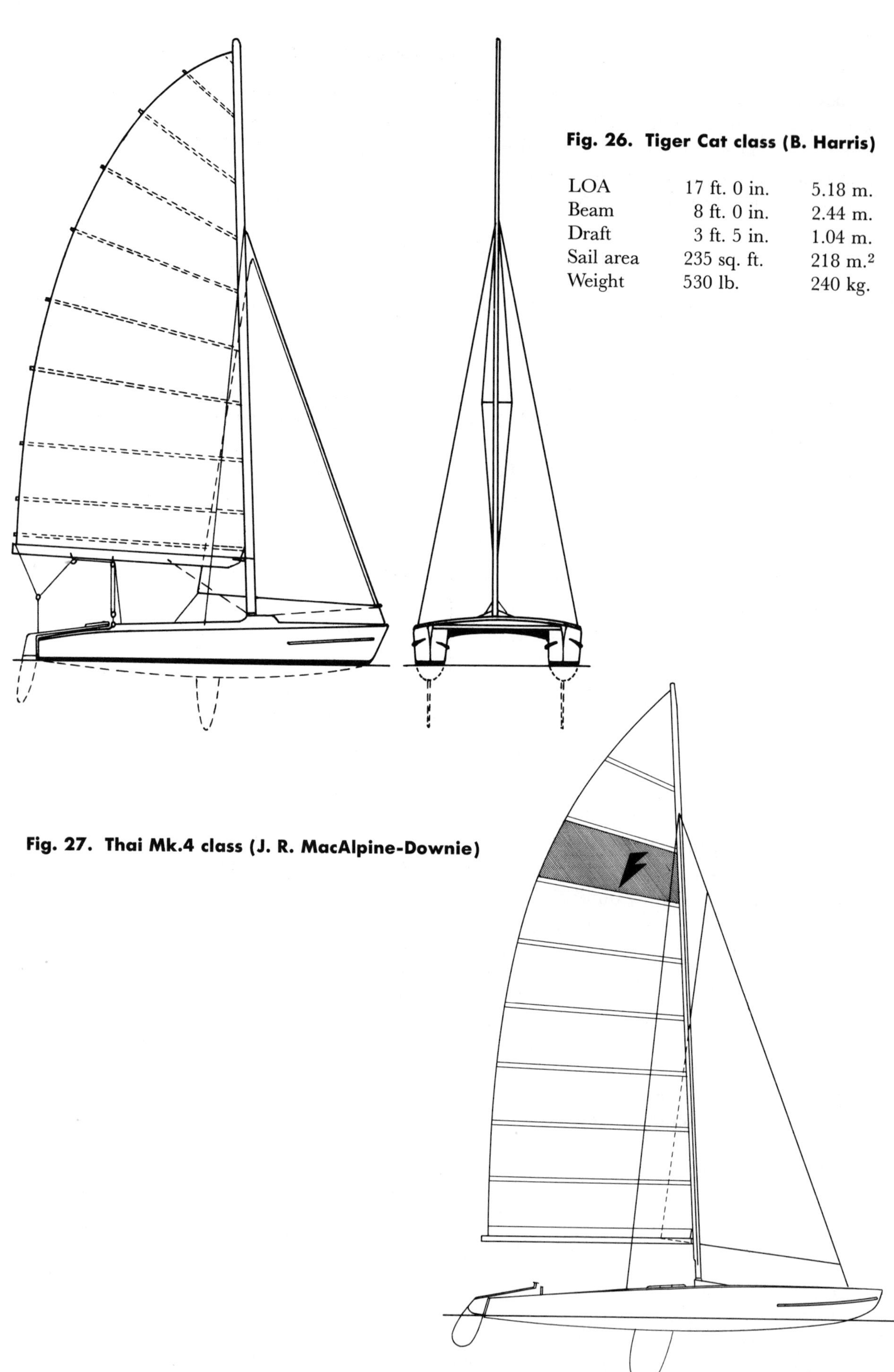

Fig. 26. Tiger Cat class (B. Harris)

LOA	17 ft. 0 in.	5.18 m.
Beam	8 ft. 0 in.	2.44 m.
Draft	3 ft. 5 in.	1.04 m.
Sail area	235 sq. ft.	218 m.^{2}
Weight	530 lb.	240 kg.

Fig. 27. Thai Mk.4 class (J. R. MacAlpine-Downie)

PART II

AERODYNAMICS OF SAILS

1. THE CONCEPT OF AN AERODYNAMIC* FORCE

No laws for a wind, an eagle, or a maiden's heart.

PUSHKIN

AUTHOR'S NOTE: This chapter is an attempt to translate into everyday language certain aspects of dynamics necessary for a full understanding of subsequent discussions. It was the most difficult to write, and will probably be the most difficult to understand. For the benefit of those unfamiliar with the basic concepts of mechanics these will be treated more fully in the Appendix.

In many cases wind effects are in agreement with common sense, easy to understand and forecast. Nevertheless, there are times when our intuition may deceive us. For an example, let us look at Fig. 28a, illustrating a wind blowing over two types of roofs, and try to determine which type is more likely to be blown off. Common sense would say that the steep, high roof is the more likely to be damaged, but in reality, it is usually the low pitched roof which gets lifted off by the wind.

* The term "aerodynamic" comes from the Greek *aer* (air) and *dynamikos* (power).

Fig. 28

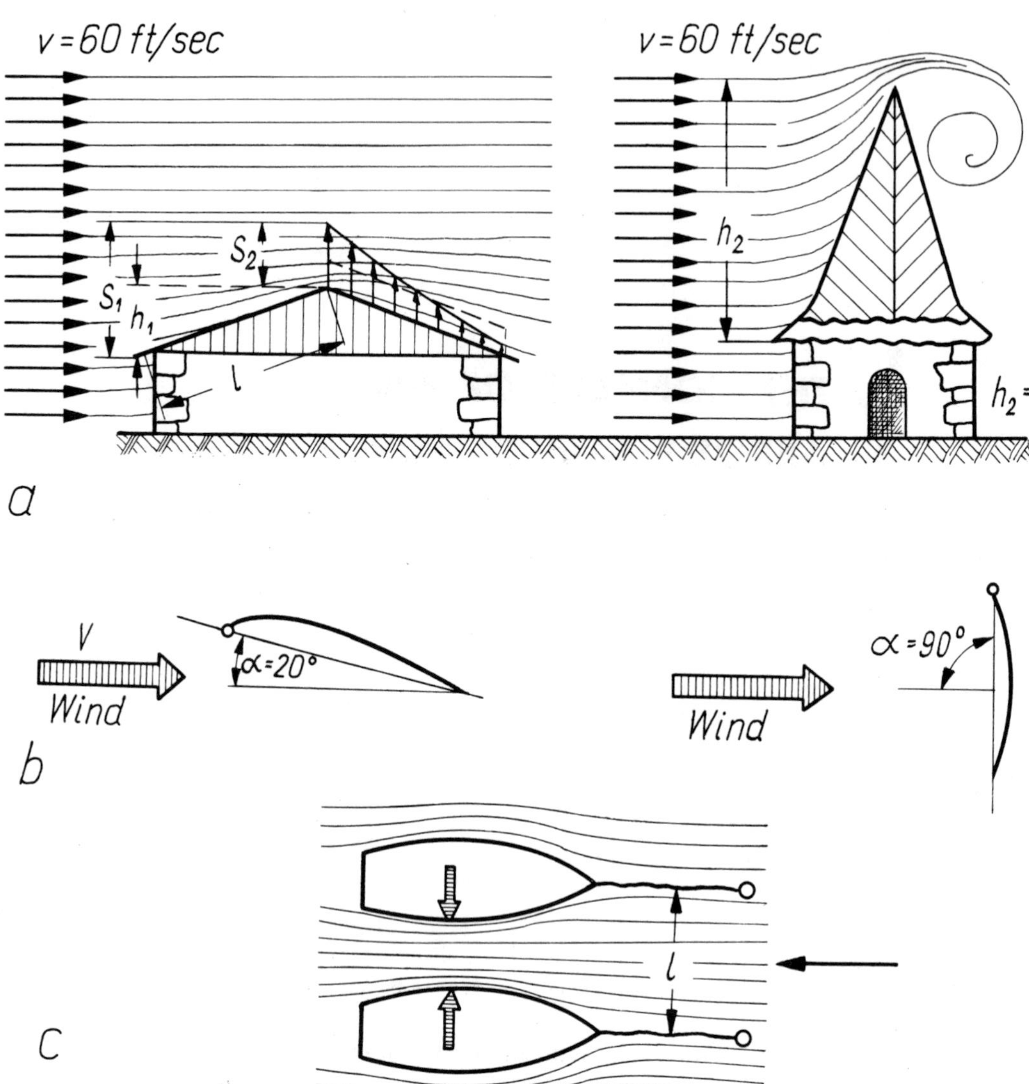

A second example can be seen on Fig. 28b. The wind here blows over two sails of the same camber (curvature). One is set at an "angle of incidence" of 20° to the wind, the other at 90°. Which sail will develop the stronger force? Contrary to expectation, it will not be the latter which does so.

A similar type of example, but one which can have unpleasant consequences for an inexperienced helmsman, is shown in Fig. 28c. Two boats are moored in a strong current. What would happen if the two boats were moored near one another? Many would answer that the water flowing between them would push them apart, and that the repelling force would be the greater, the smaller was the separation. Yet the fact is that the two boats will tend to move together, and this tendency will increase as they approach each other. Nonobservance of this apparently incomprehensible phenomenon has been the cause of many serious accidents at sea, and the law nowadays expressly forbids two ships to pass close together at high speed. Explanations for this, and the two previous examples, will emerge later.

A sailing yacht moves on the boundary between air and water, being partly immersed in each. The flow of air over the sail creates the driving force necessary to overcome the hydrodynamic resistance generated by the hull traveling through the water. In the study of flowing air and water, called respectively aerodynamics and hydrodynamics, they are both generally referred to as "fluids," as distinct from "solids." The differences between them are largely relative, rather than fundamental. Thus, for both fluids, one important characteristic is their density γ, which for sea water is about $\gamma_W = 64$ lb./cu. ft. The corresponding figure for air is $\gamma_A = 0.0765$ lb./cu. ft.

According to the laws of Newton, when one considers bodies in motion, one must know their mass, which is obtained by dividing their weight by the acceleration due to gravity.

$$\text{i.e., mass} = \frac{\text{weight}}{\text{gravity acceleration}}$$

Now, the wind is only a special case of a body in motion, in which the body happens to be continuous, rather than having a fixed size and shape. Thus one must consider its mass per unit volume or mass density,

$$\text{i.e., mass density of air } \rho_A = \frac{\gamma_A}{g}$$

where γ_A = weight of a unit volume (0.0765 lb./cu. ft.)
g = gravity acceleration = 32.2 ft./sec.^{2}

In consequence of the wind having both mass and velocity, it can be said to possess kinetic energy, the energy due to motion. This energy, expressed per unit volume of the air, is called the dynamic pressure, and is given by:

$$q = \frac{1}{2}\frac{\gamma_A}{g} \times v^2 = 0.00119 \times v^2 \text{ lb./sq. ft.}$$

where q = dynamic pressure
v = velocity of the wind (speed of known magnitude and direction, in ft./sec.)

The aerodynamic forces which appear on a sail depend almost entirely on the prevailing pressures on the windward and leeward sides: strictly speaking, on the prevailing static and dynamic pressures. Let us try to describe these pressures and their method of measurement.

Let us imagine that a glass tube of the shape shown in Fig. 29a is filled with water to the level L-L and then placed in an air stream (Fig. 29b). Inlet No. 1 of the tube is placed perpendicular to the wind direction, and inlet No. 2 is parallel to the wind direction. We would find that the difference in water levels

Fig. 29

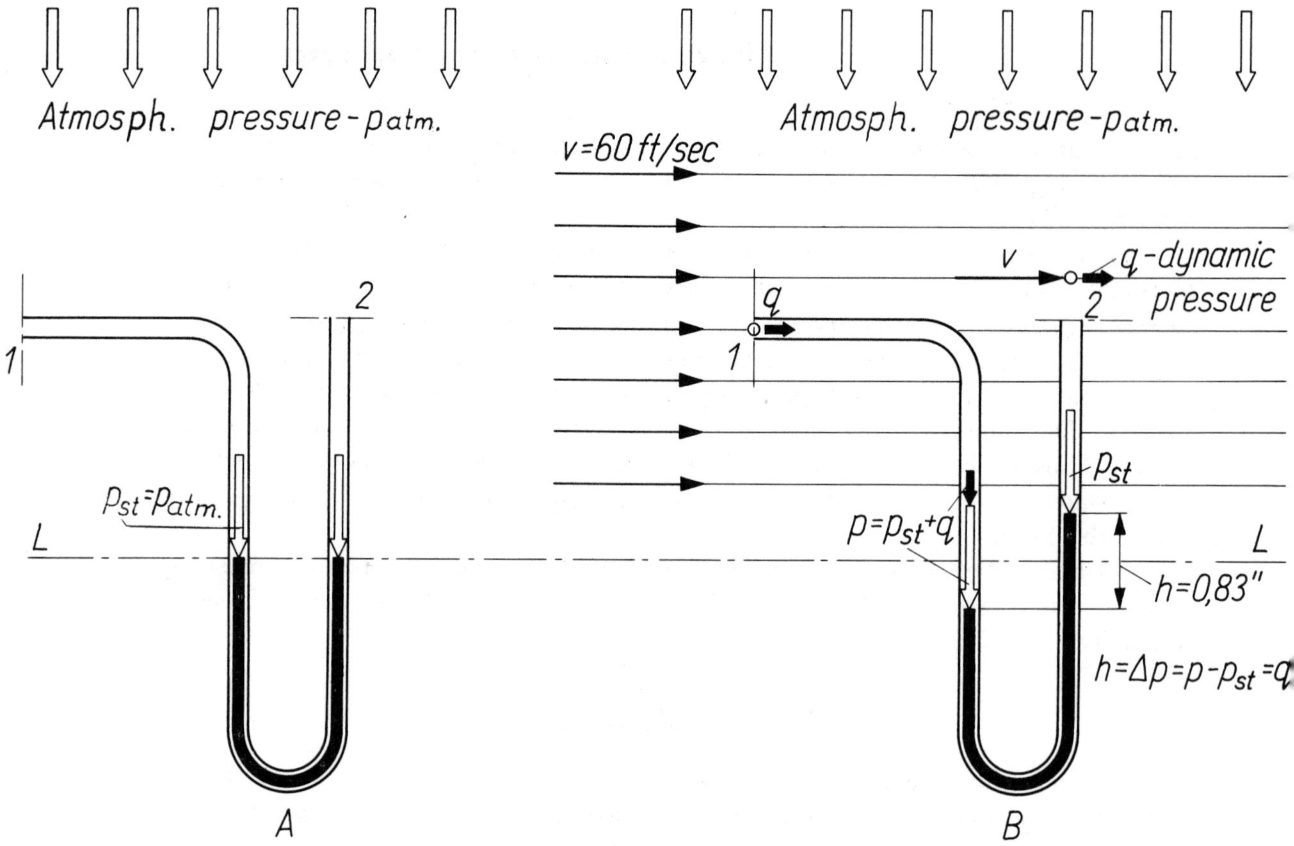

in the two tubes will be greater for greater wind speeds, v. Consider what our very primitive manometer measures. So long as there is no wind acting on the manometer, the levels are the same, since through both open tubes there is the same static pressure p_{st} acting, that of atmospheric pressure p_{atm}. At sea level, which is the bottom of our atmosphere, its pressure is 2116 lb./sq. ft., and is balanced in a barometer by a column of mercury 29.92 in. in height. If the barometer was filled with water, the height of the column would be 33.9 ft. From this we can calculate that a water column of 1 inch height is equivalent to a pressure of about 5.2 lb./sq. ft. If our manometer is placed in a moving air stream in the manner described, the static pressure acting on the water in both tubes will be the same, and equal to atmospheric, i.e., the prevailing pressure in the immediate surroundings. However, the tube 1, pointing into the flow, will receive, in addition to the static pressure, the dynamic pressure, q, of the wind, which in this case is converted into an equivalent static pressure as its motion is arrested on entering the tube.

In accordance with the physical law stating that energy cannot be destroyed but only converted into other forms of energy, the kinetic energy of the wind is here being converted into a static form equivalent to a local alteration of the atmospheric pressure.

The tube 2 will not receive the dynamic pressure, since its inlet, being parallel to the wind direction, offers no impediment to the flow.

As an example, if the wind velocity v = 60 ft./sec., then the dynamic pressure q will be:

$$q = 0.00119 \times 60^2 = 4.3 \text{ lb./sq. ft.}$$

and this value would be indicated on our manometer by a difference in water levels of $\Delta h = 0.83$ in.

The height of the water column in the manometer thus measures the dynamic pressure of the wind:

$$q = \Delta p = p - p_{st}$$

The sum of static pressure (indicated by the barometer) and dynamic pressure is called the total head, or stagnation pressure, since it is the net pressure acting if the air is brought to rest.

Let us now carry out another experiment. Between and around the two plates shown in Fig. 30 flows an air stream. The ends of the plates are covered, so that air must flow in turn past the stations S_1, S_2, S_3, S_4. At these four points are attached U-tube manometers filled with water to the common level L-L and having their outlets in, and parallel to, the undisturbed stream.

Fig. 30

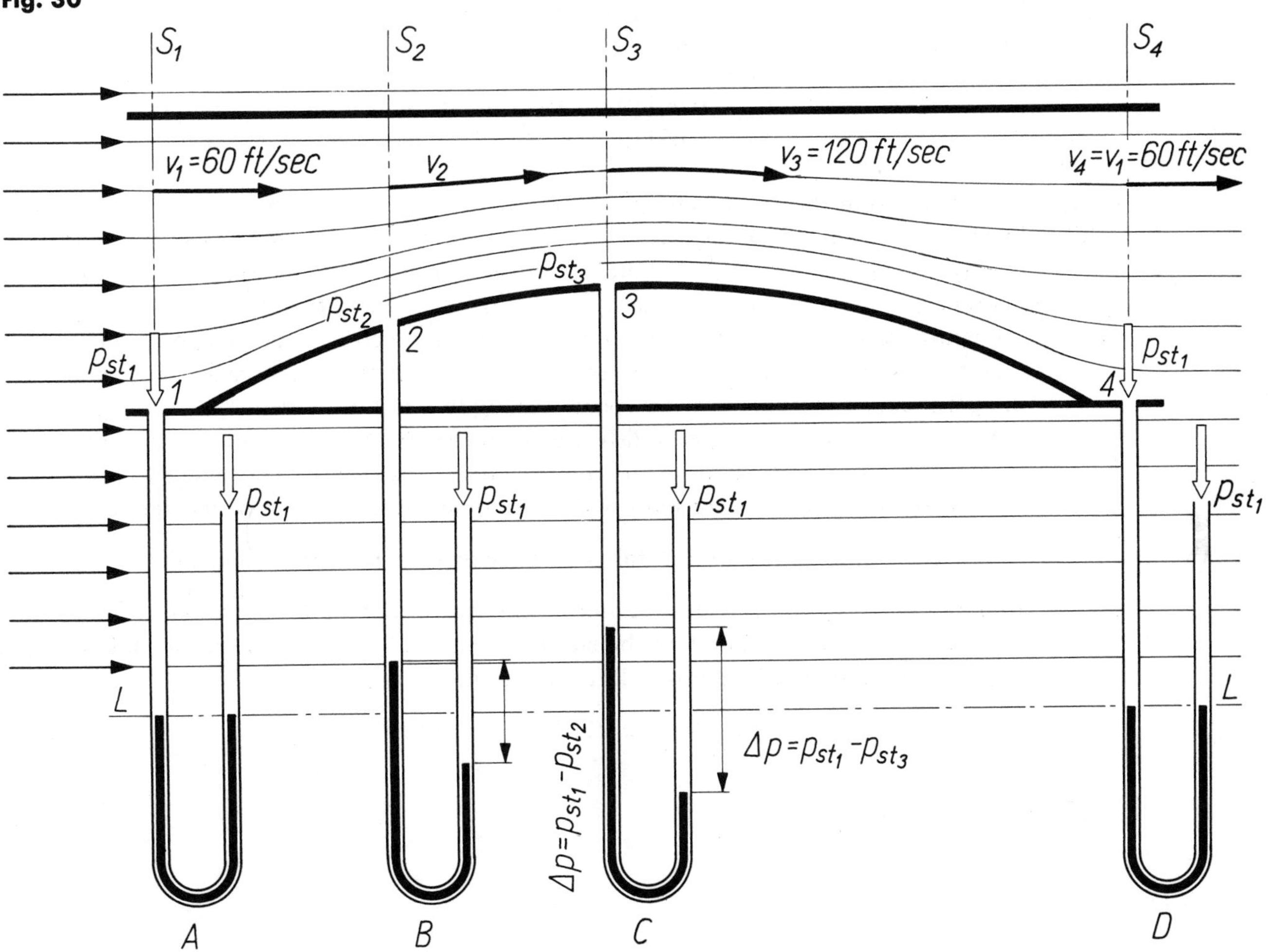

So long as there is no air flowing through the channel, the manometers will all indicate the same level. When, however, an air stream flows we see that the manometers B and C alter in level and indicate reduced pressure, or suction, the greatest change in level occurring at station S_3, that having the minimum cross section.

Let us try to answer the following questions: What is the reason for the different levels on the manometers? Why did the pressure fall at the stations 2 and 3, relative to the surrounding static pressure? Evidently these changes are caused by the varying velocity of the air as it flows in turn through sections S_1, S_2, S_3, S_4. Manometers A and D will not indicate any difference in levels, because each has both ends placed tangentially to the wind direction, measuring p_{st1}. This follows since sections S_1 and S_4 are the same, neither disturb the flow and thus both have the undisturbed flow velocity v_1. For our purposes, the air can be regarded as incompressible, and thus it must flow faster through the smaller sections S_2 and S_3 than through S_1 and S_4, in order that the quantity of air passing the sections in a given time interval shall be the same. Now, the quantity flow rate is given by the product of the area and the flow velocity, and we can therefore write:

$$S_1 \times v_1 = S_3 \times v_3, \text{ or } \frac{S_1}{S_3} = \frac{v_3}{v_1}$$

If at section S_1, the speed of the wind is $v_1 = 60$ ft./sec. and the sectional area S_3 is half that of S_1, then the flow speed at S_3 will be $v_3 = 120$ ft./sec. Hence, the dynamic pressures at S_1 and S_3 will be:

$$q_1 = 0.00119 \times 60^2 = 4.3 \text{ lb./sq. ft.}$$
$$q_3 = 0.00119 \times 120^2 = 17.2 \text{ lb./sq. ft.}$$

This means that the kinetic energy of the wind at S_3 has increased over that at S_1 by four times, which is the square of the ratio of the speeds. We know, however, that energy cannot be created from nothing, but it can be converted from one form to another, as in the previous example of Fig. 29, when the kinetic energy of the wind, expressed as a dynamic pressure, was changed to another energy form, manifest as a static pressure. In this example evidently, a reverse process is in operation, an increase of wind speed leading to a fall in pressure.

In 1738 Daniel Bernoulli established a simple relationship between the dynamic and static pressures in the same air stream, namely that the sum of these two pressures at the same point is constant within an air stream. This can be written as:

$$p_{st} + q = p_{st1} + q_1 = \text{total head or stagnation pressure (constant)}$$

In honor of the discoverer, this relation is known as "Bernoulli's equation."

We are now able to calculate the static pressures at the various stations taking p_{st1} equal to atmospheric pressure 2116 lb./sq. ft.

$$p_{total} = p_{st1} + q_1 = 2116 + 4.3 = 2120.3 \text{ lb./sq. ft.}$$

The total pressure at station S_3 must be the same to fulfill Bernoulli's equation, and we know $q_3 = 17.2$ lb./sq. ft.

$$\text{Then, } 2120.3 = 17.2 + p_{st3}$$
$$\text{or } p_{st3} = 2120.3 - 17.2 = 2103.1 \text{ lb./sq. ft.}$$

Thus the difference between p_{st3} and atmospheric pressure p_{st1} will be:

$$\Delta p = p_{st1} - p_{st3} = 2116 - 2103.1$$
$$= 12.9 \text{ lb./sq. ft.}$$

and this difference will be indicated on manometer C by a difference in water levels of:

$$\frac{12.9}{5.2} = 2.48 \text{ in.}$$

Manometer B will indicate a value intermediate between A and C, since the section, and thus the velocity v_2 are intermediate.

It is worthy of note that the air stream, initially of speed $v_1 = 60$ ft./sec., has been accelerated to a higher speed by a process which involved local changes in flow direction. This resulted in a varying pressure force over the surface causing the changes in direction, and this pressure force everywhere acts perpendicular to the surface. This is essentially the principle by which one is able to sail to windward.

We are now in a position to explain one of the examples quoted earlier. The low roof A of Fig. 28a is rather similar to the previous example of a channel. The wind, as it passes over the ridge will create suction forces tending to lift the roof, the pressure inside the building being equal to atmospheric.

Considered numerically, if at the apex of the roof the effective area for the air to flow through is half that at the eaves, and $v_1 = 60$ ft./sec., then the average suction over the roof would be about 6.4 lb./sq. ft. For a roof of plan area 750 sq. ft., the lifting force would be 4800 lb.

In the case of a steep roof the air is unable to negotiate the sharp angle and covers the lee side in a confused, turbulent flow known to aerodynamicists as "separated flow." A consequence of this is that the large suction forces are not developed over the rear half and thus the total lift force on the roof is much less than that for the low-pitched roof.

Let us now consider the air flow round a sail (Fig. 31a). The air stream divides into two parts, that traversing the lee side and that on the weather side.

We can see from the diagram that the flow on the lee side is constricted, from a section S to the section S_L. The wind speed, v_L, in this region must therefore be greater than the free stream speed, v. According to Bernoulli's equation, an increase in speed must have a corresponding decrease in static pressure p_L on the lee side. The greatest changes in speed, and hence suction, occur near the luff of the sail.

By a similar analysis for the weather side, we find that the local wind speed v_W

Fig. 31

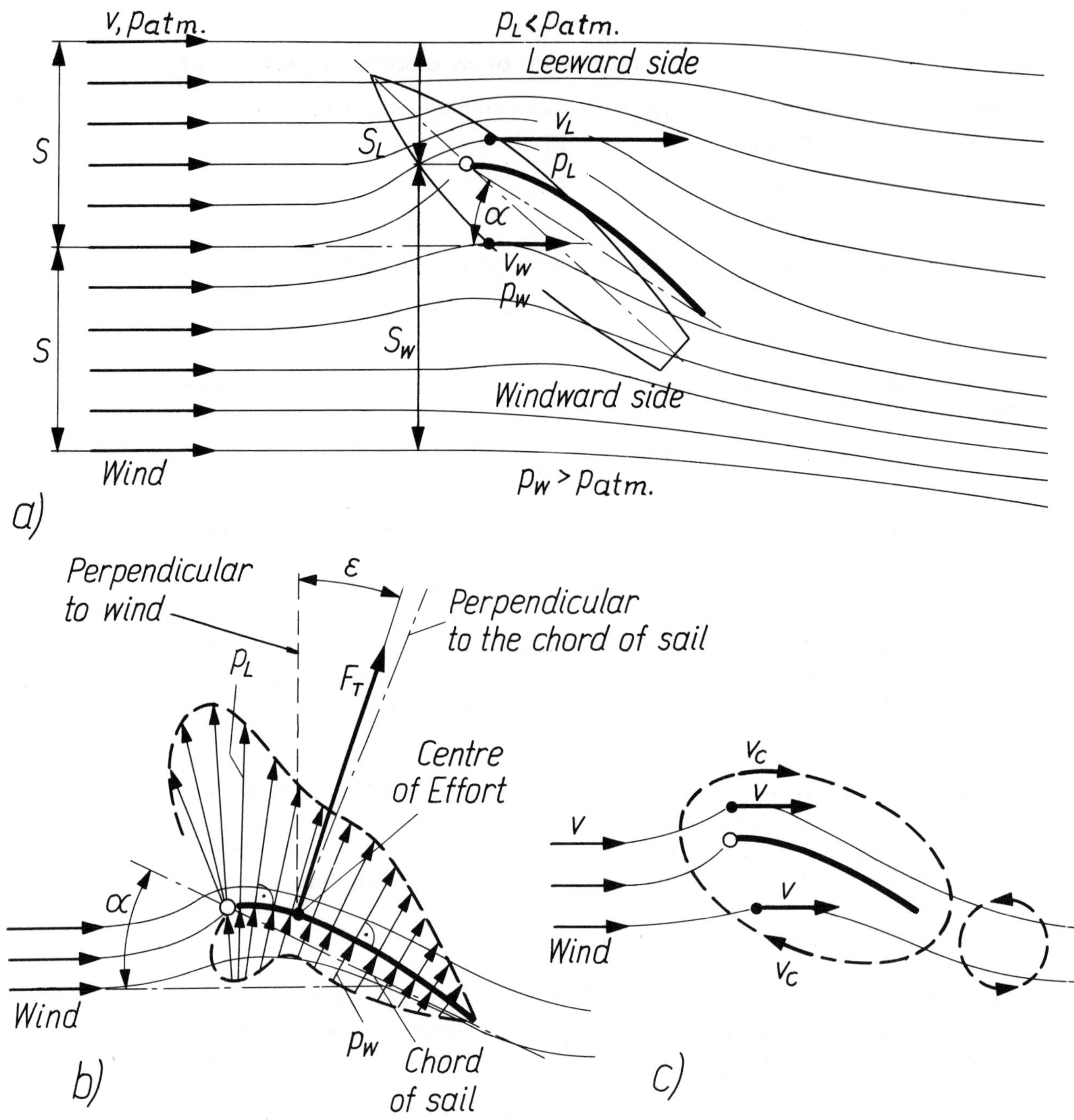

falls, and thus the static pressure p_W rises as the kinetic energy of the air is converted.

Thus on the windward side we have pressures greater than atmospheric, and on the lee side they are less than atmospheric. These can be combined to give a single resultant force F_T, acting at an angle ε to the perpendicular to the wind direction (see Fig. 31b). It will not act, in general, perpendicular to the chord line of the sail, shown on the diagram. The line of action of F_T, which will be in the forepart of the sail, passes through a point called the center of effort.

Some yachtsmen are of the opinion that on the windward side of a sail the air is being compressed. This view is erroneous, as air compression due to motion only becomes significant at speeds near and above that of sound. The aerodynamic forces depend entirely on the conversion of kinetic energy of the wind into other forms by the action of the sail, and these processes take place, so far as we are concerned, at constant air density.

The generation of aerodynamic forces of this type can be explained in another way, compatible with Bernoulli's equation. We can assume that the resultant flow round the sail is composed of two superimposed parts (Fig. 31c). Firstly there is the normal wind velocity, v, but in addition there is a circulating flow, v_c. We can easily see that the resolution of these two components will lead to reductions in velocity on the weather side and to increases on the lee side, and hence increases and decreases respectively in the pressures. It is interesting that this concept, apparently contradictory to common sense, is confirmed by experiments.

For instance, if one takes a strip of corrugated cardboard and pivots it on a pin as shown in Fig. 32a, and then, in the direction v, moves a piece of curved cardboard underneath it, one will find that the corrugated strip will move in the direction v_c, opposite to v. The curved piece of cardboard, like a sail, induces a circulation around it in the direction previously described. If there was no circulation, the corrugated strip would move in the same direction as the cardboard, under the action of air friction.

The theory of circulation can also be illustrated by the experiments first carried out by Magnus (1852). He demonstrated that if a wind of velocity v is blowing on a circular cylinder turning with an angular velocity w, there will be a force P created, acting perpendicular to the axis of the cylinder and the wind direction (Fig. 32b). This phenomenon, whereby an aerodynamic force is generated, is called the "Magnus effect." Using this principle, Flettner constructed a ship, which instead of having sails or a propeller, used vertically mounted rotors of suitable size. With the wind abeam, the driving force was directly forward. Although in practice the idea worked, it was not commercially successful due to its limited application.

Fig. 32

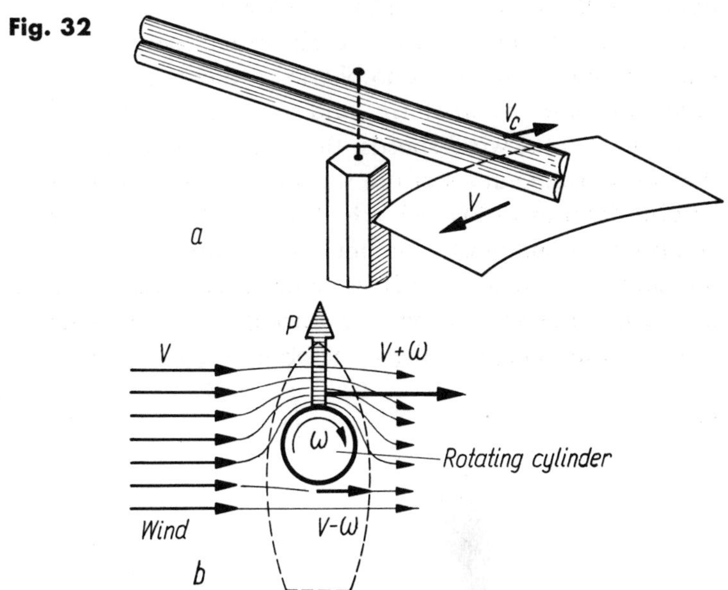

2. DISTRIBUTION OF PRESSURE ON A SAIL

The magnitude of the suction on the leeward side and pressure on the windward side varies for different parts of the sail. This can be established by carrying out measurements with manometers on sail models in wind tunnels or on the full-sized sails of a moving yacht. Pressure measurements on both sides of the sails of the American yacht *Papoose* were made in close-hauled, light weather conditions. Figure 33 shows the location of the three lines of pressure points on the mainsail and one line on the jib. Small holes in the sails were connected by rubber tubing to a battery of manometers on deck. The readings on the manometers were recorded simultaneously by photography. The principle of the measurements is illustrated in Fig. 34, which for the sake of clarity shows only one manometer connected to the sail. By tacking, the experimenters were able to obtain measurements from both the windward and leeward sides.

The manometers showed the differences between the pressure on the sail and static pressure, equal to atmospheric, at the deck. To obtain results in a convenient ratio (nondimensional) form, and to eliminate the effects of different tests being done at different wind speeds, the static pressure differences Δp were divided by the appropriate values of the wind dynamic pressure q. They were presented in graphic form as in Fig. 35, which shows the pressure distribution for one row of points on the mainsail. The horizontal scale measures the width, or chord, of the sail, and the vertical scale gives values of $\Delta p/q$, adopting the convention that positive values indicate pressure, and negative values suction. It should be noted that negative values appear above the origin O, and positive values below.

Fig. 33. Papoose

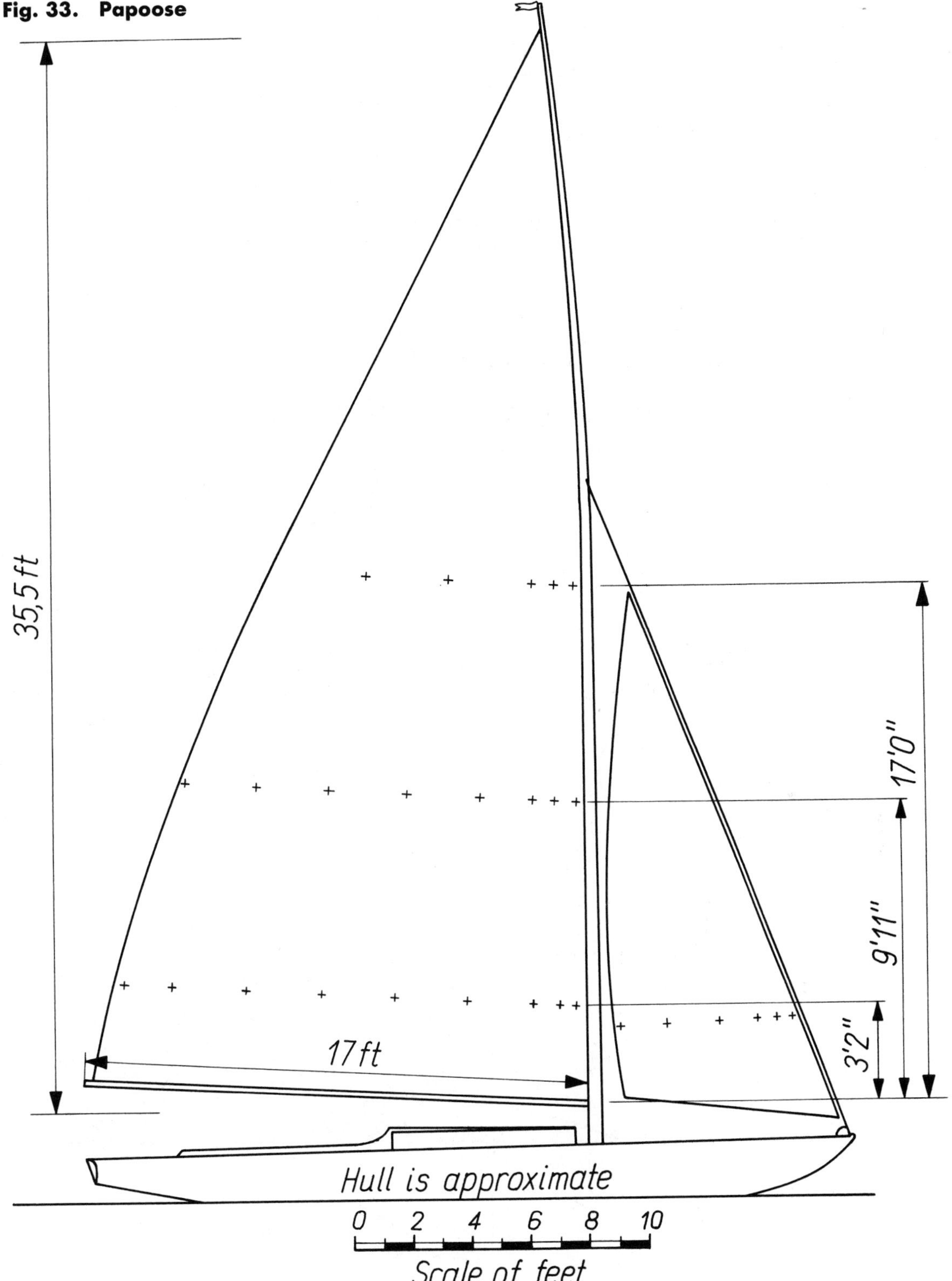

Fig. 34

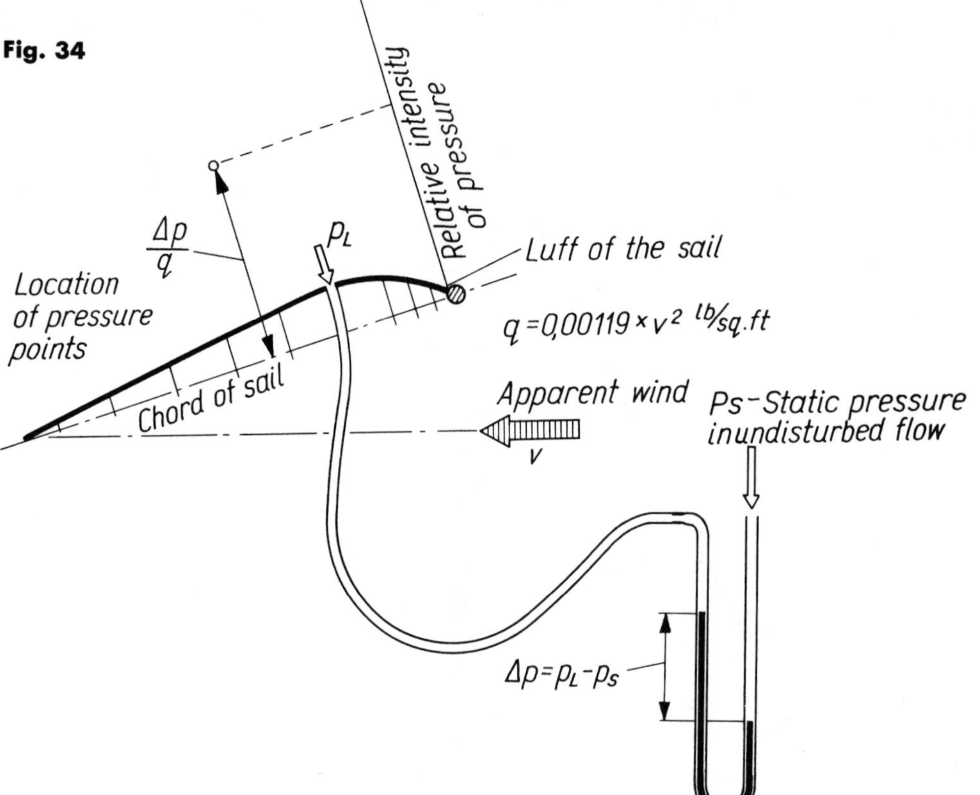

Relative intensity of pressure
Δp/q
p_L
Luff of the sail
Location of pressure points
q = 0,00119 × v² lb/sq.ft
Chord of sail
Apparent wind
v
Ps - Static pressure in undisturbed flow
Δp = p_L - p_s

Fig. 35

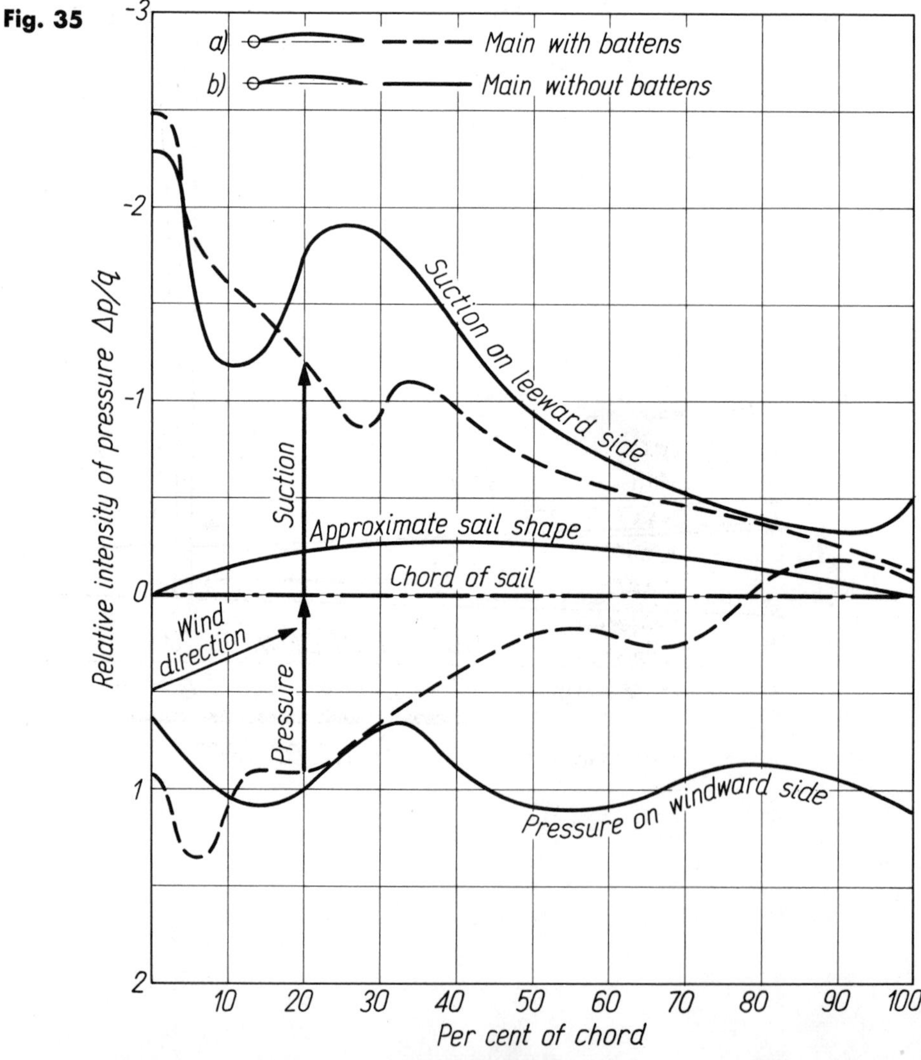

a) Main with battens
b) Main without battens
Relative intensity of pressure Δp/q
Suction on leeward side
Suction
Approximate sail shape
Chord of sail
Wind direction
Pressure
Pressure on windward side
-3
-2
-1
0
1
2
10 20 30 40 50 60 70 80 90 100
Per cent of chord

From the graphs we are able to deduce the values of the pressures at different points on the sail. If the speed of the wind is 30 ft./sec., its corresponding dynamic pressure will be $q = 0.00119 \times 30^2 = 1.07$ lb./sq. ft.; then for instance, at the point where $\Delta p/q = -2$ we shall have a suction of

$$\Delta p = -2 \times 1.07 = -2.14 \text{ lb./sq. ft.}$$

An examination of the curves of pressure distribution shows a characteristic drop soon after the mast, particularly for the suction (leeward) curves. This can be largely attributed to the mast which exerts a strong modifying effect on the flow in its vicinity. Reference to Fig. 36 showing the detailed pressure distribution round the mast can give us an understanding of its air flow. We can see that maximum suction is developed when the position of maximum width, relative to the air stream, is reached, where the local speed is greatest. Behind this point the flow is separated, and absorbs some useful energy. Hence the local kinetic energy of the wind over the foreparts of the sail is reduced, with a corresponding drop in pressures and suctions.

This example showing the disturbing influence of the mast demonstrates how critical is the dependence of the pressures, and even more so the suctions, on the precise nature of the air flow. Any disturbance reduces the local dynamic pressure and hence affects the pressures and suctions and, finally, the resultant aerodynamic force. These losses can be incurred not only by the presence of the mast but also by such things as wrinkles in the sail, protruding batten pockets, and a poor sail profile.

The second striking characteristic of the graphs of Fig. 35 is the concentration of the large values of the distributions near the luff of the sail. Away from the luff, the values fall rapidly, approaching zero at the leech.

In practice this characteristic of high pressures near the luff is of great value to the yachtsman. At any one point, the pressure on the windward side and the suction on the leeward side can be added, and represented by a vector, showing direction and magnitude, as, for example, p_1, p_2, p_3, in Fig. 37, acting perpendicular to the sail curvature. These pressures can then be split into two components, along and across the axis of the boat, the former being a driving pressure. We can

Fig. 36

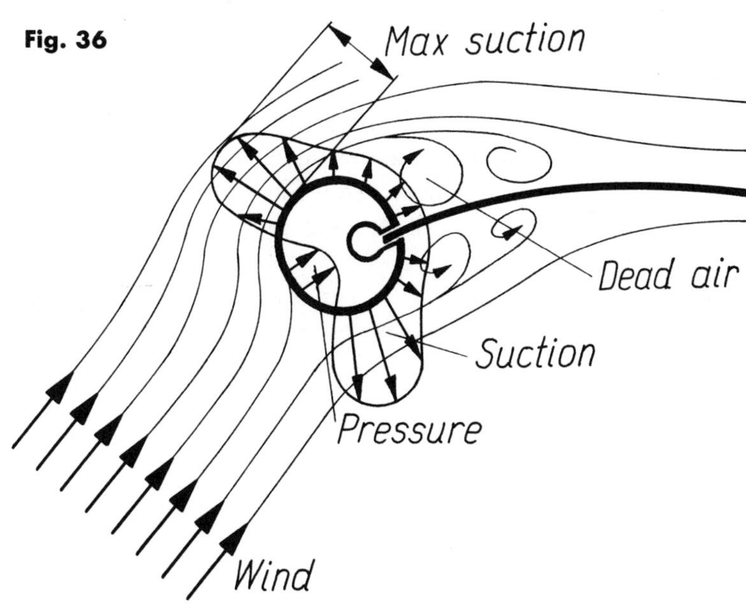

Fig. 37

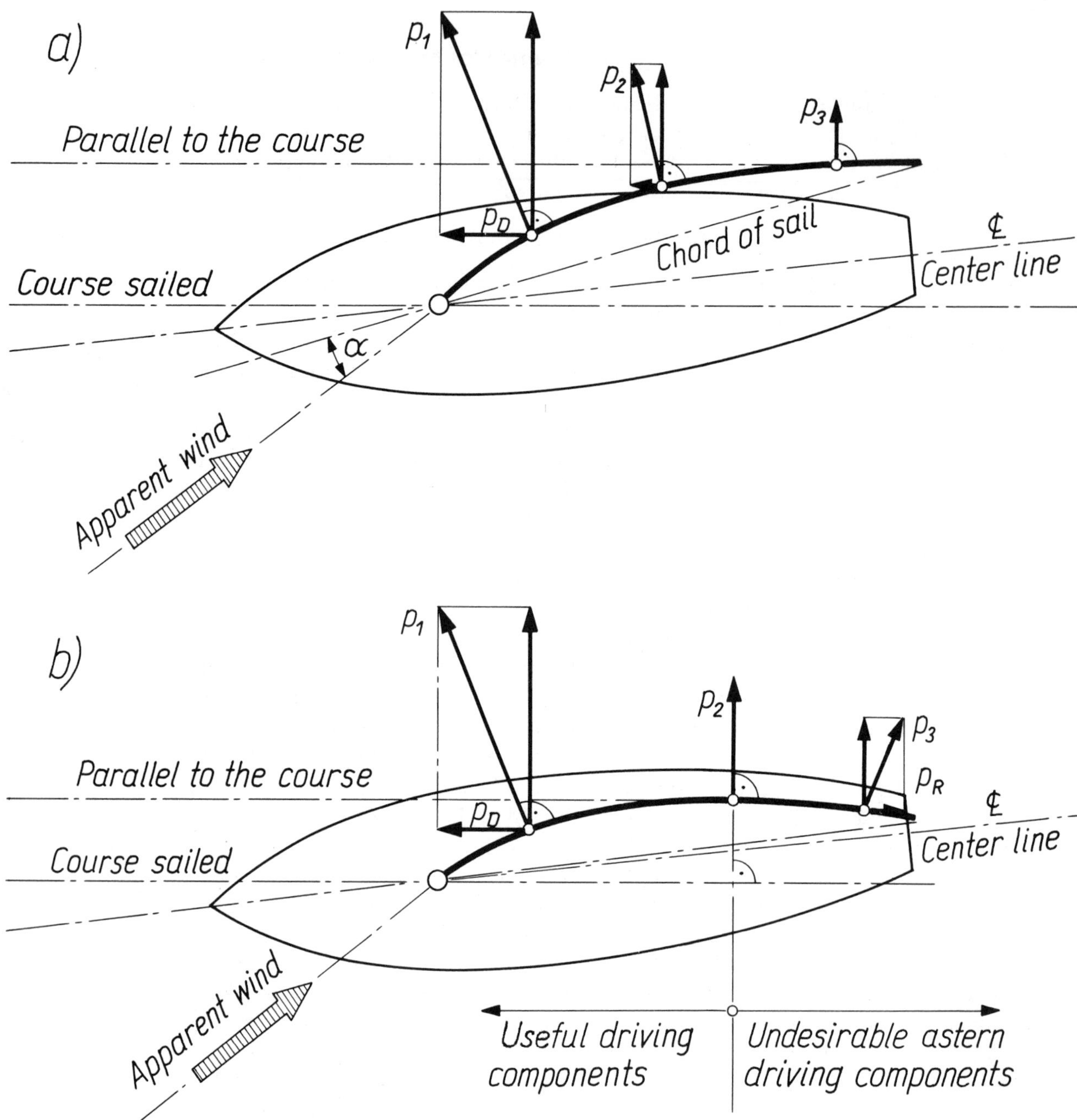

see from Fig. 37a and b that the greatest contributions to the driving force come from the foreparts of the sail, by virtue of both their magnitude and also their direction. The pressures near the leech exert no driving force, but mostly a side force, causing leeway, and in some cases can even give an undesirable astern driving force.

We can, in fact, state as a general rule that if we draw a tangent to the sail, parallel to the direction of motion, then pressures on the windward side and suctions to leeward will give a forward driving component if they act ahead of the tangent point, and if they act aft of this point they are essentially harmful.

The efficiency with which a sail produces a driving force depends to a large extent on two factors:

(a) The sail profile, largely determined by its cut
(b) The position of the sail relative to the wind direction, and to the hull centerline, controlled by the helmsman

If the sail is hauled in too far, the driving force component p_D will be reduced, and the harmful leeway component p_R increased. To obtain the greatest driving force with a low leeway force it is necessary to increase the pressures near the luff, where they are most useful, and simultaneously to reduce their magnitude in the afterparts of the sail.

In Fig. 35 are shown the pressure distributions for two sails similar in all respects except that the sail a has the roach stiffened with battens, and sail b is not stiffened, and has therefore a considerable curvature of the profile on the roach. The condition obtained on sail b could also be found when the stiffness of the battens is not sufficient, in relation to the strength of the wind, or if the sail has the fault, particularly common on Dacron sails, of exhibiting a "hard" leech. This condition is usually met with in rather strong winds, when the position of maximum camber of the sails moves aft toward the leech. On soft cotton sails one is able to flatten out the leech by hauling down on the mainsheet, but on the stiffer Dacron sail this is very often impossible. By comparing the pressure distributions for these two cases we are able to see the reason why the use of battens, particularly on a sail with a large roach, is so advantageous.

Another typical characteristic of the pressure distribution on a sail is the considerable difference in the magnitudes of the pressures on the leeward and windward sides. Comparing the pressures and suctions in the foreparts of the sail we can estimate that the leeward side contributes 60–75 per cent of the total aerodynamic force. This is a very important and rather unfortunate fact, since the flow over the leeward side is usually far more intolerant of any disturbance than that over the windward side. This is shown very clearly in Fig. 38, giving pressure distributions for a jib and a mainsail, each sail being hoisted separately. It will be seen that the value of the suction, and to a much lesser extent the pressure, of the jib is considerably greater than for the mainsail. This can be largely attributed to the presence of the mast in the one case and not in the other.

The undesirable, large values of pressure near the leech of the jib are due to its sagging to leeward, and could be avoided by using battens. The probable effect of their use has been shown on Fig. 38 by chain dotted lines.

We can estimate from Figs. 35 and 38 that the efficiency of the jib is about 2.0 times that of the mainsail. When the two sails are used together the jib makes another great contribution toward the over-all performance by virtue of its action on the mainsail. Comparison of the curves of pressure distribution for the mainsail

Fig. 38

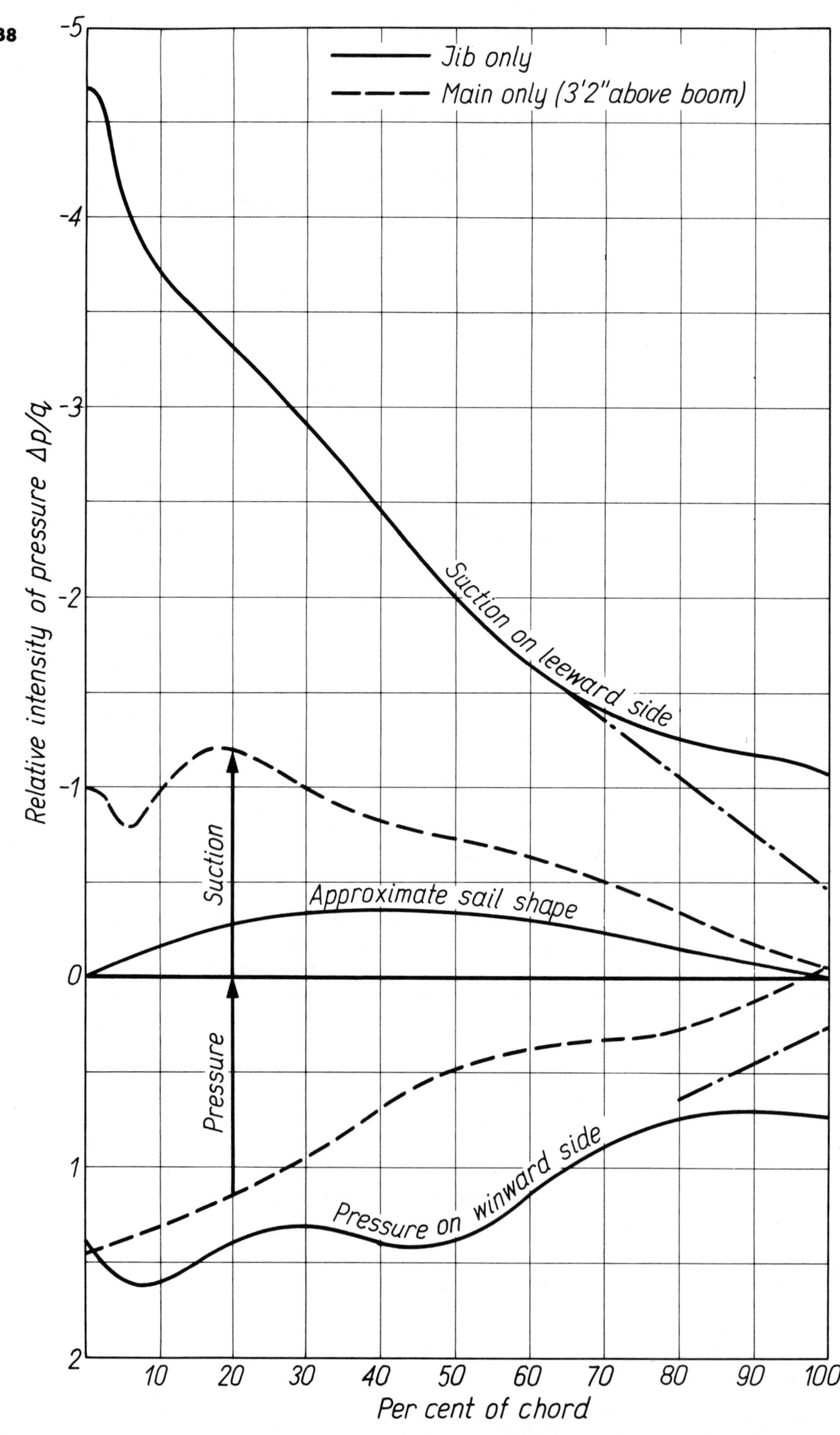

Jib only
Main only (3'2"above boom)
Relative intensity of pressure Δp/q
-5
-4
-3
-2
-1
0
1
2
Suction on leeward side
Suction
Approximate sail shape
Pressure
Pressure on winward side
10
20
30
40
50
60
70
80
90
100
Per cent of chord

in Figs. 35 and 38, where the former is behind a jib and the latter is not, shows one striking feature—the absence of a distinct suction peak in the case where the jib is absent. Due to the twist of the mainsail, the sections low down work at a larger angle of incidence to the wind than those higher up the mast, and are particularly prone to flow separation from the leeward side. The jib provides a very large stabilizing effect on the flow around the mainsail, and prevents separation of the flow, giving a more efficient mainsail.

To obtain a complete picture of the pressure distribution over the whole of a sail it is necessary to carry out the measurements along many sections at different heights. Figure 39 shows the results of such measurements for a Bermudian sail.

Fig. 39

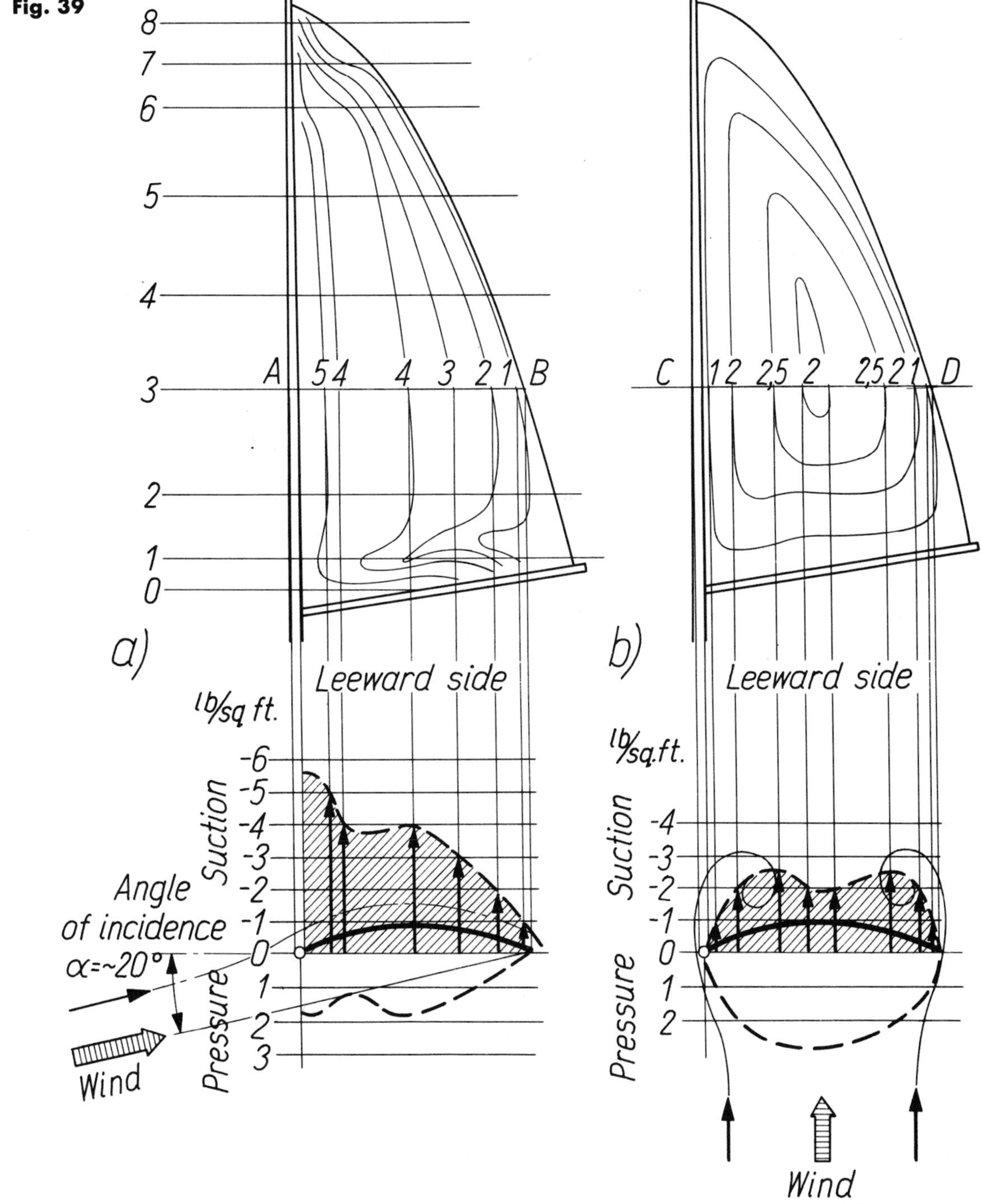

The results are plotted in the form of contours, lines joining points of equal pressure. Sail a gives the distribution of suction on the leeward side of the sail when at an angle of incidence of 20° to the wind. It will be noticed that the contour lines follow a regular pattern in the middle of the sail, but near the head and boom they have certain irregularities, indicating certain flow changes at the extremes of the sail. Sail b shows the suction distribution when the sail is at an angle of incidence of 90°. It is immediately noticeable how different is the distribution in this case from that of sail a. This can be explained by reference to the subdiagram showing the disturbed nature of the flow over sail b. As the wind attempts to flow round the mast and leech, it separates violently, forming large eddies, giving much lower values of suction. By comparing the pressure and suction fields for the two cases, we are able to conclude that the resultant force on sail a will be greater than that on b. This, however, is only true if two conditions are fulfilled, for sail a, to give the pressure distribution shown:

1. The camber of the sail should be suitable
2. The angle at which the sail is set should be large enough to obtain a fast air flow over the leeward side, but not so large that the air flow separates

3. THE EFFECTS OF AERODYNAMIC FORCES

The total, resultant aerodynamic force F_T generated by a sail can be approximately resolved into two components in a plane passing through the mast, as shown in Fig. 40a, b, c. These components are:

1. A driving force F_R acting along the direction of the course
2. A heeling force F_H acting perpendicular to both the course and the mast

The force F_H can be further resolved into two components, whose magnitudes will depend on the angle of heel, Θ, thus:

$$\text{horizontal, or lateral force } F_{lat.} = F_H \cos \Theta,$$
$$\text{vertical force } F_{vert.} = F_H \sin \Theta.$$

We can now consider in general terms, the effects of these force components on a yacht.

1. The yacht will move along a course with a velocity v_s. The magnitude of v_s depends on the driving force F_R, and will increase if F_R increases.
2. The drift of a yacht can be described by a leeway angle λ, measured between the course and the centerline of the hull. As $F_{lat.}$ increases, so also does λ.
3. The heel of the yacht is given by the angle Θ. This will depend on the magnitude of the heeling moment $M_H = F_H \times h$, where h is the distance, measured along the mast, between the "center of effort" (CE) of the total aerodynamic force F_T, and the "center of lateral resistance" (CLR), through which point passes the corresponding resultant hull force R_T. Increases of F_H and h both lead to increases in the heel of the yacht.

Fig. 40

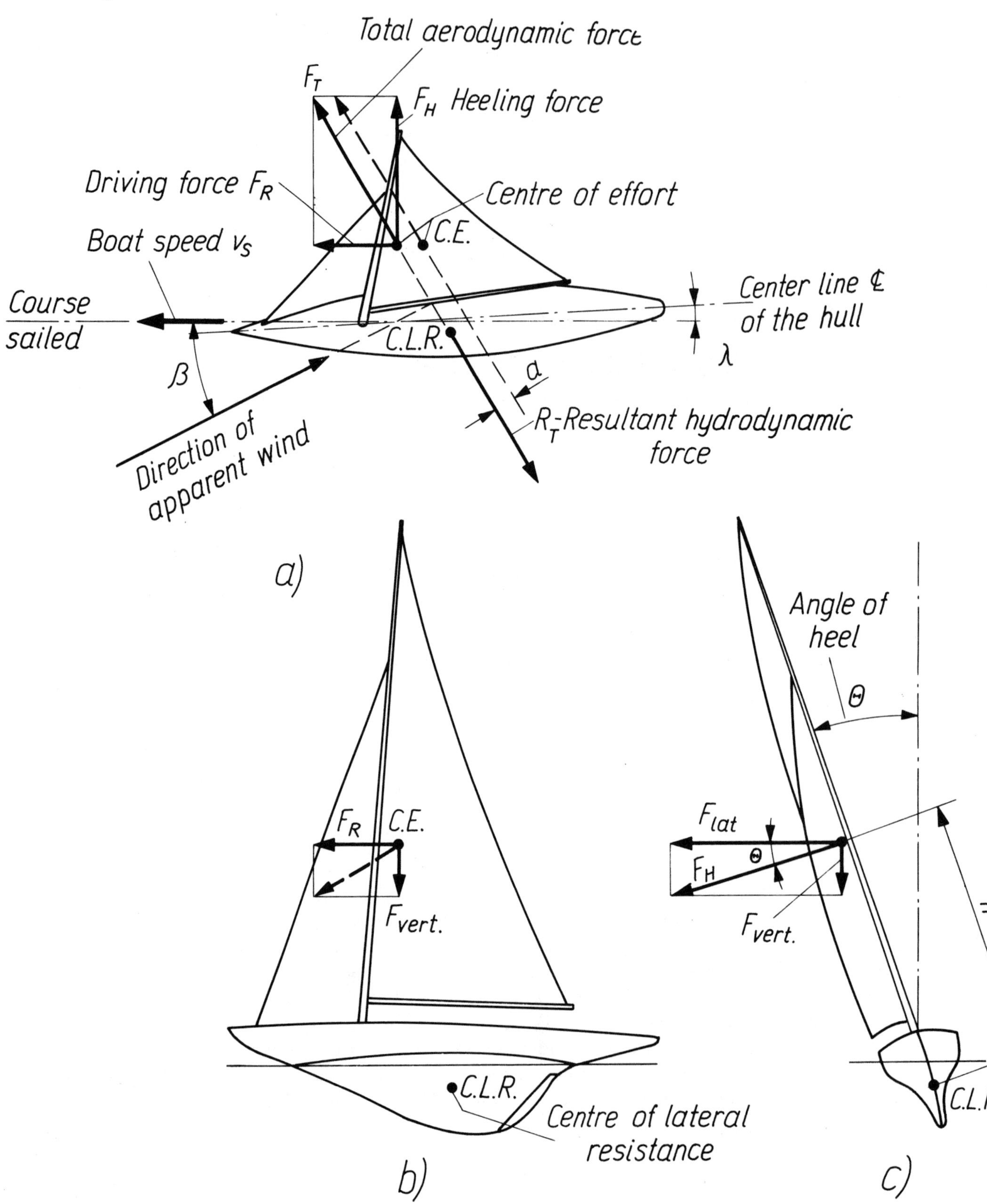

Total aerodynamic force
F_T
F_H Heeling force
Driving force F_R
Centre of effort
C.E.
Boat speed v_s
Course sailed
Center line ℄ of the hull
C.L.R.
λ
β
α
Direction of apparent wind
R_T-Resultant hydrodynamic force
a)
Angle of heel
Θ
F_R
C.E.
$F_{vert.}$
F_{lat}
F_H
Θ
$F_{vert.}$
C.L.R.
Centre of lateral resistance
C.L.R
b)
c)

4. The directional balance of the yacht can be measured by the amount of helm needed to maintain a given course. Balance is obtained when the total aerodynamic force F_T and the resultant hydrodynamic force R_T act along the same straight line, in the plan view (Fig. 40a). Large lee helm will be carried if the CE is forward of the CLR by, relatively, a large distance "a"; and if it is aft a distance "a" of the CLR, then the yacht will carry weather helm. In all cases, increases of F_H will lead to more imbalance.
5. Immersion of the hull. The force $F_{vert.}$ tends to increase the hull immersion beyond the designed LWL, and together with F_R, can affect the longitudinal trim, i.e., depress the bow and raise the stern. This will be discussed in more detail later.

The various effects described in 2, 3, 4, and 5 are all detrimental to the yacht's performance, since they increase to a greater or lesser extent the hydrodynamic resistance of the hull, and hence reduce the speed.

From the point of view of the racing yacht, the primary objective is to achieve a large driving force F_R, and simultaneously to reduce to a minimum the harmful force F_H, or its components $F_{lat.}$ and $F_{vert.}$.

To be able to predict the effect of the aerodynamic force F_T, we must clearly know its three characteristics:

(a) Magnitude
(b) Direction
(c) Point of application, here termed the CE (center of effort)

4. MEASUREMENT OF AERODYNAMIC FORCES

From experiments carried out on yachts, and in laboratories, and also from aerodynamic theory it was concluded that these three characteristics of an aerodynamic force depend on:

(a) The dynamic pressure $q = 0.00119 \times v_A^2$ of the apparent wind (v_A in ft./sec.)
(b) The sail area S_A (sq. ft.)
(c) The angular position of the sail, or sails, relative to the apparent wind, known as the angle of incidence α
(d) The shape of the sail, its cut and camber
(e) The sail cloth, its stiffness, weight, porosity, and smoothness

In considering the shape of a sail, an important quantity is its "aspect ratio" (A.R.), given by the ratio of its height to its average (mean) width.

For a rectangular sail (Fig. 41) the aspect ratio is simply

$$\text{A.R.} = \frac{L}{l}$$

Fig. 41

f

l

Camber $= \frac{f}{l}$

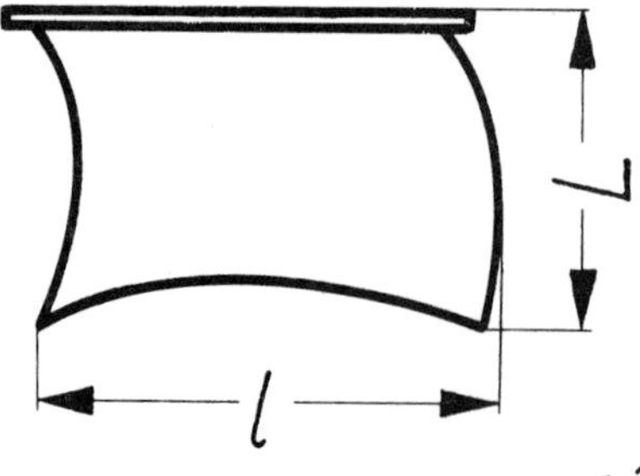

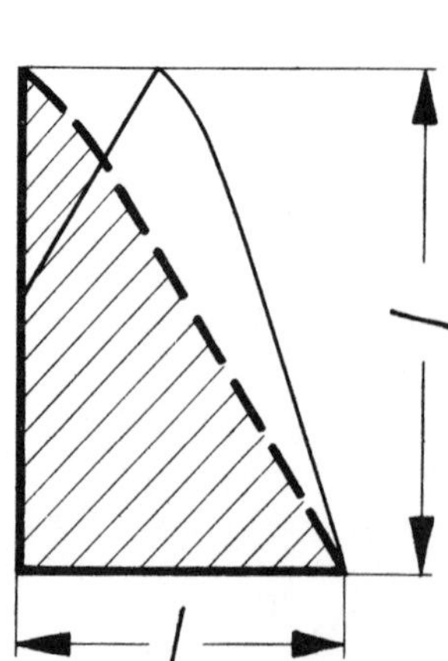

where L is the height of the sail
l is the length of the chord of the sail

For sail shapes other than a rectangle, the aspect ratio is obtained somewhat differently. If the sail area, S_A, is defined as the product of the height L and a mean chord, the mean chord is obtained by dividing S_A by L, and hence

$$A.R. = L \div \frac{S_A}{L} = \frac{L^2}{S_A}$$

The camber of a sail is measured by the ratio of the bow f of the section to its chord l.

$$\text{Camber} = \frac{f}{l}$$

With certain reservations we are able to combine the factors mentioned previously as determining the forces on a sail into a mathematical formula. The formula implies that if we have two sails of the same shape, cut, and incidence setting, but of different areas—i.e., geometrically similar—working in winds of different dynamic pressures, then the forces developed will be proportional to their respective areas and dynamic pressures. If we describe the geometrical factors by a coefficient C, then we can write:

$$\begin{aligned} F &= q \times S_A \times C \\ &= 0.00119 \times v_A{}^2 \times S_A \times C \end{aligned}$$

where F is the aerodynamic force in lb.
v_A is the velocity of the apparent wind in ft./sec.
S_A is the sail area in sq. ft.
C is the aerodynamic force coefficient

It is usually more convenient to discuss the properties of a sail in the coefficient form, since in doing so, we are not tied down to actual size and wind speed. If a model sail satisfies all the geometric conditions for similarity with a full-scale sail, then it will have the same coefficient.

The aerodynamic coefficient is derived experimentally by measuring forces on a model sail, or a full-sized sail in a wind tunnel, in which the wind speed can be accurately controlled by varying the revolutions of a fan. Usually the different geometric factors such as shape, camber, and angle of incidence are varied, and the dependence of the coefficient obtained. Experiments of this nature are often very expensive and have their limitations, as it is not possible to represent the varied conditions of wind direction and speed, and the motion of a yacht encountered in practice.

Although measurements made on models in wind tunnels are not strictly representative of true sailing conditions, they do lead to an understanding of the aerodynamic forces on sails, and it is possible to establish the influence of many different

Fig. 42A. Schematic diagram of the wind tunnel (working section) at Southampton University.

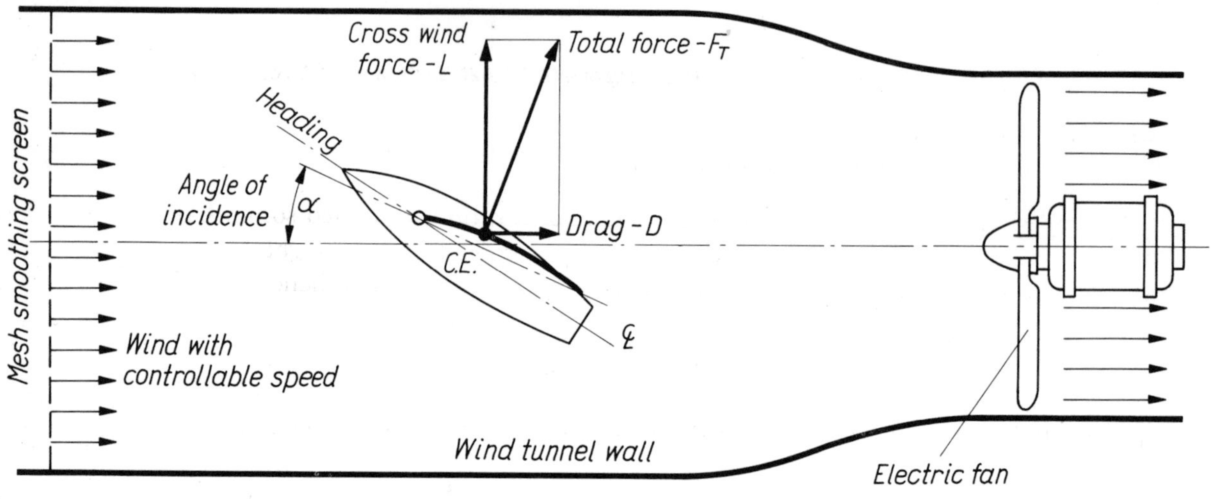

Fig. 42B. Schematic balance arrangement in the wind tunnel.

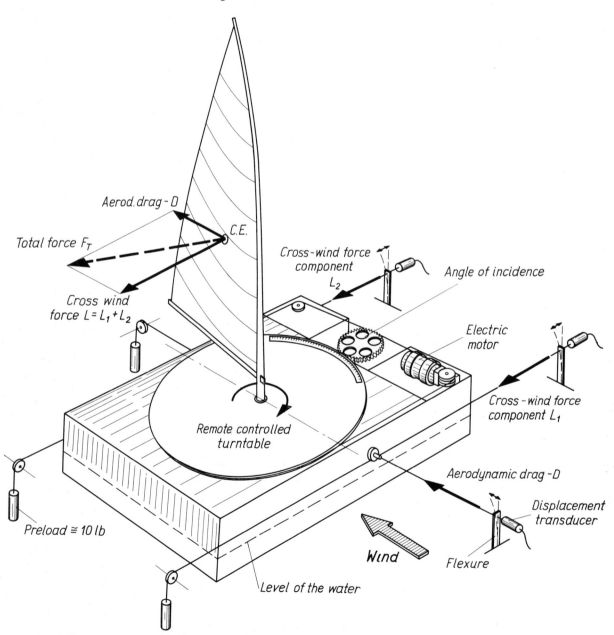

Aerod. drag - D
C.E.
Total force F_T
Cross wind force $L = L_1 + L_2$
Cross-wind force component L_2
Angle of incidence
Electric motor
Cross-wind force component L_1
Remote controlled turntable
Aerodynamic drag - D
Displacement transducer
Preload ≅ 10 lb
Wind
Flexure
Level of the water

factors such as camber, sailcloth, angle of incidence, twist of the sail, mast, etc., which can be held under close control. To understand fully the aerodynamic phenomena of sailing one must both study full-scale yachts and perform experiments on models. Each complements the other, and either one by itself is inadequate.

The significance of wind tunnel experiments will be better appreciated if the method of measuring the aerodynamic forces, and graphic presentation of the results are explained. Figures 42a and b and 43 and photographs 1a and b show the principle of the measurements of the forces on a model sail. The sail (or sails in presence of the hull) under investigation is placed in a controlled wind stream and is connected to a suitable weighing system called a balance, to measure the forces. For reason of convenience it is usual to construct the balance so that instead of measuring the total force F_T, it measures two components:

1. The cross-wind force L, perpendicular to the wind direction
2. The drag force D along the wind direction

The balance in the wind tunnel at Southampton University shown in Fig. 42b and Photos. 1a and b was designed bearing in mind conclusions based on the analyses of early sail tests carried out during the last 30 years in various wind tunnels. From many of the lessons learned in previous experiments it became obvious that to make it possible to determine the influence of important factors on sail efficiency with a reasonable degree of accuracy and reliability, it was necessary to experiment with fabric ("soft") sails on a sufficiently large scale. With one exception—Sir Richard Fairey Wind Tunnel (G.B.) of a big square section 12 × 12 ft. where the primary aim of the tests was to tune up and improve the

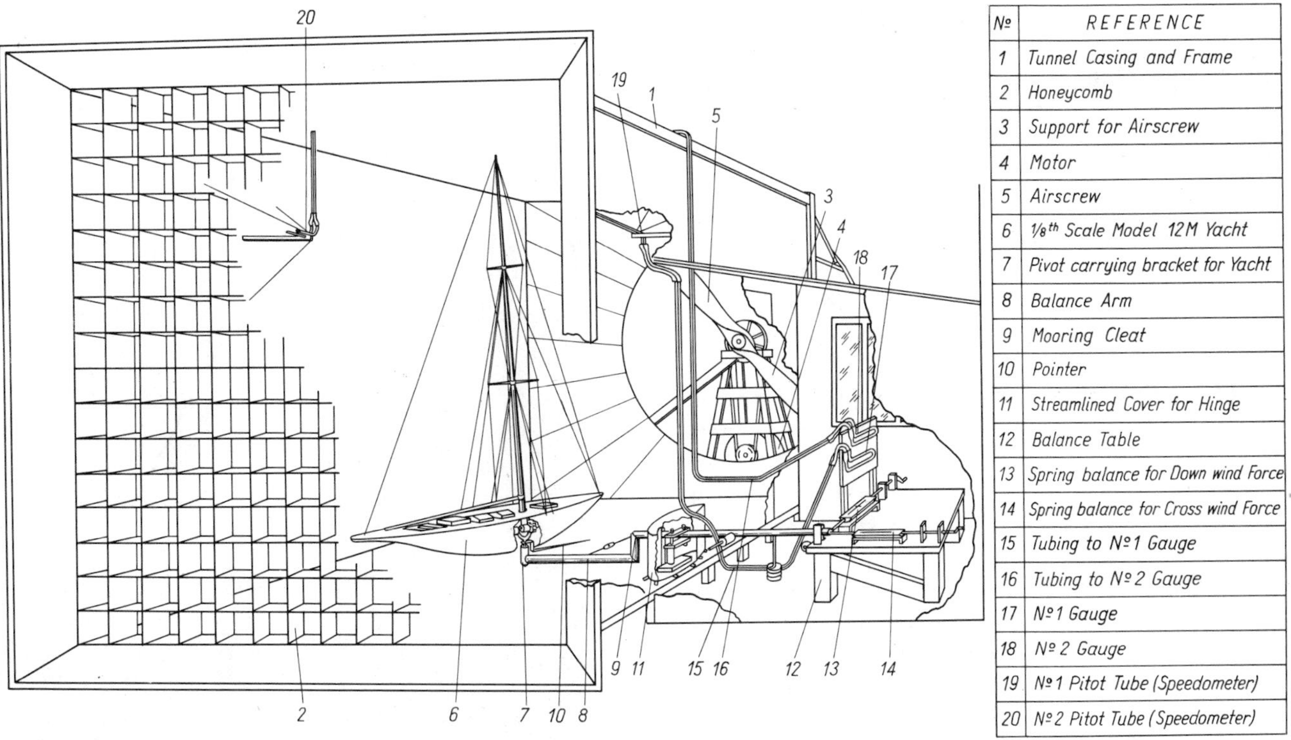

20
19
1
5
3
4
18
17
9 11
15 16
12 13
14
2
6
7 10 8
№ REFERENCE
1 Tunnel Casing and Frame
2 Honeycomb
3 Support for Airscrew
4 Motor
5 Airscrew
6 1/8th Scale Model 12M Yacht
7 Pivot carrying bracket for Yacht
8 Balance Arm
9 Mooring Cleat
10 Pointer
11 Streamlined Cover for Hinge
12 Balance Table
13 Spring balance for Down wind Force
14 Spring balance for Cross wind Force
15 Tubing to №1 Gauge
16 Tubing to №2 Gauge
17 №1 Gauge
18 №2 Gauge
19 №1 Pitot Tube (Speedometer)
20 №2 Pitot Tube (Speedometer)

Fig. 43. Experimental Wind Tunnel for Research on model sails (Sir Richard Fairey, England)

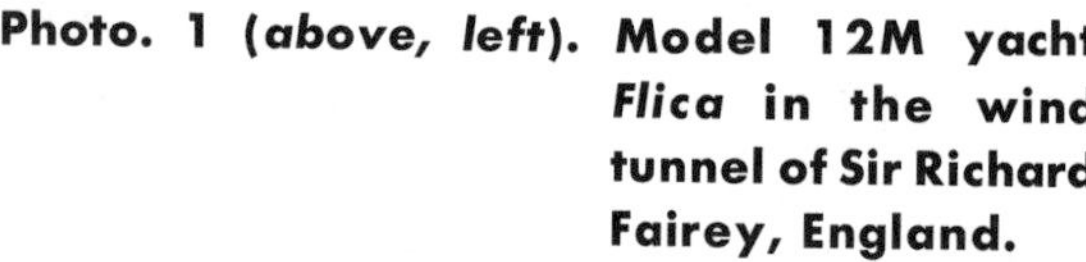

Photo. 1 (*above, left*). **Model 12M yacht *Flica* in the wind tunnel of Sir Richard Fairey, England.**

Photo. 1A (*above, right*). **Dragon model, undergoing tests in the wind tunnel at wind speed of 25 ft./2 sec.**

Photo. 1B (*right*). **A model of the sails of an X-one design class yacht being tested in the large wind tunnel at Southampton University.**

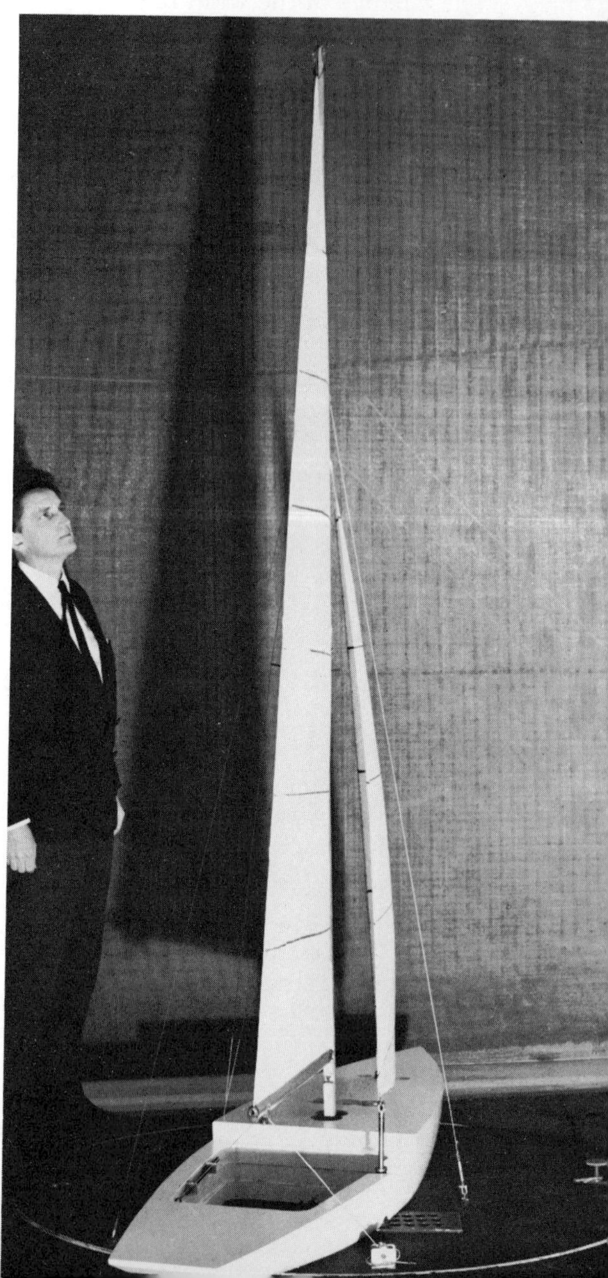

performance of J-Class yacht—all other experiments have been performed in relatively small working sections using conventional tunnel balances not suited to these purposes.

This necessarily limited experimenters to using small, in most cases, rigid, sheet metal sails. Tests on solid sails can not, of course, be completely successful as they can not simulate fabric sails, although they are very convenient tools to predict general trends and also to obtain qualitative information.

According to the opinion of leading sailmakers the length of the luff should be not less than about 7 feet to overcome problems of manufacturing a proper model of the sail. On this scale the camber of the sail could be predetermined and also the similarity between model and full sail with regard to the method of cutting, elasticity and structural details could be maintained.

In addition it is desirable to simulate the active working condition of the sail as closely as possible, namely:

1. To simulate the sea surface and hull,
2. To avoid the effect of gravity forces on the sail shape,
3. To heel the sail and hull relative to the sea surface,
4. To modify the tension in and directions of sheets and the position of other sail fastenings.

The arrangement of the balance is shown schematically in Fig. 42b and Photos. 1a and b. The sail is attached to a mast and boom connected to a pontoon floating in a water tank which is recessed into the floor of the wind tunnel. The pontoon is made large and buoyant enough to minimize pitching and rolling motion so that it remains virtually horizontal. Its motion is controlled by three flexures, the deflections of which are proportional to the force components L_1, L_2 and D. Deflection in the range 0–0.025 inches are measured electrically using inductive displacement transducers. A remote controlled turntable enables the rig to be rotated to simulate a change of heading angle of the yacht relative to the wind or to simulate a change of angle of incidence of the sail. Special fittings on the turntable allow the sheeting of the sails to be varied. In other words the vertical and horizontal position of the boom can be altered. In this way, not only the effect of the sheeting base can be investigated but also, the effect of the sea, i.e. the gap between boom and the sea surface which seems to be significant.

For various angles of incidence α from the minimum possible up to 90°, we measure the corresponding values of L and D, and by using the type of construction shown in Fig. 44, obtain the total force F_T. Along the vertical axis we mark the cross-wind force L and on the horizontal axis the drag force D. For example, when the model sail is set at an angle $\alpha = 27°$, the measured cross-wind force L will correspond to OY_A, and the drag force D will correspond to OX_A, then from a parallelogram of forces their resultant force F_T will be represented in both magnitude and direction by OA. In a similar way we treat the values of L and D for say $\alpha = 5°, 10°, 15°$, up to 90°, and hence obtain a curve giving the variation of the magnitude and direction of the resultant force with incidence. This curve, known as a "polar diagram" of the aerodynamic forces on a sail, is valid only for the particular sail, of a certain area S_A, tested at a particular wind speed v_A. It provides a ready means for determining the forces on the one sail, but lacks generality.

To make the results from tests on a model sail generally applicable to other, similar sails and to allow comparison of one sail with another, we express the results as coefficients, as described earlier, by dividing the measured forces by the dynamic pressure of the air stream in the wind tunnel and by the model sail area:

$$\frac{L, D, F_T}{S_A \times 0.00119 v_A^2} = C_L,\ C_D,\ C_T, \text{ respectively}$$

If at any time we want the actual forces which would be developed on, say, a similar full-size sail, we multiply the coefficients by the full-size sail area and the dynamic pressure of the wind in which we are interested, thus:

$$F_{T_{F.S}} = C_T \times 0.00119 v_A{}^2{}_{F.S} \times S_{A_{F.S}}$$

where the subsuffix refers to "full-size."

By plotting the coefficients in polar diagram form, we can readily compare results of tests on all manner of sails, at different wind speeds, and thus study the character of the aerodynamic forces.

Figure 45 shows the polar diagram of the coefficients of the sail forces illustrated earlier in Fig. 44. We can see that the former reflects faithfully all the characteristics of the latter, showing the correct line of action and magnitudes proportional to those of the original forces.

In subsequent discussions on aerodynamic forces, we will frequently, for the above reasons, consider them in their coefficient form.

The polar diagram of Fig. 45 shows some results obtained by T. Tanner in tests on a Bermudian sail of aspect ratio A.R. = 4.2, made of light cotton cloth. We can compare this with the polar diagram obtained from measurements made at Göttingen Institute on sheet-metal aerofoils without masts (Fig. 46).

Curve I refers to a flat aerofoil, and Curve II refers to an aerofoil having a camber of 1⁄10. The areas in both cases were the same, and A.R. = 5.

From both Figs. 45 and 46 we can deduce that both camber and angle of incidence have a large effect on the magnitude and direction of the force coefficient C_T and thus on the total force. It can also be seen that the maximum force coefficient for the soft sail (Fig. 45) occurs at an angle of incidence $\alpha = 27°$, whilst that of the cambered plate (Fig. 46) occurs at $\alpha = 15°$.

It is interesting to compare, from Fig. 46, the values of the force coefficients for the two aerofoils, one flat and one cambered. Particularly at the smaller angles of incidence the differences are very marked, both in magnitude and direction. For instance, at an angle of incidence $\alpha = 15°$, the total force F_{T2} of the flat aerofoil is about half that of F_{T1} of the cambered aerofoil, the former acts aft of the perpendicular to the sail chord, and the latter acts forward of it. This same information is

Fig. 44

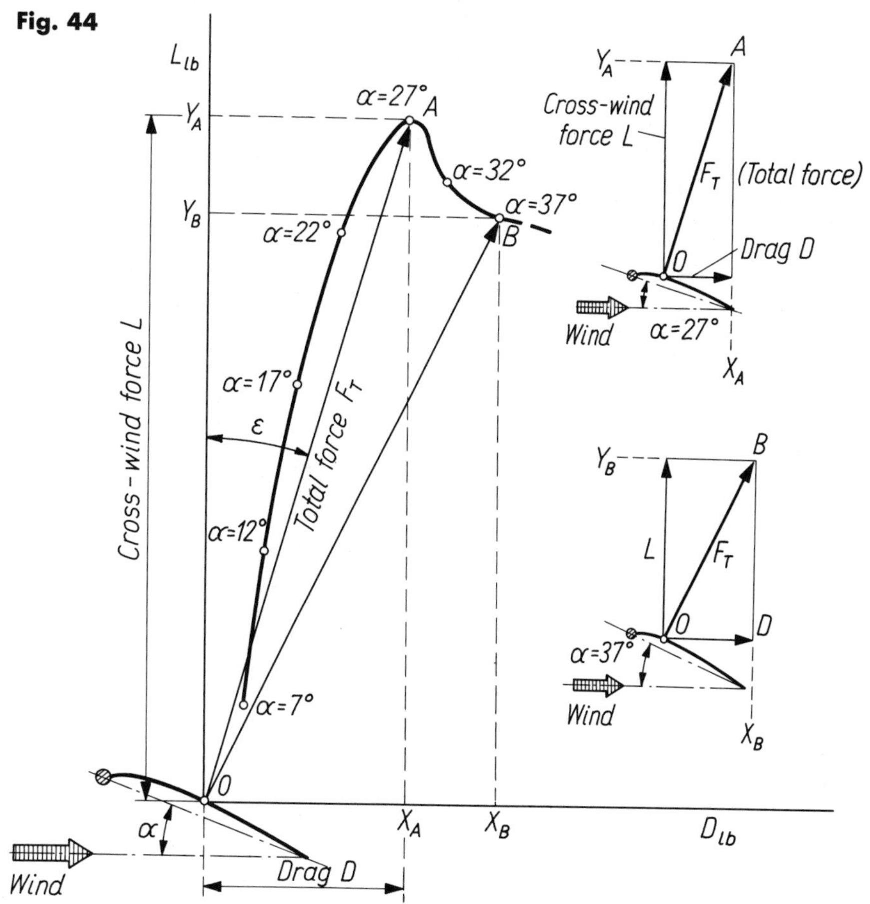

L lb
Y A
Y B
α=27° A
α=32°
α=37°
B
α=22°
α=17°
ε
Total force F T
α=12°
α=7°
Cross-wind force L
O
X A
X B
D lb
α
Wind
Drag D
Y A
A
Cross-wind force L
F T (Total force)
O
Drag D
Wind
α=27°
X A
Y B
B
L
F T
O
D
α=37°
Wind
X B

Fig. 45

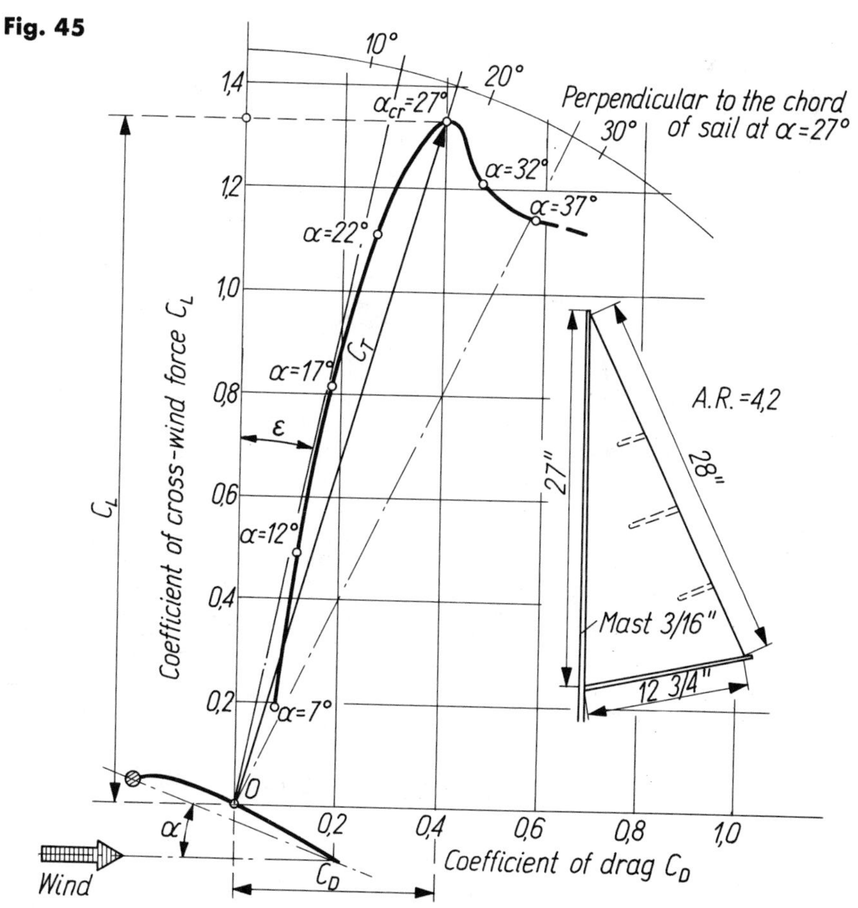

10°
20°
30°
1,4
1,2
1,0
0,8
0,6
0,4
0,2
α cr=27°
Perpendicular to the chord of sail at α=27°
α=32°
α=37°
α=22°
α=17°
C T
ε
α=12°
α=7°
Coefficient of cross-wind force C L
C L
O
α
Wind
C D
0,2
0,4
0,6
0,8
1,0
Coefficient of drag C D
A.R.=4,2
27"
28"
Mast 3/16"
12 3/4"

Fig. 46

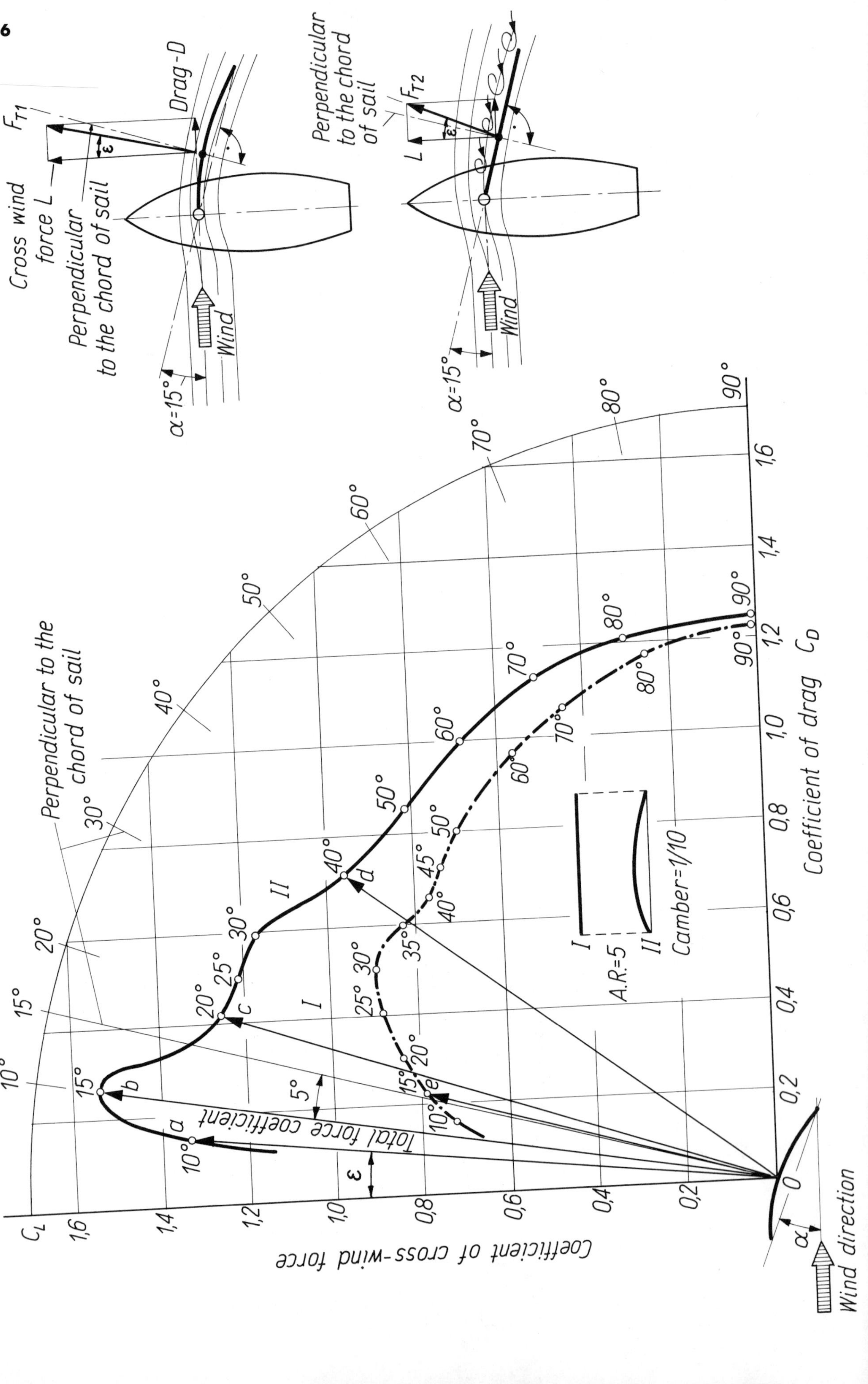

Cross wind force L

F_{T1}

Perpendicular to the chord of sail

ε

Drag-D

α=15°

Wind

Perpendicular to the chord of sail

L

F_{T2}

ε

α=15°

Wind

C_L

1,6

1,4

1,2

1,0

0,8

0,6

0,4

0,2

Coefficient of cross-wind force

10° 15° 20° 30° 40° 50° 60° 70° 80° 90°

Perpendicular to the chord of sail

Total force coefficient

ε

5°

a b c d e

I II

A.R.=5

Camber=1/10

0 0,2 0,4 0,6 0,8 1,0 1,2 1,4 1,6

Coefficient of drag C_D

α

Wind direction

conveyed in a more concise manner in Fig. 46 by the two lines Ob and Oe. The perpendiculars to the sail chord are drawn as radii from O to the outer circular arc, bearing in mind that the wind direction lies along the horizontal C_D axis.

The great differences between Curves I and II can be largely attributed to the different flows over the leeward sides, as a result of the curvature. With the perfectly flat sail, the flow finds it impossible to travel smoothly round the leading edge of the sail, and so separates, covering the lee side of the sail with eddies. One effect of camber is to introduce the leading edge more gradually into the flow, which in consequence does not separate. Instead, it passes smoothly round the lee side, accelerating as it is constricted, giving rise to a large suction. At greater angles of incidence, when the flow separates over most of the cambered sail also, the differences between the two sails tends to disappear. At an angle of incidence $\alpha = 90°$, corresponding to sailing on a run, the difference is so slight as to be negligible. At this high angle of incidence, the total sail force depends a lot less on the lee-side suction forces than on the lesser angles of incidence. The foregoing remarks explain why a perfectly flat sail is bad. Later the disadvantages of too large a camber will also be explained.

In Fig. 46 we will now consider the total force coefficients Oa, Ob, Oc, and Od at the respective angles of incidence $\alpha = 10°, 15°, 20°$, and $40°$. If these results are translated in terms of actual sailing on a reach, as in Fig. 47, we can clearly

Fig. 47

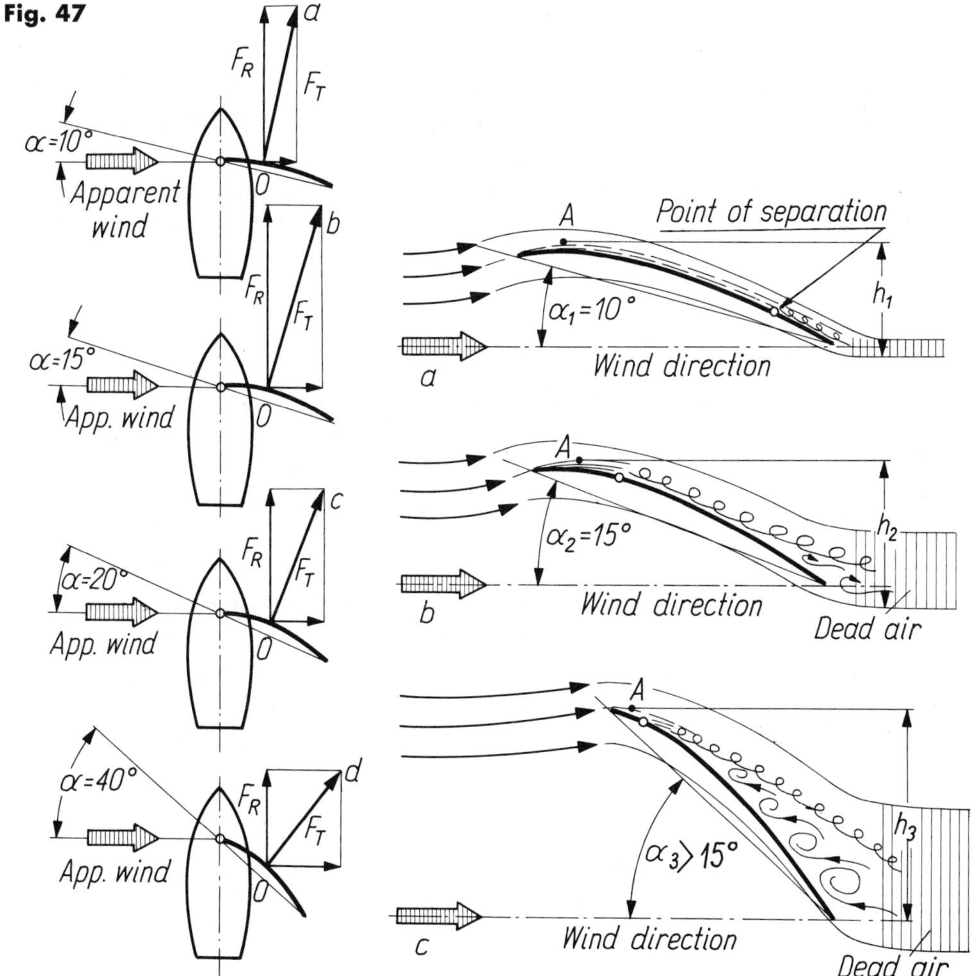

see how important is the angle of incidence for the yacht's motion. Depending on the trim of the mainsail so will the forces vary. If the sail is pulled in too hard, at too large an angle of incidence, the forward, driving component F_R of the total force F_T will be low, and will give a corresponding reduction of the speed of the yacht.

(a) Gradual Changes of Incidence

Let us look in greater detail at the changes in the aerodynamic forces illustrated in Fig. 47. The reaching case, when the apparent wind is at 90° to the hull center-line, allows us to simplify the discussion, since in this case the driving force F_R corresponds to the wind-tunnel cross-wind force L.

Although both sides of the sail are important, the lee side is particularly so, since it is largely the flow on this side which limits the forces the sail can develop. If we gradually increase the sail incidence α, and simultaneously investigate the flow on the lee side (Fig. 47a), and record F_R in a graph, as in Fig. 48a, we find that up to an incidence α_1, the graph is practically a straight line, and the flow lies smoothly on the sail, following its contour. Beyond this incidence the flow character changes somewhat, the change originating near the leech and spreading forward with increasing incidence. The flow now adheres to the sail contour only over the forward portions, it then separates from the sail and gradually diverges from it into the true, undisturbed wind direction. Over the rear portion of the sail there now exists a confused, turbulent wake in the region between the sail and the flow proper. In practical terms this means that the expected increase in F_R for a given increase in incidence is not realized and results in the graph bending from the straight line as in Fig. 48, points A and B. With increasing incidence, one reaches a value α_2 (Fig. 46 point B) when a maximum value of F_R is obtained (point B on Fig. 48a). From this point onward the sail is said to be in a fully stalled condition, with virtually the whole of the flow on the leeward side being separated. Beyond this point, F_R tends to fall to lower values such as at α_3 (Figs. 46 point C, 47 point C, and 48 point C).

(b) Rapid and Repeated Changes of Incidence (Pumping)

The preceding discussion has been confined to cases in which the incidence was increased slowly and smoothly. It has been established, however, in laboratory tests on aerofoils, that if instead the incidence is increased quickly, the character of the leeward flow is altered if one is working in the incidence region above α_1. For a short while after the incidence is increased, to a value which in the steady case would have some separated flow, the flow adheres smoothly to the sail, with a corresponding increase in F_R. One is able by this means to get temporary increases of F_R, of up to 40–45 per cent, in the region from α_1 to beyond the stall. This phenomenon is shown in Fig. 48b, where the broken line ABC represents the values of F_R obtained by slowly increasing the incidence, and the upper full line ADE the values obtained by rapid changes in incidence. This upper line represents

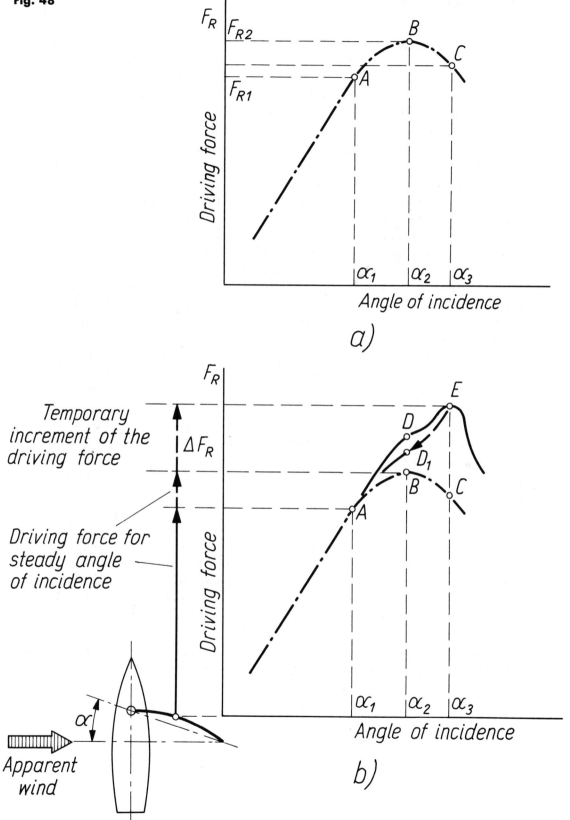

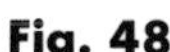
F_R
F_{R2}
F_{R1}
B
C
A
Driving force
α_1
α_2
α_3
Angle of incidence
a)
F_R
E
D
D_1
B
C
A
Temporary increment of the driving force
ΔF_R
Driving force for steady angle of incidence
Driving force
α
Apparent wind
α_1
α_2
α_3
Angle of incidence
b)

Fig. 48

only a temporary increase of F_R, and if the incidence is held, after the rapid increase, the separation will progress forward to the normal position. Thus, referring to Fig. 48b, suppose one managed to traverse the portion of the graph ADE by a single rapid change of incidence. If the sail is now held steady, then F_R would fall to C, which is clearly undesirable. If instead the sheet was eased gradually, one could return to A along ED_1A, giving a substantial increase in average F_R over the value at A. If in the first instance, one only went from A to D, still on the linear portion of the curve, then one could return along DA.

This process of changing the magnitude of an aerodynamic force on a sail by a rapid change of the angle of incidence provides the basis of a relatively new and quite successful sailing technique popular among some high performance centerboard classes such as the Flying Dutchman, 5-0-5, and Finn, when sailing off the wind. This technique has become known within the sailing fraternity by the descriptive term "pumping," which simply means a regularly repeated process of trimming the sails in which they are first sheeted in abruptly, and then the sheets eased rather slowly. The effect of pumping on increasing the boat's speed has been demonstrated conclusively, and it has been found particularly effective in planing or surfing conditions, in which planing has been achieved earlier and prolonged after the wind strength has lessened.

The helmsman, if he is to obtain the maximum advantage from pumping, must be fully aware of what the air flow is doing on the leeward side of the sail and must adjust the frequency and amplitude of his actions to suit the wind speed and his sailing conditions. He should preferably start the action from a point when the sail has little or no separated flow (point A on Fig. 48b) and ease the sheet before the separation spreads forward and the sail stalls. Pumping should be particularly effective when the sail has little twist, when all sections are working at about the same incidence. The phenomenon is not confined to the reaching case considered, but can be exploited at most points of sailing other than close hauled and on a run.

From the viewpoint of an observer, one can get the impression that the helmsman is helping to propel the boat by dint of the muscular effort he puts into alternately hardening and easing the sheets, and it is this impression which lies at the root of the controversy over pumping. There is a suggestion that pumping contravenes the basic I.Y.R.U. rule about "means of propulsion," which states: "No yacht shall employ any means of propulsion other than the natural action of the wind on the sails."

From the above discussion it is quite clear that if he applies the technique correctly, the helmsman is able to obtain significant increases in driving force, and hence speed, using ". . . the natural action of the wind on the sails." His actions are thus in accordance with the spirit of the I.Y.R.U. regulation.

5. AERODYNAMIC RESISTANCE OF THE SAIL

When beating against the wind (Fig. 49a) we should like to have the maximum possible driving force F_R, and simultaneously a minimum sideways, heeling force F_H, so that we may sail at high speed, with negligible heel and drift. We may see from the following trigonometrical relations that the values of F_R and F_H depend on the angle β between the course and the apparent wind, and on the cross-wind force L and drag D. It should be remembered that L and D are themselves derived from the total force F_T, and the more forward F_T acts, the greater will be L and the less the value of D.

Fig. 49A

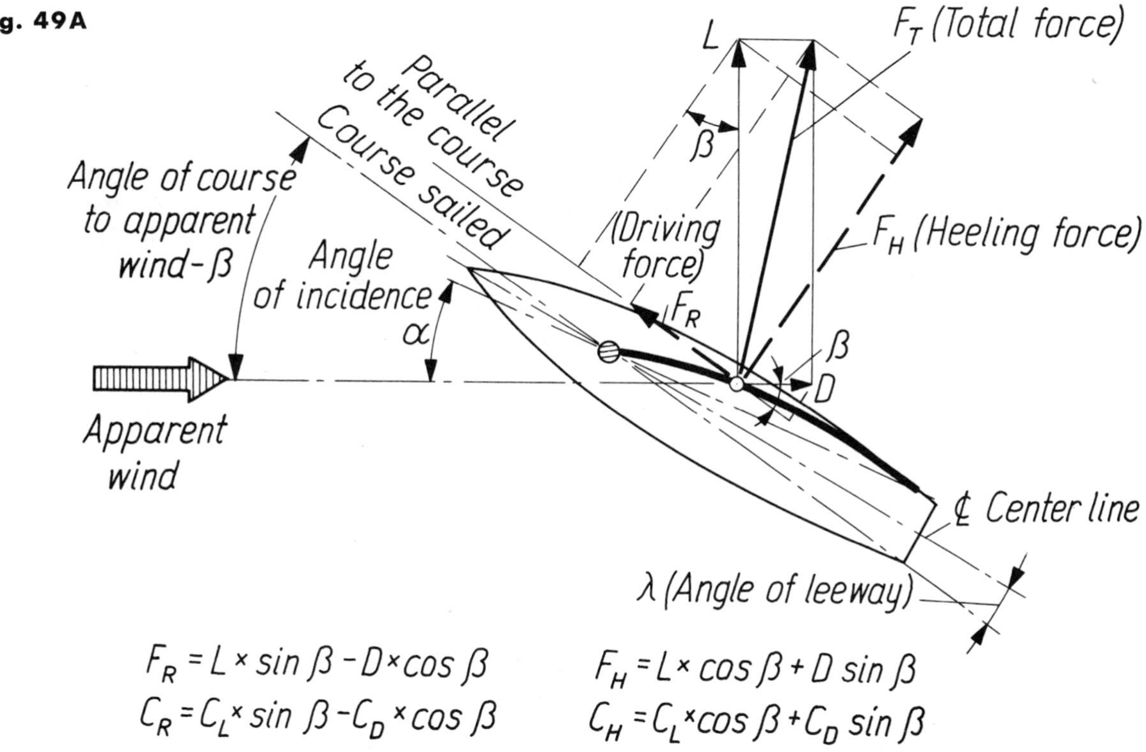

$$F_R = L \times \sin\beta - D \times \cos\beta \qquad F_H = L \times \cos\beta + D \sin\beta$$

$$C_R = C_L \times \sin\beta - C_D \times \cos\beta \qquad C_H = C_L \times \cos\beta + C_D \sin\beta$$

Fig. 49B

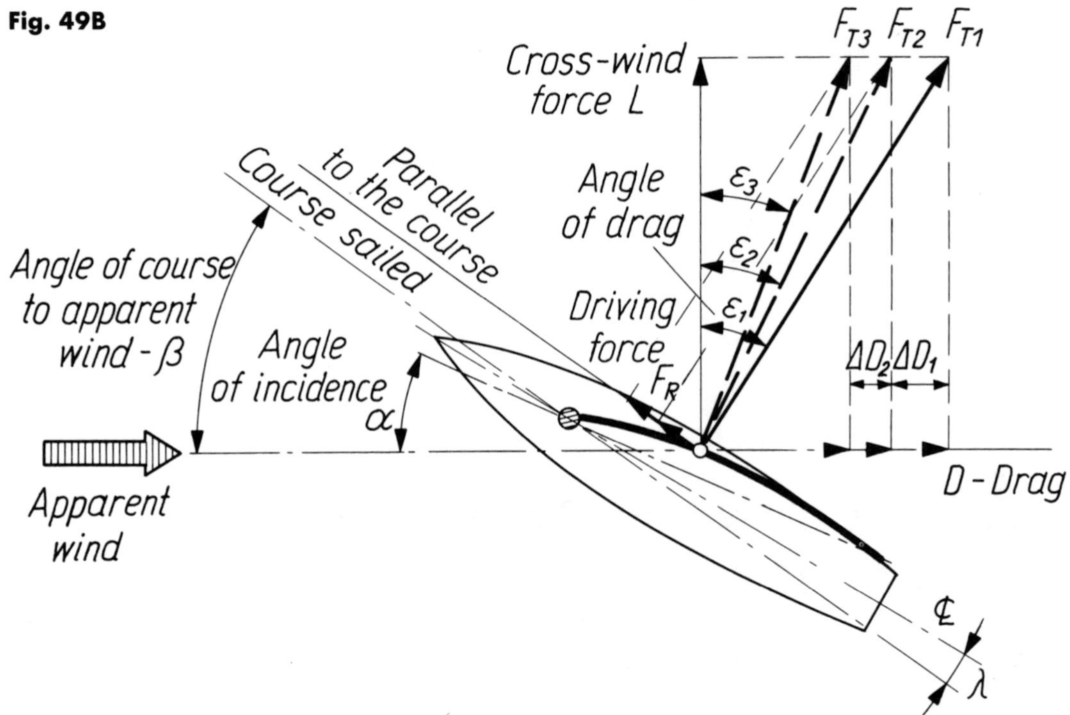

$$F_R = L \times \sin \beta - D \times \cos \beta$$
$$F_H = L \times \cos \beta + D \times \sin \beta$$

or in coefficient form,

$$C_R = C_L \times \sin \beta - C_D \times \cos \beta$$
$$C_H = C_L \times \cos \beta + C_D \times \sin \beta$$

We can conclude immediately from either pair of these equations that the drag not only lowers the driving force F_R, but also increases the harmful heeling force F_H.

The action of aerodynamic drag is particularly harmful when one is sailing close-hauled, for reasons best understood by referring to Fig. 49b.

When sailing a yacht, it is possible, by gradually luffing into wind, to reach a condition where the yacht loses forward motion and only drifts to leeward. This will occur when the total sail force F_{T1} acts perpendicular to the direction of the yacht's course, i.e., when the forward force component F_R disappears. This then represents a limiting value of β for beating to windward. We can see from Fig. 49b that if we could reduce the aerodynamic drag D of the yacht by an amount ΔD_1, we would alter the direction of the total force to F_{T2}, and the yacht would regain forward motion due to the appearance of a driving force F_R. For a further reduction of the drag by AD_2, we would obtain a further increase of speed to windward.

From the foregoing argument we can say that the angle between the course and the apparent wind direction depends to a large extent on the ratio L/D. This ratio also expresses the angle of F_T to the wind direction, termed the angle of drag ϵ, since cot ϵ = L/D. In general, a small value of the angle of drag is desirable, particularly when racing. The question now arises as to the nature of the drag D, and whether it is possible to reduce it.

Theory and experiment show that the resultant drag D is made up of three components:

(a) Induced drag
(b) Friction drag
(c) Form drag

Their individual contributions to the total drag D depend on the shape of the sail, its type of surface, and the speed of the wind.

(a) The Induced Drag

Induced drag, D_i, for a sail of aspect ratio A.R. is that portion of the total drag which is inseperably connected with the formation of the cross-wind force L. This force arises from the differences in pressure on the two sides of the sail. The air on the windward side, being generally at a higher pressure than that on the leeward side, attempts to reduce the difference by flowing to the leeward side, round the boom and at the head of the sail. (See Fig. 50 and Photo. 2 A and B.) As a re-

Fig. 50

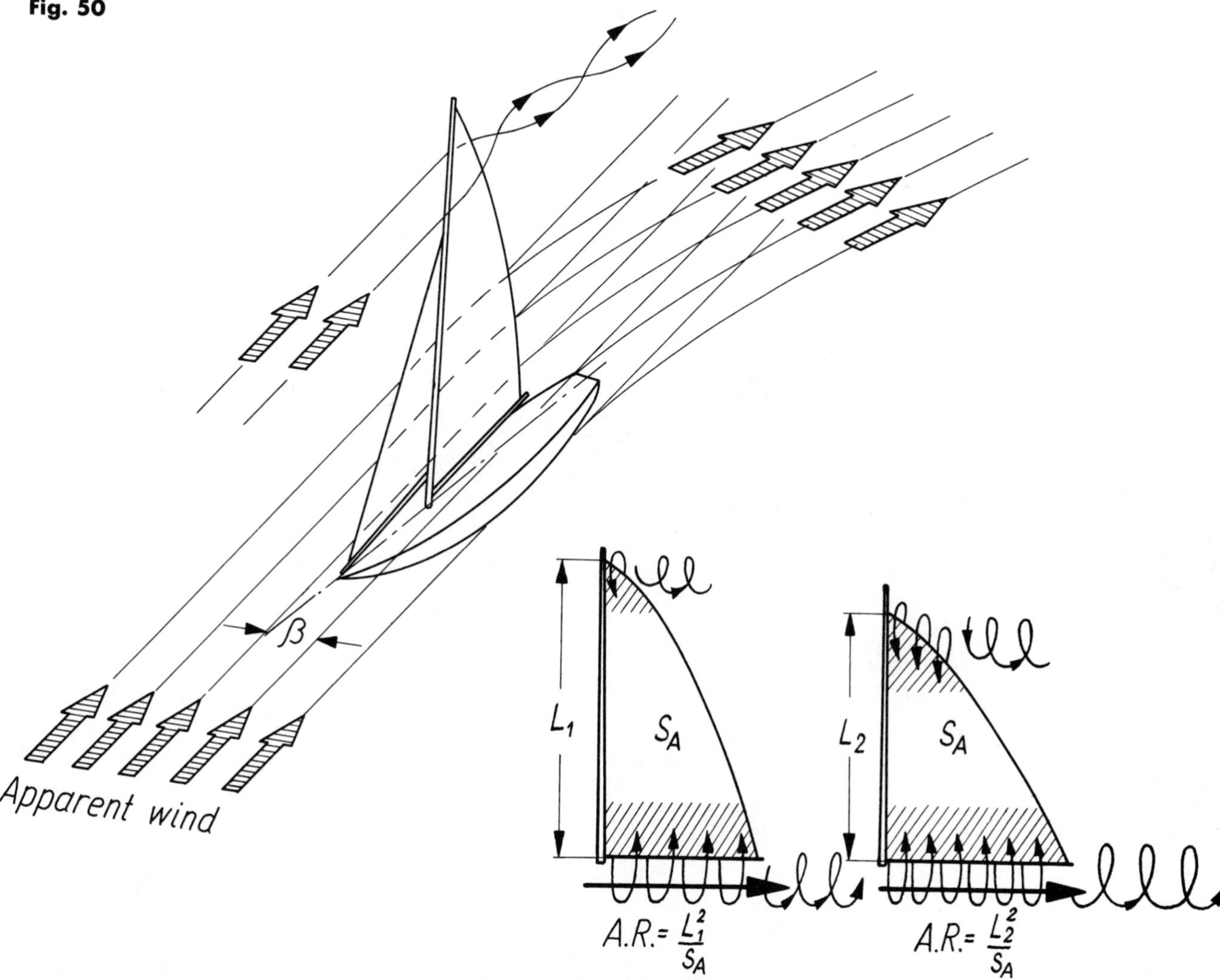

sult of this flow of air around the "ends" of the sail, the pressure differences between the two sides are reduced, and vortices are formed in the air flow.

In the course of experiments carried out at Southampton University, some photographs were taken showing the air flow in the neighborhood of a model sloop. Photograph 2 A and B show views looking from astern, and C a view looking down on the starboard bow. In A, the model is upright, and B is heeled and is also at a larger angle of incidence. They show how the flow around the head and boom from the windward to the leeward side rolls up into two vortices which extend astern of the model. C shows how the general direction of the wind stream is altered by the sails.

Taken together, these photographs demonstrate the principles behind the racing tactics of blanketing. Not only is the astern boat unable to point so high, but also she sails in very dirty air.

The magnitude of the induced drag is not constant, but depends to a large extent on the magnitude of the cross-wind force, L, and the aspect ratio, A.R., of the sail. The pressure differences on the sail depend almost entirely on L, and on these depends the amount of flow around the boom and head, and hence the induced drag. Similarly it is easy to see, in general terms, why the sail shape can affect the induced drag. The higher is the aspect ratio of a sail, the less will be the influence of the small foot and the head in comparison with the rest of the sail. We are usually able to express these conclusions approximately in a formula:

$$D_i = k \frac{L^2}{A.R.}$$

where k is a constant depending on the shape of the sail, etc.

Photo. 2. Flow visualization on a model yacht in the wind tunnel at Southampton University.

A

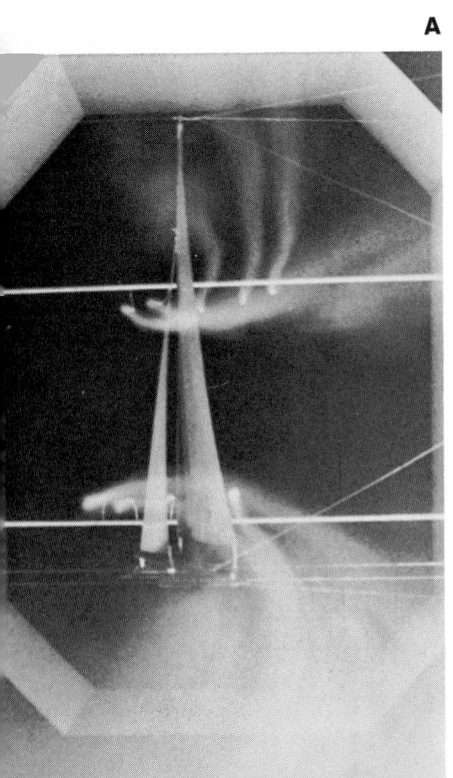

B

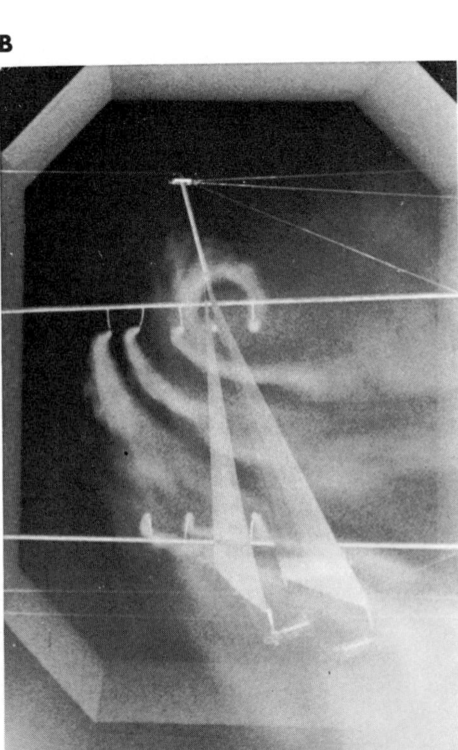

C

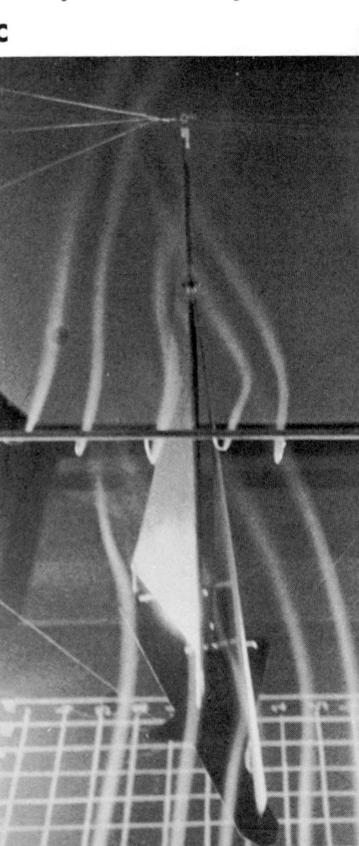

Some constructors, wishing to decrease the losses associated with the induced drag, introduced wide booms, whose function was to prevent the flow around the boom. An example of such a device was the Park Avenue boom, used on the *Enterprise,* winner of the fourteenth America's Cup, in 1930 (Photo. 3). An additional benefit to be gained from this idea was the continuation of the flow of the sail right down to the boom, since the foot was attached to the boom on transverse runners.

Some experiments were conducted in Junkers wind tunnel on a Bermudian sail with a bent mast and an end plate attached to the boom on the leeward side

Photo. 3. *Enterprise's* Park Avenue boom

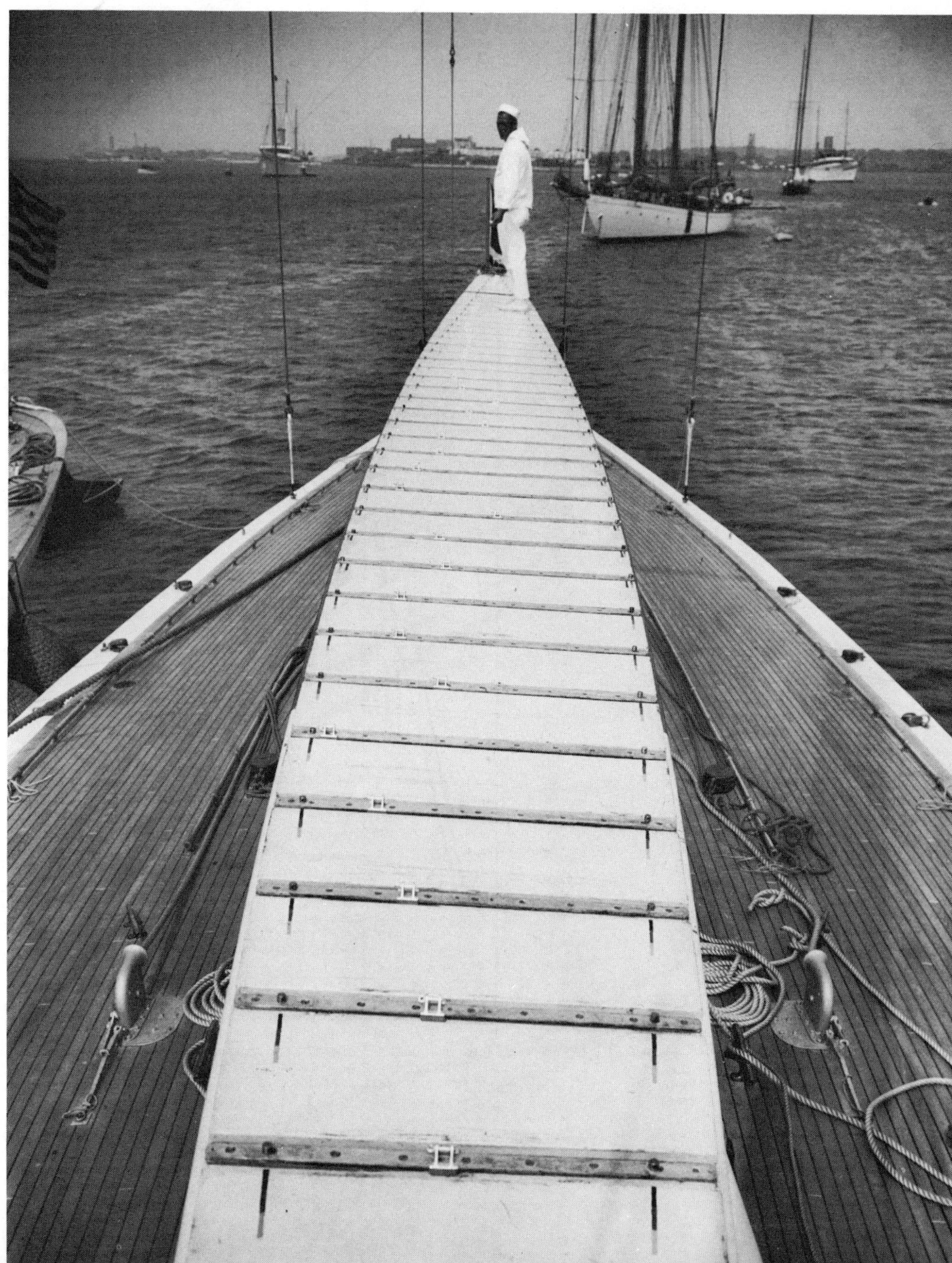

(Fig. 51). This sail A was demonstrated to be superior to a similar sail without end plate B, since the total force F_{TA} was inclined forward of F_{TB}. This is equivalent to saying that the induced drag was less by an amount ΔD, resulting in sail A having about 15–20 per cent more driving force than sail B.

Other possibilities for reducing induced drag arose with the advances in mast construction, and the discovery of the new, synthetic glues, which enabled tall, hollow masts to be made. These allowed sail plans of high aspect ratio, A.R., to be used. A good example of this can be found in the 30 Square Meter

Fig. 51

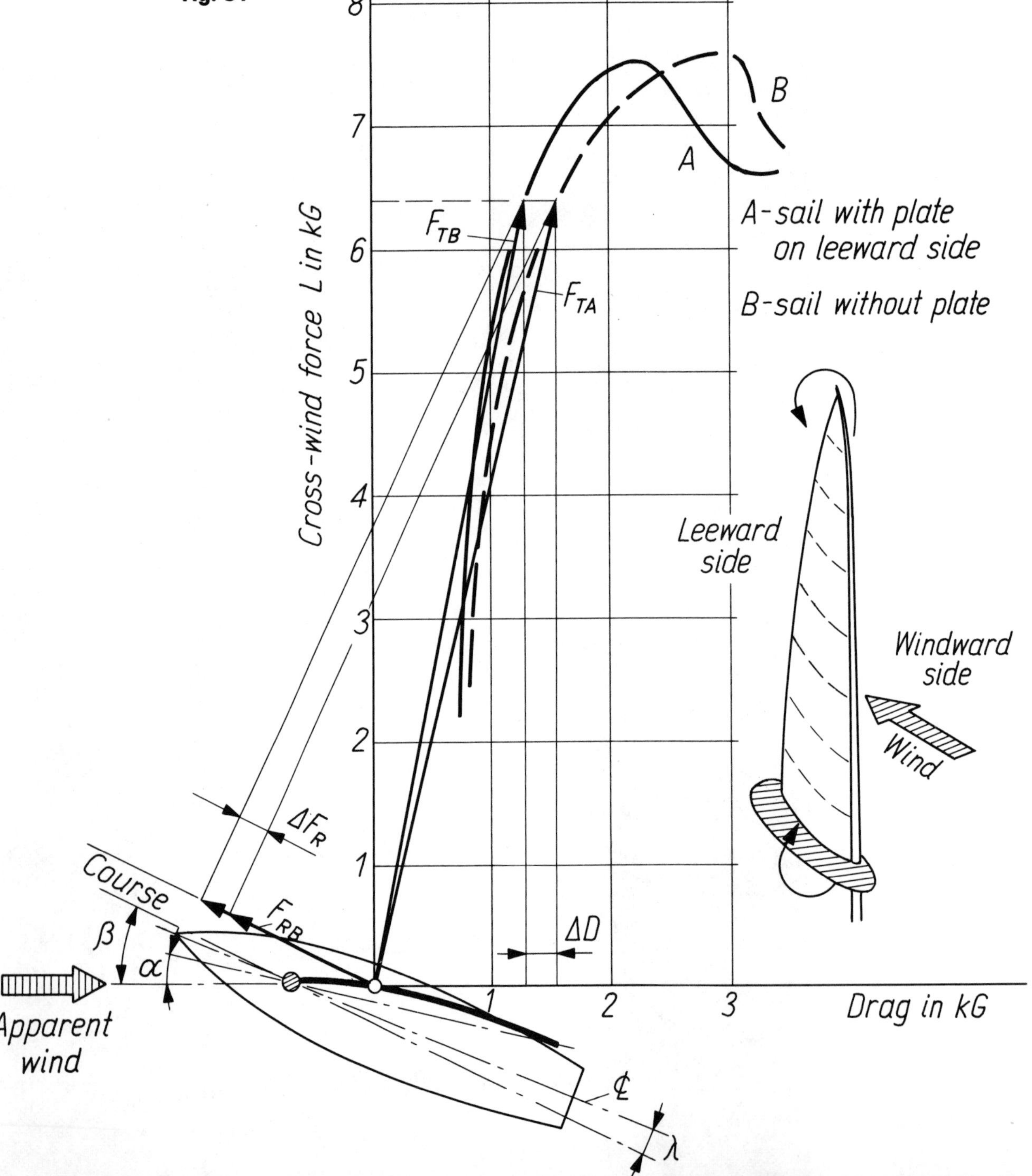

Photo. 4. 30 Square Meter

(Photo 4). The exceptionally high rigging in this class was a result of the class rule which placed no limitations on the hull, but only on the sail area. Hence the sail area could be disposed in the efficient, windward-going manner to give a low induced drag. The large amount of stability required to balance the tall rig was obtained from the relatively large, heavy hull. In the majority of yachts, under the rating rules one cannot apply such a tall rig, since the limited hull size immediately imposes problems of lateral stability and excessive heeling.

It seems that the practical upper limit to aspect ratio is about 4–4.5. Beyond this, the necessary increases in hull size and weight to avoid excessive heeling result in reduced performance.

The performance of a yacht when close hauled will also depend to some extent on the sail shape. The results of tests at Göttingen Institute on two sails of the same aspect ratio (Fig. 52) showed that a gunter sail or a Bermudian sail with

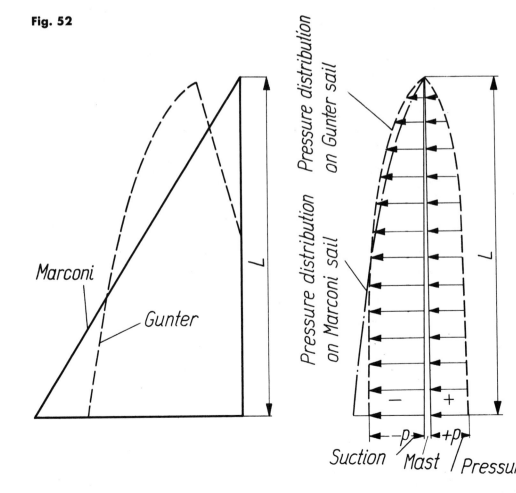

Fig. 52

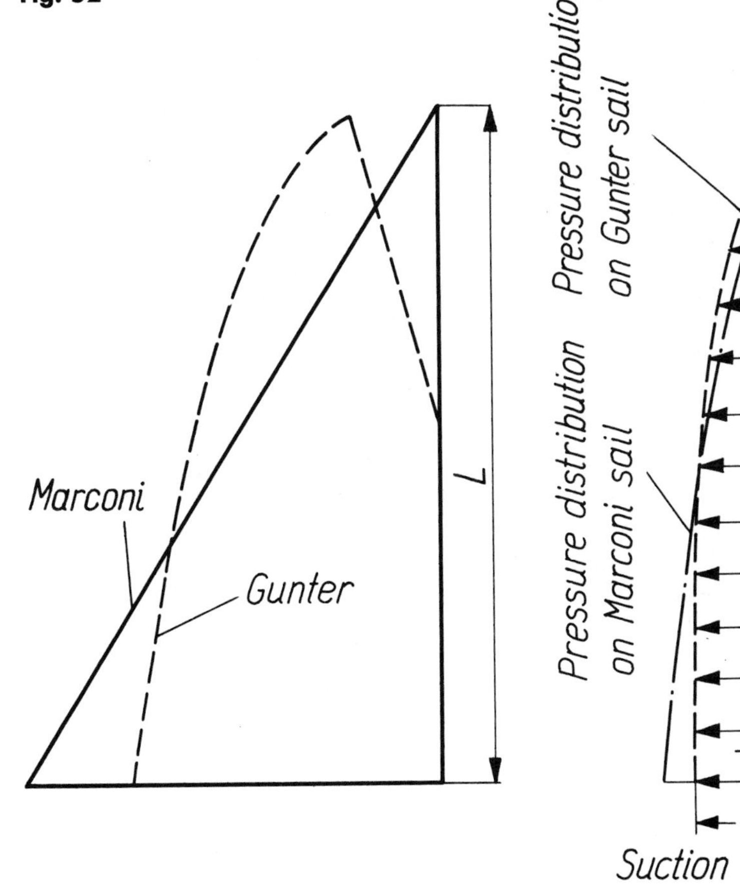

a bent mast was more efficient than one with a straight mast. Theory says that minimum induced drag will be obtained when the distribution of the cross-wind forces up the sail varies according to a type of oval called an ellipse. This is usually found to be the case when the sail shape itself is elliptic. A gunter sail, or one with a bent mast, more nearly approach this condition than a Bermudian sail with a straight mast. The induced drag of the latter is about 10 per cent higher than the ideal.

As is often the case, however, practical considerations play a part in deciding the merits of a rig. A disadvantage of a bent mast, which limits its use to racing craft, is that when reefed the sail sets badly and flutters violently. This fault is not found in the gunter sail, but, on the other hand, the spars have a higher resistance than a single mast, and the rigging is heavier and more complicated than a Marconi rig.

In conclusion, it is interesting to note that nature also appears to know about induced drag, since the majority of the birds renowned for their flying ability have elliptic and/or high aspect ratio wings.

(b) Friction Drag

When discussing the forces arising on a sail, we saw that they arise from the combination of the pressures and suction. If air was an ideal fluid, we should have had to deal only with these forces. In actual fact, however, air possesses certain viscous properties, similar to, but to a lesser degree than, water and oil. This viscosity gives rise to frictional resistances, which must be taken into account. When a stream of air flows past a sail, it is found that the particles of air immediately adjacent to the fabric are brought to rest. These particles then do not travel along the sail with the main air stream, but instead remain fixed, relative to the sail.

As a result of the viscosity of the air, which is a measure of its internal friction, the stationary air particles on the sail exert a braking action on their immediate neighbors, which are thus slowed somewhat. These, in turn, reduce the speed of the next layer of particles, and this process is repeated so that it is only at some distance from the sail surface that the layers of air reach their "full" speed (Fig. 53).

The region between the sail and the main stream, in which the particle velocities are less than the stream velocity, is termed the "boundary layer." The perfect example to demonstrate the existence of the boundary layer can be taken from the way dust settles on motor vehicles when driven at high speeds, showing that irrespective of the speed of the car (or sail), the wind velocity at its surface is zero.

As the air particles in the boundary layer are slowed down, in turn, from the main stream speed, they lose kinetic energy. This loss in energy is transmitted as friction forces through the air layers, until finally it is communicated to the sail as friction forces, acting parallel to the surface of the sail. This gradual loss in kinetic energy is shown on Fig. 53a as the shaded area. The thickness of the boundary layer on the leeward side of a sail is shown on an enlarged scale for

Fig. 53

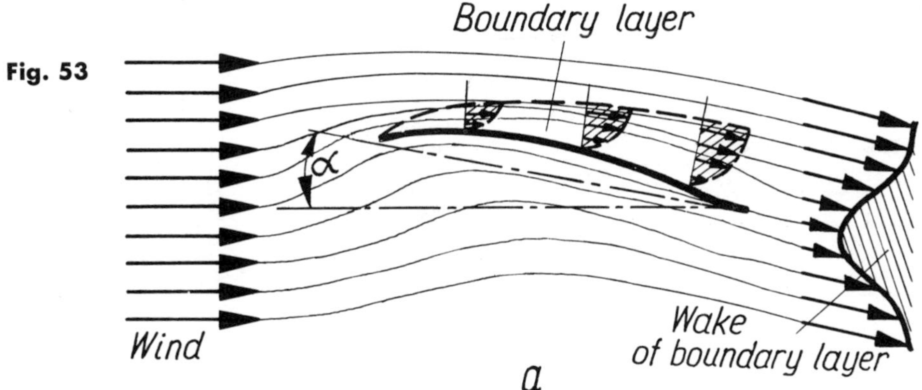

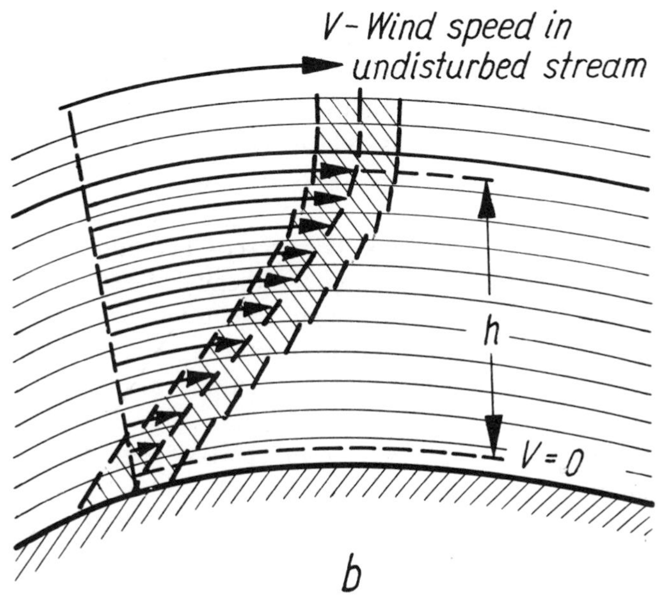

the sake of clarity. In practice the boundary layer, which exists on both sides of a sail, is quite thin.

Experiments carried out by O. Reynolds and others have shown that the characteristics of the flow within a boundary layer, and the associated friction forces, depend on a quantity known, in honor of the investigator, as "Reynolds' number,"

$$\text{i.e., Re} = \frac{vl}{\nu}$$

The magnitude of the Reynolds' number is determined by three factors describing the air flow:

v = velocity of the air flow in ft./sec.
l = some characteristic length, in feet, of the body in the flow
ν = a coefficient describing the viscosity and density of the fluid (in our case air)
$= \frac{1.57}{10{,}000} = 1.57 \times 10^{-4}$ ft.^{2}/sec.

Fig. 54

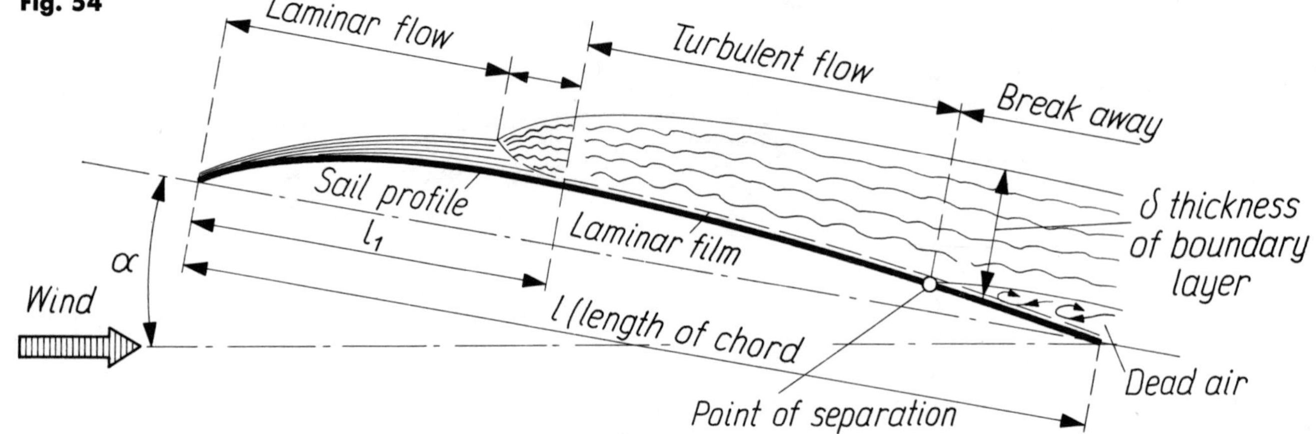

For a low value of Reynolds' number, or in other words, a low wind speed and not too long a body, the motion of the particles in the boundary layer is essentially parallel to the surface (Figs. 53b and 54). This is known as "laminar flow." The thickness of the layer is relatively small, reaching a maximum of about 0.5 per cent of the sail chord, and the corresponding coefficient of frictional resistance is low.

If, however, the Reynolds' number exceeds a certain critical value, the character of the boundary layer flow changes radically. The air particles no longer flow smoothly, in parallel lines, but instead start to oscillate in a direction perpendicular to the general flow, which is still, of course, maintained in the layer. This type of flow is called "turbulent." One immediate result is that the rate of growth of the layer is greater, and the thickness can reach about 2 per cent of the sail chord (Fig. 54), giving higher coefficients of frictional resistance. Very close to the sail surface, even in the most turbulent boundary layer, there exists a thin film of laminar flow, which has one useful effect, that in some cases it makes the effective smoothness of the fabric more than it actually is.

Let us calculate the Reynolds' number for some typical yachts in average conditions, and hence estimate their coefficients of friction:

Assume a wind velocity of $v_A = 20$ ft./sec.
Average chord length of the sail at half-mast height:

Finn and Flying Dutchman $l_1 = 6$ ft.
R-12 Meter $l_2 = 17$ ft.

Thus for Finn and F.D. $$Re = \frac{20 \times 6 \times 10^4}{1.57} = 765{,}000$$

and for R-12 Meter $$Re = \frac{20 \times 17 \times 10^4}{1.57} = 2{,}160{,}000$$

Referring to Fig. 55, we can firstly assume that the Finn and F.D. sails are very smooth. In this case, at the calculated Reynolds' number, the boundary layer might be entirely laminar, corresponding to point I, and giving a low friction coefficient $C_{fr} \cong 0.0015$. If the sail surface is not sufficiently smooth, on its forward

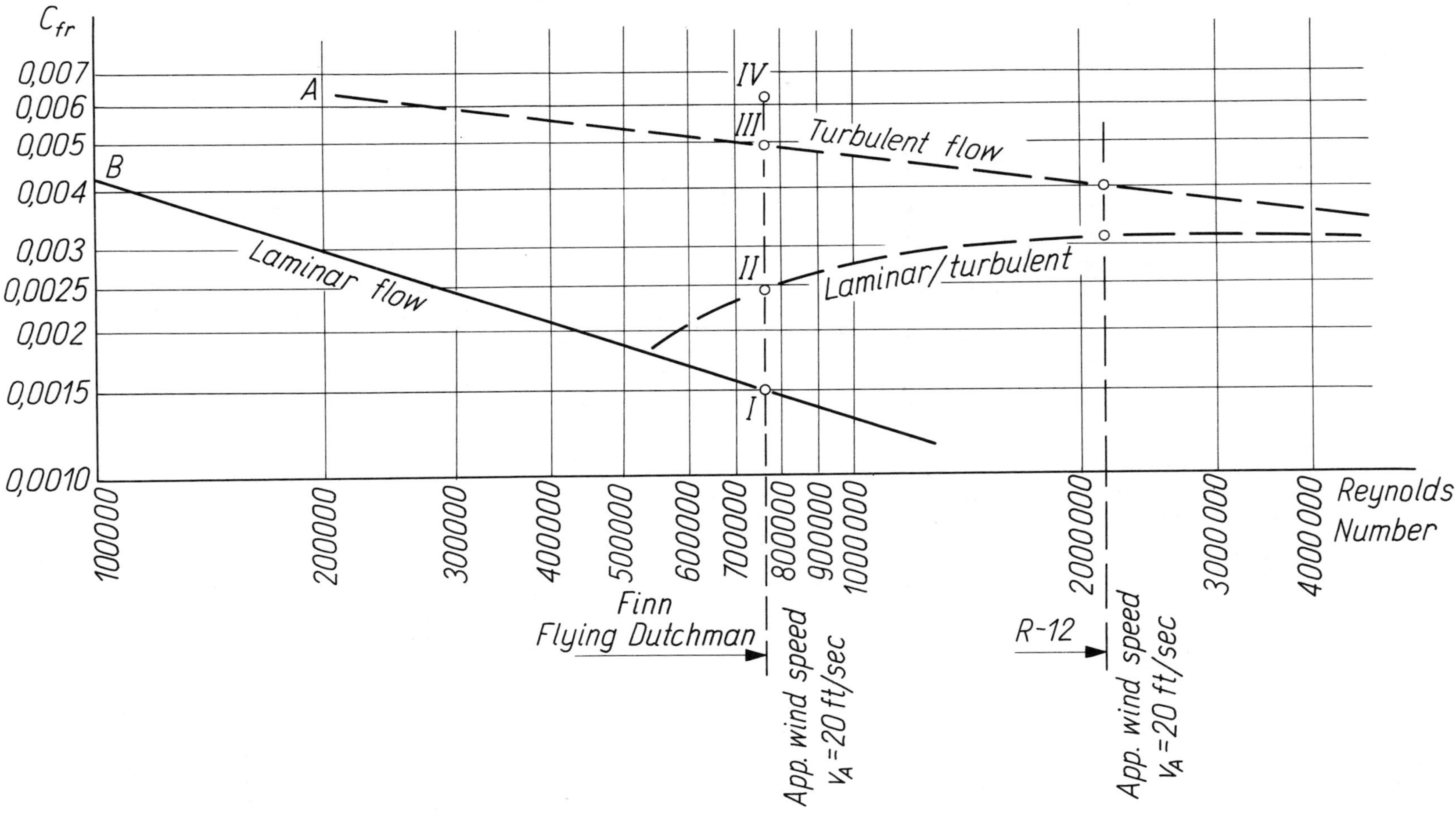

C_{fr}
Friction coefficient
0,007
0,006
0,005
0,004
0,003
0,0025
0,002
0,0015
0,0010
A
B
IV
III
II
I
Turbulent flow
Laminar flow
Laminar/turbulent
100000
200000
300000
400000
500000
600000
700000
800000
900000
1000000
2000000
3000000
4000000
Reynolds Number
Finn
Flying Dutchman
App. wind speed
v_A=20 ft/sec
R-12
App. wind speed
v_A=20 ft/sec

Fig. 55

portion the boundary layer will be laminar, and over the rest it will be turbulent, as in Fig. 54. This condition arises at point II on Fig. 55, giving $C_{fr} \cong 0.0025$, 67 per cent more than at I. Point III corresponds to conditions in which the surface is so uneven that a turbulent boundary layer is initiated right forward, and thus extends over nearly all the sail profile.

The coefficient of friction, C_{fr}, thus depends not only on the Reynolds' number but also on the smoothness of the surface (and its shape).

Line A on Fig. 55 represents values of C_{fr} when the roughness of the surface does not exceed a limiting value k, calculated from the following formula:

$$k = \frac{1200 \times \nu}{v}$$

where k = height of surface roughness in ins.
ν = coefficient of the fluid's viscosity ($= 1.57 \times 10^{-4}$ ft.^{2}/sec. for air)
v_A = flow velocity in ft./sec.

Hence we can calculate that for the wind velocity v = 20 ft./sec., the roughness of the sail fabric, k, should not exceed:

$$k = \frac{1200 \times 1.57}{20 \times 10^4} = 0.0094 \text{ in.}$$

This roughness height will be covered by the laminar film underneath the turbulent layer. If it is exceeded, the friction coefficient will increase to that at point IV.

Commercially available cotton sailcloth, together with the stitching and hems when it is made up, has an effective roughness exceeding 0.0094 in. For this reason we are not able to obtain smaller friction coefficients than those indicated on Curve A, that for a fully turbulent boundary layer, of the order of 0.004 to 0.005.

The roughness of the sail fabric influences also the magnitude of the cross-wind force coefficient C_L, more so, in fact, than it affects the friction coefficient C_{fr}. Experiments carried out on aerofoils having different degrees of roughness on the leeward side of their profile have shown that the roughness, and its location relative to the leading edge, are of great importance in determining the cross-wind force.

The experiments were performed in such a way that the effect of induced drag was eliminated, by fitting large end-plates on the aerofoils to prevent the pressure-equalizing flow round the ends. The roughness of the leeward side was varied by sprinkling sand, graded for size, onto the freshly varnished surface. With the varnish dry, the cross-wind force L and drag D, the latter being mainly frictional drag, were measured.

The polar diagrams of Fig. 56a show how the coefficients C_L and C_D were affected by gradually increasing roughness, from Curve O for the smooth aerofoil

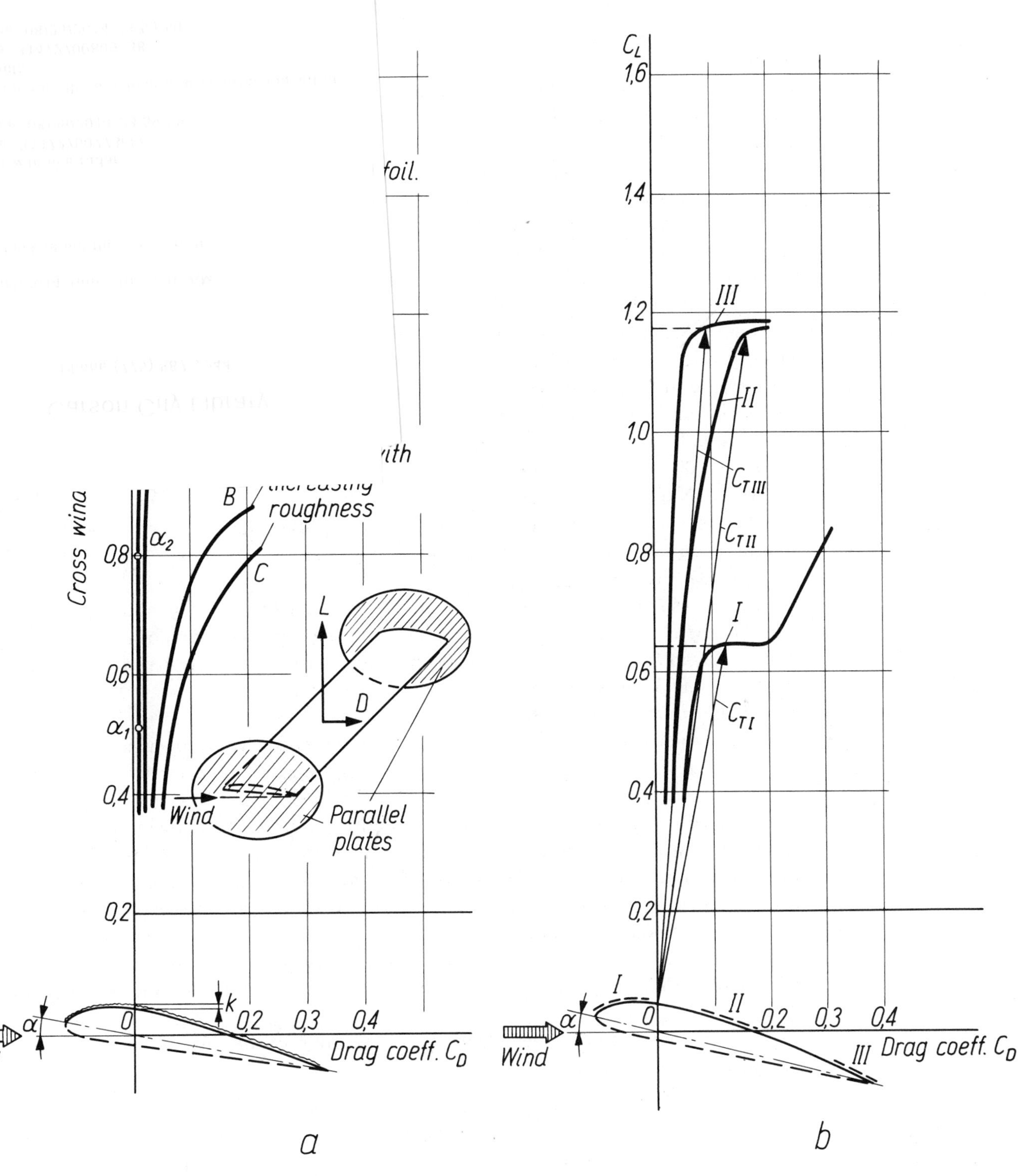

0,8
α_2
α_1
B
C
roughness
L
D
0,6
0,4
Wind
Parallel plates
0,2
k
0
0,2
0,3
0,4
Drag coeff. C_D
a
C_L
1,6
1,4
1,2
1,0
0,8
0,6
0,4
0,2
III
II
I
$C_{T\,III}$
$C_{T\,II}$
$C_{T\,I}$
0
0,2
0,3
0,4
Wind
III
Drag coeff. C_D
b

to C, the most rough. The polar diagrams of Fig. 56b were obtained on a basically smooth aerofoil, having localized rough regions. The positions of these regions is shown on the sketch of the profile, by I, II, and III. From a comparison of the curves we can deduce that the magnitude and direction of the resultant aerodynamic force is more affected by roughness near the leading edge than at the trailing edge.

We are now in a position to be able to explain, in part, the success of Dacron sails. The advantages to be gained from their smooth surface often outweigh the disadvantages of their relatively poor setting qualities, in comparison with cotton sails. This is particularly noticeable in the small racing classes. From the Portsmouth Yardstick Table III for small centerboard boats using both cotton and Dacron sails, it appears that a gain of about 7 per cent is obtained from Dacron sails.

The exceptionally smooth surface of Dacron allows some laminar boundary layer to exist, and this lowers the friction coefficient, and at the same time one gets an increase in cross-wind coefficient C_L. The advantages to be gained are greater at lower values of Reynolds' number, i.e., for small boats rather than large. This can be seen from our previous example, using Fig. 55. For the Finn and F.D., when $Re = 765{,}000$, one could realize a value of the coefficient C_{fr} in the range 0.005 to 0.0015. Naturally, we shall not obtain laminar flow on the whole sail, if only due to the effect of the mast. Nevertheless, the possibilities are there, and some laminar boundary layer will be attained. In addition, there will be a marked influence on the coefficient C_L.

The corresponding possibilities of altering the coefficients C_{fr} and C_L for a yacht of the R-12 Meter class at the same wind speed are considerably less. At the higher Reynolds' number of 2,160,000 the value of C_{fr} can only be in the range 0.004 to 0.003, and this range decreases even more as the wind speed, i.e., Reynolds' number, increases.

These conclusions are in agreement with experience. Many owners were surprised, when they fitted Dacron sails to their large yachts, that they did not obtain the increases in performance which could be obtained for small dinghy sails.

By the same argument we can explain the intriguing problem of why cotton sails improve with use. In sailing circles these old, faithful sails are well known; often after alterations and repairs they seem to be better the older they are, until finally they lose their strength. It is not uncommon to find that the owner of such a sail bears the title of a champion.

The surface of a new cotton sail has a microscopic nap. With frequent use this is worn off until finally the surface attains a kind of gloss similar to, but never quite so smooth as, Dacron.

At Göttingen Institute the following comparative coefficients of friction were obtained for cotton sails:

average, smooth fabric	83
similar fabric with protruding fibers singed off	50
similar fabric, doped three times	47

(c) Form Drag

Form drag arises from the turbulent flow which always exists over some part of a body in an air stream. This turbulence is on a larger scale than the turbulent boundary layer, although it can be influenced by it. It is called form drag because it is largely a consequence of the shape of the body.

An example illustrating the presence of such a turbulent flow is the cloud of dust which arises from a country road behind a vehicle. We know from experience that the nonstreamlined bus raises a large wake, whilst the aerodynamically smooth lines of a sports car cause very little disturbance in relation to its size. As a result, the car has a considerably lower form drag coefficient.

Form drag is a result, once again, of the air having internal friction. This can be explained and demonstrated by the air flow around a mast (Fig. 57).

In the absence of viscosity the air would flow smoothly round the mast in the manner predicted by Bernoulli's equation. From point 1 it would accelerate to its maximum velocity, and hence maximum kinetic energy, at point 2. As the velocity increased, the static pressure would fall to a minimum at point 2. It would then progress to point 4 in an exact reverse of the processes in going from 1 to 2.

Due to its viscosity, however, the air suffers an extra retardation as it travels

Fig. 57

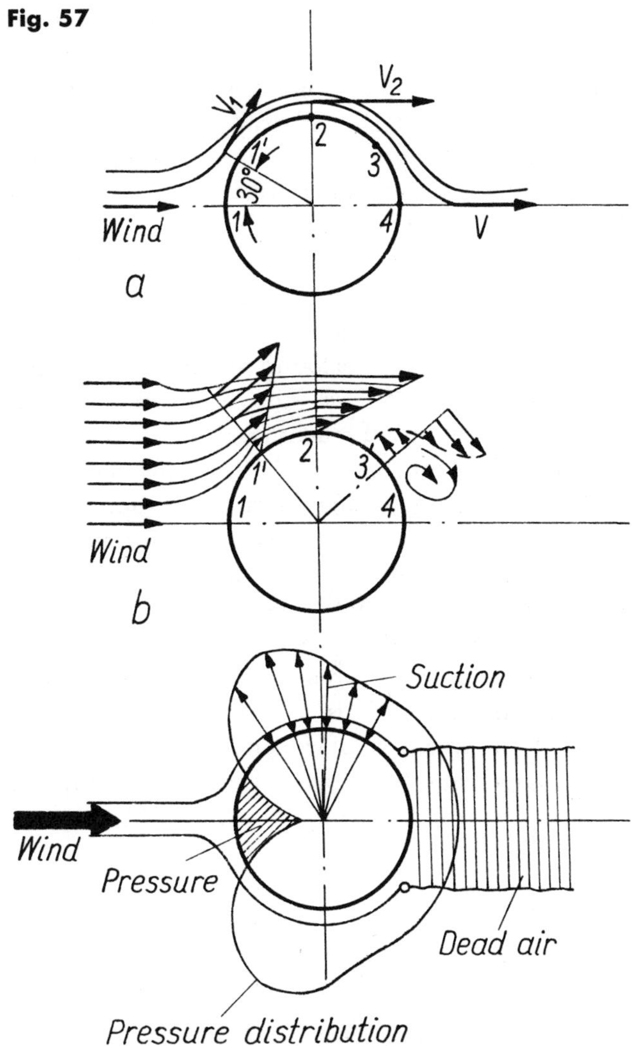

around the mast, because of the boundary layer. Hence its velocity at 2 is less than it would be in the absence of viscosity, and this implies that its kinetic energy is less than it should be. Now to travel on the path 2–3–4 would require the expenditure of the full amount of kinetic energy, and since this is not now available, the air is unable to adhere to the correct contour, separates from the mast, and flows downstream in a very turbulent manner.

The velocity distributions at various points round the mast are shown in Fig. 57b. It shows how the velocity distributions gradually get distorted until finally an eddy, having a reversed flow, is formed. The formation of these eddies results in losses in the pressure distribution on the lee side of the mast, and the extent of these losses is a measure of the form drag of the mast. An indirect indication of the form drag is provided by the area of the turbulent wake behind the mast.

One is able to examine in a general way these phenomena by introducing smoke in the air stream as shown in Photo. 2, or by introducing dye or air bubbles in flowing water. By these means one can readily observe the behavior of the eddies, the accelerations and retardations in the flow, the separation of the streamlines from the body, etc.

On the basis of numerous experiments carried out on many different profiles, it can be stated that the deciding factor influencing form drag is the shape of the body. The more highly curved is the contour, particularly over the rear portions, the more readily does the air flow cease to follow the contour, and separate. It follows then that for a low form drag, the body should be streamlined in the familiar pear shape and should present the smallest possible frontal area to the flow.

In Fig. 58a are shown drag coefficients for various mast sections. We can see from these diagrams how streamlining can reduce the drag considerably from that of the basic cylinder, but not under all conditions of the air stream. If we bear in mind that a yacht never sails closer to the apparent wind than about 20°, and mostly sails at a greater angle than this, we must conclude that, from the point of view of form drag, a circular mast is best.

In the fifteenth America's Cup Races, the challenger *Rainbow* employed a profiled mast which was found to have about 50 per cent more form drag than that of the defender *Endeavour.* The disadvantages of *Rainbow's* mast were particularly apparent when broad reaching, when it was found that the greater portion of the leeward side of the sail was adversely affected by the wake from the mast. (Fig. 58b)

The form drag arising from the standing and running rigging plays an important part in a racing yacht's performance. This is particularly true when close-hauled. As the yacht comes off the wind, the rigging drag has less effect on the driving force, until when the wind is abeam, it is only significant as to how it affects the air flow on the sails. How great the resistance of the rigging can be is testified by the many centerboard boats which have capsized on their moorings in strong winds.

The form drag of a sail at small angles of incidence is not great, the predominating components then being the induced drag and the friction drag. Looking

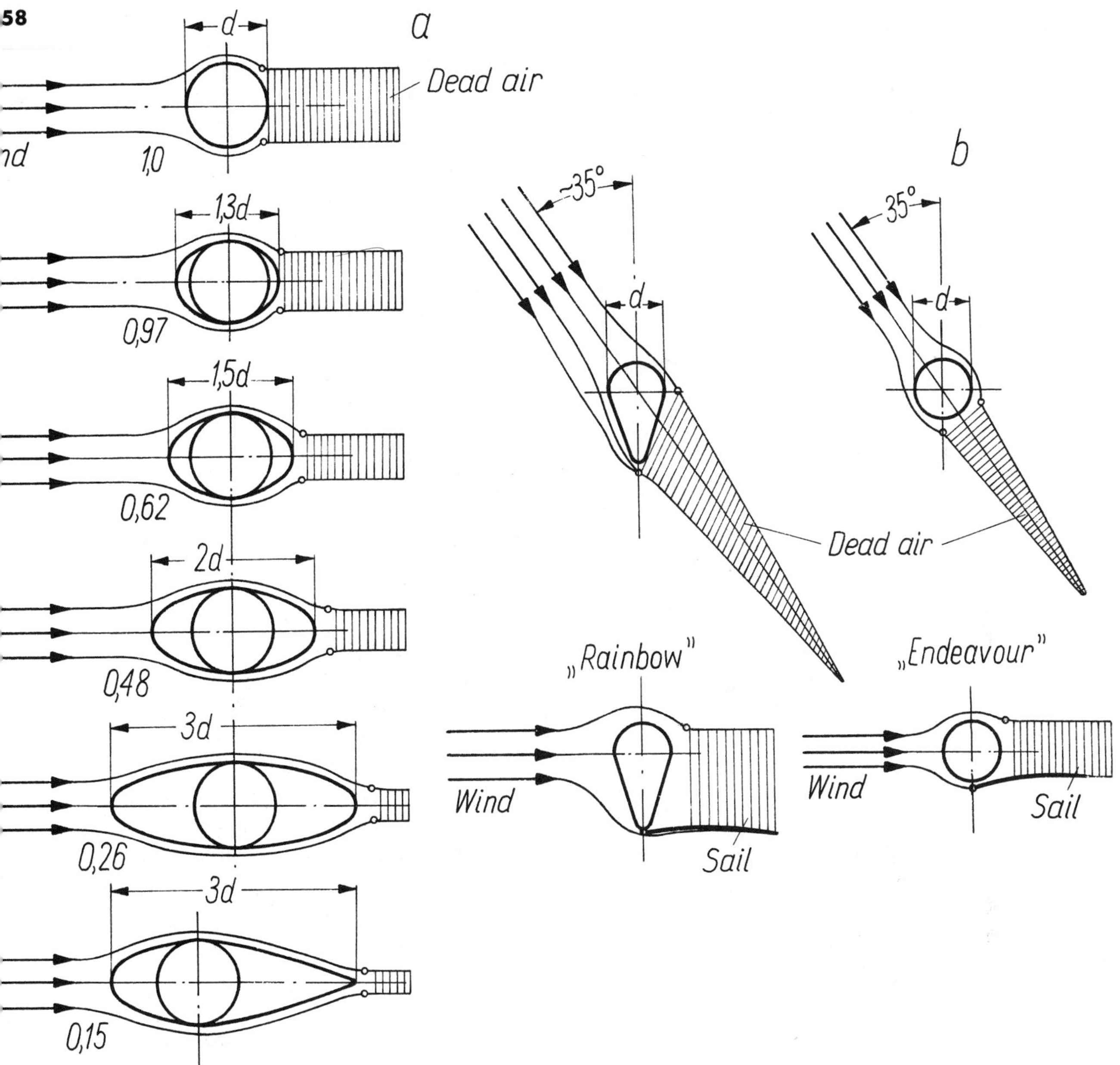

at Fig. 47 we can see that at a small angle of incidence α_1, the air particles have to traverse only a distance h_1 across the stream to reach the trailing edge, from point A. This they are able to do over nearly all the contour. As the incidence is increased to α_2 the boundary layer no longer finds it possible to adhere to all the contour, and at some point separates from it into the wake or dead air region. As the incidence is increased still further, the point of separation moves forward, until at α_3 it reaches point A at the maximum elevation. Further increases of incidence serve to increase the form drag, and at the same time reduce the cross-wind force component.

Fig. 59

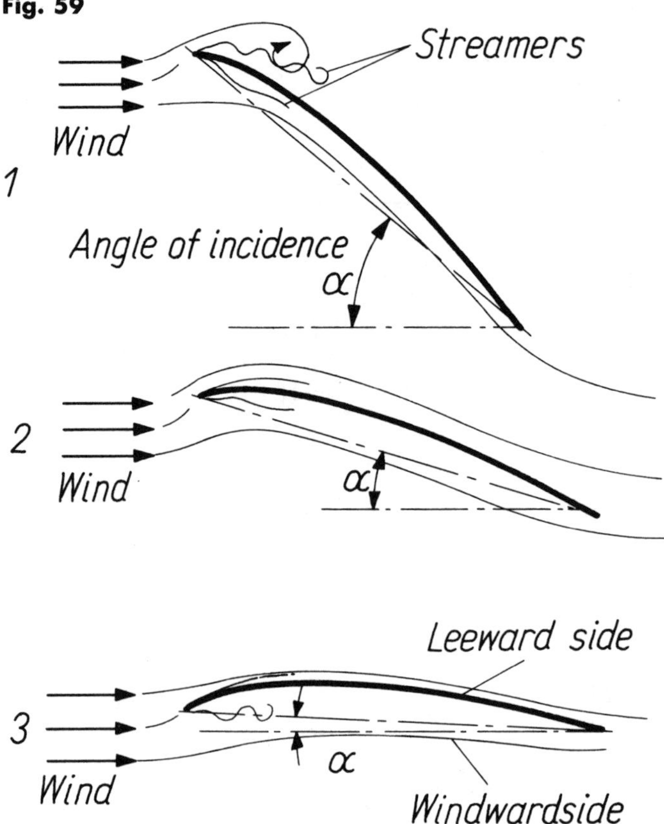

For the racing yachtsman, the condition of the flow on the lee side of the sail is of great practical significance, because separated flow serves to reduce the effective driving force and so the speed of the boat. To determine the nature of the flow it is possible to observe the behavior of streamers attached near the leading edge of the sail (Fig. 59). When sailing to windward, the streamers on the leeward side will twist and flap if the angle of incidence α is too great. They indicate that they are in a region of separated flow caused by sailing either too free or with the sheets too hard in. If the incidence is correct, both windward and leeward streamers will align smoothly with the local flow without fluttering. The windward streamers begin to flutter when the incidence is too low, and the flow separates on the windward side; the sail is then being pinched.

We now know that form drag arises from the boundary layer on the leeward side separating from the sail as a result of the loss of kinetic energy of the air particles due to friction. If it were possible to increase, in some way, the velocity of the air particles at the critical point, one could avoid this increase in sail resistance and hence improve its efficiency. In practice this is achieved by the use of a jib or some other headsail (Fig. 60).

The action of a jib is mainly based on the provision of a constriction in the flow, as a result of which the speed of the air flow increases considerably. Thus, in Fig. 60, comparing sections S_1 and S_2, the velocity v_2 at S_2 will be given by:

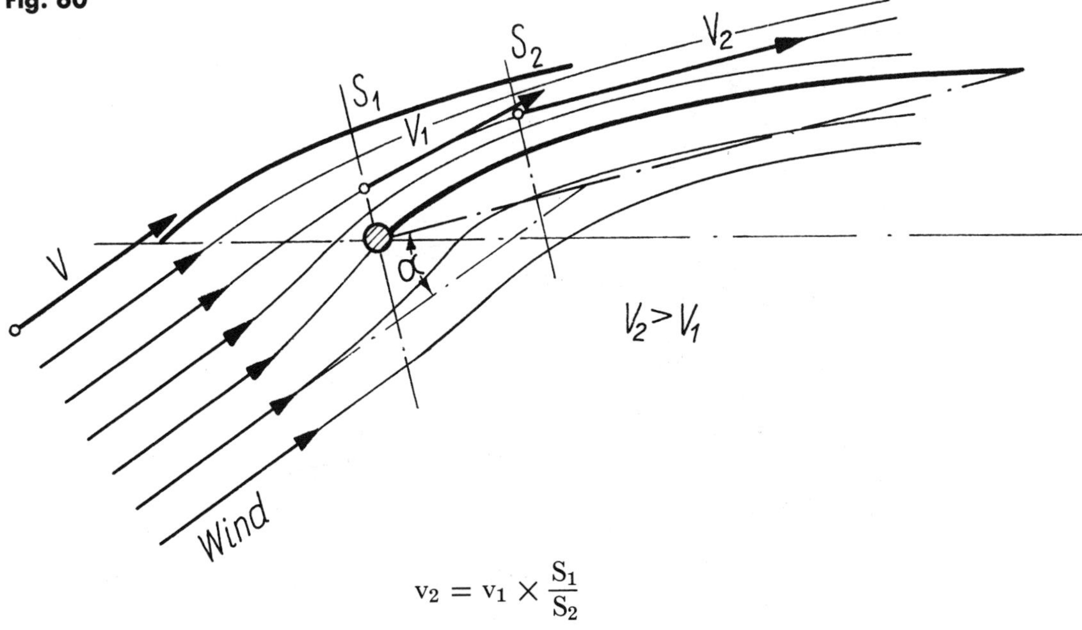

$$v_2 = v_1 \times \frac{S_1}{S_2}$$

By increasing the speed of the air flow at the section S_2, we obtain a two-fold advantage:

1. There is an increase of suction and hence the magnitude of the aerodynamic force on the sail.
2. The likelihood of the flow separating from the leeward side of the sail is reduced.

Obviously, the full effect of the headsail is only realized when both its shape and sheeting are correctly matched to those of the mainsail to obtain the required flow conditions between them. Unfortunately, the majority of yachtsmen do not fully realize the correct function of a headsail, with the result that it frequently does not improve the working conditions of the mainsail, and even reduces its effectiveness. Later we shall return to this problem once more.

The performance of the yacht could be considerably improved if we could succeed in reducing the adverse effect of the mast on the sail. As we have already mentioned, the presence of the mast at the forward edge of the sail is of prime importance in determining the nature of the air flow around the sail. Its effect is particularly harmful for the creation of suction on the leeward side. Consequently, the performance of the yacht suffers, and in particular she is unable to point so high into wind as would be the case if the adverse influence of the mast were eliminated.

We know that the maximum speed of a yacht and its ability to sail close-hauled depend upon the magnitude and direction of action of the total aerodynamic sail force F_T. The diagram of Fig. 61 gives the values of the coefficients C_T of this force for some model aerofoil sails designed to establish the effect of the mast on the sail. The sails were all identical, having a camber of 1/10 of the chord, and aspect ratio A.R. = 5. On the graphs are marked the maximum values of the coefficient C_T and the corresponding drag angles ϵ. They show in a particular way the magni-

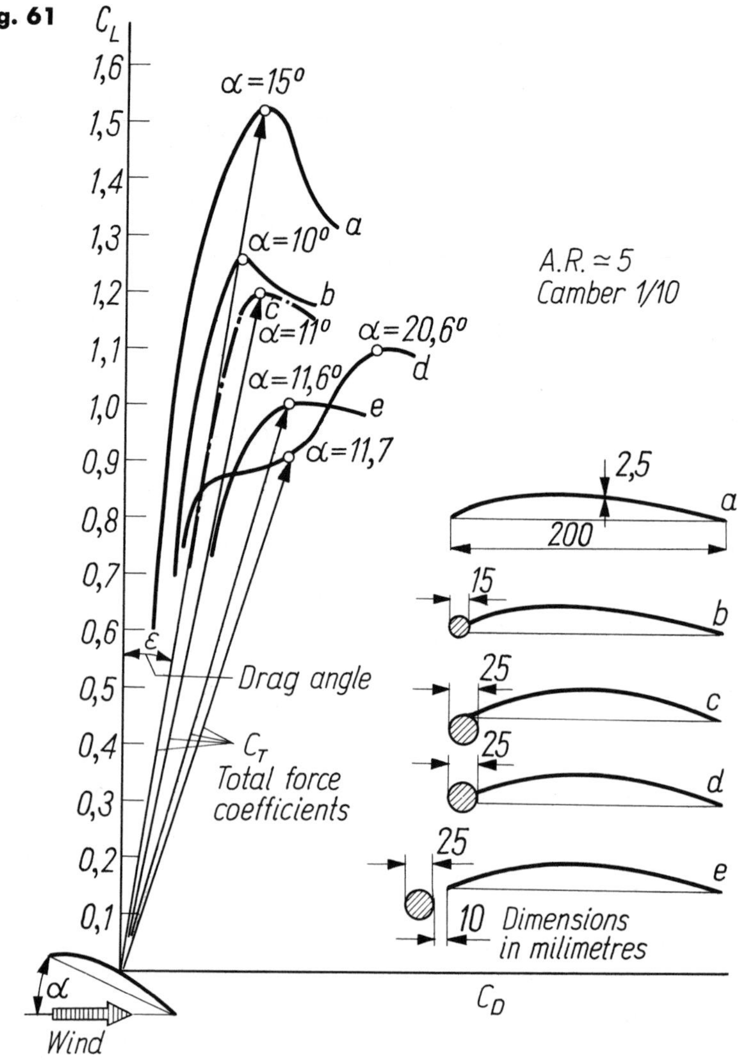

tude and direction of the total aerodynamic force F_T which can arise under conditions from beating to reaching (Fig. 62).

The reader will be able to see clearly how, when one is close-hauled, the angle of drag (ϵ) is of great importance in determining the yacht's performance, and that as one comes off the wind, the drag angle becomes of less importance, its place being taken by the magnitude of the maximum force (F_T) or its coefficient (C_T).

Taking as a datum model a, without a mast, we can see that the addition of a circular mast of diameter 7.5 per cent of the sail chord, model b, causes a fall of 18 per cent in the value of the maximum aerodynamic force. A further increase of the mast diameter to 12.5 per cent of the sail chord, model d, produces a further reduction in the sail force. At the same angle of incidence $\alpha = 11.7°$, the loss in aerodynamic force is about 30 per cent, and furthermore the direction of action of the force is altered for the worse, particularly when considering a close-hauled course.

The position of the mast in relation to the sail is also extremely important. If the mast is offset to windward, as for model c (Fig. 61), the sail performance is much

Fig. 62

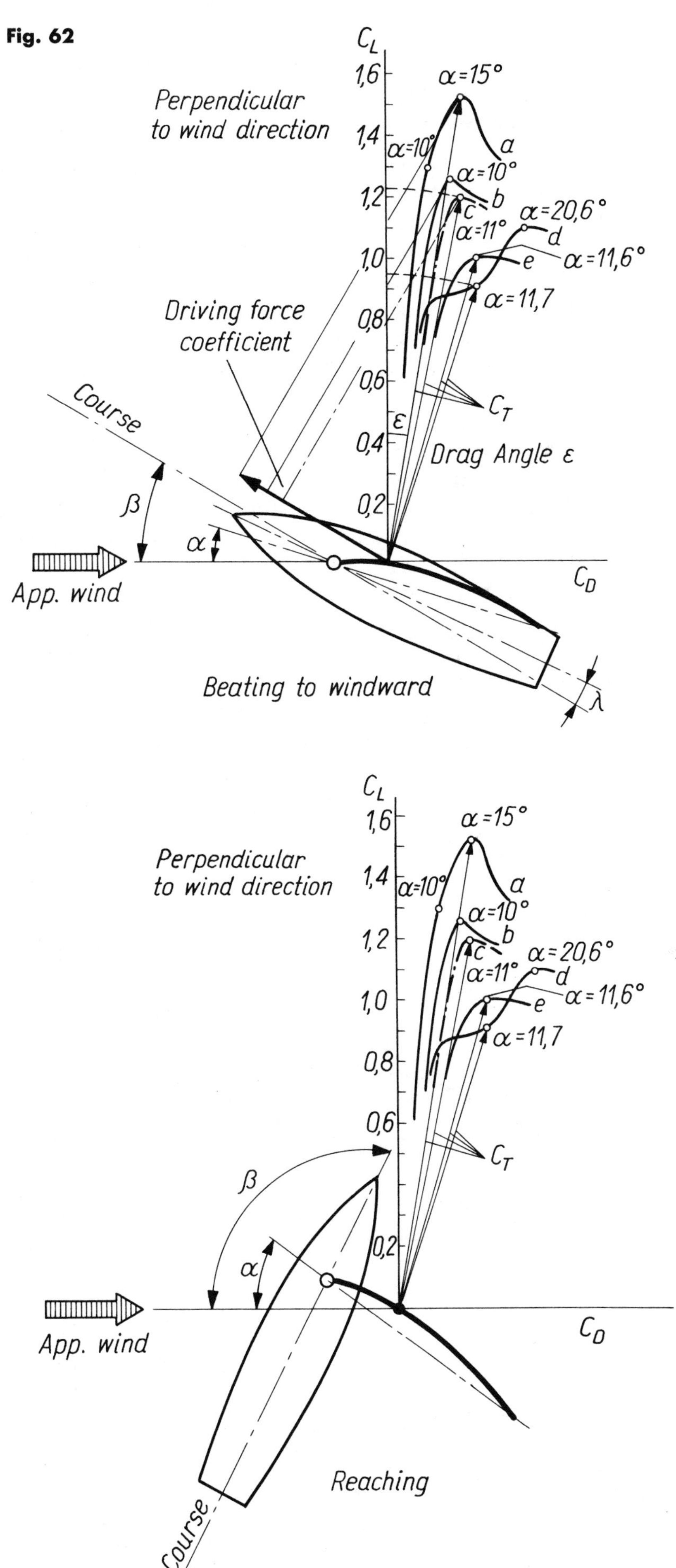

C_L
1,6
1,4
1,2
1,0
0,8
0,6
0,4
0,2
α=15°
Perpendicular
to wind direction
α=10°
a
α=10°
b
c
α=20,6°
α=11°
d
e
α=11,6°
α=11,7
Driving force
coefficient
Course
C_T
ε
Drag Angle ε
β
α
App. wind
C_D
Beating to windward
λ
C_L
1,6
1,4
1,2
1,0
0,8
0,6
0,2
α=15°
Perpendicular
to wind direction
α=10°
a
α=10°
b
c
α=20,6°
α=11°
d
e
α=11,6°
α=11,7
C_T
β
α
App. wind
C_D
Reaching
Course

improved. Roughly comparing $\alpha = 11.7°$ for model d, with a centrally positioned mast, with $\alpha = 11°$ for model c, we see that the latter shows an increase of about 28 per cent of C_T over the former, and an added bonus is that its drag angle ϵ is less, indicating that the force is directed more forward for model c. We can explain the differences between these two models if we remember that the flow on the leeward side of the sail is particularly susceptible to any disturbances. If, on this side, the sail is connected smoothly onto the mast, the flow is less likely to separate.

If the sail is attached to the mast with a gap between, as when hoops are used, model e, a particularly poor sail performance results over most of the working incidence range. This is as a result of the gap permitting pressure equalization between the two sides of the sail, and thus destroying the pressure differences where they are normally largest and most useful.

We can conclude from these tests that, if we must have a mast, its adverse effects can be reduced to a minimum by careful positioning and profiling, particularly on the leeward side. Since, however, it must work under a wide variety of conditions, it should revolve, always to point into wind. In practice, the easiest means for achieving a high sail efficiency is to site the mast to windward of the sail, as in model c, reduce to a minimum the gap between the mast and sail, and reduce to the minimum compatible with strength the diameter of the mast.

One ingenious solution to the problem of smoothly connecting the sail to the mast can be found in the Ljungstrom sail (Fig. 63 and Photo. 5), which was later developed by Vosper-Hasler (Fig. 64) and which satisfies the requirements of

Fig. 63

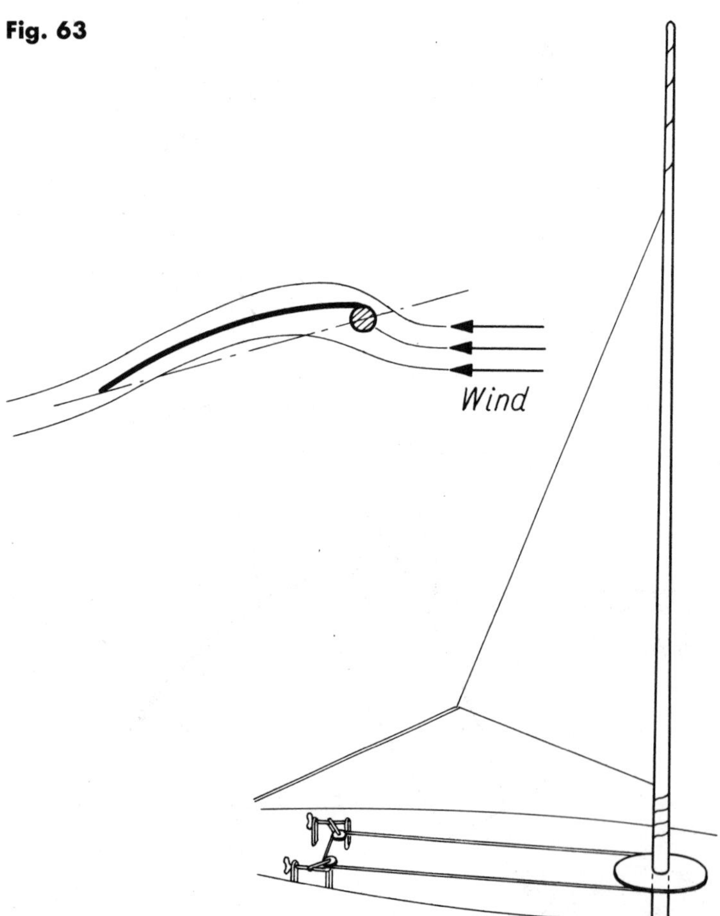

Fig. 64

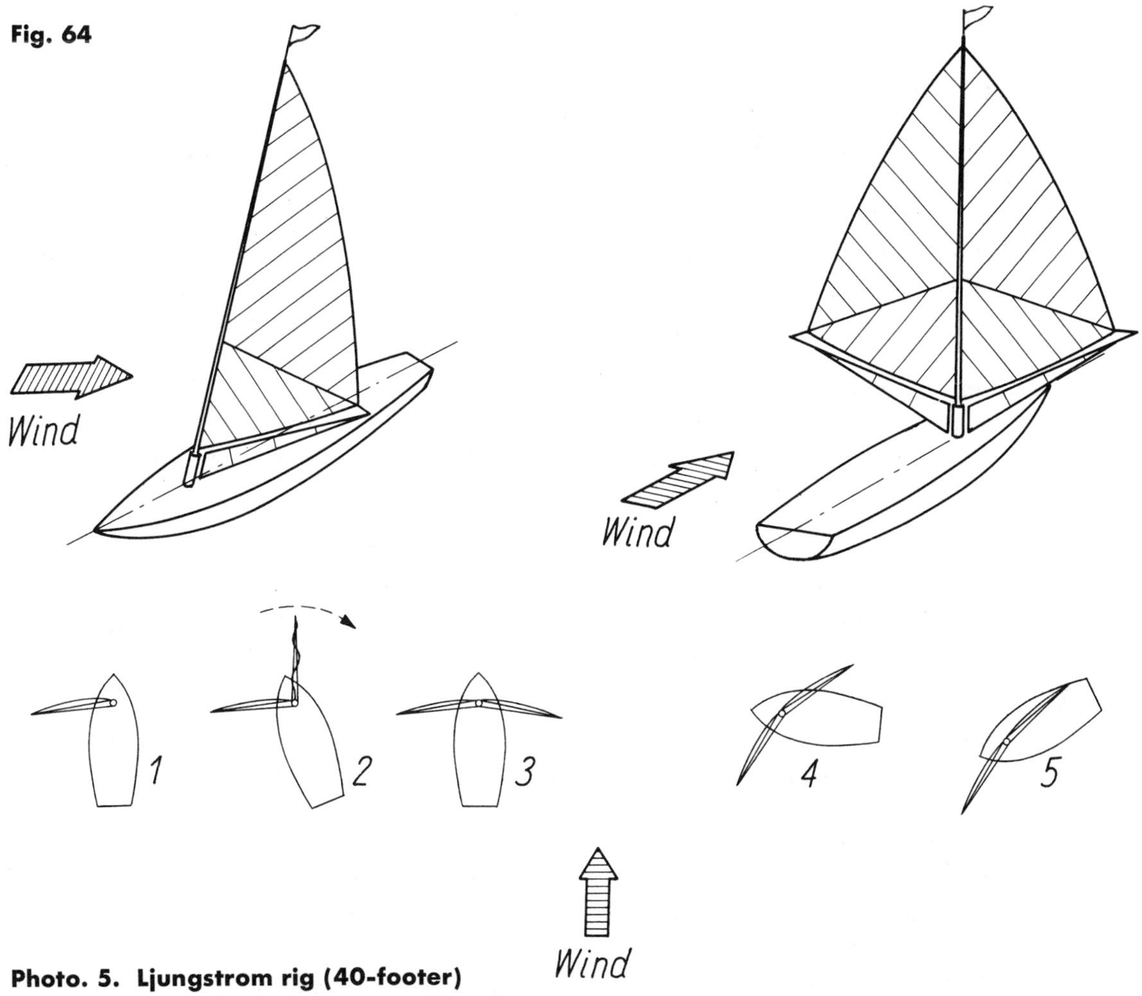

Wind

Wind

1 2 3 4 5

Wind

Photo. 5. Ljungstrom rig (40-footer)

model c (Fig. 61). A free-standing flexible mast is used, with a rigid, double boom. To these are attached twin sails, which pass round the mast. When going to windward, the two sails lie together and act as one double-weight Bermudian sail. When sailing off the wind, the two sails are separated and goose-winged, giving double the close-hauled area. Reefing is effected by rotating the mast, and thus rolling both sails onto it. By being smoothly attached to the leeward side of the mast, this type of sail has a considerably improved air flow on its leeward side, when sailing on the wind. In addition, the camber of the sail can be adjusted by regulating the tension at the clew.

In comparison with classical rigs, those of the Ljungstrom and Vosper-Hasler type have certain advantages, rather more important for cruising than racing:

1. Reefing is greatly simplified, and the rather dangerous business of the crew working in the bows when changing headsails in heavy weather is eliminated.
2. When sailing before the wind, a Ljungstrom-rigged yacht can quickly and easily double its sail area. A normal yacht must effect this by the more or less troublesome addition of extra headsails.

Another solution to the problem of supporting the sail is found on the yacht *Jester*, which was sailed by H. G. Hasler in the Singlehanded Transatlantic Race of 1960. The rig was adapted from the Chinese junk, in which the sail projects well forward of the mast (Fig. 65), and thus is not seriously disturbed by it. The rigging, although apparently complicated, is reputedly easy to handle, and reef, and in the original Chinese version could be used to adjust the camber of the sail within wide limits.

Numerous attempts have been made to eliminate the harmful effects of the mast by using semirigid sails. A typical example is shown in Fig. 66 in which a streamlined "yard" is supported on a somewhat short mast. A halyard running through the hollow mast allows the yard to be hoisted onto its bearing. The sail runs in a groove in the yard as on a normal mast.

The advantages to be gained from the use of a profiled mast are apparent from the results of experiments on Bermudian sails carried out in the Aerodynamic Laboratory of Professor Junkers. Comparing the polar diagrams in Fig. 67 of the aerodynamic forces for the two models A and B, we can see that the profiled model B has total aerodynamic forces F_{TB} and their components along the direction of motion F_{RB} about 30 per cent greater than those of model A, with a normal circular mast.

Another solution to the mast interference problem was introduced by C. O. Walker on the catamaran *Marara* (shown in Fig. 68). The mast, a braced lattice structure in the shape of the capital letter A, is mounted aft of the leech of the mainsail and hence does not disturb the flow around the sail. In this way the aerodynamic efficiency of the mainsail can be as high as that of the jib, and thus a large driving force can be developed with a relatively small sail area.

Fig. 65

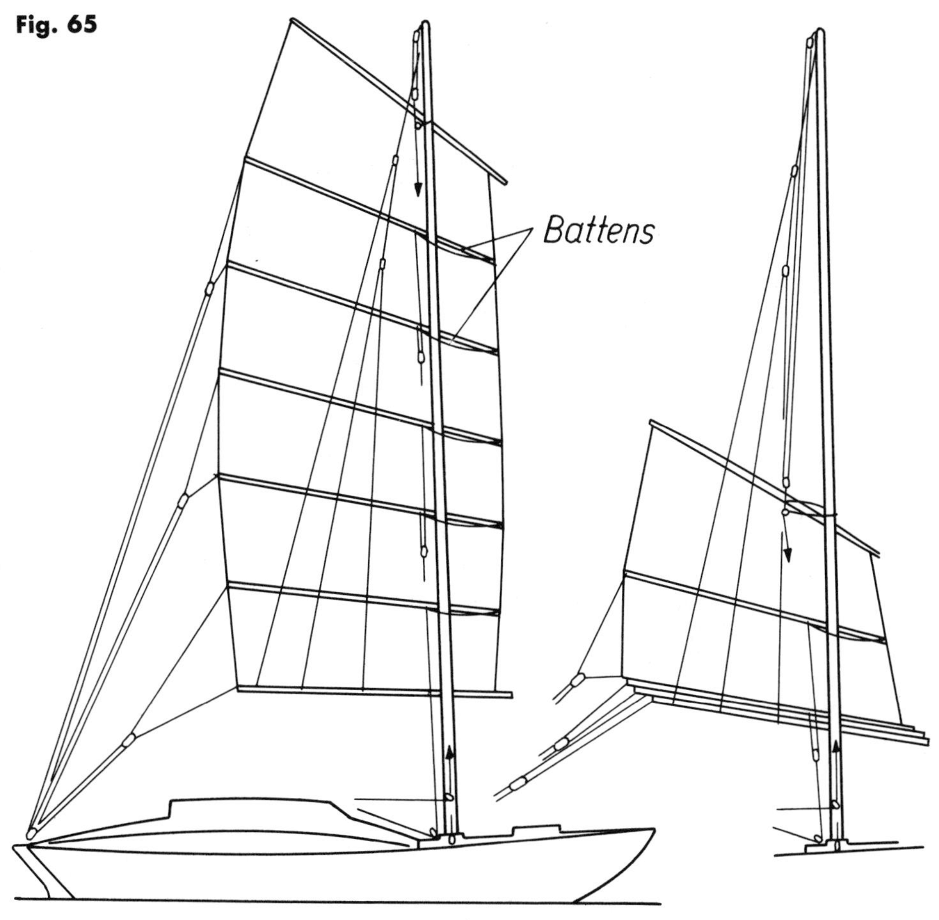
Battens

Fig. 66

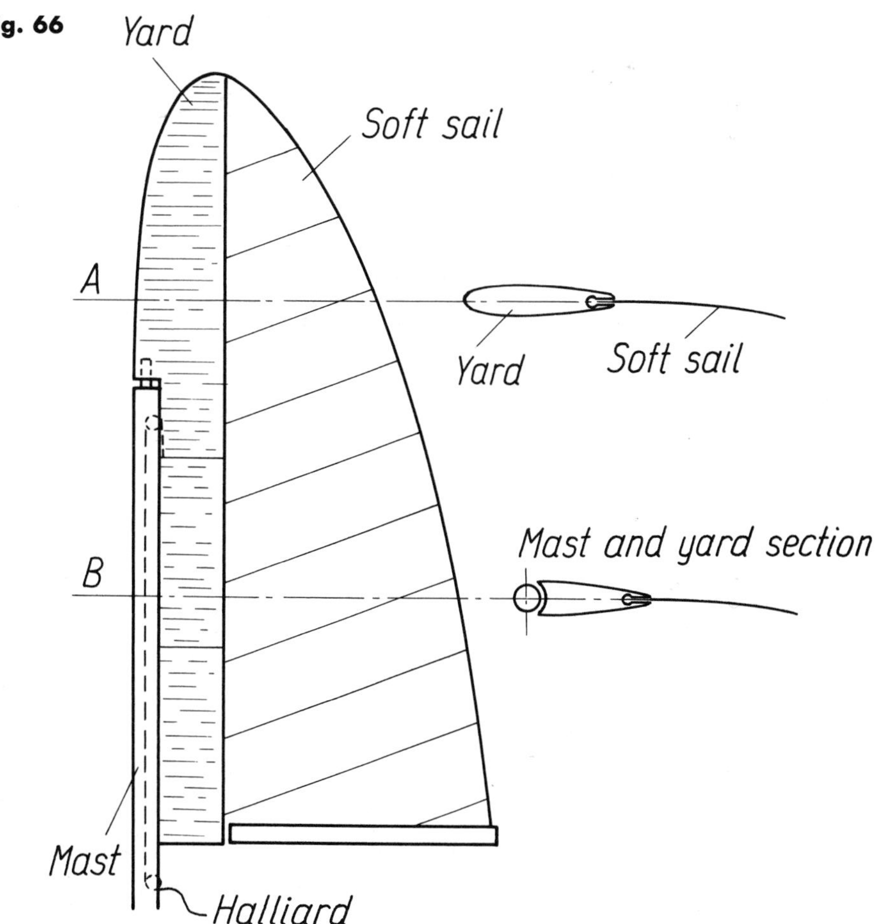
Yard
Soft sail
A
Yard
Soft sail
Mast and yard section
B
Mast
Halliard

Fig. 67

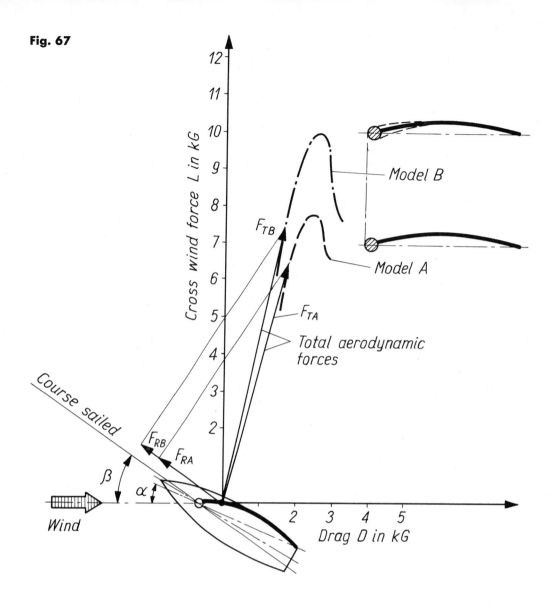

Cross wind force L in kG

12
11
10
9
8
7
6
5
4
3
2

Model B

Model A

F_{TB}

F_{TA}

Total aerodynamic forces

Course sailed

F_{RB}

F_{RA}

β

α

Wind

2 3 4 5

Drag D in kG

Fig. 68

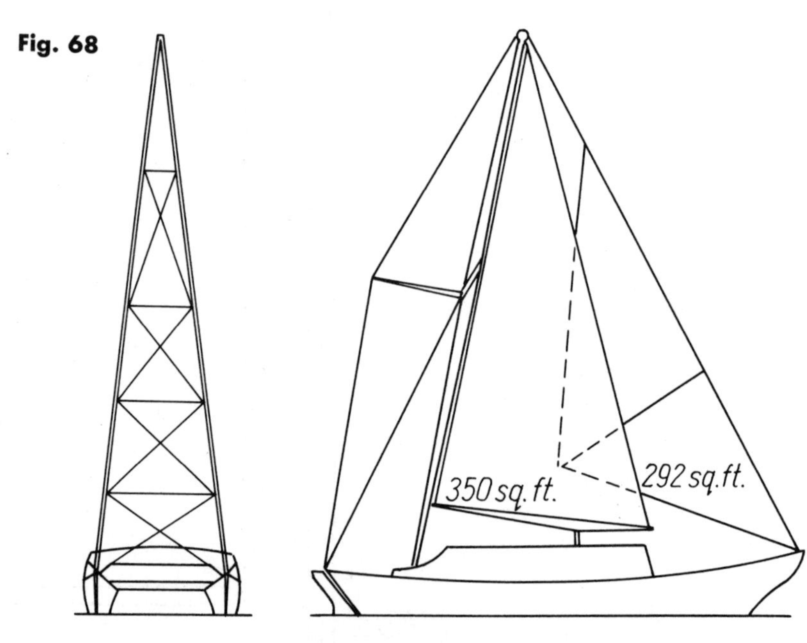

(d) Additional Aerodynamic Resistance of the Yacht

In our consideration of the aerodynamic resistance of the sail, and the way it affects the magnitude and direction of the resultant aerodynamic force, we did not include the forces generated by the wind on the hull, rigging, crew, etc. The influence of these on the resultant force F_T can be very considerable and cannot be ignored in the over-all estimation of the yacht's performance.

The total area above the waterline, that exposed to the action of the wind, can be divided into two parts:

1. Effective sail area S_A
2. Parasitic area Sp, of everything except the sail area S_A

The wind forces arising from the additional area Sp act along the apparent wind direction, and can therefore be included with the drag of the sails. The effect of this additional drag will depend on the ratio of the areas, Sp to S_A, and on the angle between the yacht's course and the wind direction. When sailing off the wind, the drag will act forward and thus be beneficial to the performance. As the yacht comes onto the wind, the drag will act more and more against the direction of motion and hence reduce the speed.

On balance, the advantages obtained from the parasitic drag when sailing off the wind do not equal the losses suffered when sailing to windward, and hence the parasitic area is undesirable. In short, it pays to reduce to the minimum the ratio Sp/S_A.

If we consider a course on the wind, as in Fig. 69, where the resultant sail force

Fig. 69

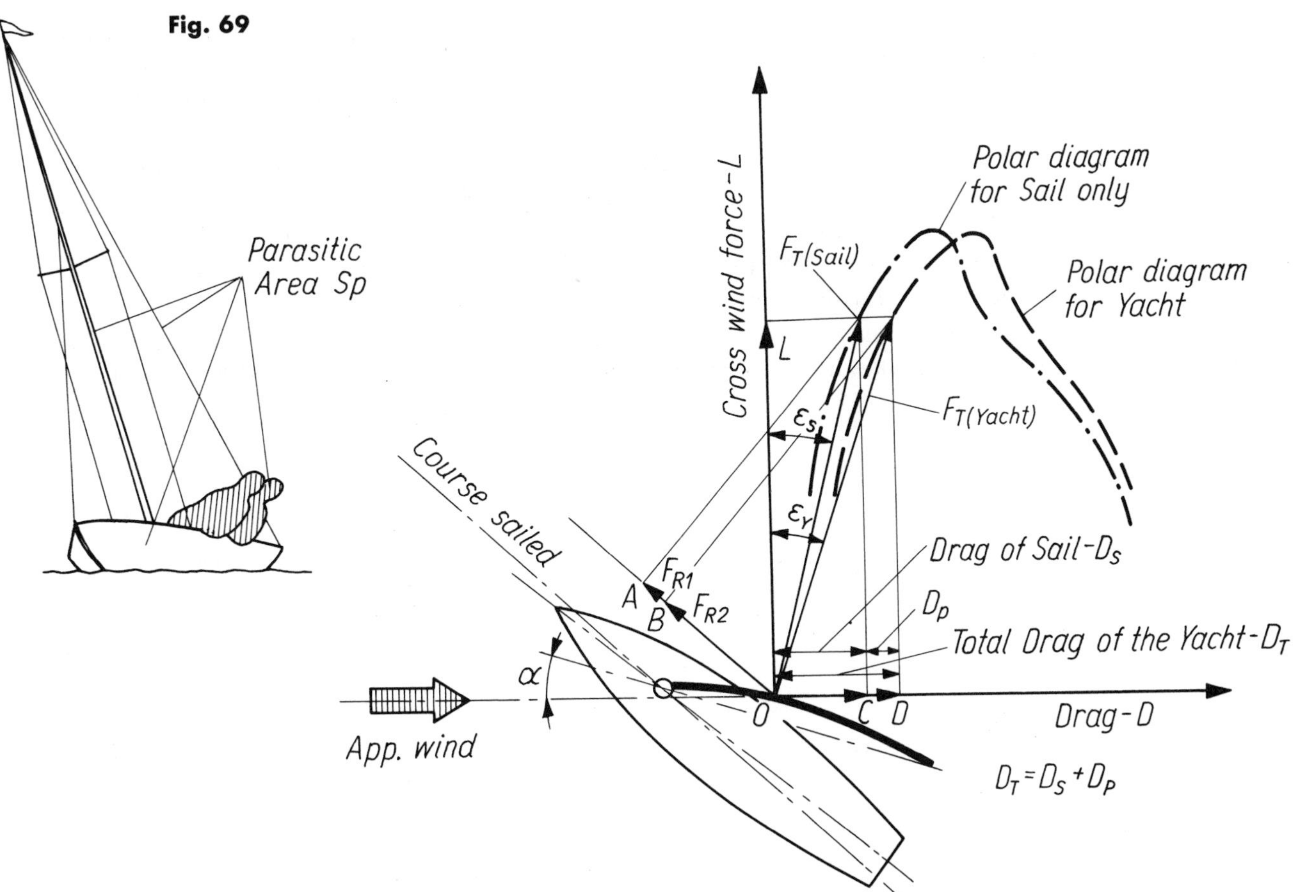

$F_{T(sail)}$ is at a drag angle ϵ_S, due to a certain sail angle of incidence, we can represent the driving force F_{R1} by the vector OA. We can see that the total sail force $F_{T(sail)}$ is made up of two components: a cross-wind force L and a drag force D_s. To represent the complete yacht, we must include the parasitic drag D_p, due to the hull, rigging, crew, etc. On the polar diagram of Fig. 69, this is shown by the additional drag vector CD. The total aerodynamic force $F_{T(yacht)}$ of the yacht is now given by the two components: the cross-wind force L of the sail, and the combined drag of the sail and hull, etc. By the usual parallelogram of forces construction, we can see that the $F_{T(yacht)}$ is inclined more to the stern, and thus its driving force component F_{R2}, shown as OB, is smaller than F_{R1}, represented by OA.

Simplifying the problem, one can now draw the polar diagram for the whole yacht (see broken curve of fig. 69) by shifting the sail polar diagram bodily to the right, by the amount of the parasitic drag D_p.

The complete elimination of unwanted drag is impossible, but some of its components can be reduced by suitable design of the superstructure and standing rigging, by appropriate positioning of the crew, and by tidying up the running rigging. There is also another possibility of reducing drag due to the hull, by taking into consideration the hull's position between the boom and the water's surface, particularly in close hauled sailing.

An exhaustive series of tests on Dragon sails at various angles of heading, and both with and without the hull, was carried out in the wind tunnel at Southampton University. The results showed that the gap between the foot of the sails and the water's surface plays an important role in generating so-called "induced drag"; this, as we already know from chapter 5a, is directly and inseparably associated with the formation of the crosswind force L. Under certain conditions regarding both the course of the yacht and the reduction of the gap between the boom and the water's surface by the hull, it was found that the hull does not in fact spoil the aerodynamic efficiency of the sails; on the contrary, it rather improves their efficiency when close-hauled.

This beneficial influence of the hull which prevents the flow of air around the boom, becomes smaller and smaller when bearing away, as the gap between the boom and the water increases. In close reaching conditions, when the boom is far off the center-line of the hull, the drag angle ϵ_Y for the whole yacht becomes greater in comparison with the drag angle ϵ_S for the sails alone.

It is apparent from these observations that it is certainly worthwhile reducing to a minimum the distance between the foot of the headsails and the deck; similarly, it generally pays to keep the boom as low as possible over the hull.

6. APPARENT WIND STRUCTURE

The aerodynamic forces produced by the wind vary as the square of the apparent wind velocity. In other words, a twofold increase in the velocity of the apparent wind will produce a fourfold increase in the aerodynamic force on the sail.

The apparent wind over the sails is not uniform in magnitude and direction, but depends on the following factors:

1. The angle between the yacht's course and the true wind direction, γ
2. The speed of the yacht, v_S
3. Variations in the true wind velocity v_T at different heights above the sea
4. Rolling of the yacht
5. Pitching of the yacht

The apparent wind felt by the crew on board a moving yacht is the resultant wind composed of the vectors of the true wind velocity and the yacht's velocity. As an example, we will consider a true wind speed of $v_T = 10$ knots and a yacht speed of $v_S = 5$ knots. For various points of sailing, we can construct the appropriate velocity triangles (as in Fig. 70).

It is evident that in the range of angles between the course and the true wind of γ_1 to γ_2, i.e., close-hauled to close reaching, the velocity of the apparent wind is greater than that of the true wind. From the angle γ_2 onward, as one comes more and more off the wind, the apparent wind velocity (v_A) decreases and reaches a minimum when running dead before the wind. In our case, the apparent wind speed has varied between 14.5 knots and 5 knots, a ratio of nearly three to one. The aerodynamic forces, all other factors remaining constant, may vary up to nine times the minimum value, depending on the course sailed.

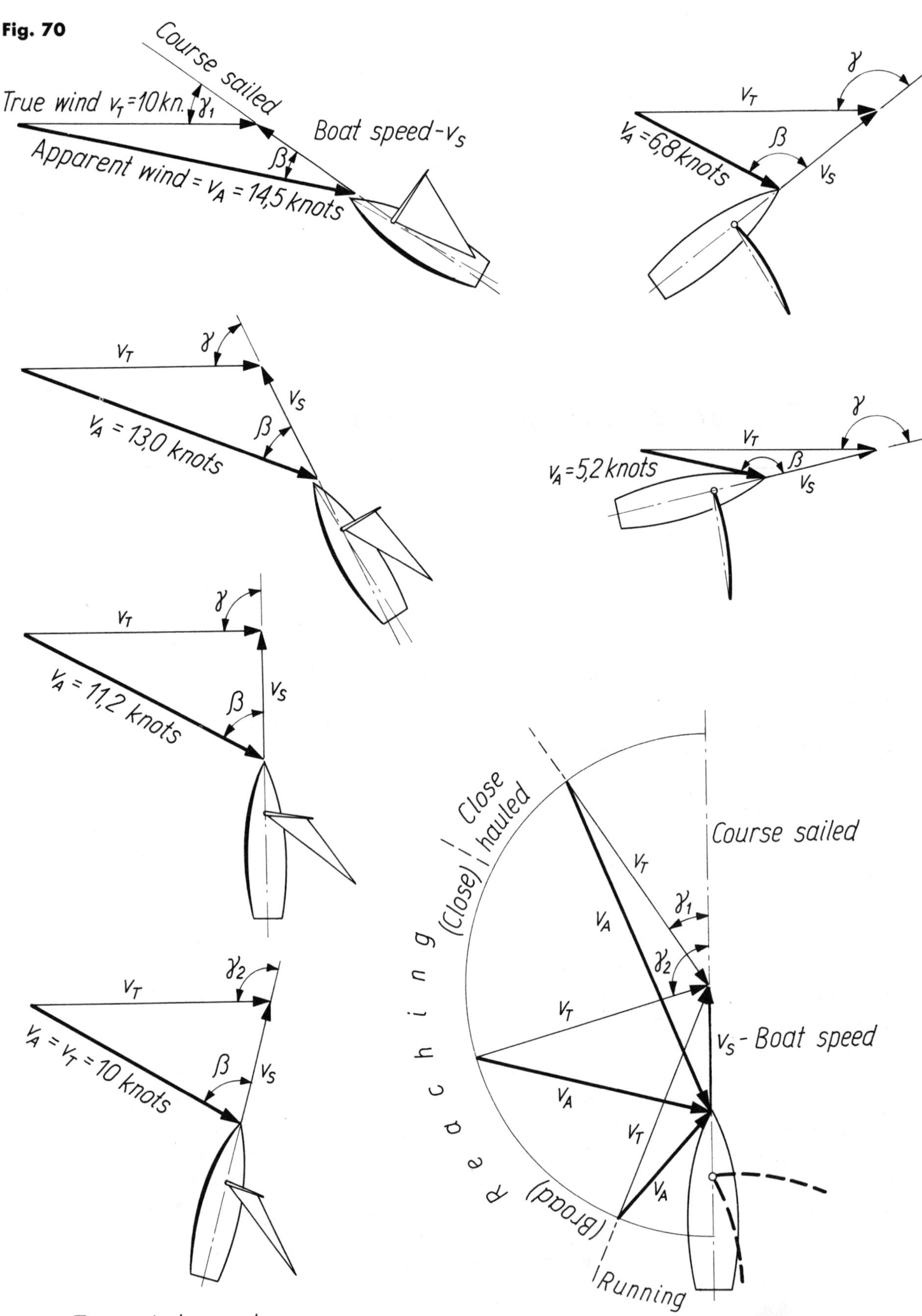

Fig. 70

v_T - True wind speed
v_A - Apparent wind speed
γ - Angle of True Wind to Course Sailed
(Angle of True Course)
β - Angle of Apparent Wind to Course Sailed
(Angle of Apparent Course)

Changes in the apparent wind speed are of considerable practical importance, especially when the question of reefing sails occurs. The degree of reefing will depend on the course being sailed. During a long-distance race, it may be possible to carry much more canvas if the leg is before the wind than if one was beating to windward. This state of affairs is sometimes a trap for the unwary, particularly when sailing before the wind in a freshening breeze or in restricted sea room. When the time comes to reef or alter course, it may be too late.

The speed of the true wind increases with the height above the sea. At the surface of the sea the motion of the air is retarded by friction, and this process is continued upward through successive layers, in a similar (though on a larger scale) manner to the formation of the boundary layers described in the previous chapter. From meteorological observations it was concluded that the rate of increase of the wind speed, the wind gradient, depends on the weather conditions and the state of the sea. Figure 71 shows a typical wind gradient curve for average sea conditions over open water. In the proximity of land or on inland waters, the shape of the curve can be quite different.

Supposing that at a height of 100 ft., $v_T = 10$ knots, then, from the curve, which shows a Dragon class yacht to scale, the true wind at the head of its mainsail will be only 80 per cent of this value, i.e., $v_T = 8$ knots, while at the center of effort of the sails it will be 6.8 knots. The variation of true wind speed v_T with height will affect the apparent wind velocity in magnitude and direction for each height. This is illustrated in Fig. 72, showing the velocity triangles for a Dragon sailing at a speed $v_s = 3$ knots. They show that for a close-hauled course, the apparent wind in the vicinity of the masthead is 32 per cent stronger than that at the height of the boom, and in addition, its direction, given by the angle $(\beta + \Delta\beta)$ is 3.5° greater than at boom height.

Similarly, considering a reaching case, we can deduce that the upper wind velocity will be about 50 per cent greater than the lower one, and the twist in the apparent wind direction will be 11.5°.

In light winds, when we are not limited by stability considerations, it is very profitable to hoist additional sails (such as a spinnaker) as high up as possible. They can then exploit the greater wind strength at a more advantageous angle than that lower down, and hence develop a greater aerodynamic force.

We have just seen how the direction of the apparent wind is twisted up the height of the mast. This is very relevant to the problem of the twisting of the sails, which often provokes strong discussion among sailing men. Broadly speaking there are two schools of thought: those who think flat sails are good, and those who do not.

As a criterion for estimating the permissible twist of a sail we can assume that a constant angle of incidence for all sections of the sail is desirable. We can then consider the variations in the direction of the apparent wind up the height of the mast.

For close-hauled sailing it is clear that we should try to reduce the sail twist as much as possible, since the twist in the apparent wind is very small. Thus for the

Fig. 71

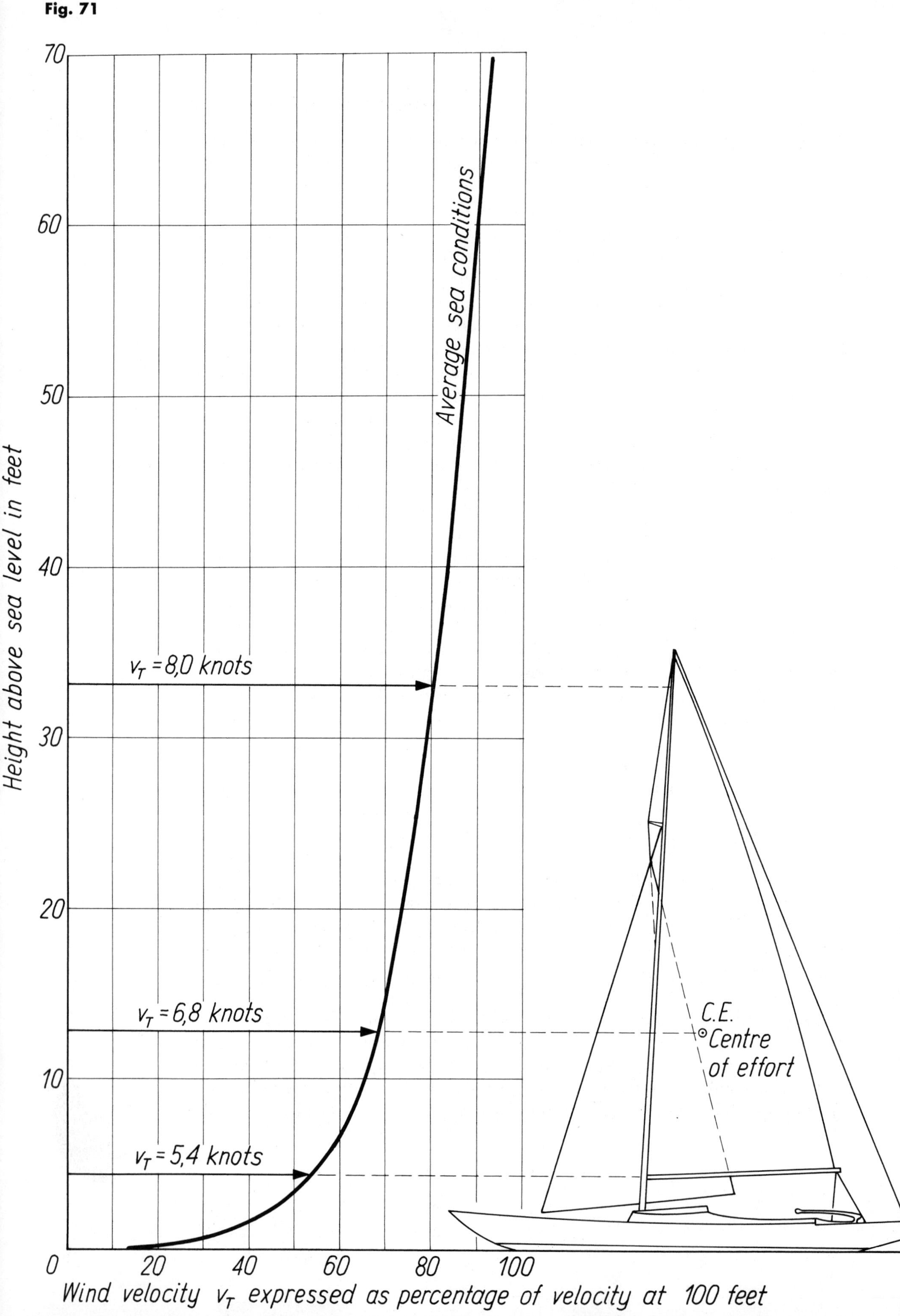

70
60
50
40
30
20
10
0
20
40
60
80
100
Height above sea level in feet
Wind velocity v_T expressed as percentage of velocity at 100 feet
Average sea conditions
v_T = 8,0 knots
v_T = 6,8 knots
v_T = 5,4 knots
C.E.
Centre
of effort

Fig. 72

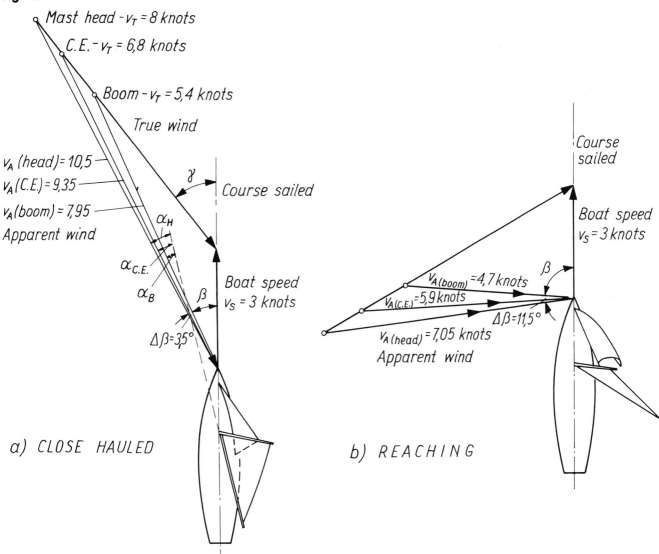

Dragon just considered the wind twist between boom and truck is 3.5° (Fig. 72). In practice it is very difficult to reduce sail twist to this sort of figure, in spite of the ingenious mainsheet leads on a special midships track and kicking straps one can use.

On a reaching course the twist of the wind is greater, e.g., $\Delta\beta = 11.5°$ for the Dragon example. Nevertheless it does not justify setting sails having twist of the order of that shown in Photo. 6. Under no circumstances can one excuse, on aerodynamic grounds, having sails twisted nearly 50°. It could be argued, however, that heavily twisted sails have a greater aesthetic appeal than flat ones.

Rolling and pitching can also influence the apparent wind strength and direction because of the associated movements of the mast and sails (Fig. 73). The effect is greatest toward the top of the mast, where the motion is most violent. Considering say, the rolling case, we can see that as the top of the mast oscillates between the positions 1 and 2, it can reach a velocity w_1 as it rolls to leeward, and a

Fig. 73

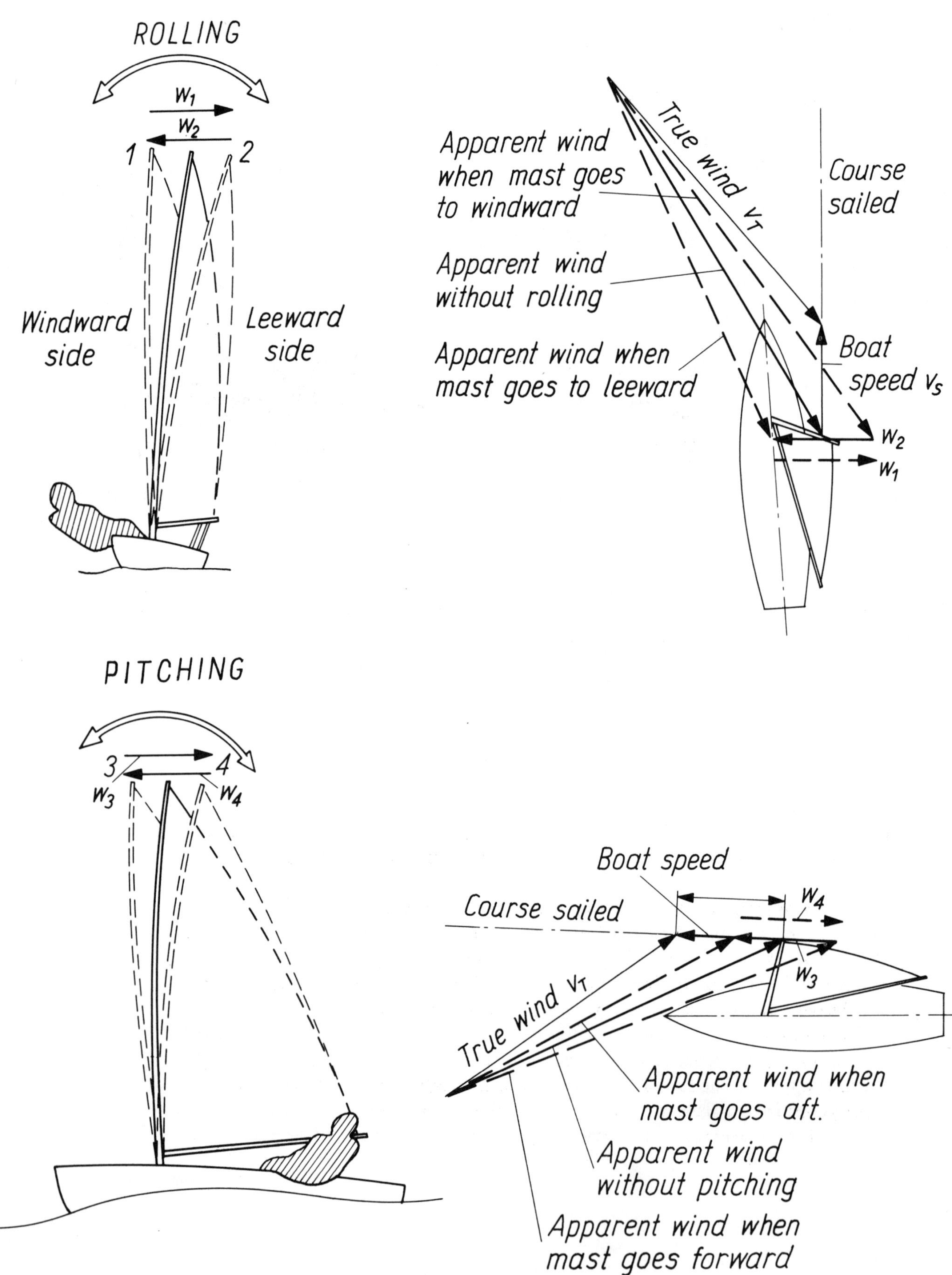
ROLLING
W_1
W_2
1
2
Windward side
Leeward side
True wind v_T
Apparent wind when mast goes to windward
Course sailed
Apparent wind without rolling
Apparent wind when mast goes to leeward
Boat speed v_S
W_2
W_1
PITCHING
3
4
W_3
W_4
Boat speed
Course sailed
W_4
W_3
True wind v_T
Apparent wind when mast goes aft.
Apparent wind without pitching
Apparent wind when mast goes forward

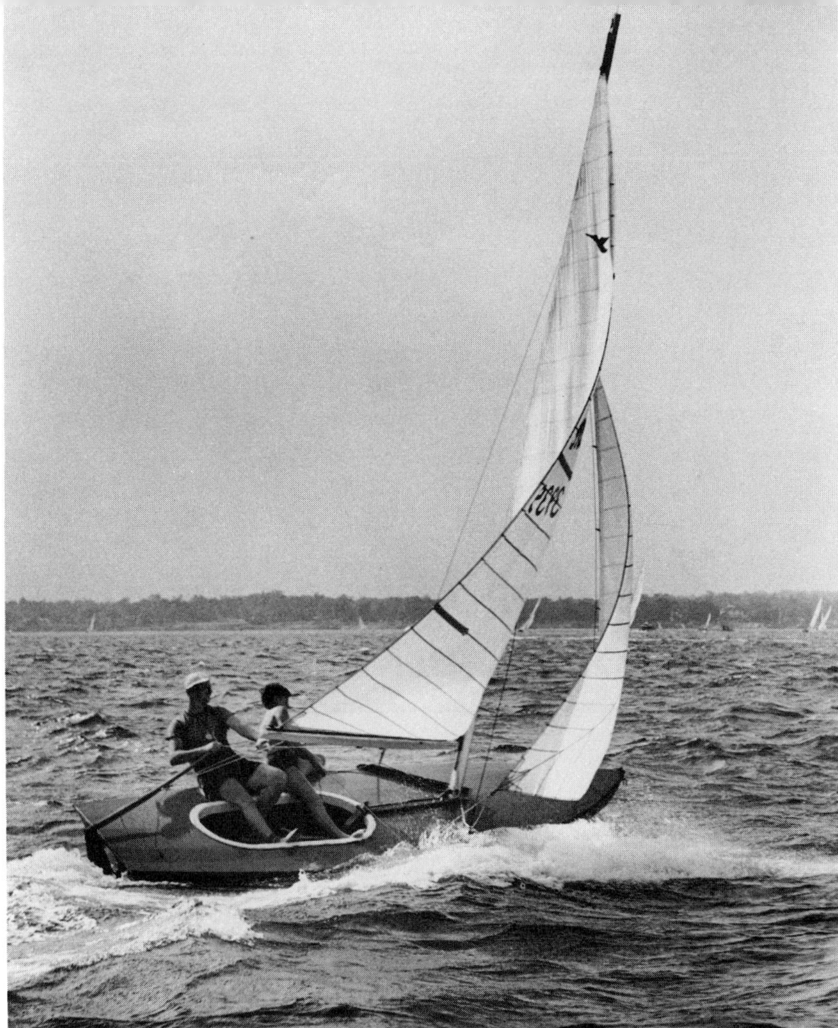

Photo. 6

velocity w_2 as it recovers. These can be treated in velocity triangles as in Fig. 73, which show the resulting changes in the apparent wind.

The angle of incidence of the upper portions of the sail can vary within wide limits and can be appreciable when rolling is violent. As a result of the fluctuations in the apparent wind, periodic changes in the magnitude and direction of the aerodynamic force will be obtained, similar to the process of "pumping" described previously. Particularly on a reaching course, the periodic changes of incidence will produce an effect like those obtained by making rapid and repeated changes in the mainsheet position.

In a similar analysis, one finds that the pitching motion of a yacht induces alterations in the apparent wind as in the rolling case.

Both pitching and rolling are particularly undesirable in weak winds and a large sea. Under these conditions the sail finds it difficult to fill in its usual form, and only shakes. It is then better to use sails of a fairly heavy fabric, which are not so easily shaken about as light sails. Although this conclusion is contrary to the generally adopted practice of using light sails for light winds, the results obtained by yachtsmen using heavier sails justify its adoption. Naturally, this does not apply to spinnakers, which should be of lightweight fabric, but then these are more parachutes than sails.

7. IMPORTANCE OF THE ANGLE OF INCIDENCE

Knowing the nature of the apparent wind up the height of a sail, we will now turn our attention to the importance of the angle of incidence of this wind to the sail.

Let us consider two cat-rigged yachts having identical sails of 100 sq. ft. area, and sailing on the same course as in Fig. 74. Also let us assume that the aerodynamic characteristics of their sails are as those given in Fig. 45 and that the average

Fig. 74

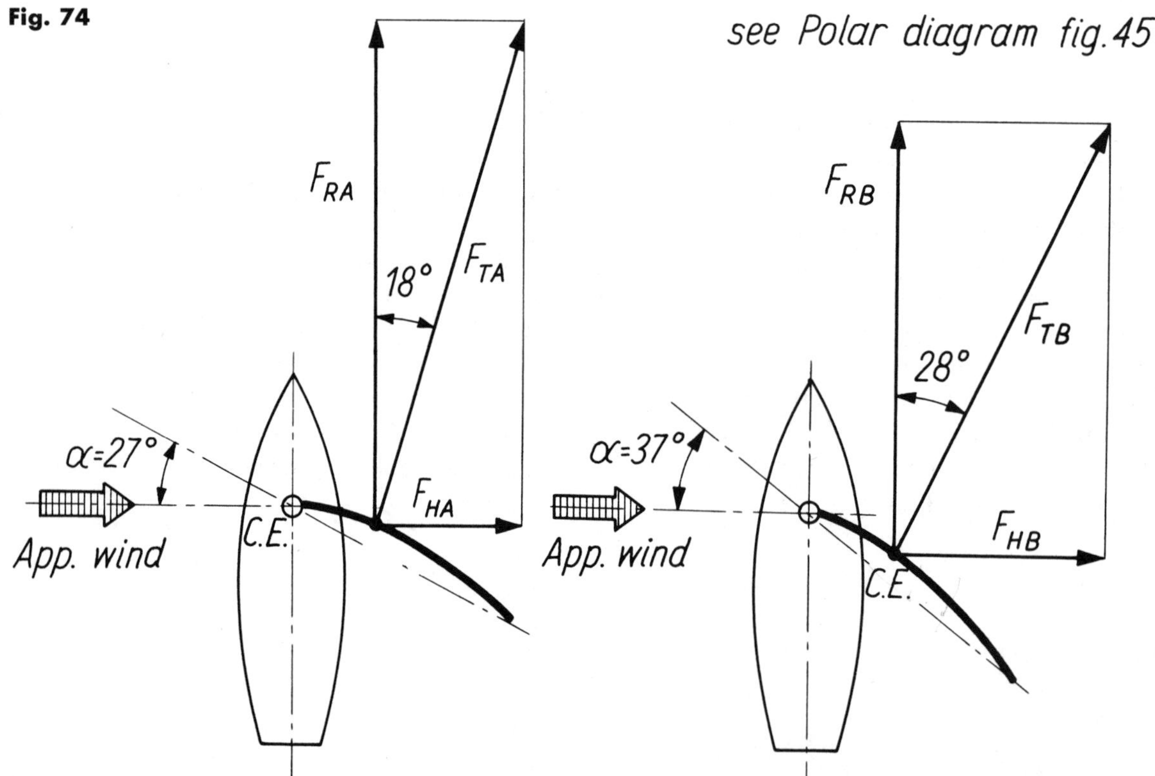

apparent wind is $v_A = 10$ knots (16.9 ft./sec.), and in addition both sails are twisted so that each maintains its chosen angle of incidence over all the sail. Now if helmsman A keeps his sail at the angle $\alpha_A = 27°$ to the apparent wind, then the corresponding coefficient of the total aerodynamic force will be $C_T = 1.38$. On the other hand, if helmsman B sheets his sail harder, to an angle of incidence $\alpha_B = 37°$, his corresponding coefficient will be $C_T = 1.28$.

Hence we can calculate the total forces.

$$\begin{aligned} \text{yacht A: } F_{TA} &= 0.00119 \times V_A{}^2 \times S_A \times C_T \\ &= 0.00119 \times 16.9^2 \times 100 \times 1.38 \\ &= 46.8 \text{ lb.} \\ \text{yacht B: } F_{TB} &= 0.00119 \times 16.9^2 \times 100 \times 1.28 \\ &= 43.5 \text{ lb.} \end{aligned}$$

From Fig. 45 we can also obtain the directions of these forces, and thus resolve them to get corresponding driving forces F_{RA} and F_{RB}.

$$F_{RA} = F_{TA} \times \cos 18° = 46.8 \times 0.951 = 44.5 \text{ lb.}$$
$$F_{RB} = F_{TB} \times \cos 28° = 43.5 \times 0.883 = 38.4 \text{ lb.}$$

This example, which is encountered frequently when sailing, demonstrates the importance of correctly trimming the sail. Here a fall in driving force of 13.7 per cent has been obtained by having the sail too far inboard, and in addition, it could have been shown that the harmful side force F_{HB} would have been much greater. At the other extreme, if the sail is used at too small an incidence, it again will not be working at its full efficiency. The maintenance of the correct angle of incidence on the sail as the wind varies is of the greatest importance if we wish to maintain optimum sailing speed at all times. This is particularly so in light winds, when small changes in driving force affect the performance considerably.

When we were discussing how aerodynamic forces are generated we saw how the maximum aerodynamic total force coefficient C_T was limited by the flow separating from the leeward side of the sail. Particularly when one is reaching, the correct setting of the sail requires one to sail near the stall without generating separated, turbulent flow, as is obtained if the sheet is hauled in too far. From the graph of Fig. 45 it can be seen that the maximum sail force is obtained only in a limited range of angle of incidence, at about 27°. This optimum angle applies to a sail with negligible twist, a camber of about 1/10, and aspect ratio A.R. = 4.2. For sails of characteristics other than these, this angle will also be different.

If a sail is twisted, it is quite possible for the luff in the upper part to be fluttering, a sign taken by many helmsmen to indicate that the sail is working at too small an incidence, while the lower parts are stalled, i.e., at too high an incidence. This results inevitably in the sail not producing a force coefficient C_T as high as could be obtained on a sail in which all heights are working at the same optimum angle of incidence.

Fig. 75

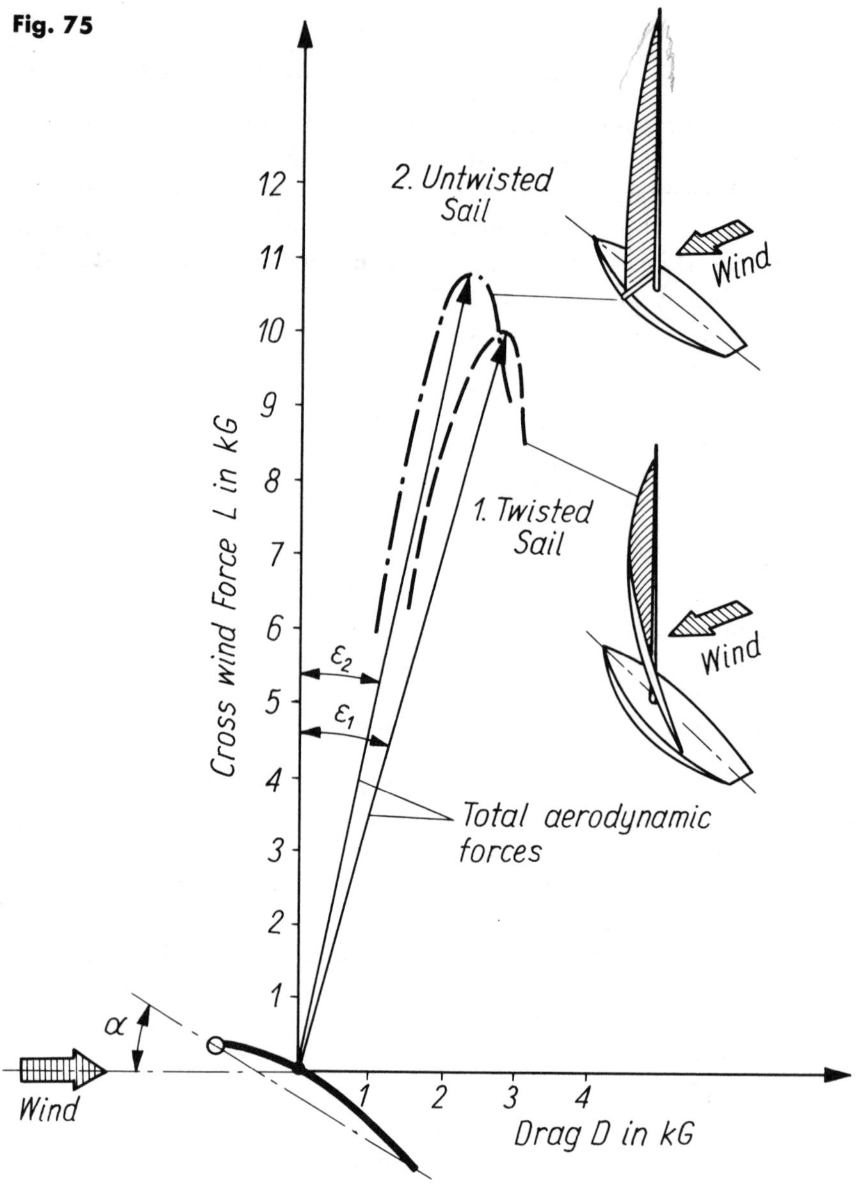

The curves of Fig. 75 show to some extent how the force coefficient, and in particular its maximum value, can be lowered by twisting of the sail. They were obtained from wind tunnel tests on Bermudian sail models. Comparison of the results shows that not only is there a decrease in the coefficients, but also a greater drag angle (ϵ) is obtained, which would result in the boat with the twisted sail not going so well to windward.

Twisting of the sail is particularly marked when sailing on a reach, or broad reach, when the tendency of the boom to lift is not counteracted effectively by the tension in the mainsheet. The working condition of such a sail can be greatly improved by the use of a kicking strap, which pulls the boom downward. Its ideal action is when it secures uniform working incidence for all sections of the sail. The regulation of the kicking strap tension should produce such a twist in the sail as there is in the apparent wind. The proof of a well-regulated kicking strap will be the flutter of the whole length of the luff of the sail when the sheets are eased or the boat luffed slightly. If the tension is not correct, either the upper or lower part will flutter first, indicating uneven working conditions at the different heights of the sail. It is possible that in spite of correctly tensioning the kicking strap, all parts of the sail do not flutter together. When this occurs the sail cut may be at fault and should be rectified. The use of kicking straps is met with in all sizes of yacht, and ones so equipped with an efficient mechanism can have a decisive superiority over their rivals.

The ability to sail close to wind is also affected by the manner in which the mainsheet is attached. Leading the mainsheet to the centerline of the hull, some distance above the keel, should be discouraged (see Fig. 76a). If the tension N_1 in the sheet is resolved into two components N_{a1} and N_{b1}, the component N_{b1}

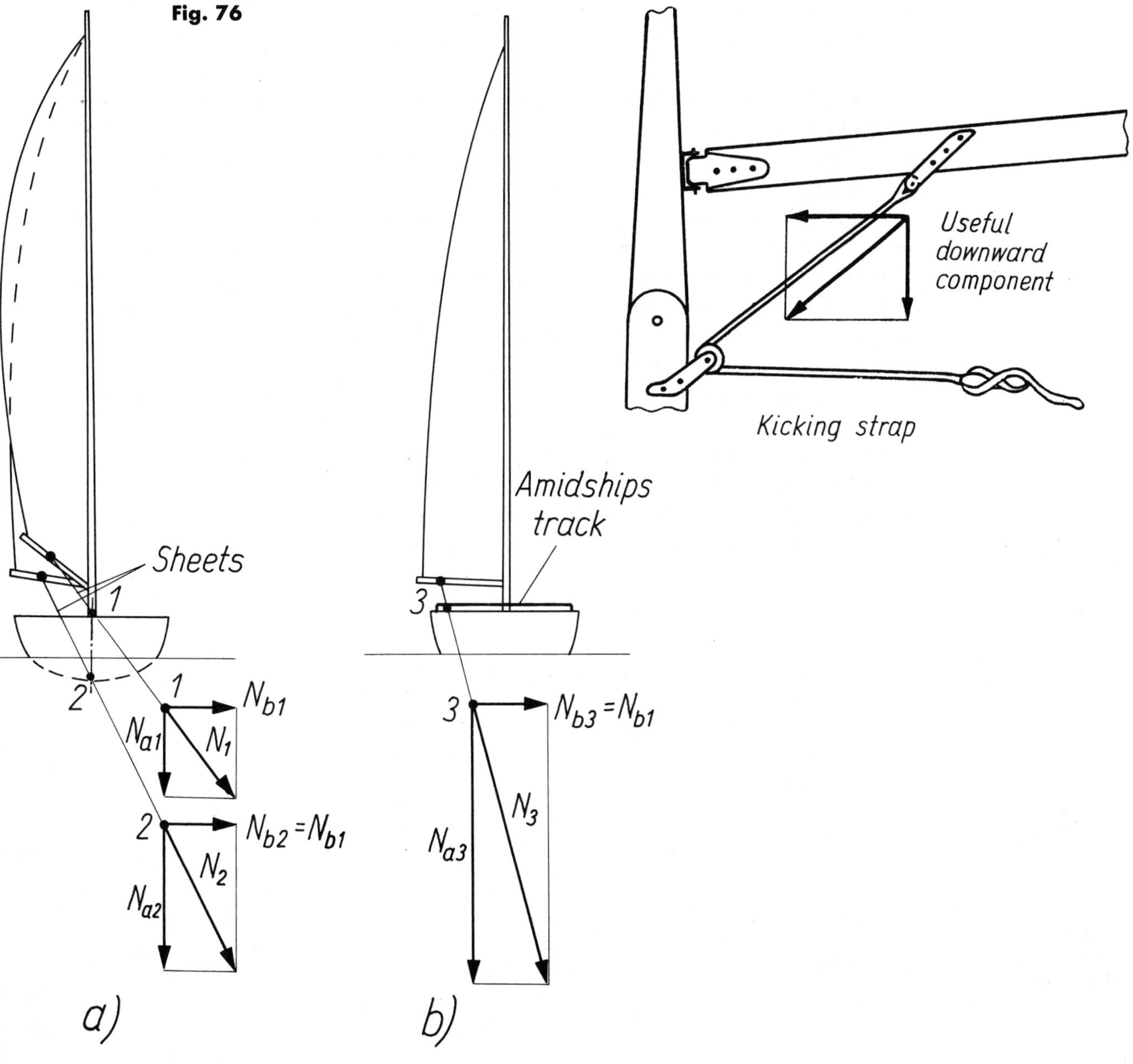

serves to keep the boom in the required position, and N_{a1} acts against its tendency to rise. The larger is this component the better, and this can be achieved by leading the sheet directly to the keel. Then to get the same athwartships force $N_{b2} = N_{b1}$ a greater total tension N_2 is required, and this leads to a larger downward component N_{a2}. One of the best ways to reduce the twist of the sail is to use a mainsheet track mounted amidships (Fig. 76b). This allows a near vertical mainsheet to be used, and consequently, a large component of the tension is available to pull the boom down.

A well-designed kicking strap should automatically counteract the tendency of the boom to rise as changes of course are made, so leaving the mainsheet free to perform its main function of controlling sail incidence. This requirement is very difficult to achieve in practice.

From the example of Fig. 74, we can come to the conclusion that the maximum resultant force F_T is attained only when we set all the sail at a certain optimum angle of incidence α_1 equal to 27° for the sail considered. The question now arises, must we try to attain this optimum angle for setting the sail relative to the apparent wind for all points of sailing? The example shown in Fig. 77 will explain that this is not always the case.

In Fig. 77a a yacht is shown sailing on the wind. The yacht sail is set at an angle of incidence $\alpha_1 = 27°$ at which it derives the maximum aerodynamic force F_{T1}. The component of this force acting in the direction of motion of the yacht, called the driving force, is shown by the vector F_{R1}.

Figure 77b represents a yacht with the mainsail set at the smaller angle of incidence $\alpha_2 = 24°$. The aerodynamic force F_{T2} is now less, but when resolved into a driving force component F_{R2} and a heeling force F_{H2}, causing drift, it is seen that the former is larger, and the latter smaller, than the corresponding components for yacht a. Hence yacht b will sail faster and make less leeway than yacht a. In addition, the force F_{H1}, larger than F_{H2}, will cause yacht a to heel more than yacht b. This again detracts from its performance, since the extra heel causes more hull resistance.

The example quoted shows that to derive the maximum possible speed for a yacht on any selected course, the angle of incidence of the sail must be so adjusted that not only the magnitude of the resultant aerodynamic force, but also the direction in which it acts, are taken into account.

Fig. 77

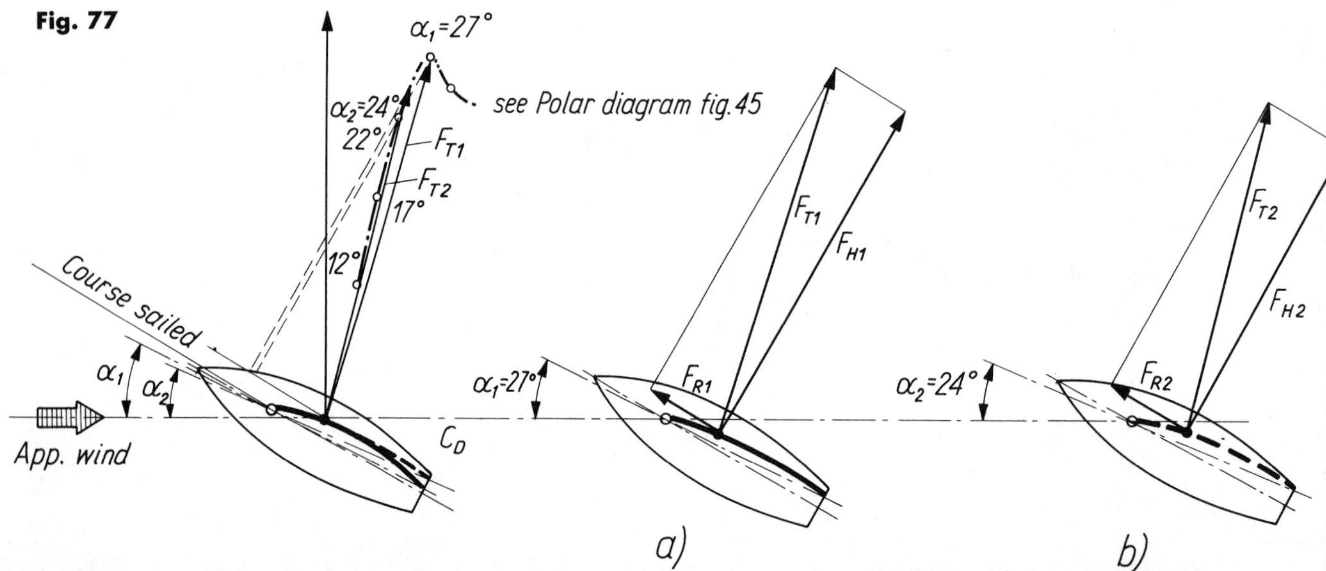

8. THE DEPENDENCE OF SAIL TRIM ON WIND STRENGTH AND APPARENT COURSE, β

In this section we will attempt to discuss how the correct sheeting of the sails depends not only on the sail characteristics but also on those of the hull, and in addition, the strength and direction of the wind. Such a problem can only be done exactly by calculations of a rather tedious nature, but some general conclusions can be drawn by inference, knowing sail and hull characteristics. Typical curves representing aerodynamic properties of the single sail have been given previously. Now the reader will have to accept as valid some simplifying assumptions concerning hydrodynamic characteristics of the hull, which are based on information to be found in later chapters of this book.

We have already mentioned (Fig. 40) how the forces produced by the sail must be exactly balanced by similar forces on the hull. This is illustrated in Fig. 78a which shows the polar diagram of forces for a sail at a certain apparent wind speed and direction. Opposing the sail polar diagram there is a resultant hull force R_T which can be seen to be balanced at only one point on the sail curve, that at point A. Thus with the configuration shown it is possible to sail with the sail at only one incidence α_A, i.e., sheeted in one particular position δ_A. If α_A is altered to, say, α_B by hardening the sheets to δ_B, conditions elsewhere must of necessity, alter too. Two such quantities which might alter are the speed of the yacht v_s, and the angle λ between its course and the hull centerline.

The two quantities just mentioned control to a very large extent the hydrodynamic forces on the hull. In Fig. 78a the outlines are shown of some hull sections, or waterlines, of a fixed-keel yacht sailing to windward at a certain angle

Fig. 78

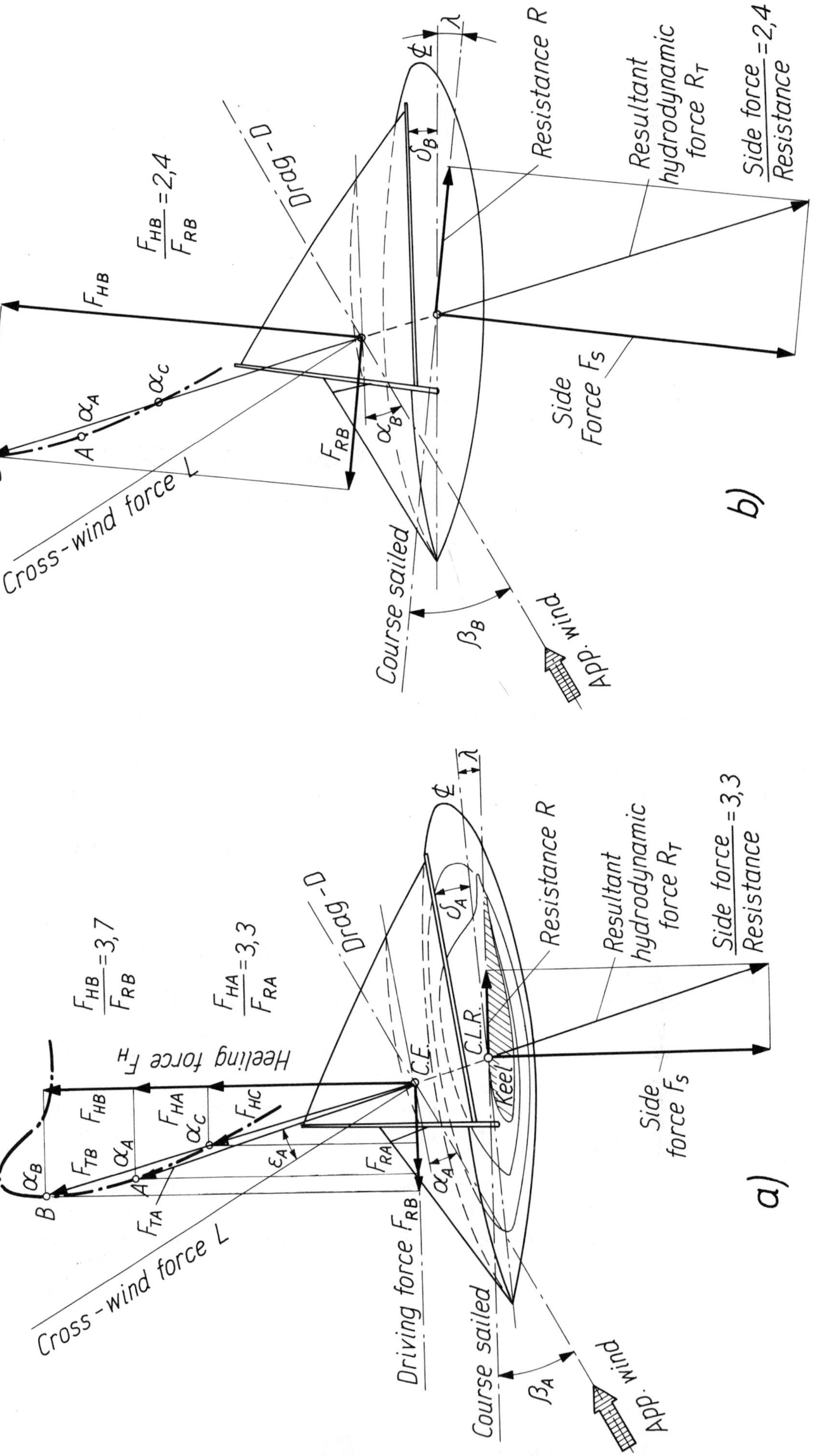

a)
Cross-wind force L
Driving force F_{RB}
Course sailed
App. wind
β_A
Heeling force F_H
$\frac{F_{HB}}{F_{RB}}=3{,}7$
$\frac{F_{HA}}{F_{RA}}=3{,}3$
Drag-D
C.E.
C.L.R.
Keel
Resistance R
Resultant hydrodynamic force R_T
$\frac{\text{Side force}}{\text{Resistance}}=3{,}3$
Side force F_S
α_B α_A α_C F_{TB} F_{HB} F_{HA} F_{HC} F_{TA} F_{RA} ε_A δ_A λ
b)
Cross-wind force L
Course sailed
App. wind
β_B
$\frac{F_{HB}}{F_{RB}}=2{,}4$
F_{HB}
F_{RB}
Drag-D
Resistance R
Resultant hydrodynamic force R_T
$\frac{\text{Side force}}{\text{Resistance}}=2{,}4$
Side Force F_S
α_B α_A α_C δ_B λ

of heel and leeway angle λ. Under the asymmetric conditions shown, the underwater part of the hull acts as a hydrofoil and develops a side force F_s and a drag, or resistance R, by a process similar to that of the sail. We can say that in general as the leeway angle λ (angle of incidence of hydrofoil) increases, so will both side force F_s and resistance R.

In addition to the variation with leeway angle, the hull forces also vary with speed v_s. The side force F_s will change as the ratio of speeds squared, as do the aerodynamic forces, but the resistance will increase at a greater rate. Thus, at a fixed leeway angle the hull force R_T will vary similar to that shown in Fig. 79, which presents some results obtained from experiments carried out at the Turkish Shipbuilding Research Institute on a hull model of the *Pirate* centerboard dinghy. We can see that at a low value of velocity through the water, v_{s1}, the ratio side force/resistance = 4.5. As the speed increases, this ratio gradually falls to 1.8 at the velocity v_{s4}. This state of affairs can be compared with those for the sails, in which the same ratio of forces F_H/F_R can be taken not to vary with wind speed.

A fixed-keel hull will demonstrate characteristics similar to those of the center-

Fig. 79

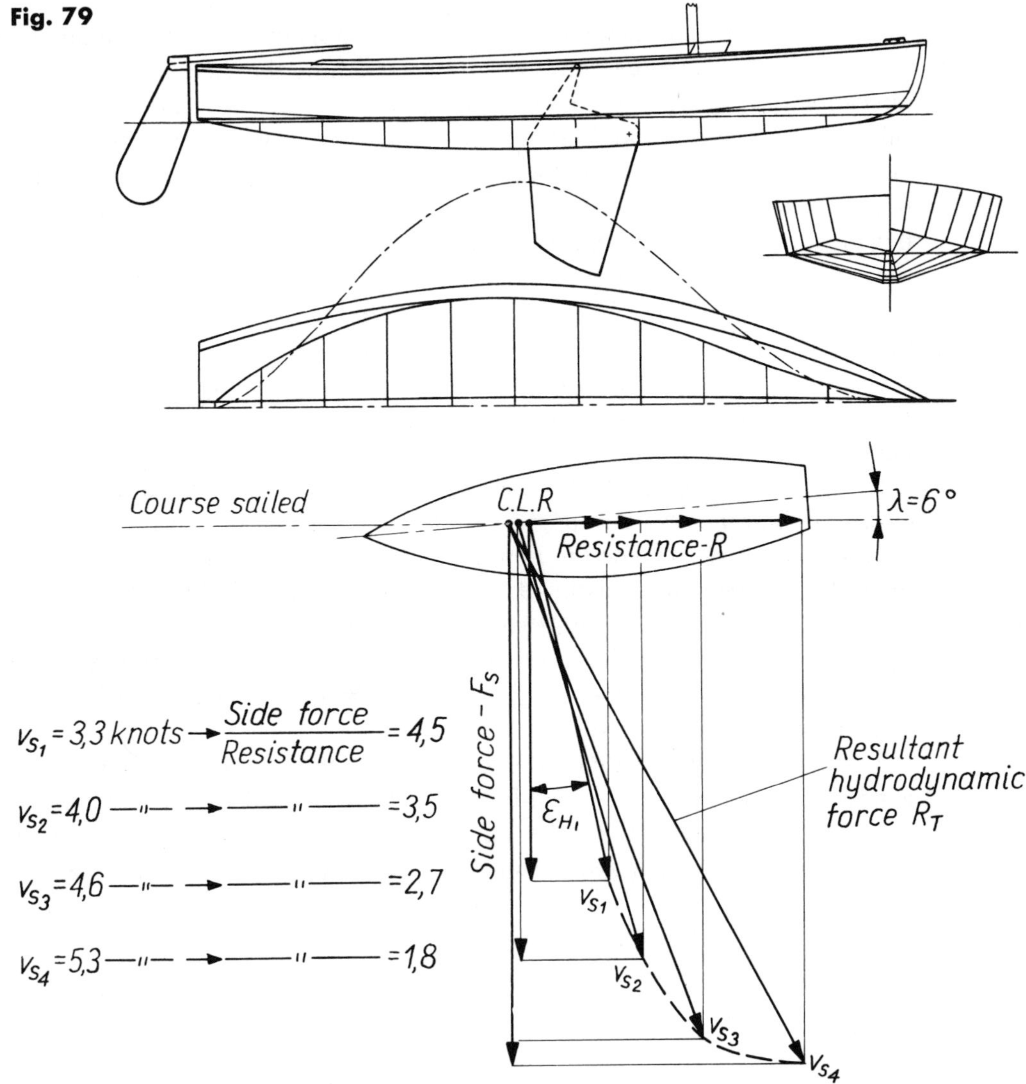

board dinghy, but the values of the ratio F_S/R will be generally lower, due to the poorer hydrodynamic efficiency of the hull in generating the side force F_s at a corresponding resistance R. We can see how this hydrodynamic efficiency depends on the shape (aspect ratio) of the hull, or centerboard, if we compare the shape of centerboard of the *Pirate* with the International 10 sq. meter Canoe (Fig. 25) which can produce a maximum value of F_S/R, at the leeway angle $\lambda = 6°$, of 7.5. The same general behavior is found to be true for sails also.

A yacht's hull is therefore strictly limited in its possibilities of producing side force F_S for a given velocity v_S and the unwanted component of resistance R.

We are now in a position to consider how to achieve maximum speed through the water. The allied problem of close-windedness, which together with the speed decide the yacht's performance on the wind, will be treated in a later section.

In the example shown in Fig. 78a we have taken a ratio for the hull $F_S/R = 3.3$ appropriate to an I.Y.R.U. Class 6-meter yacht sailing at a speed $v_S = 5.9$ knots, on the wind, whose true velocity is $v_T = 12$ knots. If the yacht is sailing at a steady angle β_A between the course and the apparent wind direction, the hydrodynamic force will be in equilibrium with the sail force when the latter is working at the angle of incidence α_A.

The question now arises as to what will happen if the helmsman decides to increase the driving force from the sail by hardening the sheet, without making any alteration of rudder. The angle of incidence of the sail will increase to α_B and result in an increase of the total aerodynamic force to F_{TB}, and a change in its line of action; i.e., the ratio F_{HB}/F_{RB} will increase to 3.7. In general the hull will not be able to achieve a similar ratio of F_S/R by an increase in the angle of leeway λ only, but must also increase its speed to balance the forces. This it will do by bearing off the wind and so increasing the angle β, until equilibrium is reached. In the process the ratio of F_{HB}/F_{RB} will reduce, since the heeling force/driving force axes will rotate relative to the apparent wind. The final state of equilibrium, when $F_{HB}/F_{RB} = F_S/R = 2.4$, is shown in Fig. 78b, where it can be seen that the angle β_B equals 36.5°, an increase of 6.5° over β_A, and that the leeway angle λ has also altered.

If, on the other hand, the helmsman had eased the sheet, from the sail incidence α_A to α_C, then the resultant aerodynamic force will fall drastically to about 70 per cent of F_{TA}. If we suppose the new force F_{TC} acts along the same line as did F_{TB}, then the corresponding ratio of the forces F_H/F_R will be 3.7. As a result of the smaller driving force F_{RC}, the yacht's speed v_S must decrease. Reference to Fig. 79 shows that this increased ratio required of the hull forces may be met solely by the reduction in v_S, with possibly a small change in leeway angle λ and the apparent course β_A.

The two examples just considered demonstrate how one may affect changes in windward performance of a well-balanced yacht by making alterations only in sail setting. Thus, starting from the initial point A (Fig. 78a), hardening the sheet causes the yacht to bear away from the wind, and increase its speed, while freeing the sheet reduces the speed with probably only a small change in the course.

The arguments on which these conclusions, well known to many dinghy sailors, are based assumed that alterations in speed did not appreciably alter the apparent wind strength or direction. For the condition chosen this is quite a reasonable simplification to make, and one which will be used throughout this section. We also assumed that the heel angle did not alter: this is justified in such a general discussion because increasing angle of heel adversely affects both the aerodynamic efficiency of the sail and the hydrodynamic efficiency of the hull, in the same manner.

Let us now consider some of the geometrical relationships between the apparent course β and the aerodynamic and hydrodynamic forces. Figure 80 illustrates the relative angular positions of the sail and keel forces on a yacht sailing on the wind. This drawing is more simple than that of Fig. 78a. It assumes that the yacht is sailing upright, and that the center of effort (CE) of the sail and the center

Fig. 80

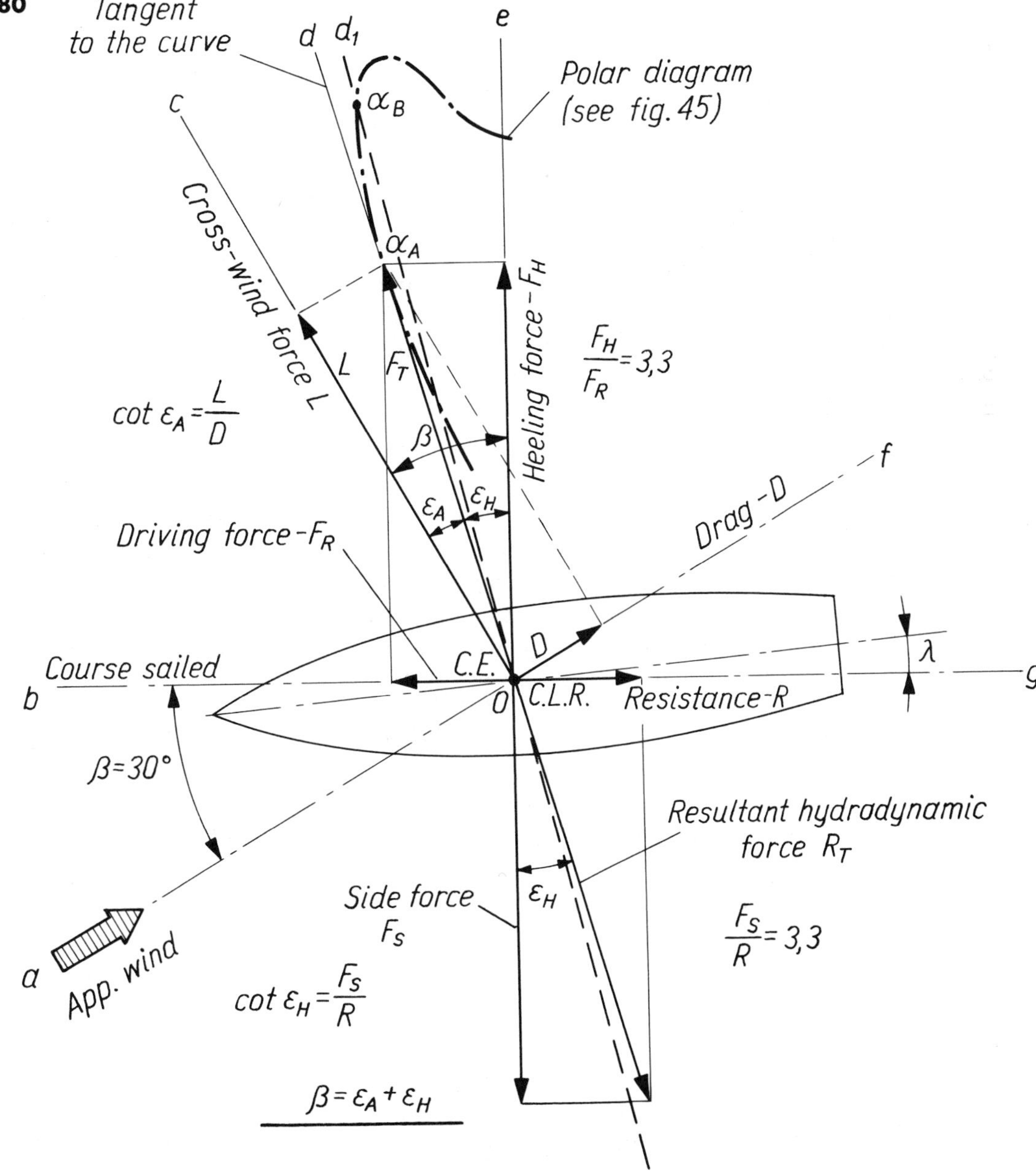

of lateral resistance (CLR) of the submerged hull are coincident at the point O. These simplifications do not affect the geometrical relationships we shall derive. The line of action of the resultant aerodynamic force F_T is defined by the aerodynamic drag angle ϵ_A. This term was described in the section dealing with the "Aerodynamic Resistance of the Sail" (Fig. 49b). The angle is measured between the direction of the resultant aerodynamic force and the cross-wind axis CO, which is perpendicular to the apparent wind direction. Its magnitude can be calculated from the relationship between the cross-wind force component L and the drag component D, so that $\cot \epsilon_A = L/D$. Similarly we can calculate the hydrodynamic drag angle ϵ_H from $\cot \epsilon_H = F_s/R$, where F_s is the hull side force and R its resistance.

Under steady sailing conditions, when v_s is constant, the resultant air and water forces, F_T and R, are of the same magnitude and act along the same line. Thus, from Fig. 80 we can say:

$$\epsilon_A = \angle\, c\,o\,d,$$

and $$\epsilon_H = \angle\, d\,o\,e,$$

and hence $$\epsilon_A + \epsilon_H = \angle\, c\,o\,e.$$

but $$\angle\, c\,o\,e = \angle\, a\,o\,b = \beta$$

thus $$\beta = \epsilon_A + \epsilon_H$$

It can be said therefore that the sailing angle to the apparent wind or, in other words, the apparent course β is the sum of the aerodynamic and hydrodynamic angles of drag, ϵ_A and ϵ_H. This simple geometrical relationship is of fundamental importance in understanding the principles of the performance of yachts. We can derive from it a number of practical conclusions which are particularly important for competitive sailing.

It is clear that one way we might juggle with the equations we have just derived from Fig. 80 is to maintain β constant using the rudder. Then if we increase ϵ_A using the sheet, ϵ_H must decrease by the same amount, i.e., the line of action of the resultant aerodynamic and hydrodynamic forces rotates about O from Od to Od_1. Bearing in mind that there is a correspondence between apparent wind speed v_A and yacht speed v_s, increases in the former in general leading to an increase in the latter, we can also take the hull characteristic from Fig. 79, with the leeway angle λ remaining constant. Then as ϵ_H varies, provided that the apparent wind strength v_A is sufficient, so must the yacht's speed v_s vary as follows:

$v_{s1} = 3.3$ knots	$\cot \epsilon_{H1} = 4.5$	$\epsilon_{H1} = 12.5°$
$v_{s2} = 4.0$ knots	$\cot \epsilon_{H2} = 3.5$	$\epsilon_{H2} = 16.0°$
$v_{s3} = 4.6$ knots	$\cot \epsilon_{H3} = 2.7$	$\epsilon_{H3} = 20.3°$
$v_{s4} = 5.3$ knots	$\cot \epsilon_{H4} = 1.8$	$\epsilon_{H4} = 29.0°$

It is interesting to attempt now to decide at what incidence α we should set the sail to obtain the maximum speed on this apparent course $\beta = 30°$.

Using the equation derived earlier, and the above values of ϵ_H, we can obtain the corresponding values of ϵ_A, thus:

$$\epsilon_A = \beta - \epsilon_H$$

Hence for $v_{s1} = 3.3$ knots $\epsilon_{A1} = 30° - 12.5° = 17.5°$
$v_{s2} = 4.0$ knots $\epsilon_{A2} = 30° - 16.0° = 14°$
$v_{s3} = 4.6$ knots $\epsilon_{A3} = 30° - 20.3° = 9.7°$
$v_{s4} = 5.3$ knots $\epsilon_{A4} = 30° - 29.0° = 1°$

Thus it appears that if we can set the sail incidence to give a drag angle $\epsilon_{A4} = 1°$, then for the apparent course $\beta = 30°$ we should obtain a yacht speed of about 5.3 knots. Unfortunately this condition is unobtainable. Looking at the sail polar diagram (see also Fig. 45), it is clear that a minimum possible value of ϵ_A is obtained at the point where a line from O is a tangent to the curve. This point, shown as α_A on Fig. 80, yields a value $\epsilon_A = 12.5°$.

Using this minimum value, intermediate in the above table, we can estimate that the maximum speed v_s under the conditions chosen is about 4.3 knots.

The arguments we have used were not completely sound, since in general the leeway angle λ would not have remained constant under these conditions, and it was tacitly assumed that the wind and water speeds were such that a balance of forces as well as their ratios could be obtained. Nevertheless an important point emerged: the great significance of the minimum attainable angle of aerodynamic drag. This is particularly true when considering racing One-Design classes, such as the Finn, Flying Dutchman, Star, Dragon, when all hulls are nominally identical and thus have the same hydrodynamic characteristics. In these cases the limit of velocity v_s will depend almost entirely on the rigging, trim, and set of the sails, since on these will depend the angle of aerodynamic drag ϵ_A attainable under any given conditions.

Taking the last example as a starting point, when we estimated the maximum speed a particular yacht could attain on a given apparent course β, let us now consider what happens if the wind reduces in strength. If the angle β is maintained, we know that the yacht's speed v_s must fall. The effects of changes in v_s will in general be greater than any alterations in leeway angle λ; so as was shown in Fig. 79, the hydrodynamic angle of drag ϵ_H will decrease. Hence the aerodynamic drag angle ϵ_A must increase by a like amount, and this is done by increasing the sail incidence to α_B (Fig. 80). A limit beyond which it will not pay to increase sail incidence can be found by drawing a tangent to the polar diagram such that it is also perpendicular to the course (Fig. 78a). This construction defines the maximum attainable driving force. It is clear that any increase in incidence beyond this point serves to reduce the driving force, at a very large heeling force, which is obviously undesirable.

From this example we can conclude that the best sheeting position of the sail on a given apparent course depends on the wind strength, harder sheeting being necessary as the wind falls. This is in agreement with practical experience, particularly of small boat racing helmsmen, who know that sail sheeting must never be static, but must vary continuously with wind strength if the best performance is to be obtained.

The amount by which sail incidence should be altered if the wind strength varies depends to some extent on the apparent course β being sailed. Figure 81 shows our sail polar diagram drawn for four points of sailing between close-hauled and broad reaching, obtained by considering the yacht as fixed in direction and rotating the wind vector around it. Hence the horizontal and vertical axes through O give scales of driving and heeling force respectively. Each axis has two scales, appropriate to $v_A = 10$, 15 knots, and also are drawn scales giving the values of the coefficients of the forces based on a sail area of 100 sq. ft. Comparison of this figure with Fig. 80 will show that the cross-wind direction is given by the axis cO, drawn at the appropriate angle of $\beta = \epsilon_A + \epsilon_H$ to eo. This line, for $\beta = 30°$, is shown on Fig. 81.

We have already demonstrated that the minimum aerodynamic drag angle ϵ_A, corresponding to the point A for $\beta = 30°$ on Fig. 81 is of great importance for windward sailing in strong winds. For the polar diagram shown this minimum ϵ_A is attained at a sail incidence $\alpha = 17°$, corresponding to the minimum possible value of C_H/C_R. In other words, we have at this point the best compromise, in the absence of any other considerations, between the unwanted heeling force F_H and the useful driving force F_R. The incidence at which this minimum drag angle is obtained is clearly independent of the point of sailing, but it will be found later that its significance is reduced as one comes off the wind.

A different situation arises, however, in lighter winds, when the correctly trimmed sail should tend toward realizing the maximum driving force, F_R or equivalent max C_R (driving force coefficient). For $\beta = 30°$, the maximum driving force is attained at point B, at $\alpha = 24°$, but as β varies, the optimum sail incidence also changes so that at $\beta = 50°$, the maximum driving force is attained at an incidence $\alpha = 27°$. Thereafter, for the sail characteristic shown, the incidence value changes little, but this will depend on the shape of the top of the curve, i.e., on the particular sail configuration being used. Thus, depending on the wind strength, we have a range of incidence, α from 17° to 24°, at which to set the sail when close-hauled; and in addition, the upper limit, at least, of this range depends on the point of sailing, increasing to 27° when well off the wind.

It is of interest to consider the magnitude of the changes in the forces for different incidences and wind speeds. At an apparent course $\beta = 30°$, a light breeze condition ($v_A = 10$ knots) for the sails at an incidence $\alpha_B = 24°$ gives a heeling force F_H of 40 lb. On the other scale of Fig. 81, for a moderate breeze $v_A = 15$ knots, a heeling force $F_H = 60$ lb. is obtained with the sail at $\alpha_A = 17°$. If now the breeze is fresh, say $v_A = 20$ knots (33.8 ft./sec.), the helmsman will try to trim the sail to the optimum incidence $\alpha_A = 17°$, with the luff on the verge of fluttering.

Fig. 81

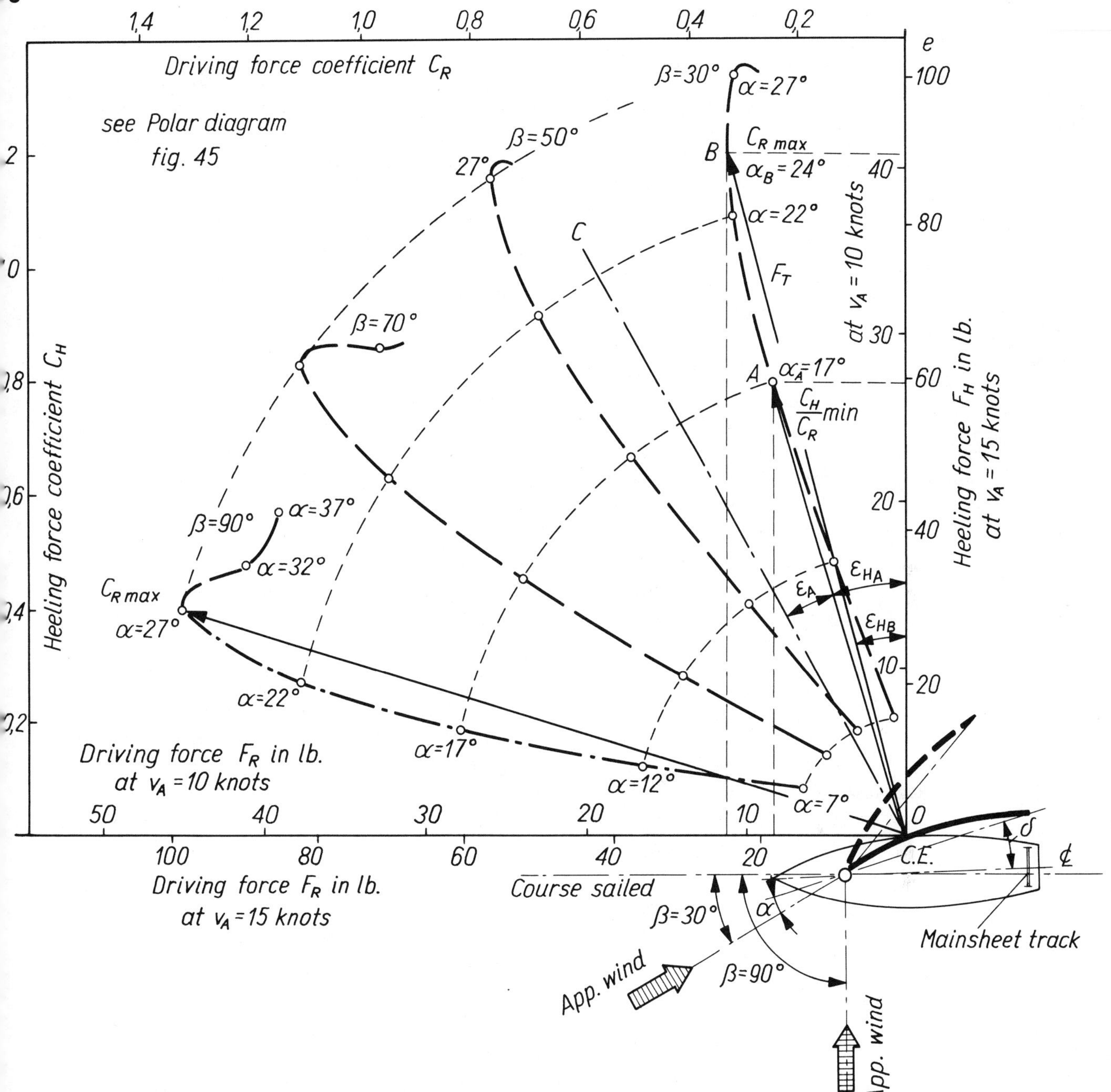

The corresponding heeling force coefficient C_H is 0.795, and hence the heeling force F_H, for a sail area S_A = 100 sq. ft.:

$$F_H = 0.00119 \times v_A^2 \times S_A \times C_H$$
$$= 0.00119 \times 33.8^2 \times 100 \times 0.795 = 108 \text{ lb.}$$

Now if the crew is not able to balance such a large heeling force, or if the yacht

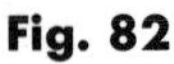

Fig. 82

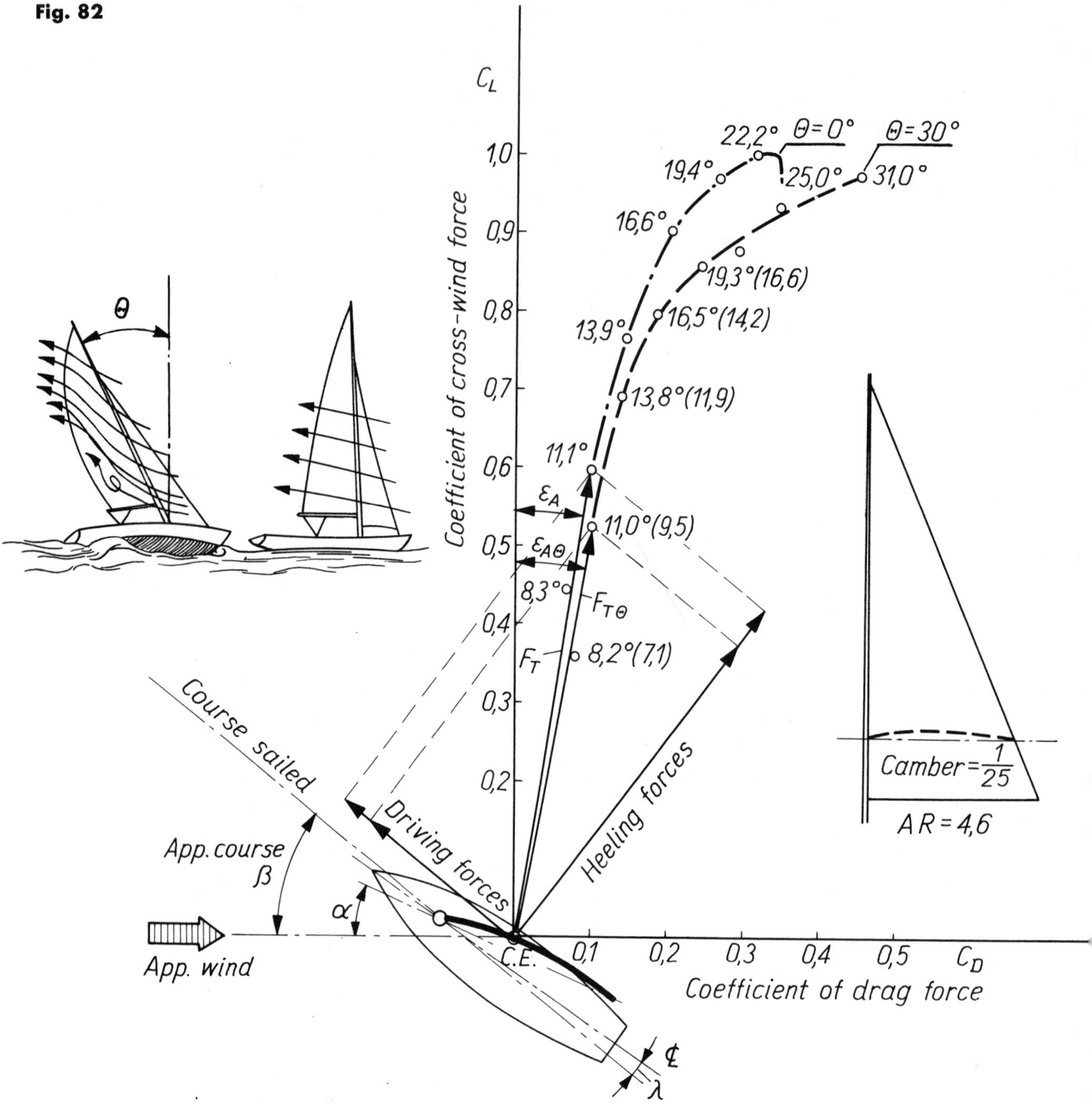

is a keel boat, the yacht will heel until a stable angle is reached. This is partly a result of the natural stability of the hull, and partly because of changes in the sail and hull forces due to heeling, changes which are to the detriment of the performance.

Figure 82 shows some results of experiments carried out at Southampton University on a rigid sail of aspect ratio A.R. = 4.6, and camber 1/25 of the chord, on a mast of constant diameter. Comparing the two polar diagrams for heel angles $\Theta = 0°, 30°$, we can see that the latter curve has moved generally to the right, and has incurred obvious disadvantages over that for the upright position. Thus the value of the minimum drag angle $\epsilon_{A\theta}$ for the heeled yacht is greater than ϵ_A for $\Theta = 0°$, which will result in reduced speed. Some of the difference between the two curves arises because when a sail is heeled, the effective incidence α of the sail becomes less, both for geometrical reasons, and because of the greater influence of the sea on the sail. The effect of this can sometimes be seen when a yacht is heeled to a very large angle, usually on the verge of capsizing, when the sail may get the wind on the lee side. The polar diagram for $\Theta = 30°$ (Fig. 82) shows in brackets the reduced angles of incidence due to heeling, and the accompanying sketch shows how the air flow over the sail changes for the worse as the yacht heels.

Since the effective sail incidence is reduced when the yacht heels, a sail which is already working at a low incidence, as it should be in strong winds, may flutter at the luff. The flapping parts of a sail contribute little driving force, but plenty of resistance, and so the crew who cannot ballast their boat upright carry a penalty. Other ways to avoid excessive heel are to reef the sail, or if it is possible, to flatten it, i.e., decrease the camber.

The sail losses when heeled are not the only ones to contend with. The hull resistance also increases, and its side force reduces and therefore the hydrodynamic drag angle ϵ_H increases. Since the aerodynamic drag angle ϵ_A also increases, it follows that the sailing angle β does so too, i.e., the yacht does not point so high as when upright.

The unwanted heeling force, which is the price we pay to obtain a driving force is not such a problem when sailing on a reach. Referring to Fig. 81, it can be seen that the heeling force falls considerably as the apparent course β is increased, with the sail at the best incidence, near to $\alpha = 27°$. As the angle β increases the hull is called upon to produce less side force to balance the sail heeling force. Hence driving force becomes of increasing importance and it pays to trim the sail near to its maximum driving force, irrespective of the wind speed.

To summarize our discussion we can say that, with the aid of some specific sail and hull characteristics, we have established certain broad principles to obtain the best performance from a yacht. Although for other hulls and sails of different aspect ratio and camber the values will be different, the principles will remain unaltered.

The chief point to emerge is that the well-known rule for trimming the sail, to free it until the luff is just about to flutter, is inadequate. Instead, a range of best sail incidence is found, which depends on the wind strength and the point of sailing. Two limits to this range were found:

1. The sail incidence at which the ratio of heeling force F_H to driving force F_R or C_H/C_R and thus the drag angle ϵ_A are minimum, being applicable when sailing close-hauled in strong winds. This incidence corresponds roughly with the incidence given by the "near-fluttering-luff" rule.
2. The sail incidence at which the maximum driving force F_R or equivalent $C_{R\,max}$ is obtained, being applicable when sailing close-hauled in light winds and when reaching in any wind strength.

Bearing in mind the previous discussion on sail twist it is worth noting that in the present context, the sheet should pull to the hull centerline when sailing close-hauled in light airs, but as the wind strength increases, the sheet should run to a point on the lee side of the boat.

So far, then, we have discovered two fundamental criteria, the minimum ratio of C_H/C_R and the maximum value of C_R, by which to assess the merits of sails. In another section we shall consider the question of the best course β to adopt when sailing to windward, largely by taking as examples some well-known Olympic classes.

9. THE IMPORTANCE OF SAIL CAMBER

The magnitude and line of action of the aerodynamic forces depend to a large extent on the shape of the sail and its camber.

In the majority of cases, class rules, in some form or another, place restrictions on the choice of sail area and how it is disposed. There are no such limitations on the amount of flow or camber in a sail, and crews are therefore able to set sails of different cambers according to their needs.

Views on the importance of camber, and on how much it should be, have varied considerably throughout the history of yachting. Up to the middle of the last century, sails were universally used having large camber. This was a consequence of their being made of flax. In those days yachts were unable to sail closer to the wind than about 55° to 60°. The traditional conviction that a bellying sail was best underwent a radical change only after the racing victories of the schooner *America*. This yacht, which in comparison with her rivals had very flat sails, demonstrated a marked superiority when going to windward, being able to sail about 6° closer to the wind than her opponents. Designers imitating *America* soon confirmed that her victories could largely be attributed to her flat sails, and so the full sail went out of fashion.

With the progress made in aerodynamics, and through racing experience, the position has again reversed, and sails of considerable camber are again in favor. The old controversy has been revived: is camber a good or a bad thing? The fact is, both types have their advantages and disadvantages, and the choice of a suitably cambered sail must be made with regard to the prevailing racing conditions, the course, and the wind strength. There is no such thing as a universal sail. What may be an excellent sail under certain conditions may, as a result of incorrect camber, be hopelessly bad in some other conditions.

Fig. 83

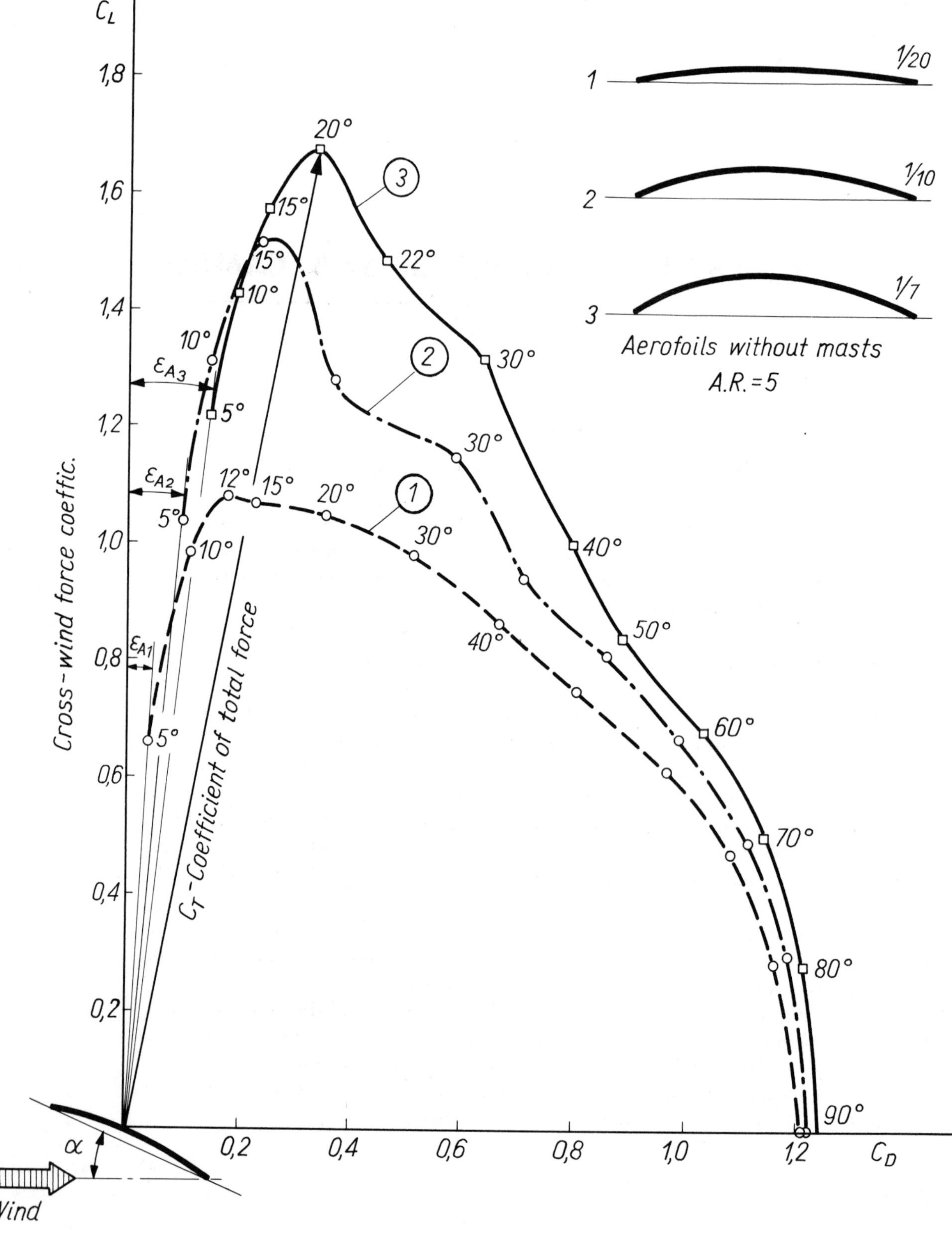

C_L
1,8
1,6
1,4
1,2
1,0
0,8
0,6
0,4
0,2
0,2
0,4
0,6
0,8
1,0
1,2
C_D
Cross-wind force coeffic.
C_T-Coefficient of total force
ε_{A3}
ε_{A2}
ε_{A1}
α
Wind
1
2
3
1/20
1/10
1/7
Aerofoils without masts
A.R.=5

(a) Selecting the Best Camber

In Fig. 83 are given the polar diagrams for three rigid, untwisted, aerofoils having cambers of 1/7, 1/10, and 1/20 respectively and a common aspect ratio A.R. = 5. Although the results are for aerofoils without masts, they illustrate the influence of camber, in a general way, for most sails. They will represent the behavior of a jib quite well, but would be modified in shape if a mast were fitted.

We can see immediately that there are profound differences among the three polar diagrams: for instance, in the maximum value of the total aerodynamic force coefficient C_T. For the aerofoil of 1/7 camber this is about 1.7, for 1/10 camber it is 1.55, while for the 1/20 camber it is only 1.1.

Let us arrange these three polar diagrams (Fig. 84), in the manner of Fig. 81, so that we can assess their relative merits for the apparent courses β = 30°, 60°,

Fig. 84

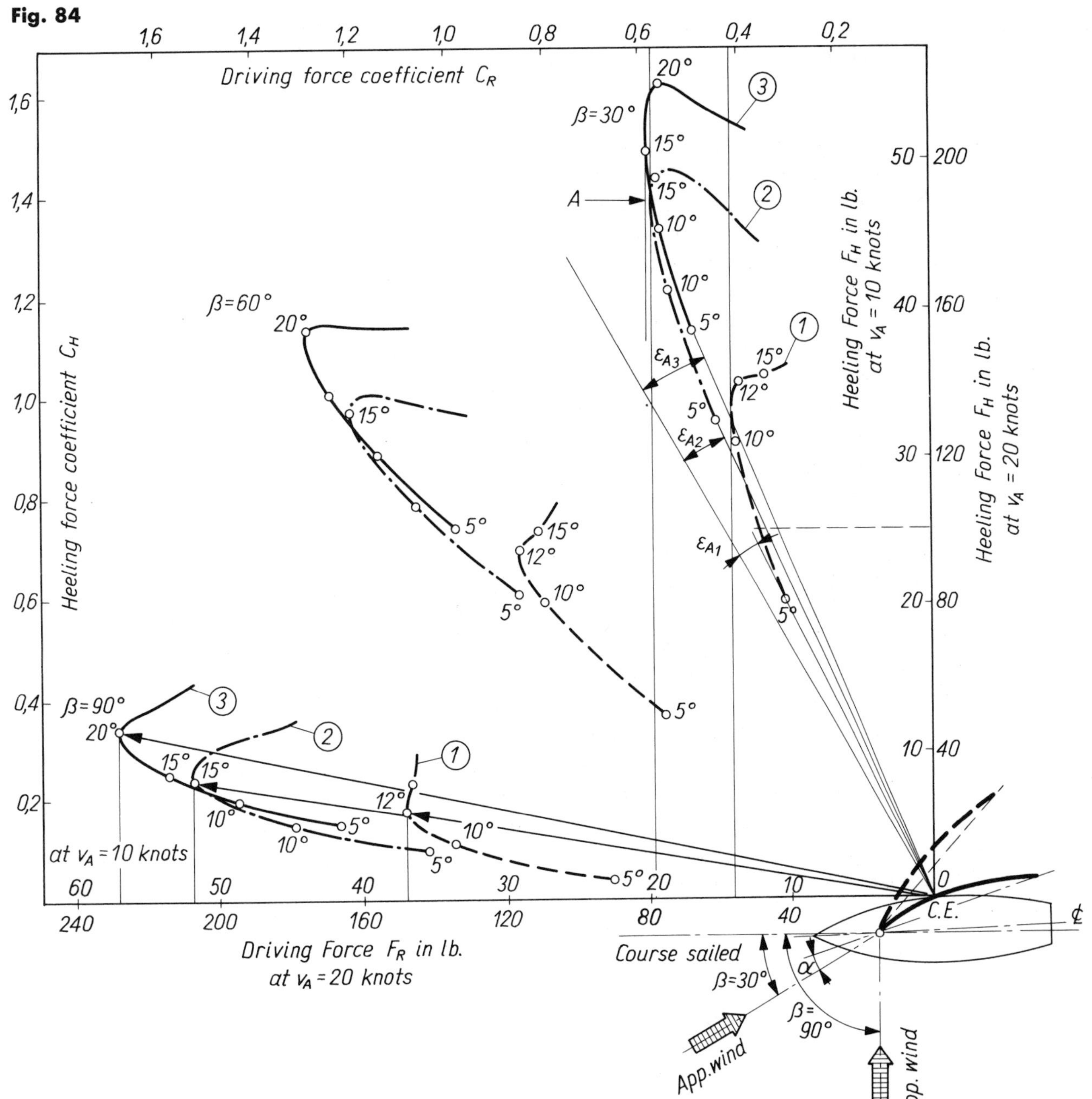

and 90°. On the vertical axis is marked the scale for the heeling force coefficients C_H, and the corresponding values of the heeling force F_H for a sail area $S_A = 100$ sq. ft. and wind strengths of $v_A = 10$ knots (gentle breeze) and $v_A = 20$ knots (fresh breeze). On the horizontal axis we have driving force coefficients C_R and driving force F_R.

We will consider initially the case $\beta = 90°$, i.e., the apparent wind abeam. If three yachts are similar in all respects except for the camber of their sails, it is easy to predict that the yacht with sail 3, of 1/7 camber, will be one of the fastest. Comparing the values of the maximum driving force, for $v_A = 10$ knots we have:

for sail 3 — 57 lb.
for sail 2 — 52 lb.
for sail 1 — 37 lb.

It is clear that the large discrepancy between 1 and his opponents (57 per cent and 40 per cent greater force) is unlikely to be reduced appreciably by any amount of skill in tactics. Naturally, we are assuming here that all three helmsmen are able to trim their sails to the appropriate angles of incidence for maximum driving force. It should be noted that these angles are different for each sail, being respectively 20°, 15°, and 12° for sails of camber 1/7, 1/10, and 1/20.

If the yacht with sail 3 sets her sail at a smaller angle of incidence, say $\alpha = 10°$, then her speed will be less than the yacht with sail 2 set at the best angle $\alpha = 15°$. For these conclusions to be valid it is important that the sails do not exhibit excessive twist.

We can conclude from this example that when sailing well off the wind a sail with large camber is desirable. This is particularly true when sailing in fairly light winds, when velocity increases are almost proportional to increases in driving force. In strong winds, when hull hydrodynamics dictate a practical limit to speed, particularly for heavy-displacement vessels, the advantages to be gained by increasing driving force are much less marked.

Let us now compare the merits of these sails when beating to windward at, say, $\beta = 30°$.

In light winds, when considerations of stability and hull hydrodynamic efficiency do not impose serious limitations on the output we may obtain from the sails, our criterion for comparison is the maximum driving force coefficient $C_{R\ max}$. For the flattest sail, with 1/20 camber, the value of $C_{R\ max}$ is approximately 0.4, corresponding to a driving force of 13 lb. for a wind speed $v_A = 10$ knots. For the sails of 1/10 and 1/7 camber, their maximum coefficients are just under 0.6, giving driving forces of 20 lb. Clearly, then, in this case also, sail 1 is inferior to 2 and 3, but the differences between 2 and 3 are very small. For incidences below the intersection of these last two polar diagrams, point A, sail 2 will have some slight advantage, since at the same driving force as 3, it has a little less heeling force. This is another way of saying that the angle of drag ϵ_{A2} for sail 2 is mostly less than ϵ_{A3} for sail 3.

A somewhat different pattern emerges if we increase the wind strength to 20 knots, when the aerodynamic forces increase fourfold over that at 10 knots. As was mentioned in the previous section, a good criterion for comparison in this case is the minimum ratio C_H/C_R, i.e., the minimum drag angle ϵ_A. On this basis, from Figs. 83 and 84 it appears that sail 1 will now be better than 2 and 3, since it has the least minimum ϵ_A. If, for example, one assumes that a heeling force of 100 lb. is the maximum that can be tolerated, for balancing a dinghy or for sailing a keel yacht without excessive heel, and also that an angle of 5° is the minimum at which all three sails will set, then sail 1 will have a heeling force of only 80 lb. at this incidence. Sail 2, on the other hand will have a heeling force of about 130 lb., and although it will also have a larger driving force than sail 1, it will not be able to take advantage from it, because of the excessive drift and heel.

The desirable amount of camber on a sail for windward courses will therefore depend on the strength of the wind. Beginning in weak winds, when a camber of 1/10 is needed, this should be successively reduced with increasing wind strength to a practical minimum of about 1/25 to 1/30. A sail should be selected which will not heel the yacht more than 30°, and allow it to be sailed as nearly upright as possible without spilling wind from the sail.

Figure 85 shows how the driving force coefficient varies for various points of sailing, with the camber of the sail. Marked on the horizontal scale of camber are the ranges of wind strength and apparent course for which the various cambers should be used. Thus when sailing close-hauled in light winds we require a maximum camber of 1/10, whilst when sailing right off the wind a camber of more than 1/8 is required, since the curves VI and VIII are still rising at this point.

The camber of the sails is not only placed there by the sailmaker; it is to some extent under the control of the crew, and Fig. 86 shows how this can be achieved. In light winds, when the sail is working at a large angle of incidence, the jib fair-

Fig. 85

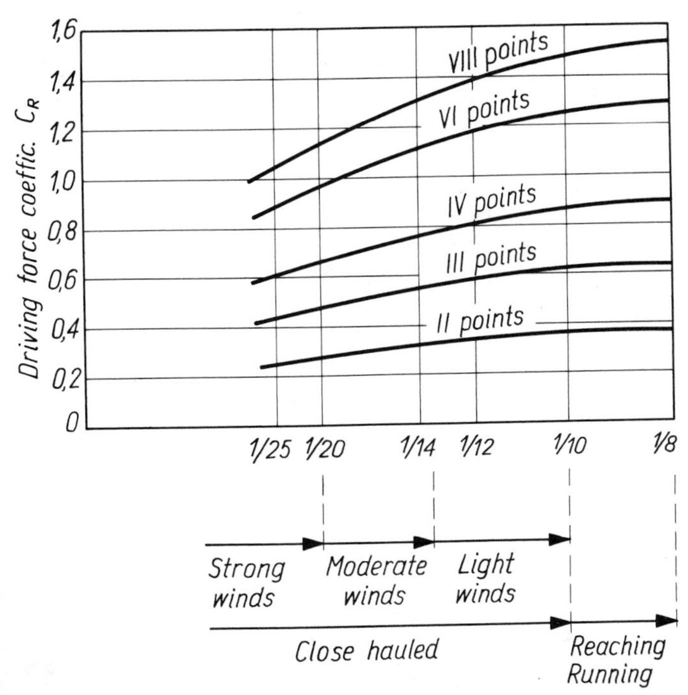

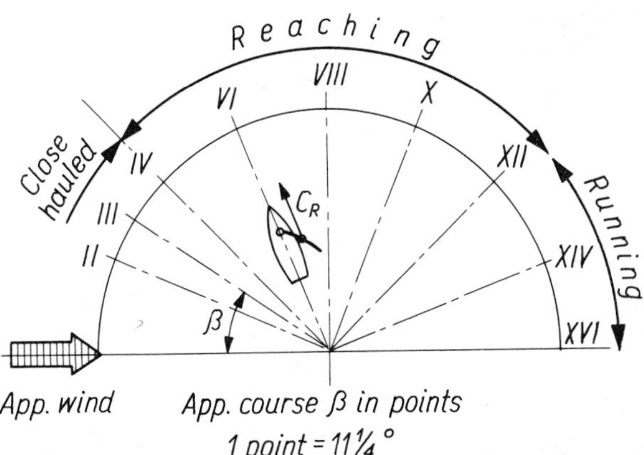

Fig. 86

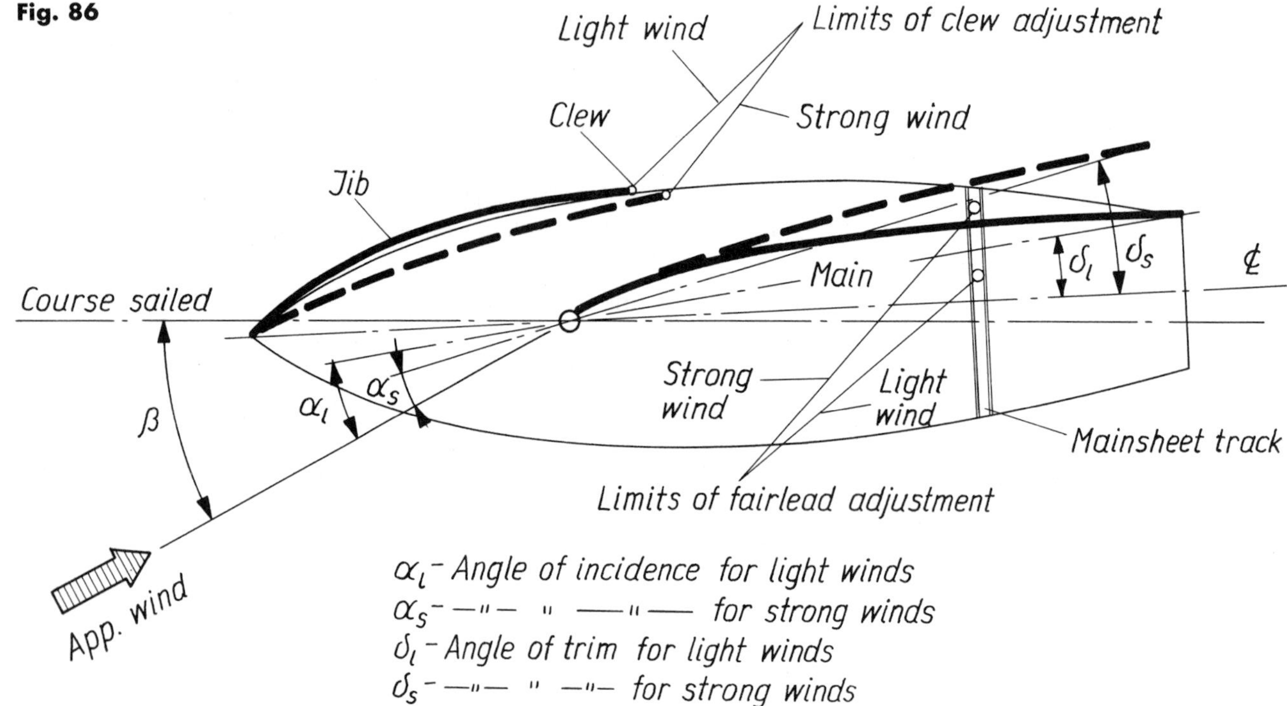

Photo. 7

Photo. 8

lead and mainsheet block should be adjusted well inboard. With increasing wind speed, the sail incidence is reduced by paying out the sheets, then to avoid excessive twist and to flatten the sails, the leads should be further outboard, and if possible, further aft. The advantages of a wide mainsheet horse are particularly apparent when sailing on a close reach. Without one, the necessary easing of the sheets allows the boom to lift, and the sail to belly, and makes this a very difficult point of sailing indeed (see Photo. 7).

The ideal solution to this problem would be to have the facility to make continuous and "automatic regulation" of the camber when sailing in varying conditions. This is partly obtained in such classes as Star, Finn, Flying Dutchman, and even Dragon, by the use of a flexible mast and sometimes boom (see Photo. 8). The bending of these flexible spars serves to reduce the sail camber and the effect is most marked in strong winds, when it is required. Nevertheless this is not all profit, since a sail which sets well on a straight mast will not do so if the mast is then bent. For this reason it is a normal practice in such classes to carry several sails to suit the prevailing conditions.

Although it is possible to reef heavily cambered sails, or sail with them fluttering, when the wind is too strong, these practices are definitely disadvantageous compared with setting a sail with the correct camber. The owner of many sails, however, has to pay one penalty, he has to forecast what conditions will be like during the race, and choose his sails accordingly. This is far from easy as the choice will depend on not only the weather and the course, but also the type of yacht and even her crew. Stiff, lightly canvassed craft can carry full sails in a wind in which a tender, overcanvassed yacht must reef or flatten the sails. In this respect a heavy crew helps to stiffen the yacht.

(b) Reefing and Flattening Sails

After predicting what the weather conditions will be throughout a race, we must select sails of such a camber that reefing should not be necessary to avoid excessive heel. In extreme cases sails having as little as 1/25 to 1/30 camber may have to be used.

Being able to carry full rather than reefed sails confers advantages in addition to those obtained on the windward leg. A reefed boat will have to shake out the reefs when coming off the wind, when lateral stability is not so important a factor, and later may have to reef again, all of which wastes precious time.

If the wind strength is such that even the use of the flattest possible sails will not prevent excessive heel, then the sail must be reefed to such an area that the yacht can be sailed properly without spilling wind from the sails. This will also guard against the unconscious and harmful tendency to luff too much in the gusts. This results in pinching and the yacht loses way.

A reduction in speed reduces the apparent wind speed and thus the sail forces, making the yacht slow but easy to control, but also gives an impression of sailing close to the wind.

Fig. 87

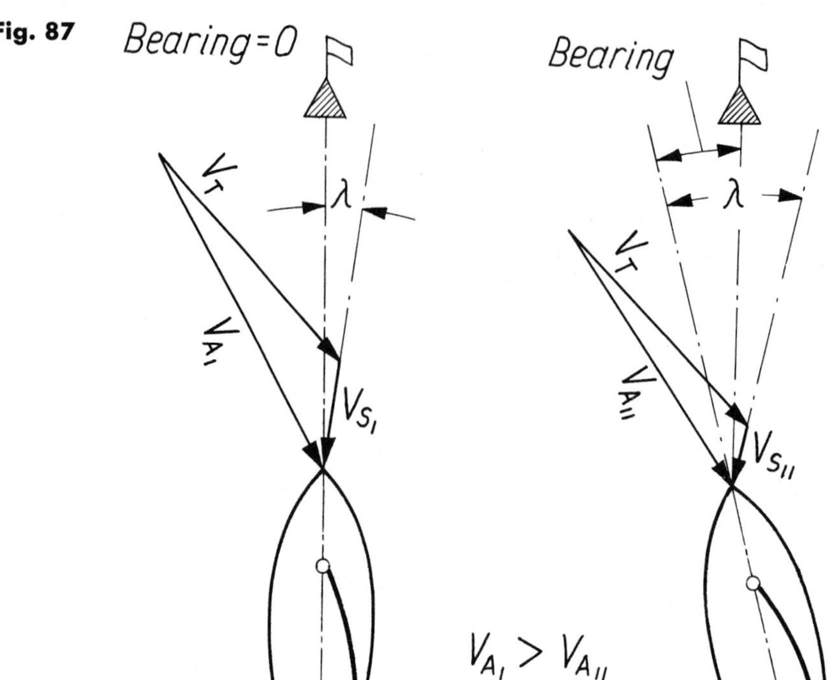

The difficulties and dangers of estimating the close-windedness of a yacht from the apparent wind, are illustrated in Fig. 87. Boat b, carrying too much sail, has a false impression from the apparent course that she will easily clear the mark albeit rather slowly. In practice, boat a, sailing faster, with less canvas and flatter sails, will sail closer to the wind and reach the mark before boat b.

Thus one must approach the problem of reefing very carefully, paying due regard to the weather, yacht, crew, and sails. Many helmsmen attempt to evade the issue by taking in one reef less than their opponent, but this is manifestly wrong, since even if the two yacht hulls are identical, their sails and crews will not be. Each skipper must judge for himself.

To some extent the camber of the sails can be controlled whilst sailing by increasing the tension in the clew outhaul and in the luff, both serving to flatten the mainsail. This is a useful remedy, but must not be taken to excess, since incorrect tension at the edges of a sail has a great effect on its setting and hence its other aerodynamic qualities.

It is also possible to flatten the mainsail by a judicious bending of the mast. This is done by the adjustment of the tension in the forestay, backstay, and jumper stay, more bending being required in stronger winds.

In most classes of yacht this process can only be carried out before a race, which again requires an intelligent forecast of conditions, but some, as the Star and Flying Dutchman, have facilities for adjusting the curvature of the mast whilst sailing. Still others, such as the Finn, employ cantilevered, rotating masts (no standing rigging) which automatically bend in accordance with the wind strength and the corresponding aft pull of the mainsheet.

One must remember, however, when employing a bending mast, that the sail, which at times will be set on a straight as well as a curved mast, must be specifically cut, and afterward trimmed, with this special purpose in mind. In practice one finds that all these sails, while setting well on one particular point of sailing, will on another course exhibit an uneven camber distribution at various heights up the mast.

(c) The Effect of the Position of Maximum Camber

There is a general idea among sailing men that the position of the maximum camber should be ⅓ of the local sail chord, aft of the mast. This shape is supposed to produce the most effective aerodynamic performance. It originated by taking an analogy between sails and birds' wings and with the usual position of maximum thickness of aeroplane wings. Nevertheless, experiments on sails have shown that this traditional view is not correct.

Figure 88 gives the results of measurements made on three sail models, having the same camber of 1/13.5, but three different positions of the maximum. Sail I

Fig. 88

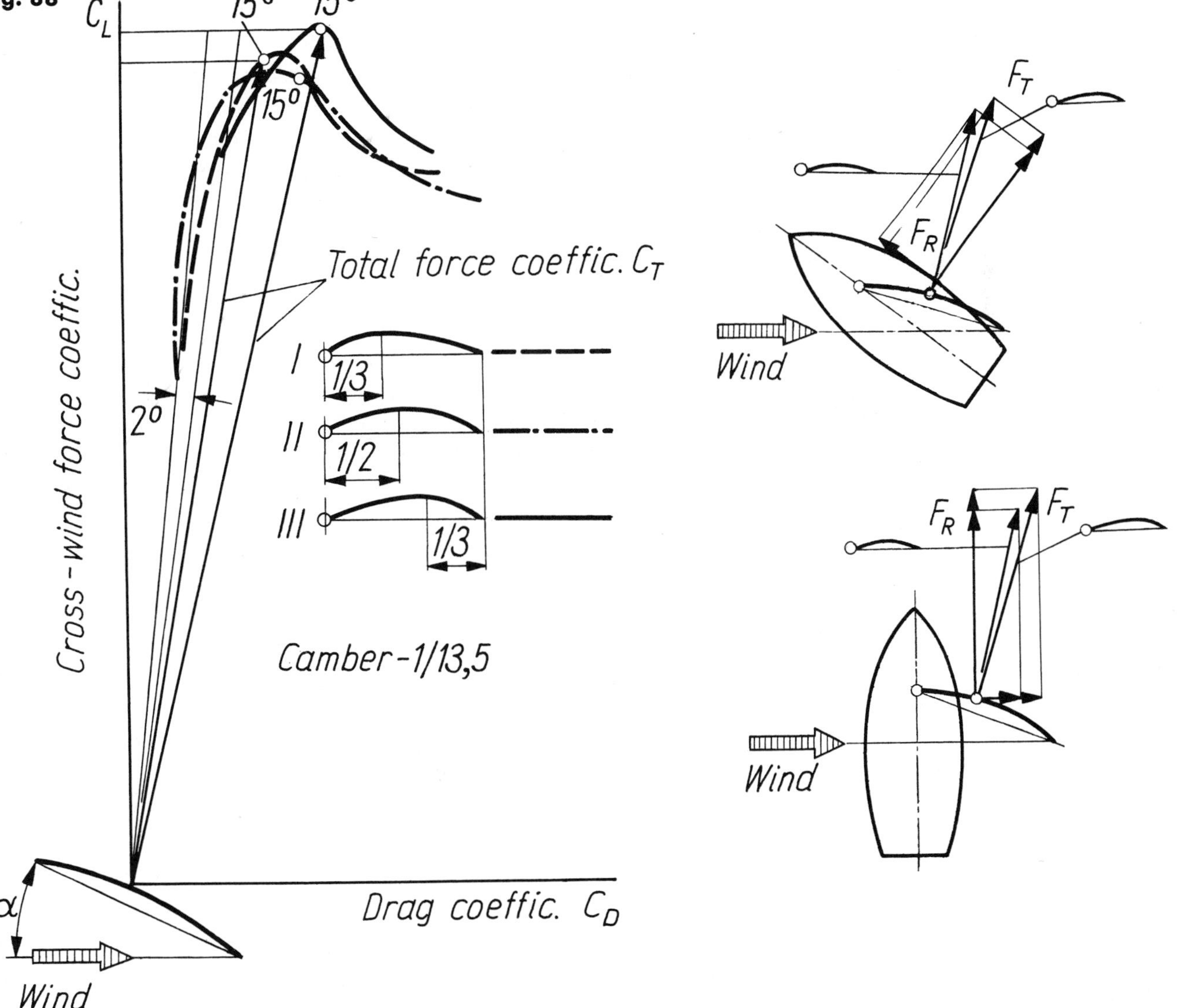

has the maximum camber position at ⅓ of the chord length from the mast, sail II in the middle, and sail III at ⅔ of the chord. The differences between their resultant total aerodynamic force coefficients at similar incidences are very small, and do not exceed 4 per cent, yet the sails are not alike and their merits will depend on the yacht's course.

On windward courses sail II is the best, since it has an aerodynamic drag angle typically about 2° less than its rivals. When reaching, sail III shows some superiority of driving force F_R. Sail I is everywhere inferior to either sail II or III or both. The best all-round compromise is sail II, with its maximum bow at the mid-point of the chord and flat after-part of the sail. It is most important to emphasize that these remarks are only applicable to a single working sail. If two or more sails are working together many other considerations apply (see the chapter on Sail Interaction).

When sailing full, we can change the position of the maximum camber by means of the leech-line, increasing tension moving the camber aft.

From the performance point of view, the amount, rather than the position of the maximum camber is the more important. Changes in the former affect the aerodynamic forces by amounts which are large compared with those obtained from the latter. Nevertheless these small changes cannot be neglected if one is interested in tuning one's equipment to its greatest efficiency.

The value of the sail force can also be influenced by the use of a flexible boom. If a sail is fitted on a straight, stiff boom, its camber must necessarily fall to zero at the boom, resulting in a loss of efficiency of the sail as a whole. Experiments conducted in the Junkers Aerodynamic Institute showed that a sail with an elastic boom, which took up the curvature of the sail, gave about 8 per cent more driving force than when fitted on a rigid boom. This gain was greatest for reaching courses and least when close-hauled or running.

Ideally the elasticity of the boom should be such that for all wind strengths its curvature is the same as that of the sail, but unfortunately this cannot normally be achieved. The amount of bending of the boom will depend largely on the attachment point of the mainsheet. If this point is at the after-end of the boom, the curvature will be a maximum and will approach closely that of the sail. If, however, the attachment point is further forward, the bending will be less and may even be reflex. This can sometimes be used in strong winds, when a relatively flat sail is required.

One method of obtaining the advantages of both a rigid and flexible boom was that used on *Enterprise* (Photo. 3). Here the foot of the sail was attached to the wide, flat boom by means of slides, running athwartships. This allowed the desired sail shape at the foot to be set regardless of the course or conditions, at the cost of some complication.

Another solution to the problem is to employ a loose footed sail or one only attached to the boom at its tack and clew. By suitable adjustment of the line of the sheets in the first instance, and of the clew outhaul in the second, the sail camber can be partly controlled (see, for example, the Hasler rig of Fig. 64).

10. SAILING OFF THE WIND

When sailing on apparent courses from close-hauled to those with the wind a little aft of abeam, the helmsman is able to trim his sails within quite a large range of angles. For fuller courses than these, the mainsail fouls the shrouds and so his ability to trim this sail is greatly restricted. The interaction between the main and fore sails then becomes of prime importance.

Before considering the interaction between sails off the wind we must first look at a single sail only. It can be seen from Fig. 89 that the big differences between two sails of camber 1/20 and 1/7 respectively, which were apparent for courses on the wind, become much less so as one bears away. Thus we can compare relative values of the total aerodynamic force coefficient C_T, at the apparent courses $\beta = 90°$, 130°, and 180°. These are given by A', A''; B', B''; C', C'' respectively. For the wind abeam the difference is 50 per cent; at $\beta = 130°$, is about 17 per cent; and on a dead run is only about 3 per cent.

This leads to the conclusion that sail area and not profile is the deciding factor when the wind is aft. The unimportance of sail camber when running is amply demonstrated by yachts racing, when they show very small differences in speed, one with another.

The diminishing difference between sails at large incidences is explained by the stalling of the sail. As the incidence is increased the air flow on the leeward side gradually separates, until finally the whole of the lee side of the sail is covered with separated, turbulent air.

When running, the apparent wind speed and the forces on the sail are at their minimum. In addition they act along the line of maximum hull stability. It would seem that sailing a yacht on a run should not present any difficulty, yet in practice it is frequently very unpleasant and difficult, especially for certain dinghy classes.

Fig. 89

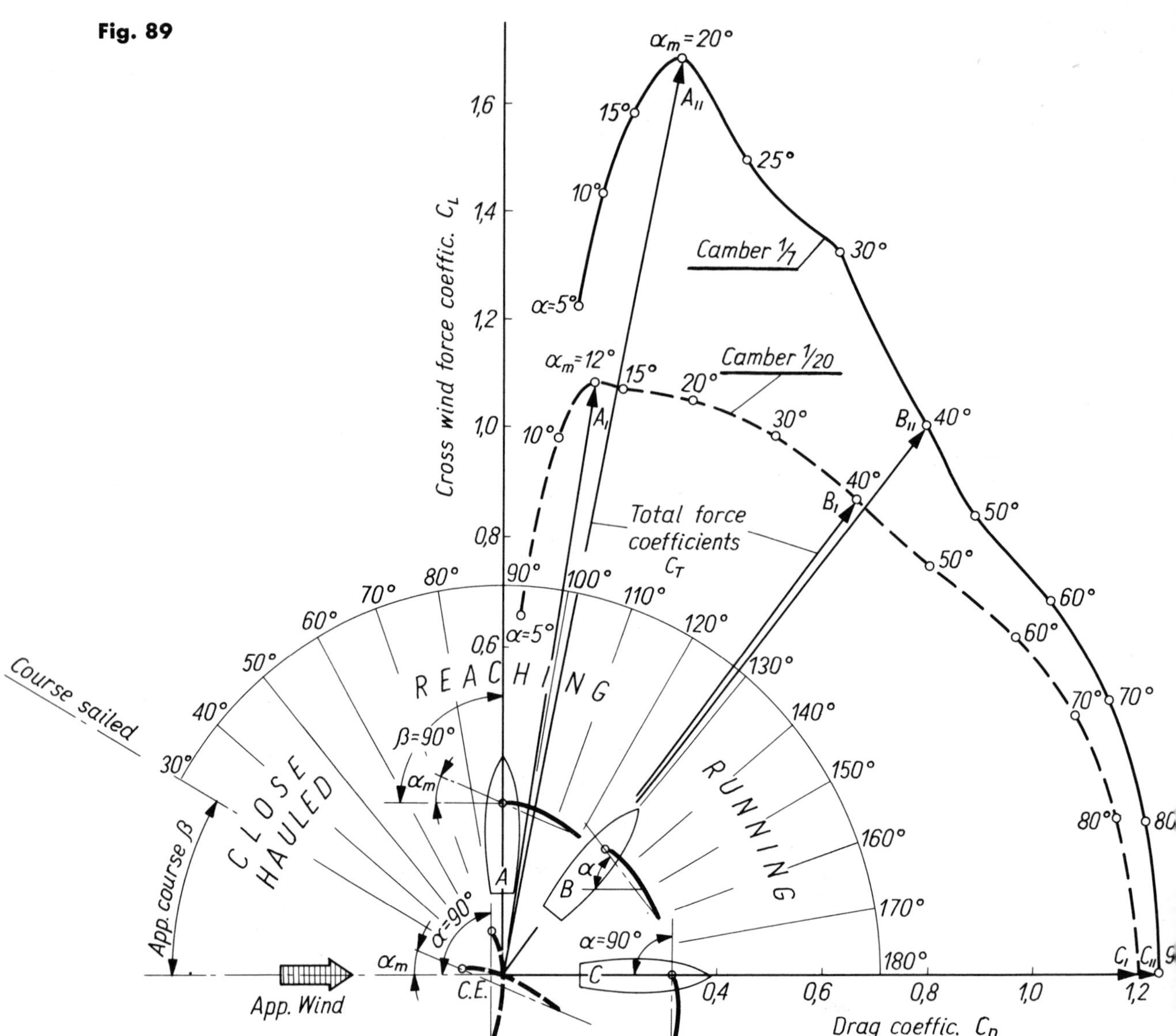

This is usually associated with rolling of the boat, which may get out of control and end in capsize.

What is the reason for this dangerous characteristic of yachts when sailing before the wind? We shall discuss this phenomenon in relation to the Finn class, which is one of the worst offenders in this respect. An explanation must be sought in terms of the aerodynamic and hydrodynamic forces acting on a yacht. Let us consider them in turn.

The turbulent air flow behind a sail when it is set approximately perpendicular to the flow is not quite so irregular as it first appears. If it is examined carefully we find that large eddies are formed alternately from each edge which then leave the sail and travel downwind (Fig. 90). The distance between the two rows of eddies, called Karman vortices, so formed is $d \cong 1.5\ l$, where l = average width of the sail,

Fig. 90

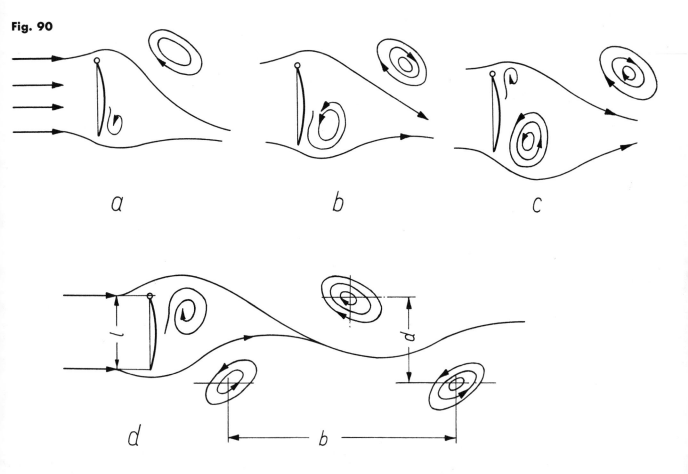

and the distance between successive eddies on one side is b = 3.5d.

We can see therefore that the wake behind such a sail sways rhythmically from side to side, and this gives rise to a corresponding rhythmic heeling force F_H, alternately to port and to starboard, which together with the driving force F_R give the total force F_T on the sail (Fig. 91).

As a result of these alternate side forces the boat will start to roll, and we then find that the motion of the boat induces further changes in the aerodynamic forces. Let us consider what happens when the boat rolls to port, from O toward A on Fig. 91. Suppose the yacht is sailing at an apparent course $\beta = 170°$,

Fig. 91

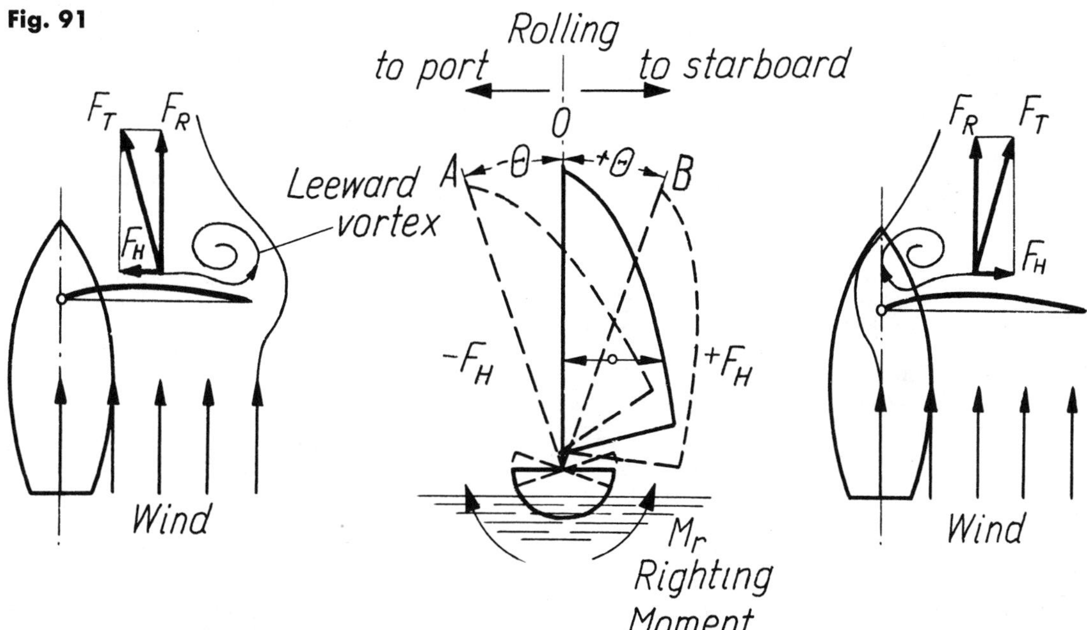

Fig. 92

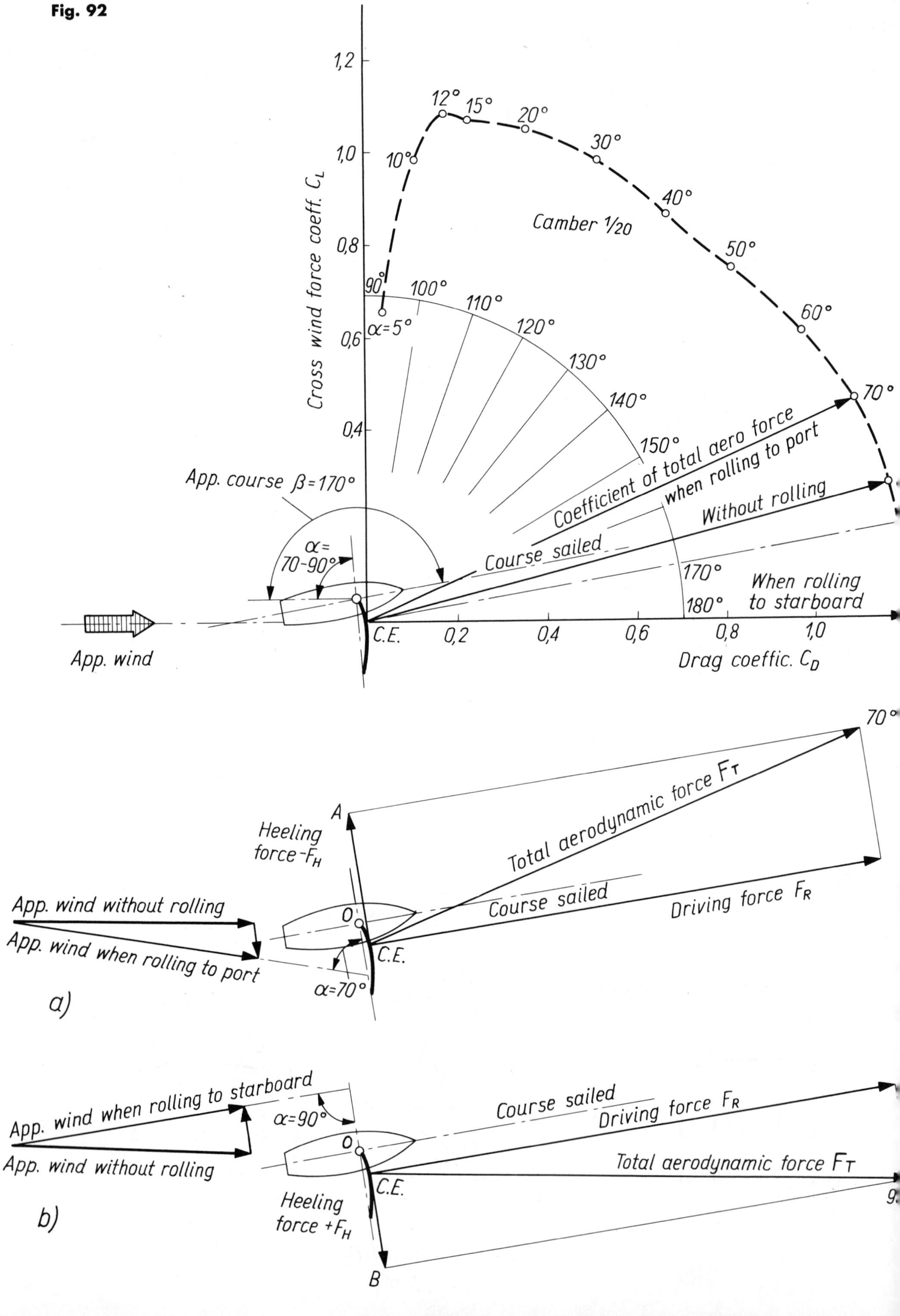
1,2
1,0
0,8
0,6
0,4
Cross wind force coeff. C_L
12°
15°
20°
30°
40°
50°
60°
70°
10°
90°
α=5°
Camber 1/20
100°
110°
120°
130°
140°
150°
App. course β=170°
Coefficient of total aero force when rolling to port
Without rolling
Course sailed
α= 70-90°
170°
180°
When rolling to starboard
App. wind
C.E.
0,2
0,4
0,6
0,8
1,0
Drag coeffic. C_D
70°
A
Heeling force $-F_H$
Total aerodynamic force F_T
Course sailed
Driving force F_R
App. wind without rolling
App. wind when rolling to port
O
C.E.
α=70°
a)
App. wind when rolling to starboard
α=90°
Course sailed
Driving force F_R
App. wind without rolling
O
Total aerodynamic force F_T
C.E.
Heeling force $+F_H$
b)
B

and has the sail polar diagram of Fig. 92. If, in the steady case the sail is working at an angle of incidence $\alpha = 80°$, then as the boat rolls to port the direction of the apparent wind will alter (Fig. 92a) in the manner described earlier. This will change the sail incidence from 80° to say 70° and simultaneously the direction of the total aerodynamic force; the driving force will be slightly reduced, and a large heeling force, acting in the direction of motion, will appear.

The boat is now rolling to port under the action of a sail force induced by the velocity of roll. As the heel angle increases (Figs. 91 and 92), the righting moment M_R from the lateral stability of the hull opposes the rolling, and finally starts to return the yacht to the upright position. The boat now swings from A to O with the sail force acting with the hull moment M_R, since the sail incidence will now be increased to say 90°. Finally, the motion from O to B, and then B to O is a reverse of the O-A-O motion, with the sail and hull moments opposing over the portion O-B and adding on the return swing B-O.

Thus a single "kick" from an eddy from the sail or from a chance gust of wind has produced a large rolling motion which may or may not die out. Further complications can arise if the yacht is allowed to change course as it rolls.

This rolling motion is said to be "self-induced," and the time taken to roll one complete cycle (OAOBO) is called the periodic time T_1.

Provided that, on each swing, the hull moment M_R is always able to overcome the sail forces $\pm F_H$ before a capsize or filling-up occurs, the motion of the yacht can be shown graphically as in Fig. 93. As the yacht runs before the wind it rolls rhythmically from side to side through the angle $-\Theta$ to $+\Theta$.

The existence of the periodic forces which are necessary to sustain such a motion can easily be shown. If a spinnaker is hoisted without a spinnaker boom, it shows a tendency to swing from one side to the other in a regular manner. Similarly, if a pole is moved through water in the direction perpendicular to its length, it will oscillate in the same way.

Fig. 93

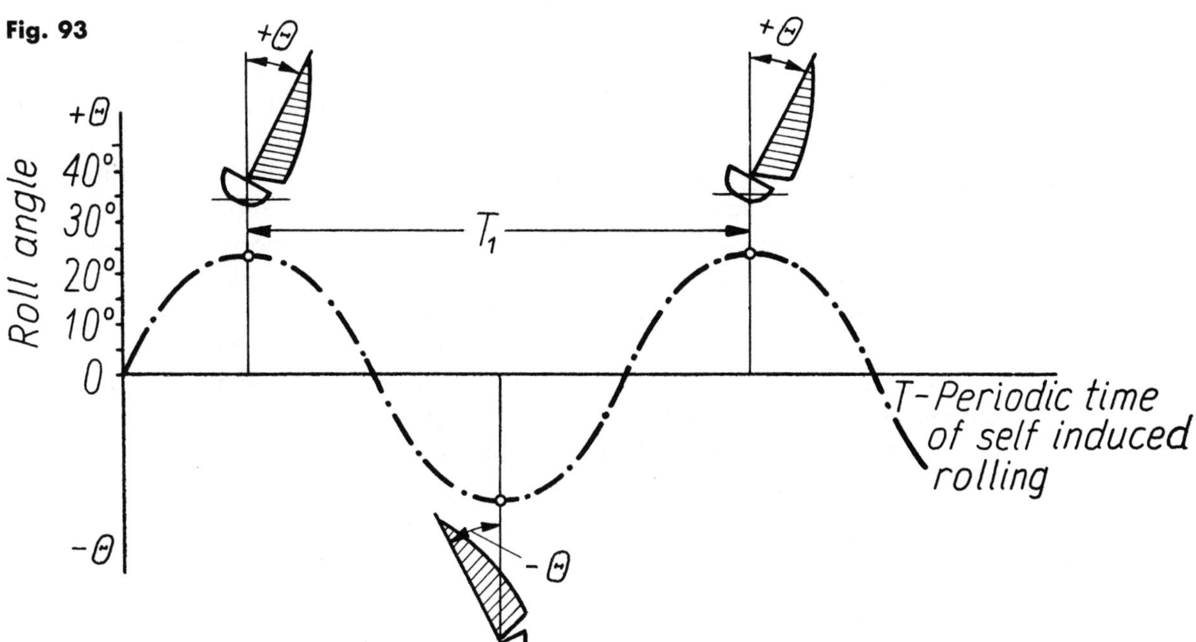

Let us now look in more detail at the forces on the hull affecting rolling of a yacht. Figure 94 shows a moored yacht which is heeled to the position A, at an angle $-\Theta'$ by some force. If this force is removed, the yacht, under the action of the couple M_R formed by the force W and Δ (W is weight, Δ is displacement), will swing toward O. The swing, however, will overshoot to B, at an angle Θ'', where this angle will be less than the previous one, because of the damping action of the water. At B a reverse righting moment will operate and thus the yacht will perform successive rolls to port and starboard, each being less than the previous, until it finally comes to rest at O.

Such a damped oscillation is shown in Fig. 95. The periodic time T_2 of this, so-called free oscillation can be shown to be a characteristic which is constant for each boat in a given configuration. It can be seen that the periodic time T_2 remains constant as the amplitude of rolling diminishes. This means that the angular speed of rolling also reduces.

The periodic time of free oscillations depends on two factors, the rolling stability of the hull and its "moment of inertia." The moment of inertia is a measure of mass and also its distance from the axis of roll, and a large moment of inertia serves to increase the periodic time T_2. Thus, on a given boat, lowering a heavy centerboard or the standing up of the helmsman will both achieve this. If there is a crew of two or more they can also increase the moment of inertia by sitting to the sides rather than on the centerline of the hull.

The rolling stability affects the oscillations such that a large stability reduces the periodic time. This factor is chiefly controlled by the design of the hull. A stiff hull will perform faster free oscillations than a tender hull. Some control can be obtained by fore-and-aft trim. When most boats are down by the bow, their lateral stability is usually reduced, due to the narrower waterline sections forward. This factor is strongly impressed on the many dinghy sailors who have attempted to disembark from the bow, and so earned a ducking. The converse is true for trimming down at the stern.

The damping of free oscillations of the hull, which controls the dying away of the motion, is greatest for a beamy hull with a deep keel or centerboard and rudder lowered as far as possible.

The third type of rolling which is possible is that said to be "forced." The only commonly encountered external force of a rhythmic nature, is that of the waves (Fig. 96). The periodic time of rolling forced by the waves will depend on the relative velocity of the yacht to the waves, i.e., the frequency of encounter.

Now, in problems concerning oscillations of bodies, one meets the phenomenon called "resonance." This occurs when the periodic time of a body oscillating under the action of some external forces approaches the periodic time for the oscillations. At this condition the amplitude of the oscillations increases considerably.

In the case of a yacht, such resonance will occur if the periodic time T_1 of the self-induced rolling due to the sails, or of the forced rolling due to waves, coincides approximately with that of the periodic time T_2 for free oscillations. The angles of

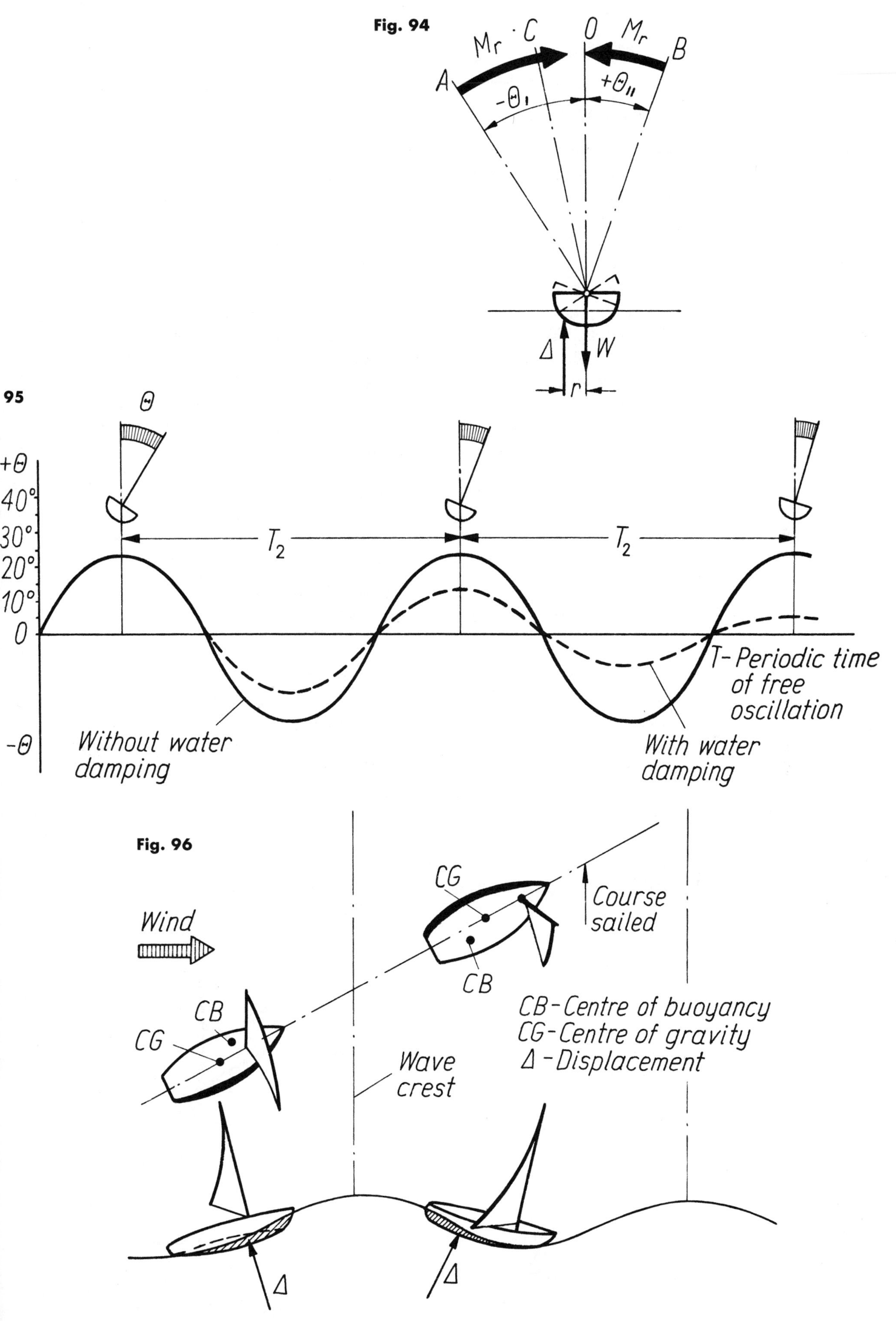
Fig. 94
M_r
C
O
M_r
B
A
$-\Theta_I$
$+\Theta_{II}$
Δ
W
r
95
Θ
+Θ
40°
30°
20°
10°
0
-Θ
T_2
T_2
T - Periodic time of free oscillation
Without water damping
With water damping
Fig. 96
CG
Course sailed
Wind
CB
CB
CG
CB - Centre of buoyancy
CG - Centre of gravity
Δ - Displacement
Wave crest
Δ
Δ

heel will become very large and may exceed the limiting value of hull stability, when the yacht will capsize. Since either sail or wave forces can cause rolling, it is possible for them to add together or subtract. In general they will not be of the same frequency, and then a condition known as "beating" will occur. In this case a period of little or no rolling, when the two sets of forces act against one another, is shortly succeeded by a period of violent rolling, when they add. The cycle is then repeated continually.

The most frequently committed error in the Finn class when rolling occurs is to ease the sheets. This is a natural reaction learned from "spilling" the wind when close hauled, but in this case it usually ends in a forced bath. What happens to the sail if the mainsheet is eased when sailing nearly before the wind? Figure 97 shows how the main effect is that of rotating the total force F_T. This is equivalent to reducing the driving force F_R and introducing a heeling force F_H acting to windward. Yachtsmen are not accustomed to capsizing to windward and are taken by surprise by such a turn of events. In the Finn class it is usually not even necessary to ease the sheets to capsize, merely doing nothing can suffice.

What action can be taken? We mentioned earlier that resonance, i.e., excessive rolling, occurs if the free and forced periods of oscillation are the same. This suggests some remedies open to us:

(a) Changing the periodic time of the aerodynamic heeling forces
(b) Changing the periodic time of free rolling
(c) Opposing the rolling motion by suitable balancing

The first suggestion can be achieved by hauling in the mainsheet or by altering course from a run to a reach, i.e., by tacking downwind and jibing between gusts. A useful rule of thumb in this case is for the sail setting to be not more than 70° from the yacht's centerline when properly trimmed. The aerodynamic rolling forces are largest when running dead before the wind, and also they are then most likely to force resonance. Some artificial damping can be introduced on the sail, as a last resort, by giving a quick, even brutal, tug on the mainsheet as the sail swings to windward.

Each case must be judged on its merits, and one can only learn by experience, backed by a thorough understanding of the phenomenon, what is the best action to adopt to counteract rolling. No hard and fast rules can be given, since the normal period of free rolling is such that one can usually encounter forcing periods

Fig. 97

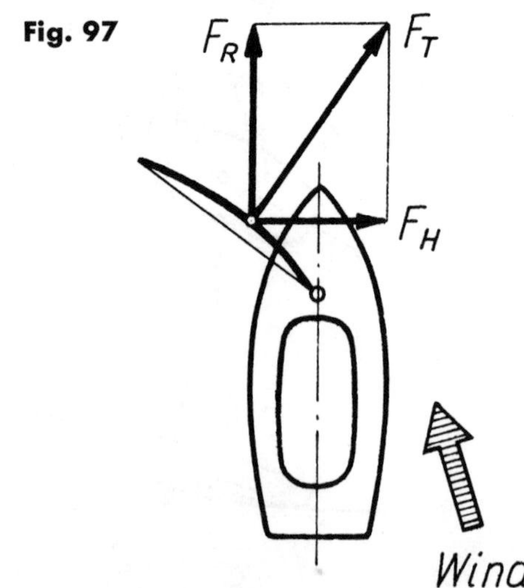

Fig. 98

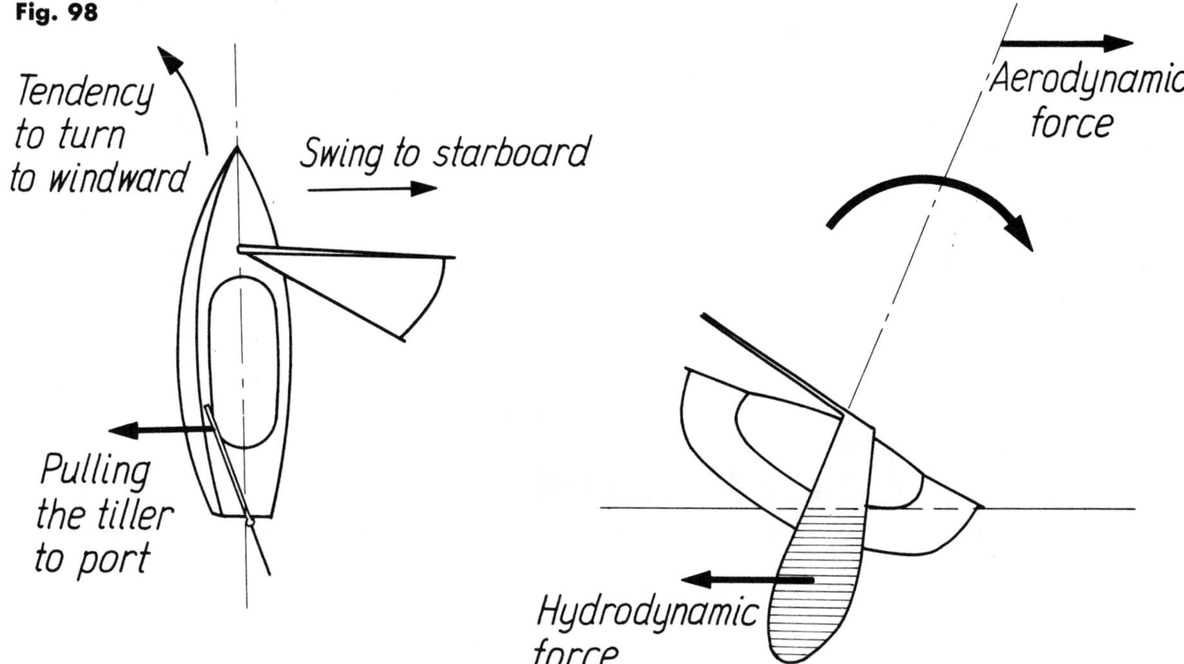

both less and greater than it. Thus in one case one might need to increase the period of free rolling and in another to decrease it.

Suppose that the free rolling period is a little greater than some period of forcing from waves or sails. Then to prevent rolling, the period of free rolling should be increased. This can be done by standing up well aft and by lowering the centerboard and rudder. These last two will be, in fact, more useful for increasing the damping rather than the moment of inertia.

Thus, in the Finn class, the proper position for the helmsman in such cases is to be standing well aft, where the waterlines are of greatest width, with the tiller between his legs. He can then sway from side to side so as to oppose the motion. His sway should be timed to oppose the angular velocity of roll and not the roll angle; e.g., if the boat is rolled to port, but is rolling to starboard, the helmsman must lean to port. A helmsman with poor reflexes, due possibly to nervous strain, may inadvertently aid rather than oppose the motion by this means.

It is most important that the helmsman should not use the rudder, as he might have to when sailing to windward, to counteract the tendency of the boat to luff as it rolls to leeward. If he does so, the rudder force (Fig. 98), situated as it is below the rolling axis, will contribute an additional moment increasing the angle of roll. In addition, the action of luffing affects the sails such that they reduce a little their rolling moments. Thus the correct procedure is to use very little rudder or even to give lee helm when the boat rolls to leeward, and vice versa, and to allow the yacht to pursue a somewhat undulating course.

We have talked about the Finn because it is particularly bad in this respect. Nevertheless, many other yachts exhibit in a lesser degree this tendency, which can only be regarded as undesirable.

11. SAIL SHAPE

The early days of yachting were characterized by yachts carrying the maximum possible sail area. It was generally considered that the speed of a yacht was directly proportional to the size of the sails. For reasons of stability the sail area had to be distributed close to the waterline, and consequently the length of the hull was exploited to the full, and even extended by means of a bowsprit. The many different types of sails used were, as a rule, of small aspect ratio (A.R.).

With the growth of knowledge of aerodynamics, greater attention was paid to the shape of, and mutual interaction between, sails (e.g., results of wind tunnel tests published in 1910 by Eiffel). It was realized intuitively that it was desirable to increase the driving force available from a given sail area and, at the same time, to make yachts sail closer to the wind.

These improvements were effected by increasing the aspect ratio (A.R.) of the sails, reducing the harmful effects of the mast and rigging, improving sail combinations, and introducing new types of sails for specific purposes (e.g., spinnaker).

Experiments carried out on both model sails and aerofoils have shown that the shape of a sail and its A.R. have a large effect on its aerodynamic force characteristics. Figure 99 shows the polar diagrams of force coefficients for four sails having the same camber 1/13.5 (7.4 per cent) of the chord but different shapes and aspect ratios, A.R. = 6, 3, 1, and ⅓.

From a comparison of the curves we can see that for small angles of incidence, up to 10°, the sails can be placed in order of merit corresponding to their aspect ratios, A.R. = 6 being the best. This shape, the characteristic Bermudian sail, can achieve larger driving forces at smaller drag angles ϵ_A. This is largely a consequence of it having a low induced drag, dealt with in an earlier chapter.

Fig. 99

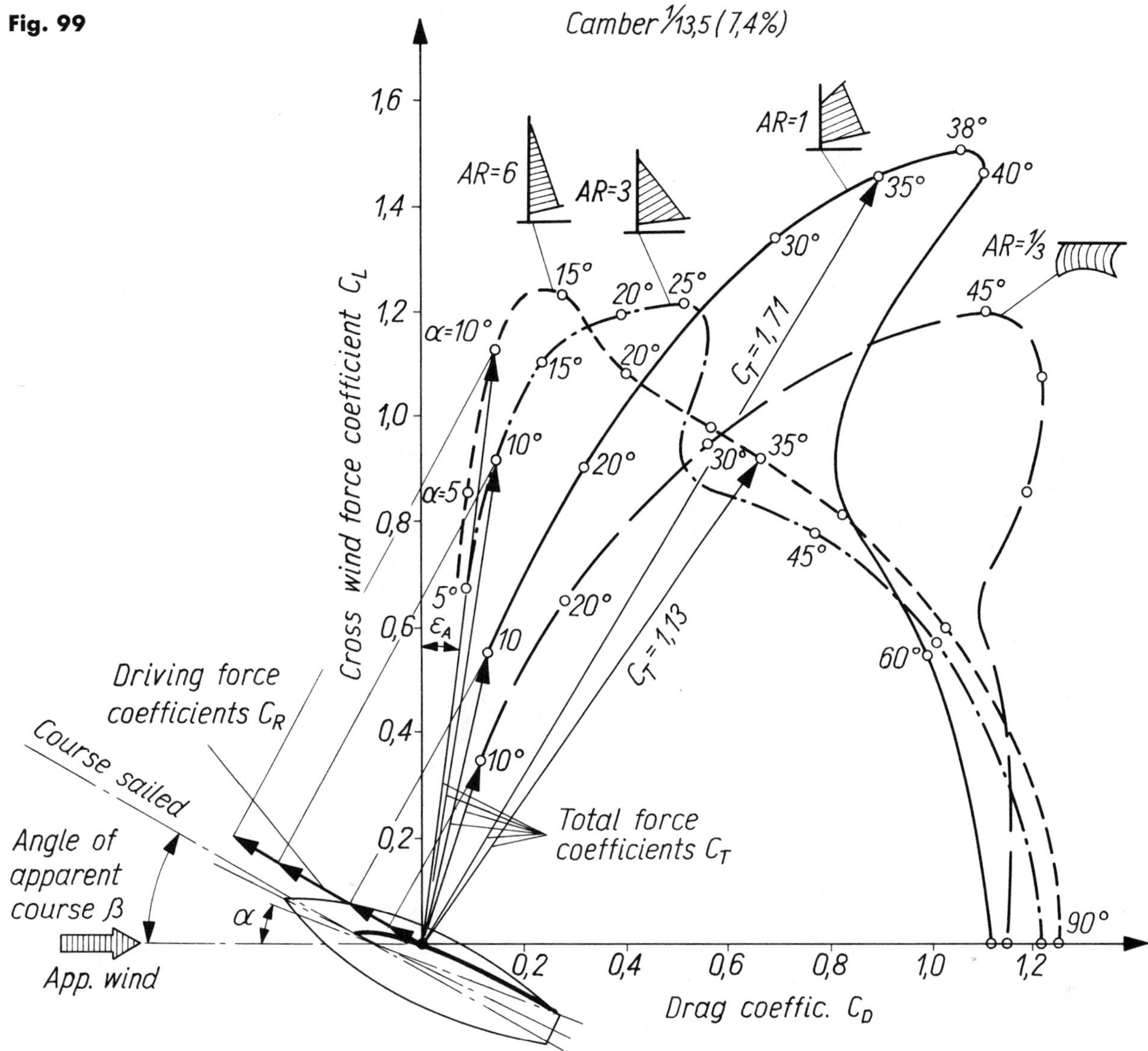

Let us now compare our sails in a different way. Comparing the angles at which they achieve maximum total aerodynamic force, we find that these angles are $\alpha = 15°, 25°, 38°, 45°$, for A.R. = 6, 3, 1, ⅓, respectively; i.e., the lower aspect ratios require the largest angles to develop maximum force. It should be noted that the lower aspect ratios also develop the largest forces C_T, A.R. = 1 being outstanding; thus the values of $C_T = 1.13, 1.71$ for A.R. = 6, 1 respectively.

Similar results were found in tests on rigid sail models at Southampton University. Some of these results for three models A, B, C are shown in Fig. 100. All models had untapered masts of the same diameter, 0.375 in., and sails of 1/25 (4 per cent) camber. In each case the position of maximum camber was at 15 per cent of the local chord behind the mast.

At first sight these results are not entirely consistent with those of Fig. 99. So far

Fig. 100

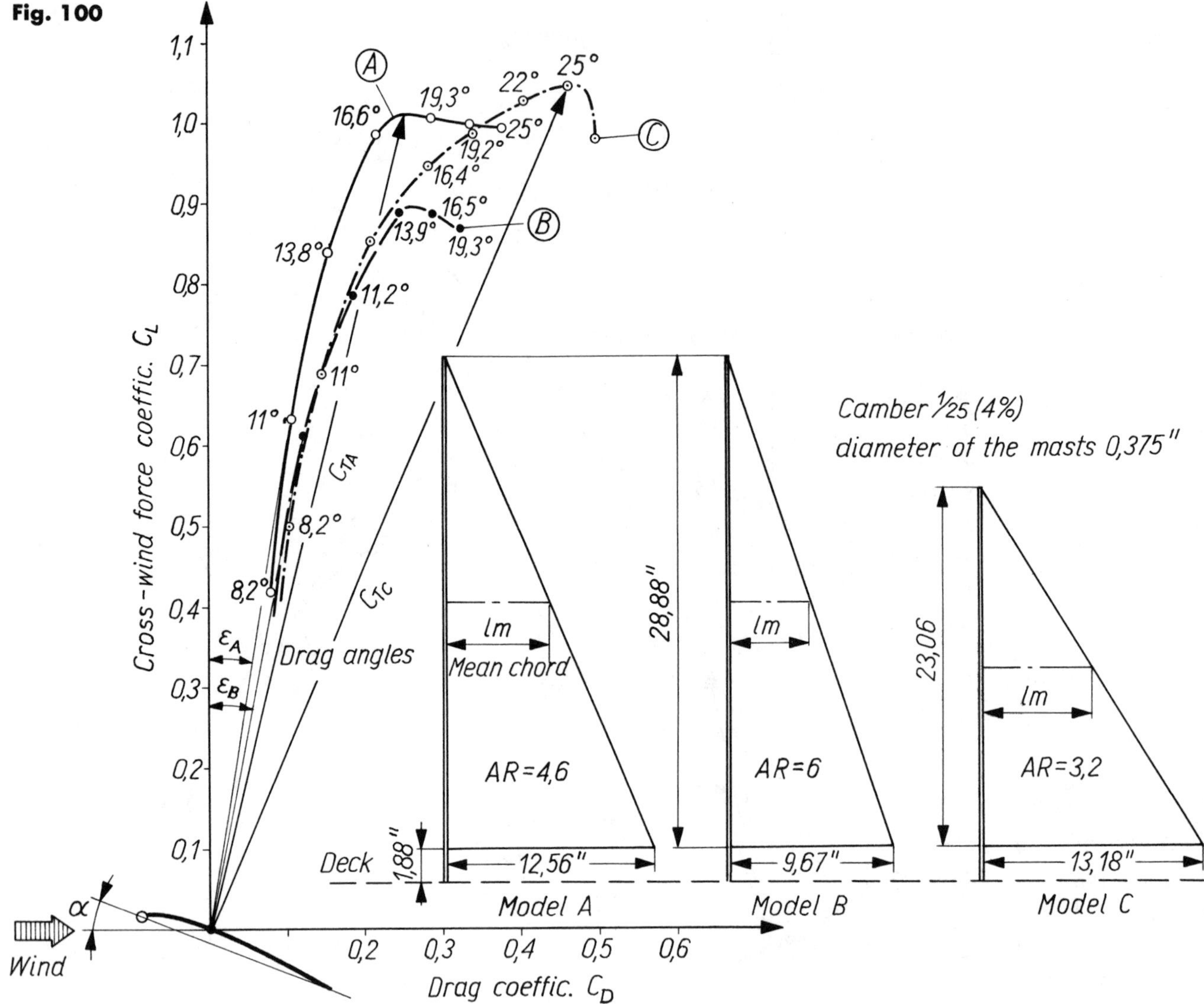

as can be judged from the restricted ranges of incidence taken, the angles for maximum force increase for decreasing aspect ratio. When, however, one comes to consider the drag angles at moderate incidence, it is clear that Model B does not occupy the position of merit as it should, by virtue of having the largest aspect ratio. Thus, in sailing to windward, Model B would be less efficient than A. This can be attributed to the effect of the mast, which adversely affects the flow round the sail. In each case the mast diameter is the same. Thus the ratio of this diameter to the average or mean chord lm will be larger for Model B, of higher aspect ratio than Model A, and its adverse effect will be correspondingly greater.

An example of how the mast can upset theoretical predictions of an efficient sail plan can be found in the 6-Meter *Atrocia* (Photo. 9), on which Sherman Hoyt tried, without success, an unusual distribution of sail area between main and foresail. The area of the mainsail was reduced, its aspect ratio increased, and a large foresail used. Although the main reason why this setup was so inefficient is mainly connected with

Photo. 9

Fig. 101

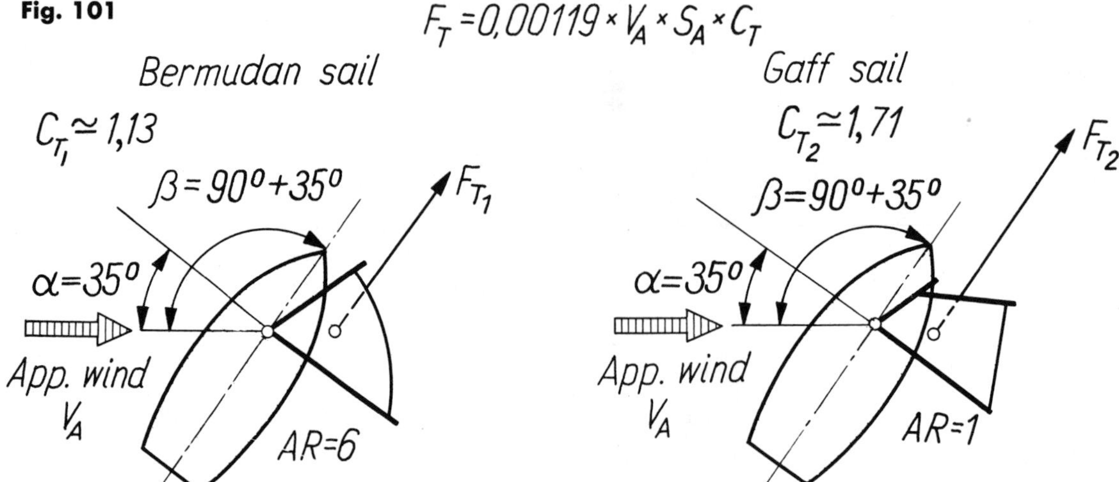

the problem of interaction between sails, which will be discussed later, undoubtedly a very large proportion of the small mainsail was inoperative, working as it was behind a mast of normal diameter.

The importance of the mast and the flow in its vicinity cannot be overemphasized. It is often not fully appreciated that it is as powerful a factor on mainsail efficiency as camber and aspect ratio.

Referring again to Fig. 99, let us examine the relative values of total aerodynamic force coefficient for different A.R.'s. We saw that the coefficient C_T for the model of A.R. = 1 has a greater maximum than those for sails of higher A.R., i.e., A.R. = 6, 3. The superiority of sails with high A.R. when sailing close to the wind will not be maintained when off the wind. Comparing a Bermudian sail of A.R. = 6 and a gaff sail of A.R. = 1, let us consider their aerodynamic forces on a broad reach, sailing at 125° to the apparent wind (Fig. 101). If both sails are working at an angle of incidence $\alpha = 35°$ and have the same area, the driving forces will be nearly proportional to the coefficients C_{T1}, C_{T2}, i.e., 1.13 and 1.71 respectively (from Fig. 99). In other words the gaff sail will develop about 50 per cent more driving force than the Bermudian sail, and hence on a broad reach the yacht with the gaff sail will be the faster.

It would seem therefore that there is no ideal type of sail superior for all points of sailing. The curves of Fig. 102 show how driving force varies for sails of different A.R. for all points of sailing. Sails of high A.R. are superior from close-hauled to close-reaching courses when the apparent course angle β is less than about 70°. When further off the wind than this, lower A.R. sails show advantages, in particular, those with A.R. $\cong$ 1. On very full courses, from a broad reach to a run the square rig is superior. This is the explanation of why the square-rigged clippers were unchallenged on a broad reach, but yielded to gaff schooners when close reaching.

Hence to assess the advantages of one rig over another it is necessary to consider the sailing course. On races over a triangular course, where ability to windward is

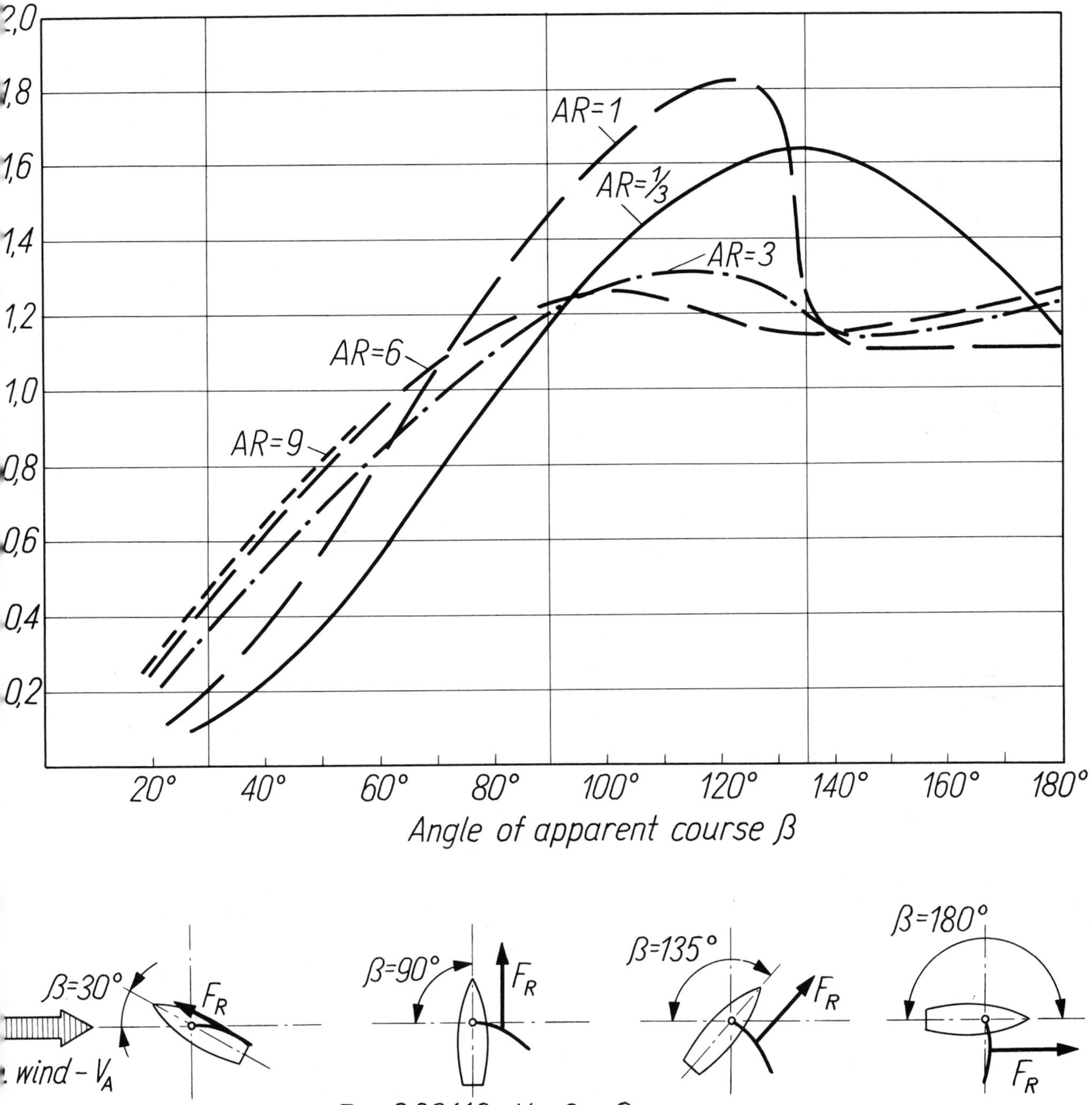

2,0
1,8
1,6
1,4
1,2
1,0
0,8
0,6
0,4
0,2

AR=1
AR=⅓
AR=3
AR=6
AR=9

20° 40° 60° 80° 100° 120° 140° 160° 180°

Angle of apparent course β

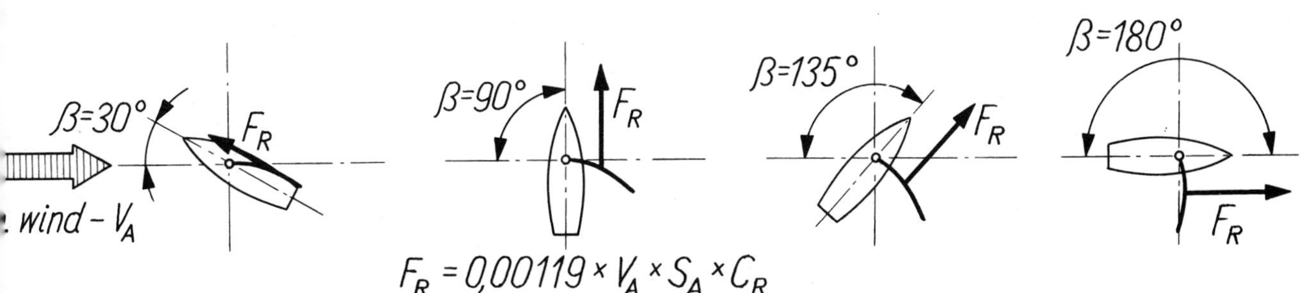

of prime importance, the Bermudian rig is pre-eminent. In passage and offshore races, on the other hand, where reaching is most common, the lower aspect ratio gaff-rigged yacht may well prove superior.

It is useful to remember that to obtain the maximum speed when sailing off the wind, when a wide range of sail incidences can be used, one must select that incidence which gives about the largest driving force. This optimum angle will be greater for a gaff sail than for a Bermudian. Under these conditions, the popular rule, to set the sail just not to flutter at the luff, is particularly misleading. There is no general formula giving the correct angle of incidence for all types of sail, and even for one particular type, this correct angle depends on the sail cut, wind strength, apparent course, etc.

12. SAIL INTERACTION

Interaction between sails, particularly between the main and fore sails, is certainly the most controversial subject amongst sailing theorists. Broadly there are two schools of thought: those who maintain that the foresail accelerates the air past the leeward side of the mainsail, increasing the suction, and those who argue that the function of the foresail is as a sail in its own right, and a very efficient one at that. The first of these theories is sometimes called the nozzle or Venturi effect, and owes a lot of its support to analogy with a slotted aircraft wing.

Depending on which idea one uses, one can argue that the best position for the foresail relative to the main and its trim, over a wide range, is correct, and one can usually quote an example to prove it. At various times, the correct close-hauled angle of trim of the foresail has been recommended as being anything from a trim angle $\delta_F = 7°$ to $\delta_F = 20°$ (see Fig. 103).

103

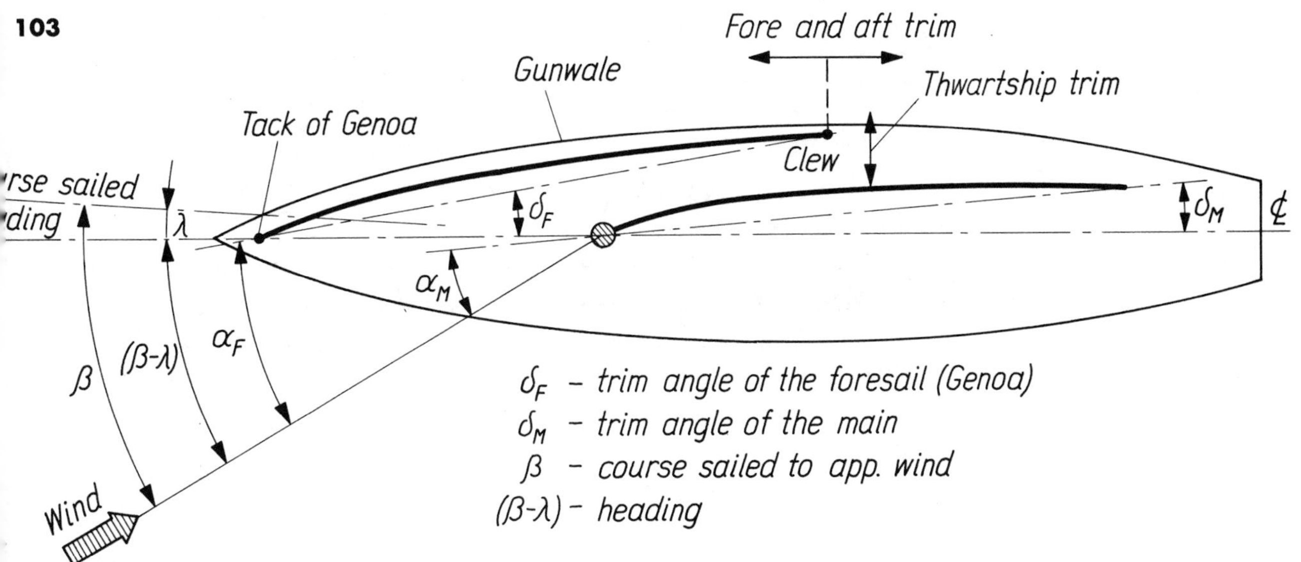

Who is right? As often happens, the truth lies between the two extremes. Unquestionably a foresail can be itself a very efficient sail. This was confirmed in the second chapter, Distribution of Pressure on a Sail. At the same time it can greatly improve the air flow over the leeward side of the mainsail, particularly if there is some overlap. To obtain the maximum advantage from both conditions simultaneously is difficult and for certain classes impossible. Some class rules are so framed that the most efficient configuration cannot be employed, or else is heavily penalized elsewhere.

On one point we can be quite definite. The question of sail interaction, and in particular, the problem of backwinding of one sail by another is very complicated, and not fully understood. The following discussion can only be a very simplified treatment indeed.

(a) Influence of the Foresail on the Mainsail

As an example of sail interaction, let us consider the commonly encountered case of a Bermudian sloop with a large overlapping genoa.

Figure 104 presents some observations of the air flow over the leeward side of some model sails, made in the wind tunnel at Southampton University. The positions of the sails are given with reference to Fig. 103. Trim angle δ_F for

Fig. 104

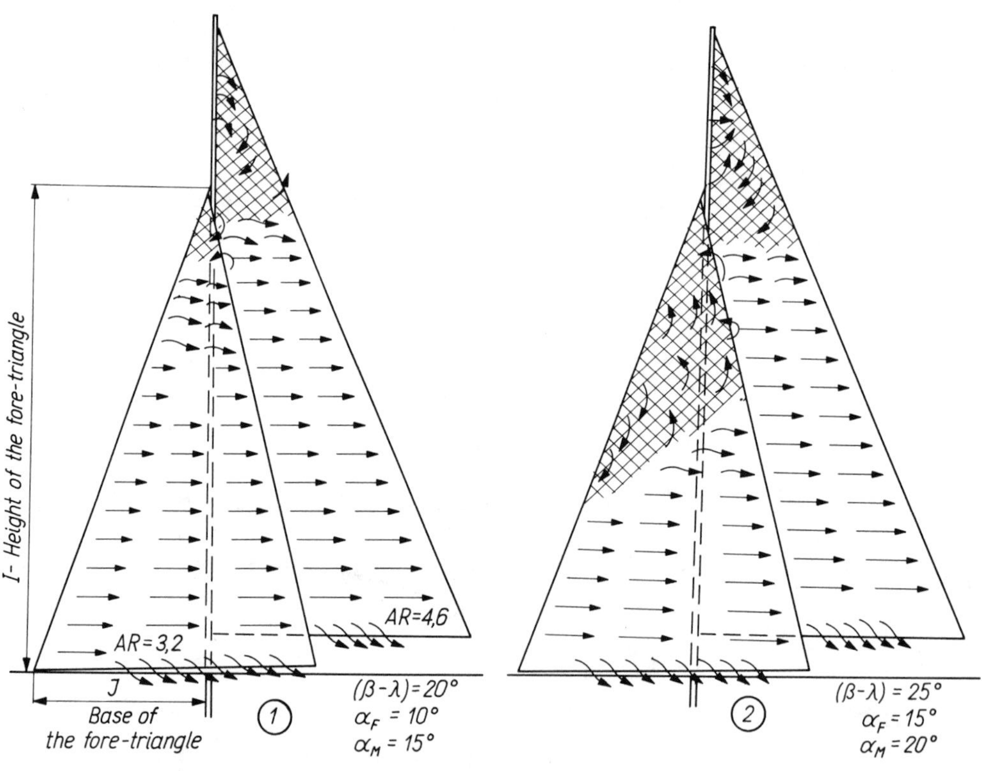

the foresail was 10°, and that for the mainsail δ_M was 5°. Both sails had a camber of 1/25 (4 per cent) and were almost without twist, so that at all heights above the "deck" the setting angles δ_F and δ_M and the incidences α_F and α_M were the same. The four sketches of Fig. 104 show the yacht model at various apparent headings β-λ, i.e., the angle between the hull centerline and the apparent wind. Thus the angles of incidence α_F and α_M were varied together, but the relative disposition between the two sails was constant.

Various types of air flow are mapped on the sails, and are explained in the accompanying key. Type A, steady flow, represents the condition when all the air particles in a certain area are moving in the same direction in an orderly manner (cf. Fig. 47a). The unsteady flow, B, indicates the presence of random movement of the air in addition to its main velocity (cf. Fig. 47b). The steady reversed flow, C, occurs when the flow separates from the sail and corresponds to the mechanism of stalling, (cf. Fig. 47c). All these types of flow are often encountered in water. Type A is seen in a deep, slowly flowing river; type B in a fast, often shallow river; and type C behind a headland or on the inside bend of a river, where a local current in opposition to the main stream can be found.

In interpreting Fig. 104 we must bear in mind that to obtain a high aerodynamic efficiency the flow on the leeward side of the sail must be steady. Sketch No. 1 shows

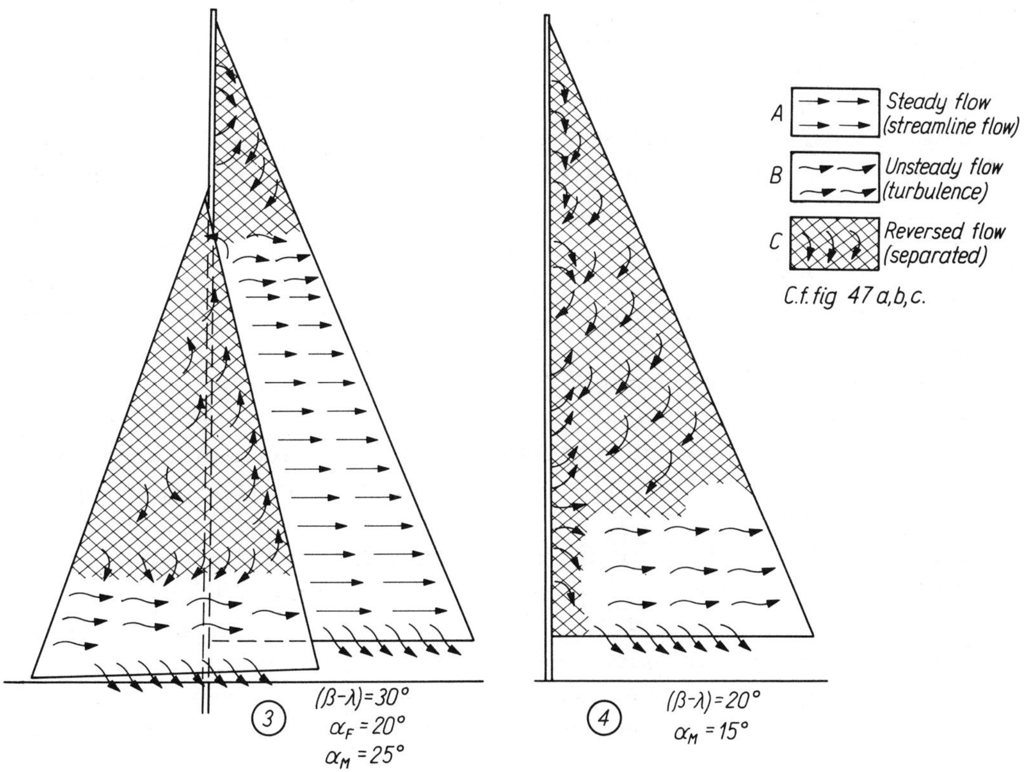

that at the small heading, β-$\lambda = 20°$, when $\alpha_F = 10°$, $\alpha_M = 15°$, steady flow occupies the major part of both sails. Only in the regions at the head of the genoa and above this point on the mainsail is the flow turbulent (B) or separated (C).

If the angle β-λ is now increased to 25°, the disturbance on the mainsail progresses downward slightly. The upper parts of this sail are most affected because the influence of the genoa is least, and the ratio of mast diameter to sail chord is greatest. The amount of the genoa, on the other hand, which is now stalled is considerably greater.

A further increase of β-λ to 30° leads to the stalling on the foresail to spread almost to the foot, but the mainsail still has a largely steady or slightly turbulent flow. This condition is maintained until at least β-$\lambda = 40°$.

Sketch No. 4 shows the mainsail only, at the same condition as that of No. 1, and clearly demonstrates to what extent the foresail stabilizes the flow over the leeward side of the mainsail against unwanted turbulent or separated flow, particularly just abaft the mast. It does this by introducing high velocity air which compensates for losses caused by the mast and by friction.

Figure 105 shows the air flow over a mainsail of small aspect ratio at an angle of attack $\alpha \cong 35°$. Case a, for the mainsail only, shows the turbulent nature of the flow on the leeward side, whilst the added foresail in case b eliminates this turbulence. Case c demonstrates backwinding and subsequent deformation of the mainsail, caused by a badly trimmed foresail. It is thus evident that the desired aerodynamic effect will be obtained only when the slot between the foresail and the mainsail is of a suitable shape.

The most important condition for effective interaction between the two sails is that the foresail should be trimmed in such a way that a substantial increase in air velocity occurs in the slot without the mainsail being backwinded. In other words, it is necessary that the general direction of air flow on the leeward side of the mainsail in the overlapping region be tangential to the surface of the mainsail. If the camber of the foresail is too large or if it is sheeted too hard, excessive convergence of the slot produces a velocity component perpendicular to the surface of the mainsail.

This condition is illustrated in Fig. 105c. The air stream at point X is resolved into two components, tangential and perpendicular to the mainsail surface. The harmful effect of the perpendicular component, which reduces the suction on the mainsail, will be most prominent immediately abaft the mast. From the earlier study of pressure distribution (Figs. 35 and 38) we know that the suction just behind the mast is not very great. It is a particularly sensitive place on the mainsail and gives the helmsman the first warning that he is pinching the sail. When the suction at this point is reduced to such an extent that the pressure difference between the windward and leeward sides is nearly zero, the sail will flutter.

Once a sail starts to flutter near the luff, its smooth contour is destroyed, and with it the streamlined flow over the rest of the sail. In the course of experiments carried

Fig. 105

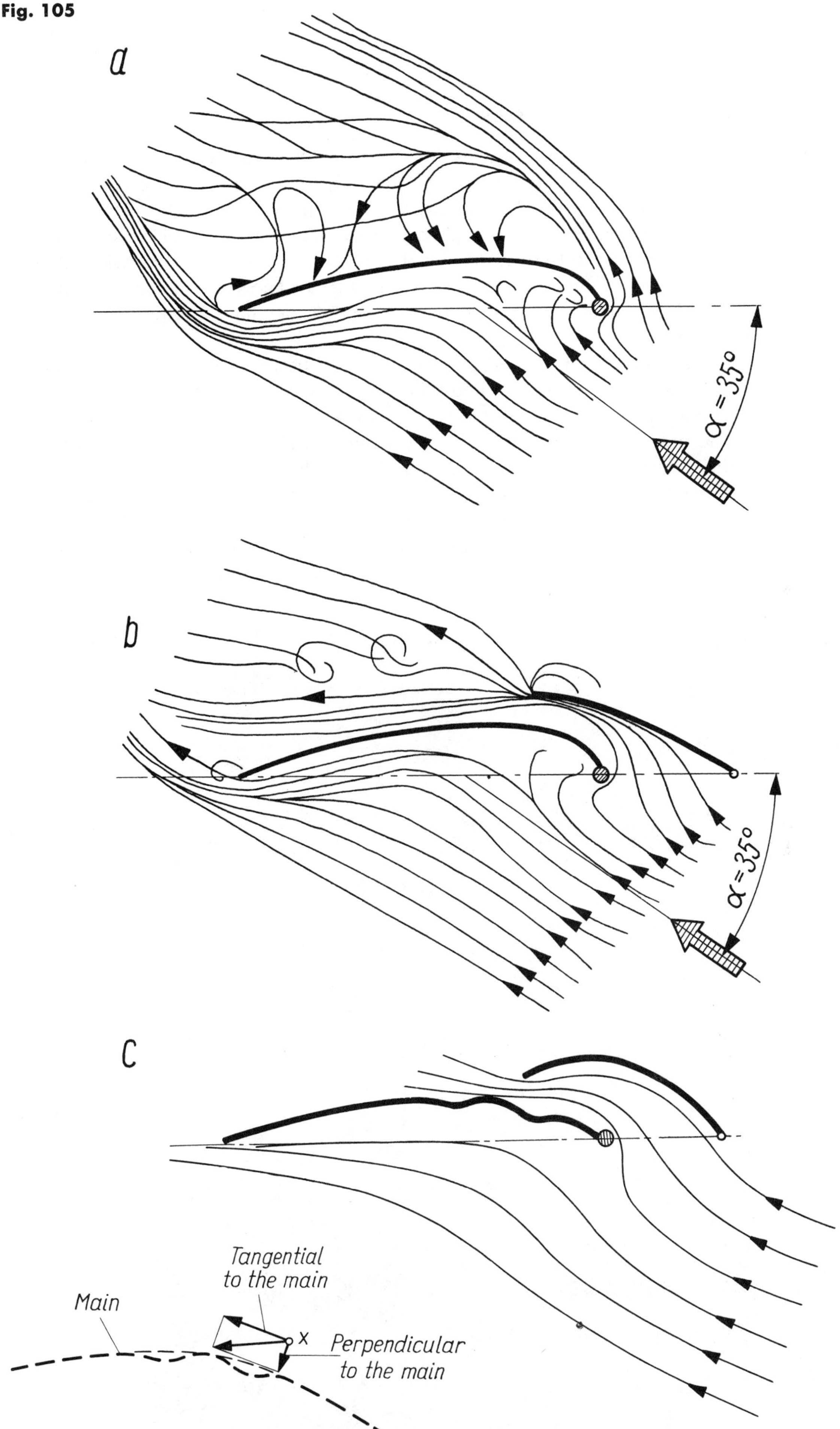

a

α = 35°

b

α = 35°

c

Tangential
to the main

Main

x

Perpendicular
to the main

out on sail pressure distributions, Warner and Ober concluded that if sufficient rigidity was supplied to a sail near the luff, to prevent shaking occurring at that point, the sail as a whole would be able to point higher. This idea was fully confirmed in practice. Sails equipped with full-length battens can be set closer to the wind, without fluttering, in spite of them being backwinded. The sail stiffness can be increased by using battens of suitable thickness and fixing them under longitudinal compression in their pockets, so that they have a natural curve, even in no wind.

Having established the best profile for the slot between two sails, it is necessary that the same general shape should be maintained at all heights. One frequently finds that the ineffectiveness of a foresail can be attributed to its having the correct profile near the foot but an excessive camber higher up, causing backwinding of the mainsail (Fig. 105c). Photograph 10 shows how this can be caused by sag in the forestay and in the leech of the foresail. The sail in the region of the third batten is backwinded, while lower down, where the foresail is relatively flat, this does not occur. This state of affairs is commonly met; the mid-height of the foresail, where its profile is most difficult to control, usually causes the trouble.

Photo. 10

From this discussion, and Figs. 105b, c and Photo. 10 we can suggest that to minimize backwinding we should:

(a) Use a flat foresail in conjunction with a fairly well-cambered mainsail in the overlapping regions, rather than vice versa
(b) Position the sails so that they are substantially parallel

These two rules imply that not only is the convergence of the slot important, but also its shape. Since the supporters of the Venturi theory would not wholly agree with this—as with them, the more convergence the better—we must qualify our statements by reference to Fig. 106. The sails shown are approximately parallel, yet the slot between them is convergent, as measured by the reducing distances O-O, A-A, B-B. It is important to remember that an effect of acceleration of the flow between two sails is conferred by a change in speed, or direction in a flow. The gap can, and should, be nearly parallel in the overlapping region, yet the foresail will still exert a powerful influence on the mainsail, by virtue of its turning the air flow to the latter's advantage.

The experiments referred to in Figs. 103 and 104 were performed using models on which the sails were almost parallel where they overlapped, yet the beneficial effect of the foresail on the flow was readily apparent.

(b) Sheeting of Main and Fore Sails

There is another aspect of the interaction between main and fore sails in favor of reducing the convergence of the slot between them. This depends on the foresail, which we know to be a highly effective sail in its own right, if only it is allowed to be so. Compare sketches 2 and 3 of Fig. 104 showing typical angles for close-hauled sailing, i.e., the heading β-λ in the range 25°–30°, angle of incidence of foresail α_F between 15° and 20°, and its angle of trim $\delta_F = 10°$. We can see that this sail is not itself very efficient, since although the flow over the mainsail is steady, that over the foresail is not. At the apparent heading β-$\lambda = 25°$, about half of the leeward surface of the foresail suffers from turbulent flow, and when β-$\lambda = 30°$, almost all its surface is affected. This means that the angle of incidence α_F is too large, and should be reduced, by increasing its trim angle δ_F.

Fig. 106

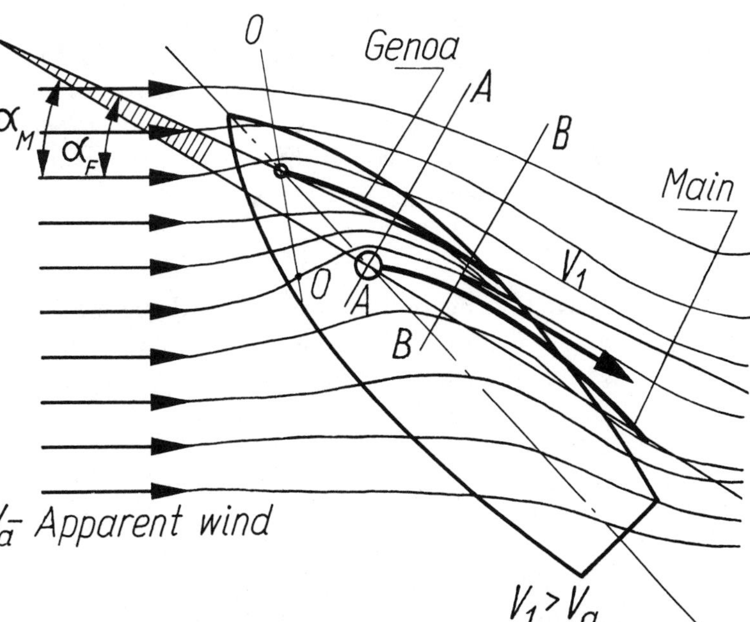

In racing circles it is well known how vitally important is the trim angle of the foresail when close-hauled. Sheeting the foresail too hard can reduce speed as no other factor can. Freeing the foresail sheet by only two inches, or a small outboard shift of its fairleads, may make a radical improvement in the performance of a yacht.

This was proved by further measurements performed in the wind tunnel at Southampton University, by the results shown in Fig. 107. The sail models were the same as in Fig. 104, but the camber of the foresail was 1/25 (4 per cent) and that of the mainsail was 1/12.5 (8 per cent). The trim angle of the mainsail was kept constant at $\delta_M = 10°$, and the aerodynamic forces for both sails were measured at headings β-λ = 22°, 25°, 28°, 31° for various angles of trim of the foresail, δ_F = 10°, 12½°, 15°, 17½°. The heading β-λ = 22° will only be attained by the highest performance yachts such as 12- and 6-Meters, that of β-λ = 25° will apply to boats like the Dragon and 5.5-Meter, while the larger values will apply to centerboard dinghies and ocean cruisers and racers.

Let us consider Fig. 107, which gives driving force coefficient C_R and heeling force coefficient C_H, for the case when the heading β-λ = 22°. For the various foresail trim angles δ_F = 10°, 12½°, 15°, 17½°, there are corresponding total aerodynamic forces represented by the vectors CE-A, CE-A_i, CE-A_{ii}, CE-A_{iii}, respectively. The curve A-A_{iii} tells us that by increasing the slot between the two overlapping sails we may increase the driving force coefficient C_R and at the same time reduce the heeling force coefficient C_H. For instance, when $\delta_F = 10°$, $C_R = 0.085$ and $C_H = 0.71$ and when δ_F = 17½°, $C_R = 0.13$ and $C_H = 0.65$. Thus by increasing the foresail angle δ_F from 10° to 17½° we obtain an increase of 50 per cent in driving force and a reduction of 10 per cent in heeling force. A further increase in δ_F above 17½° will reduce the heeling force still further, but at the expense of the driving force.

Looking in turn at the similar curves for headings β-λ = 25°, 28°, 31°, it is evident that the same general conclusions are true. Extending the curves by eye into the region where no measurements were taken, it is clear that when sailing close-hauled, the foresail should be set at an angle greater than 17½°, and that this angle should increase slightly as the heading β-λ increases. The exact angle, about 20°, will therefore depend on the type of boat and the strength of the wind, according to whether maximum driving force C_R or the ratio driving force to heeling force, C_R/C_H, is the more important.

These conclusions refer in particular to the Bermudian sloop specified in Figs. 103 and 104 where both sails were almost without twist. Experiments on other models of different aspect ratios confirmed the general dependence of the efficiency of the rig on foresail trim angle.

(c) "Tuning Sails"

We saw above that the optimum setting of the foresail when close-hauled is not less than about $\delta_F = 17°$. This is outside the capabilities of many yachts. Limitations in most class rules prohibit the use of outriggers to extend the foresail

Fig. 107

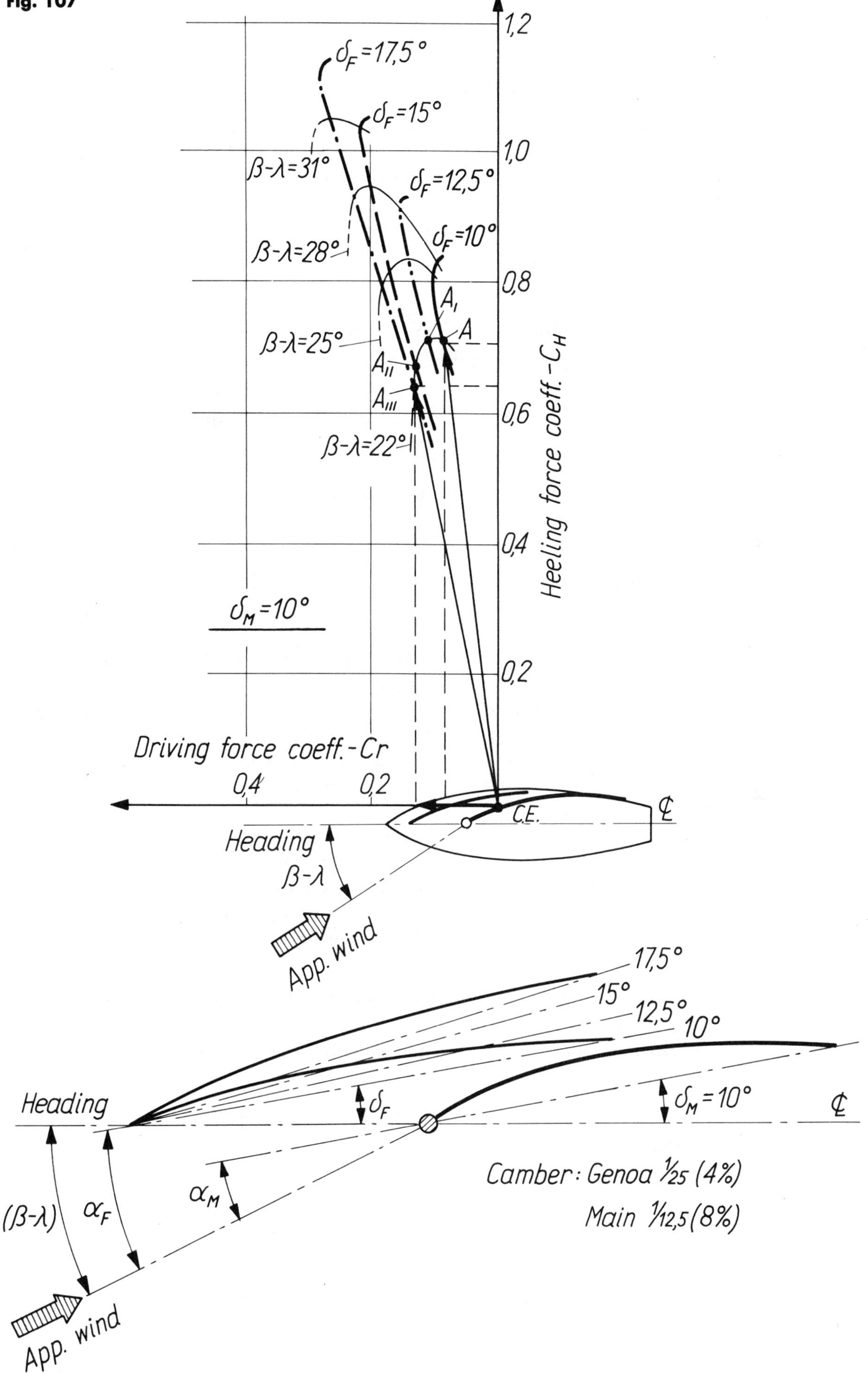

1,2
1,0
0,8
0,6
0,4
0,2
δF=17,5°
δF=15°
δF=12,5°
δF=10°
β-λ=31°
β-λ=28°
β-λ=25°
β-λ=22°
A
A_I
A_II
A_III
Heeling force coeff. -C_H
δM=10°
Driving force coeff. -Cr
0,4
0,2
C.E.
℄
Heading
β-λ
App. wind
17,5°
15°
12,5°
10°
Heading
δF
δM=10°
℄
αM
(β-λ)
αF
Camber: Genoa 1/25 (4%)
Main 1/12,5 (8%)
App. wind

sheeting outboard of the gunwale, with the exception that in some cases the foresheet can be guided by a boom. In general practice then, the outboard position of the clew of the foresail is limited, since the fairlead cannot be fixed outside the gunwale.

From Fig. 103 we can see that the trim angle of the foot of the foresail depends on:

(a) The deck width at the fairleads
(b) The length of the foot

Bearing in mind these limitations we can find from plans the maximum possible foresail angle of trim for various racing yachts:

I.Y.R.U.	R-12 Meter	$\delta_F = 8°–9°$
	R-6 Meter	$= 9°–10°$
	Star	$= 11°$
	Dragon	$= 14°$
	R-5.5 Meter	$= 15°$
	F.D.	$= 18°$
	5-0-5	$= 20°$

The limitations on trim angle for the extreme type of fine keel yachts are not so apparent for beamy dinghies, and hence it will be easier to tune the sails on the latter type of boat.

In the worst case, that of the R-12–Meter yachts, traditional design and the class rules prevent one exploiting their rig to the full. From the discussion on Fig. 107 of the advantages to be gained from increasing the foresail trim angle from $\delta_F = 10°$, we can appreciate to what extent the narrow sheeting base of the deck of a 12-Meter limits the potentialities of the sails. One can but feel that it might be better to accept some compromise in hull design for the sake of the efficiency of the sails.

For a given hull, the question will arise of how to improve the working conditions of the sails in spite of the trim angle limitations on the foot of the foresail. The primary condition to fulfill, particularly on yachts with large overlapping genoas, is to attach the fairleads as far outboard as possible. Having done this, the foresail should now be allowed to twist, to increase the average angle of trim δ_F.

The aim in tuning sails should be:

(a) To decrease the angle of incidence α_F of the foresail with a view to improving its own working efficiency
(b) To shape the slot between the sails to minimize the backwinding on the mainsail

The shape of the slot will depend on the following factors:

1. Position of the fairleads
2. Point of attachment of tack of foresail

3. Trim of mainsail and foresail sheets
4. Sag in the forestay
5. Shape of the foresail (e.g., high-cut jib, low-cut genoa)
6. Camber of mainsail and foresail.

The crew of a yacht have therefore several courses partly under their control by which they may attempt to tune the sails to the requirements a and b. Naturally, it will not normally be possible to obtain the optimum tuning in cases where the class rules or the basic design philosophy limit the hull and rigging. Nevertheless, a compromise between the various effects can be found which will yield the best performance.

To illustrate this problem in practical terms, we will analyze several photographs of yachts sailing. An extreme example of the difficulties of sail tuning is the R-12–Meter class which is notorious for its limited trim angle available for the foot of the foresail. Let us consider the case of tuning a low-cut genoa having about ⅓ of its foot overlapping the mainsail.

Photograph 11 is that of the 12-Meter *Norsaga.* The black, horizontal stripes on the sails were used to estimate the camber by photography. We can see that camber of the genoa, relatively small at the foot, increases considerably with height. As a result, the mainsail is badly backwinded in the region of the second and third stripes up, in spite of the angle of incidence of the genoa being less there than at the foot, due to twist. A section through both sails at this height would remind us forcibly of Fig. 105c. Sailing on *Norsaga*, the author was able to see how approximately 20 per cent of the mainsail area suffered from backwinding when the genoa was in normal trim for sailing to windward. Bearing in mind that the area affected is near the luff, where the suctions should be highest, we can conceive to what extent the efficiency of the mainsail was reduced.

Photo. 11

Photo. 12A

Photo. 12B

Photo. 13A

Photo. 13B

In this case, easing the genoa sheets, with a view to reducing the convergence of the slot between the sails, would not help (see Photo. 12a). The camber and twist of the genoa would immediately increase (Photo. 12b), and it would not be possible to point so high. Particularly in strong winds, it is desirable for the headsail to be flat throughout its height, have little twist and the correct slot between it and the mainsail (Photo. 13a and b).

To obtain a flat genoa, it is sometimes necessary to alter its cut. We mentioned before how the forestay sagging aft (Photo. 14) will increase the camber. In strong winds one can obtain backwinding from this cause, even though the same sail, at the same trim, may not offend in lighter winds. To some extent one can compensate for sag in the forestay by cutting the upper part of the genoa with a hollow luff. If this proves to be insufficient for a large sail in strong winds, the leech may also be cut with a hollow (see Photo. 14). Both these measures produce horizontal tensions in the fabric (shown by the arrows in Photo. 14) as a result of the tension along the edges of the sail, and so flatten the sail. The magnitudes of these horizontal forces will be largest for sails with a large hollow and a short leech.

Photo. 14

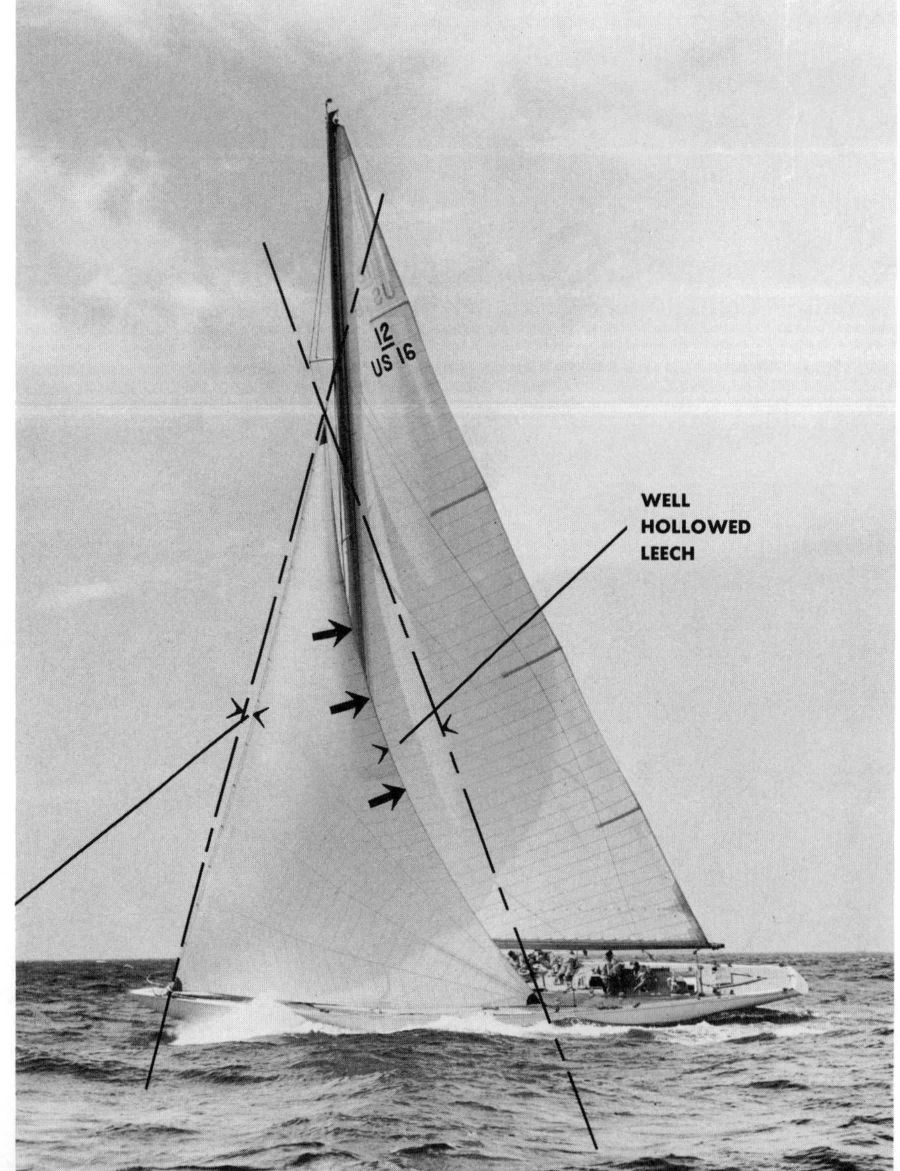

The amount of hollow in the leech of the genoa will be dictated by its proposed application. In 12-Meters, the heavy genoa for strong winds should be well hollowed, while only slight hollowing is required for the light genoa. This arises from the forestay sag being less in light winds, and also more camber can be tolerated in these conditions. Sails for reaching will have straight leeches, since then more camber is desirable.

The length of the leech also has an effect on the amount of twist in the sail (i.e., longer leech, greater twist); therefore a compromise must be found between the required flattening of the sail and the amount of twist required, consistent with minimum backwinding of the mainsail and the limitations of the foresail sheeting base.

So far we have only considered the effect of trimming a low-cut genoa on our sail combination. The shape of the slot, however, will depend also on the trim of the mainsail. By hardening the mainsheet and even leading it to the weather side of the horse, the boom can be pulled amidships, so reducing the convergence of the slot and hence the backwinding. On the extreme types of racing-keel yachts, where the sheeting base for the headsail is limited by the small beam, the main boom is generally pinned in hard. Figure 108 shows the effect of changes in trim angle δ_M of the mainsail. The measurements were made on the same model sails as those of Figs. 103 and 104. The trim angle of the genoa was kept constant at $\delta_F = 12\frac{1}{2}°$, and measurements taken of driving force coefficient C_R and heeling moment coefficient M_H for trim angles of the mainsail $\delta_M = 0°, 5°, 10°$, and for headings $\beta\text{-}\lambda = 20°, 22\frac{1}{2}°, 25°, 27\frac{1}{2}°, 30°$. For our purposes, we can regard the heeling coefficient M_H as being synonymous with the heeling force coefficients C_H previously encountered.

Let us examine the case of the mainsail trimmed to an angle $\delta_M = 10°$, on a heading $\beta\text{-}\lambda = 22\frac{1}{2}°$. The corresponding values of driving force coefficient are $C_R \cong 0.135$ and the heeling moment coefficient $M_H = 0.175$. Hardening the mainsheet to $\delta_M = 5°$, the coefficients become $C_R = 0.16$, and $M_H = 0.265$, an increase of driving force of about 18.5 per cent, but also an increase of 50 per cent in heeling moment. If the boom is pulled still further toward the hull centerline, the driving force starts to fall, and the heeling moment increases rapidly.

Considering these forces at greater sailing angles we find that the mainsail trim angle δ_M is even more important. At a heading $\beta\text{-}\lambda = 30°$, changing δ_M from 10° to 5° produces a negligible increase in C_R compared with the large increase in M_H also obtained.

Comparing Figs. 107 and 108, a very important conclusion can be reached as to the respective roles played by the foresail and mainsail. Figure 107 shows that altering the trim angle of the foresail, with the mainsail held fixed, gives large changes in driving force, up to 100 per cent in extreme cases, but relatively small changes in heeling force. On the other hand, Fig. 108 shows that changes in trim of the mainsail largely affect heeling moments.

When tuning the sails the above remarks must be born in mind. The dual role

Fig. 108

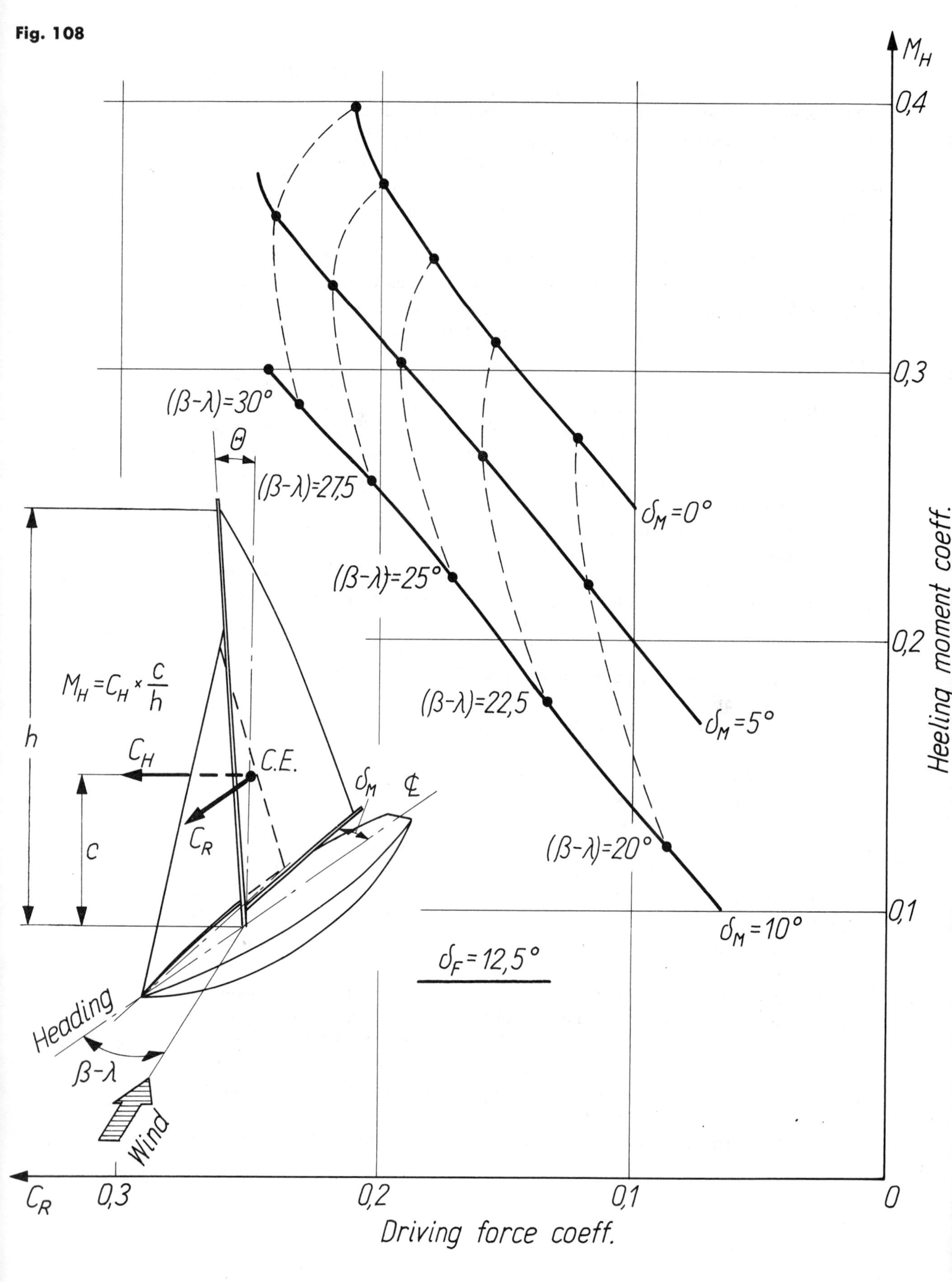

M_H
0,4
0,3
0,2
0,1
0
Heeling moment coeff.
(β-λ)=30°
(β-λ)=27,5
(β-λ)=25°
(β-λ)=22,5
(β-λ)=20°
δ_M=0°
δ_M=5°
δ_M=10°
δ_F=12,5°
Θ
M_H = C_H × c/h
h
C_H
C.E.
C_R
c
δ_M
℄
Heading
β-λ
Wind
C_R
0,3
0,2
0,1
Driving force coeff.

of the foresail, as a sail itself and as one which has a profound effect on the mainsail, results in its effect, following a change in trim, being felt more strongly than that following a change in the mainsail setting. One should therefore give it priority when tuning the sails, and if any compromise is required, this should be made on the mainsail rather than the foresail.

Let us now consider (from Fig. 108) what should be the guiding factor when selecting the mainsail trim angle. Sailing in light winds, when the main objective is to attain the maximum driving force $C_{R\,max}$, trimming the main boom nearly amidships when close-hauled can be useful, but should not be carried to excess. At the first sign of the heeling moment becoming too large, with increasing wind strength, the sheet should be eased. This will bring the operating conditions closer to the strong weather criterion of (C_H/C_R) min or (M_H/C_R) min. In no case should the yacht be allowed to heel past the point, usually around 30°, at which the speed is appreciably affected. The practice of some crews of keel yachts to set the mainsail regardless of wind strength or the precise course cannot be commended.

On small centerboard boats, the question will arise what to do first when the wind strength increases and the boat becomes overcanvassed. This becomes of particular urgency on boats with rigid masts, on which the mainsail is difficult to flatten by hardening the mainsheet. A similar situation can arise on keel yachts in gusty conditions, when the boat heels excessively in the gusts, but not otherwise. Under these conditions it is best to ease the mainsheet for the gusts and maintain the trim of the foresail constant. As a rule the foresail is a splendid driving sail, with its center of effort relatively low. Easing the mainsheet will cause backwinding, which is controllable from a slight shaking of the luff to the whole sail flogging, and so reduce the driving force, but will also produce a large diminution in heeling moment. This expedient becomes unworkable when the mainsail flogs violently, when the reduction in driving force becomes excessive. If, instead, the foresheets are eased, the effect will be to increase its camber and twist, causing what is sometimes a large increase in heeling moment and resulting in reduced speed.

Another advantage resulting from keeping the trim of the foresail constant is that it allows one to follow accurately shifts in wind direction. The effect of these is easily seen at the luff of the sail (see Fig. 59), particularly if one has some streamers of wool in this region.

Another reason for easing the mainsheet lies in the weather helm which most hulls carry when heeled (dealt with in the chapter 1e and 3c, part III). This requires a forward shift in center of effort (CE) of the sails to balance, which can be achieved by spilling wind from the mainsail. Easing the foresail would merely increase the weather helm.

An interesting method of tuning the foresail has been evolved for the Flying Dutchman for sailing to windward. The weakness of the design of this unusually light boat lies in the relatively low rigidity of the hull. Too large a tension in the forestay can deform or even damage the hull structure. In light winds, correctly tuning the genoa is comparatively simple because of the wide sheeting base for the

Fig. 109

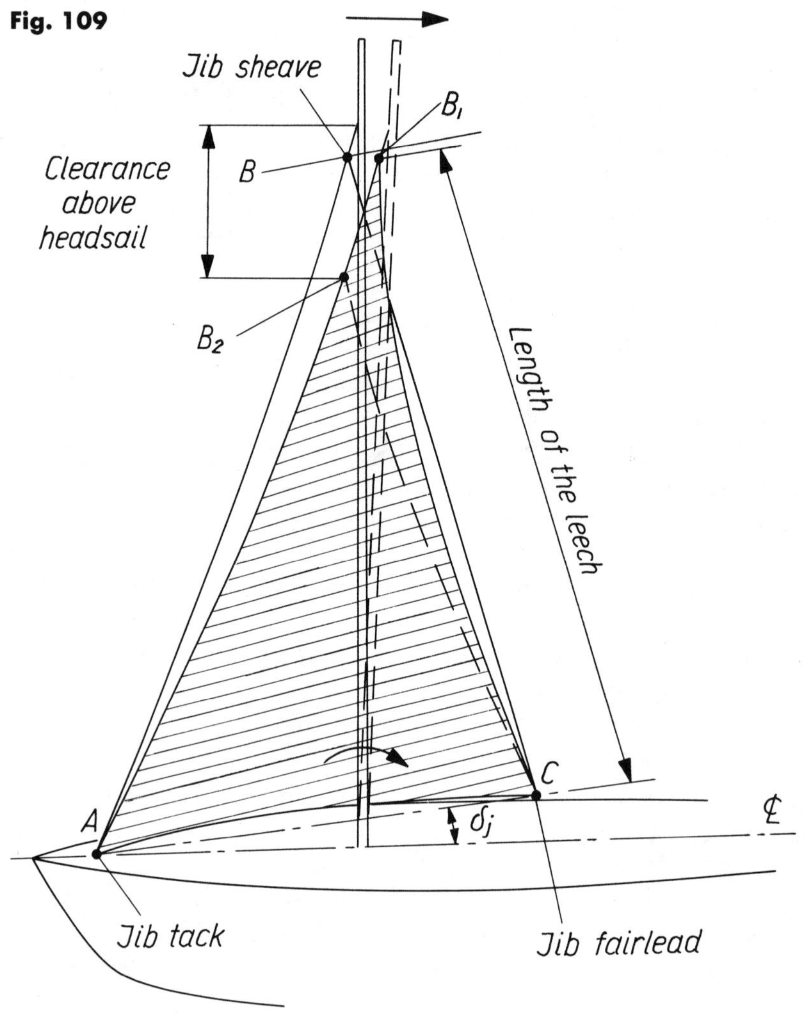

foresail. Difficulties arise, however, in strong winds when the forestay sag becomes excessive, increases the camber of the upper parts of the genoa, and so causes backwinding. By raking the mast aft (Fig. 109), it is possible to maintain a tight foot to the sail and at the same time to slacken the leech. This follows since the clew C of a low-cut genoa is virtually fixed on the deck and the distance B_1C is less than BC. Hence the genoa sags to leeward, increasing the slot between the sails. When this method proves insufficient, the genoa is changed for one of lower aspect ratio, AB_2C. This not only reduces the sail area, but also increases the clearance between the sails in the most important region near the jib halyard sheave. Thus the technique for tuning the F.D. genoa can be summarized as follows.

light winds	mast upright foot relatively slack (controlled by sheets) leech tight

strong winds	mast raked aft foot light leech slack
very strong winds	low A.R. genoa increased clearance above head of sail

The problem of tuning a low-cut genoa is a simplified one, since the clew is so close to the fairlead that the only effective alteration one can make to the fairlead is athwartships (Fig. 103), which directly alters the trim angle δ_F at the foot of the sail. In the case of a high-cut foresail an extra complication arises in that the fairlead can also be moved fore and aft. Once again opinions differ as to its best position for sailing close-hauled. Some say that the line of the sheet should be along the miter line of the clew; others maintain that it should lie above it, or below it.

The value of these prescriptions lie not so much in their actual statement as in their recognizing that fairlead position is important. Correct setting of the fairleads is a problem of attaining a balance between sail twist and camber. In Fig. 110a the tension force N in the sheet can be resolved into two components, N_1 and N_2, acting respectively along the leech and foot of the sail. The tension in the foot will be greater than that in the leech, and consequently the foot of the sail will be flat but the upper parts will be twisted and will flutter first if the sail is pinched. In case b the leech tension is increased at the expense of the tension in the foot, and hence the sail will twist less but will be more cambered, and the leech will have a tendency to curl over.

The best compromise in fairlead position can be found by the same method employed in setting the mainsail. Without changing the setting of the sheets, the boat is gently luffed. If the fairleads are positioned correctly the whole of the luff of the foresail should start to flutter almost at one moment. If the upper parts flutter first it indicates either that the sail is too full there because of its cut, or else its twist is too large. This corresponds to case a of Fig. 110, and the remedy is to move the fairlead forward. If the lower parts flutter first, the fairlead should be moved aft.

Fig. 110

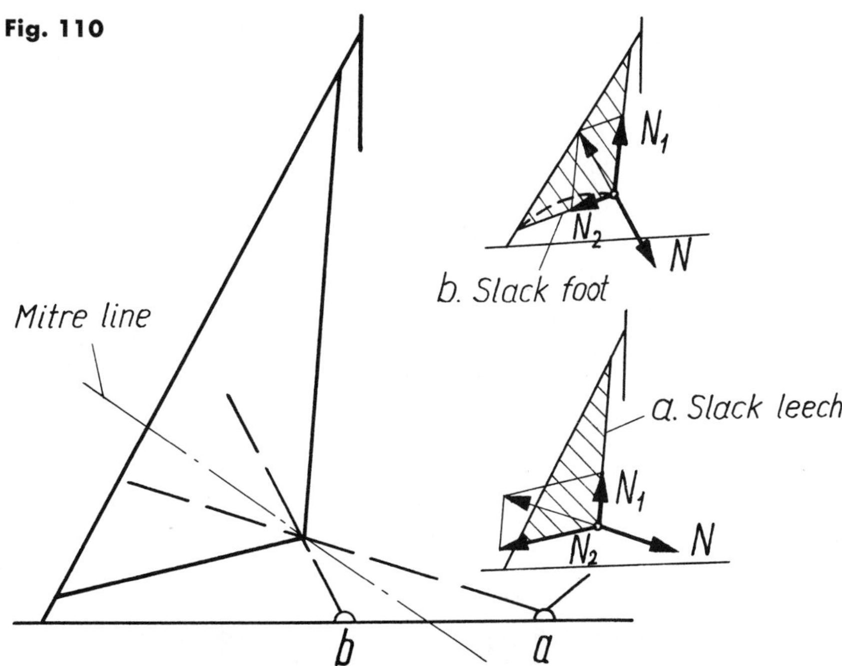

Fig. 111

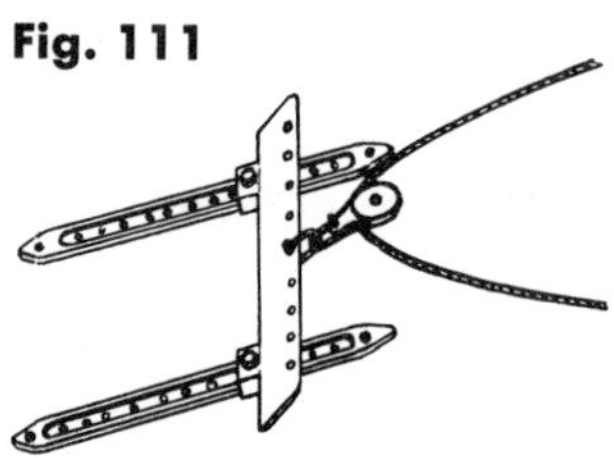

On beamy boats it is quite easy to arrange that the whole of the foresail flutters simultaneously, but in the case of narrow, racing craft, sail twist can be quite a problem.

Siting the fairleads should be considered in relation to the course sailed and the type of foresail being used, i.e., the current weather conditions. A fairlead correctly set for a close-hauled course will not be equally satisfactory on a close reach. Unless class rules forbid it, it is advisable to have several fairleads or else to make provision for adjustment of its position in both directions. Figure 111 shows one example of a system giving wide regulation of the position of the fairlead.

The limited width of foresail sheeting base of many, particularly racing, keel yachts has been responsible for the evolution of a certain "tradition" in trimming sails. Even on boats where the deck width offers no restrictions, one frequently finds the fairleads set too far inboard. Catamarans have an exceptionally wide sheeting base giving almost unlimited scope in positioning the foresail fairleads and the mainsheet horse for maximum efficiency, yet Photo. 15 of a Shearwater III illustrates how these advantages are often ignored.

Photograph 16, on the other hand, is a good illustration of how the sails can be trimmed if proper use is made of the available deck width. It can be seen how little twist there is in the mainsail, and that the foresail fairlead is positioned right to produce very little camber, and efficient interaction between the sails.

(d) Overlap

For a long time (until 1956, when the R.O.R.C. and I.Y.R.U. rules were almost completely revised), the effective area of the headsail under both formulas was rated as 85 per cent of the triangular area between the mast, deck, and forestay. The coefficient 0.85 in the formula $0.85 \times (I \times J)/2$ (see Fig. 104-1) indicated the approximate proportion of the fore-triangle area $(I \times J)/2$ which was occupied by the headsail, before the introduction in 1927 of the genoa. In those early days, the foresail was usually cut high in the foot and did not overlap the mast to any great extent.

The discovery of the highly efficient genoa, cut low in the foot and having a large overlap on the mainsail, encouraged designers to exploit the low tax on foresail area. The balance of areas began to change, with the mainsail getting smaller and more and more overlap, which was not taxed, being used. A new R.O.R.C. rule was introduced limiting overlap of the foot of the foresail over the mainsail to 50 per cent of the fore-triangle base, while in the larger I.Y.R.U. classes the overlap was limited to 40 per cent of the rated length, yet in spite of these restrictions, on most yachts only about 40 per cent of the area of their largest genoa would be included in the rated sail area.

Photo. 15. *Shearwater III*

Photo. 16

The low tax on headsails had a great influence on yacht design and on sailing techniques. One of the most famous examples of this is the English cutter *Myth of Malham* (Fig. 112, Photo. 17). The mast is set nearly amidships and carries a very small mainsail, but there is a wide selection of headsails. The sail list is reproduced to compare their areas.

No. of Sail	*Sail*	*Area (in sq. ft.)*
0	mainsail	305
1	large genoa	637
2	light genoa	516
3	large Yankee	300
4	second jib	185
5	third jib	100
6	genoa staysail	250
7	first staysail	216
8	second heavy staysail	141
9	baby staysail	72
10	large R.O.R.C. spinnaker	875
11	small spinnaker	600
12	small Yankee	250
13	second light staysail	143
14	trysail	120

Photo. 17. *Myth of Malham*

Fig. 112

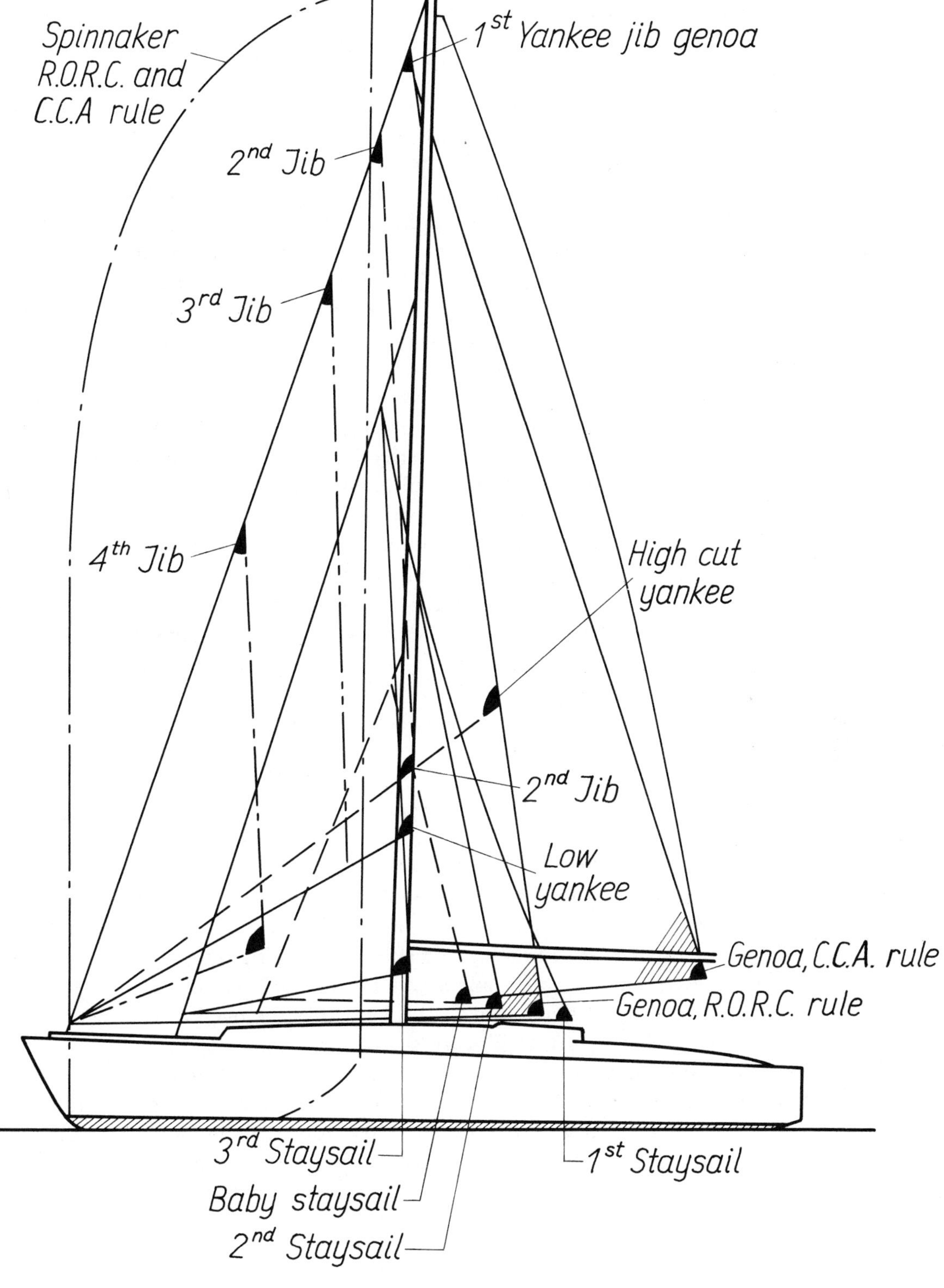
Spinnaker
R.O.R.C. and
C.C.A rule
1st Yankee jib genoa
2nd Jib
3rd Jib
4th Jib
High cut
yankee
2nd Jib
Low
yankee
Genoa, C.C.A. rule
Genoa, R.O.R.C. rule
3rd Staysail
Baby staysail
2nd Staysail
1st Staysail

Because of the greater than normal proportion of headsail area to total sail area, there had to be a large number of headsails so that the correct combination could be selected for any weather condition and course. This is expensive and demands considerable skill from the crew when changing and trimming the sails for each course and wind strength.

After the revision in 1956 of the R.O.R.C. and I.Y.R.U. formulas, it was agreed to take the area of the headsails as $(I \times J)/2$, in other words, the total area of the fore-triangle. The overlap was limited to 0.5J.

In the American C.C.A. Rule the foresail area is taken as 1.2 × fore-triangle area, and there is no limit or tax on overlap. Figure 112 shows the genoa according to both R.O.R.C. and C.C.A. Rules, and Photo. 17 shows *Myth of Malham* carrying her enormous masthead C.C.A. genoa. The straight luff testifies to a successful solution of the problems of rigging having been found.

However headsails are taxed in the future, the question of how they should overlap the mainsail will always remain. Some light is thrown on the subject from results obtained at Southampton University of force measurements on a model sloop with rigid sails. The proportions of the sails are shown in Fig. 113, and the 4 per cent camber profile in Fig. 103. Investigations were made of various models, A_i, A_{ii}, A_{iii}, having different positions of maximum camber of the sails, at 15 per cent, 25 per cent, and 50 per cent, respectively, of the local chord. A general conclusion was reached that the position of maximum camber of the mainsail should be forward of the leech of the foresail for the maximum advantage. Figure 113 shows some of the results, giving curves of driving force coefficient in the practical range of conditions for sailing to windward; i.e., heading β-$\lambda = 20°$–$30°$, trim angle of genoa $\delta_F = 12\frac{1}{2}°$, trim angle of mainsail $\delta_M = 5°$. Model A_i was shown to be superior over model A_{iii} by virtue of its higher driving force, up to 7 per cent, and also its heeling moment being about 20 per cent to 25 per cent lower. The results for model A_{ii} were between those of A_i and A_{iii}. This pattern was largely repeated for different sail trims.

The most likely reason for the relative performance of these three models can be argued with reference to Figs. 103 and 113. The main effect of the foresail on the mainsail would be to delay separation of the flow from the leeward side of the latter. In the absence of a foresail, this is most likely to occur at, or aft of, the position of maximum camber. If the leech of the foresail is forward of this position, it is doubtful whether it will have a big effect in delaying separation.

From these tests we can give some practical guidance to sailmakers. The position of maximum camber of a mainsail should be within the overlap area between the sails, and probably the further forward the better.

Another experiment in the same series concerned tests on models having different sail plans. Two of the models and some results are given in Fig. 114. Model A_i has been previously described (Figs. 103, 104, and 113); model C had the same sail area and camber, but the ratio of fore-triangle area to mainsail area was 50 per cent as against 35 per cent for model A_i. Model A_i had the typical proportions

Fig. 113

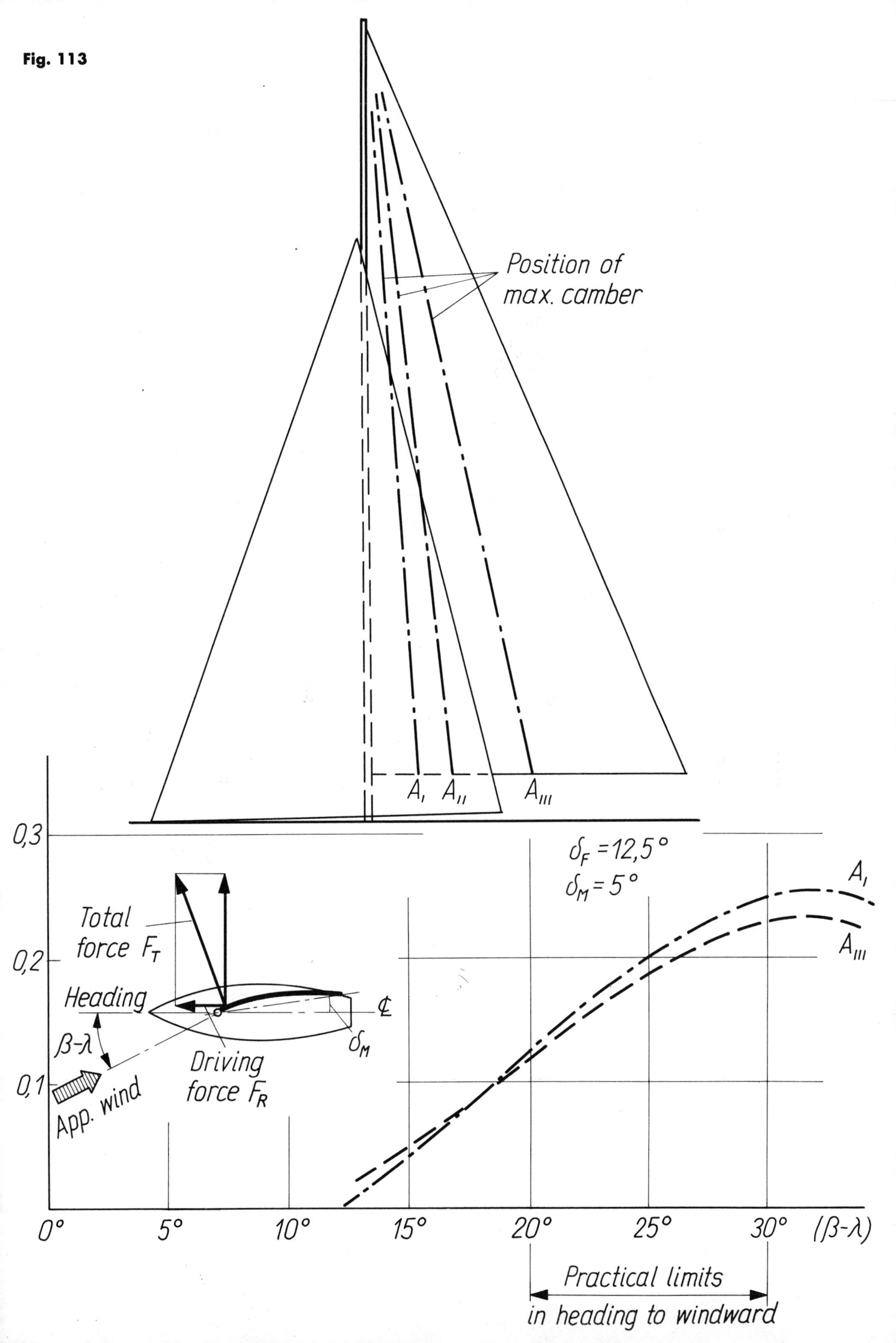

Position of
max. camber
A_I
A_{II}
A_{III}
0,3
0,2
0,1
$\delta_F = 12,5°$
$\delta_M = 5°$
A_I
A_{III}
Total
force F_T
Heading
β-λ
℄
δ_M
Driving
force F_R
App. wind
0°
5°
10°
15°
20°
25°
30°
(β-λ)
Practical limits
in heading to windward

Fig. 114

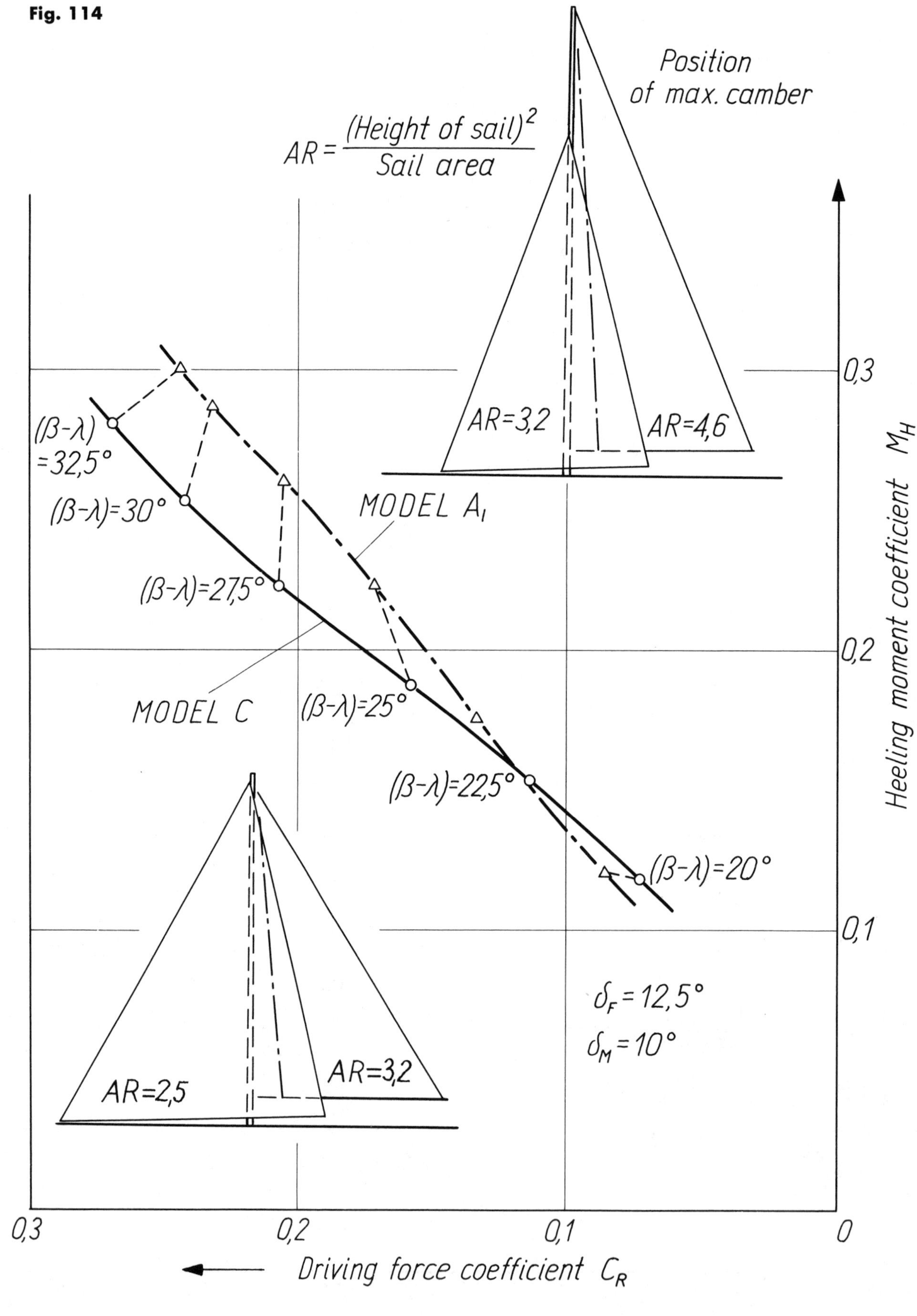

Position
of max. camber
AR = (Height of sail)² / Sail area
AR=3,2
AR=4,6
(β-λ) =32,5°
(β-λ)=30°
MODEL A₁
(β-λ)=27,5°
MODEL C
(β-λ)=25°
(β-λ)=22,5°
(β-λ)=20°
δF = 12,5°
δM = 10°
AR=2,5
AR=3,2
0,3
0,2
0,1
0
Heeling moment coefficient MH
0,3
0,2
0,1
0
Driving force coefficient CR

of such yachts as the I.Y.R.U. classes 12-Meter and 6-Meter, and R.O.R.C. offshore racers, in which the ratio of mainsail luff to foot is, as a rule, between 2.7 and 3.2. Model C, with a masthead genoa, could be considered as a rather extreme example of a yacht built to C.C.A. rules. Here the high tax on aspect ratio results in the mainsail luff seldom being more than twice the length of the foot. For both models, the values of driving force coefficient and the heeling moment coefficient were measured for headings β-λ = 20–32½°, covering close-hauled sailing. Both foresail and mainsail trim angles δ_F and δ_M were varied, but the curves of Fig. 114 refer only to $\delta_F = 12½°$, $\delta_M = 10°$. Nevertheless these curves are typical of those obtained at other sail settings.

In cases where a model has, at the same heading β-λ, a larger driving force coefficient C_R and an equal or smaller heeling moment coefficient M_H than another model, then it can be considered superior. Some doubt as to relative merits will arise in cases where, say, C_R is greater and M_H too. Then the question of wind strength will have to be considered, as in strong winds heeling moments get important, while in light airs the driving force is the predominant factor to be considered.

Thus at a heading β-λ = 20°, model A_i is superior since for the same heeling moment, it has a higher driving force than model C.

At β-λ = 22½° and 25°, it is difficult to say which is the better model, since A_i has in both cases more driving force, but also more heeling moment. It is likely, however, that model A_i would be the better in light winds and model C in strong winds. Above β-λ = 25°, model C is undoubtedly superior. Thus at β-λ = 27½° it has the same driving force, but less heeling moment, and this improves as the heading increases.

It is clear therefore that no one rig is superior over the whole range of courses considered. Model A_i will certainly be better on extremely close-hauled courses while model C will excel when close reaching. On triangular courses round the buoys, when the windward leg usually decides the race, model A_i, of higher aspect ratio, should finish in front of model C. In ocean races, where good all-round performance is required, model C will be superior.

It is encouraging for us to note that the conclusions we derived in Chapter 11, when dealing with single sails of different aspect ratio, are fully confirmed by these later experiments on sloop rigs having overlapping sails.

A current question of great interest to English yacht designers is the rather shattering success in offshore races of beamy, shallow-draft American centerboarders built under the C.C.A. rules. Both on rating and handicaps these have virtually eliminated the competition of the narrow, deep-keeled yachts. This rather unexpected result is being attributed to the differences between the hull types, particularly to the supposed high efficiency of fins having a large centerboard. Even the recently introduced changes in the C.C.A. formula support this view by taxing, more heavily than before, broad-beam shallow-draft centerboarders. Without decrying the advantages to be gained from these hull conceptions, it would be worthwhile considering also their effects on the sails. It has been conclusively shown that for ocean racing, where close-hauled performance is not usually of predominant importance, a low aspect ratio sail rig on a wide sheeting base is considerably superior to the usual rig found on the traditional narrow hulled English yachts.

(e) The Spinnaker

The R.O.R.C. and C.C.A. formulas define the maximum dimensions (Fig. 115) of the spinnaker, which will not carry a penalty, as:

width of the spinnaker at any height $= 1.80 \times J$
length of luff and leech $0.95 \times \sqrt{I^2 + J^2}$

The length of the spinnaker boom, measured from the yacht's centerline to its outboard end, should not exceed the dimension J.

Taking, for instance, the sails of *Myth of Malham*, it may be remembered that the area of the R.O.R.C. spinnaker, of 875 sq. ft., is almost three times that of the mainsail. In the 12-Meter class, this factor is 4.4 (5570 sq. ft.). Although not all yachts have such enormous spinnakers, nevertheless, their areas are usually larger than that of their mainsails. This fact alone underlines their importance as sails providing a powerful driving force. Their position in the sail list has improved considerably as their mode of operation has become understood. Initially treated as a bag to catch the wind when running (Photo. 18), the spinnaker was promoted into the role of a headsail, and has now usurped the large genoa on courses from a run to a close reach.

Fig. 115

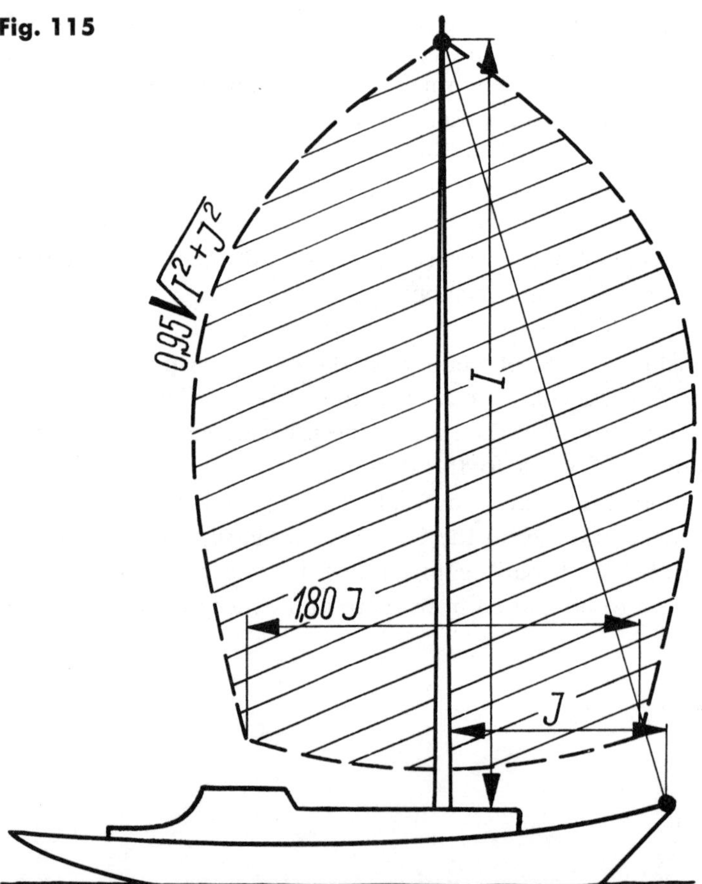

Photo. 18

Fig. 116

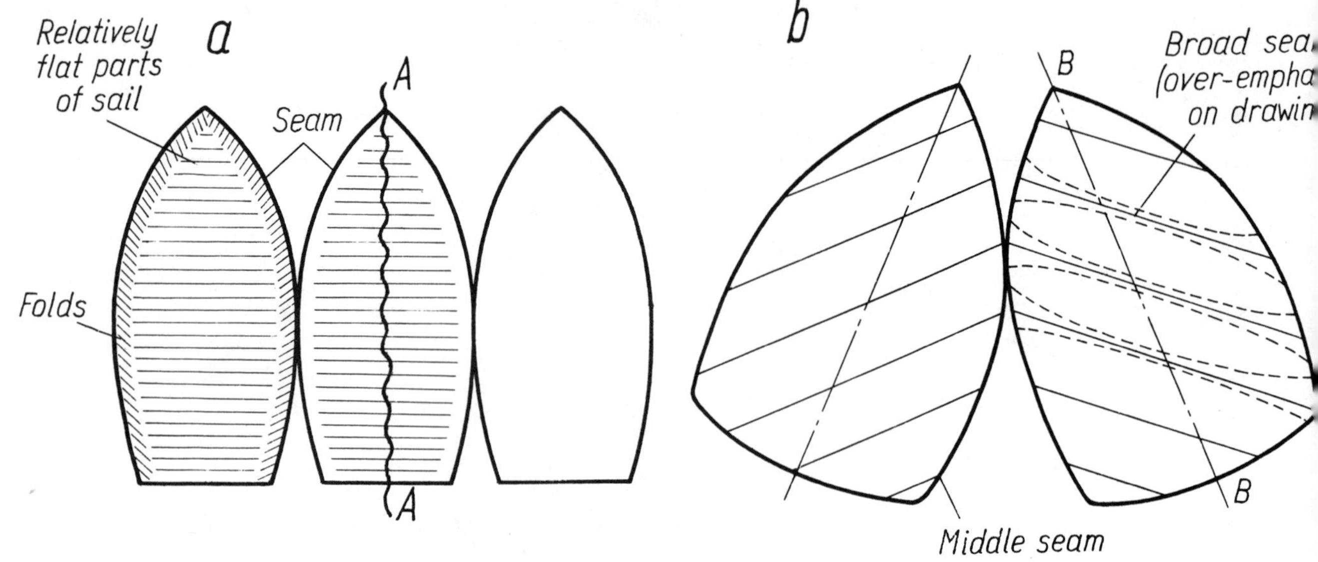

The evolution of the modern spinnaker can best be understood by considering how it is cut and the influence of its cut on its shape and properties at different angles of incidence. The spherical shape of old spinnakers was obtained by cutting the panels as in Fig. 116a. These spinnakers suffered from folds, which appeared at the seams. These were due to the differences in fabric strengths along the warp A-A and along the seams, which over most of their length are running at an angle to the warp and weft. (Before continuing, it might be better for the reader to refer to Chapter 14 (a) where this problem is dealt with in some detail.) The fewer panels in the spinnaker, the larger were the folds. This method of sewing was eventually replaced by a system of double panels, laid diagonally (Fig. 116b). The diagonally laid spinnaker has less tendency to form folds, due to the better disposition of fabric strength. Hence the amounts of stretch along the largely diagonal line B-B and on the middle seam, also diagonal, are similar. The amount of camber is controlled by the number of panels and the broad seams (which are shaped) joining them. Photograph 19 shows a splendid Herbulot spinnaker cut on the above principle, and used by the English yacht *Sceptre* in the 1958 America's Cup Races.

Comparing Photos. 18 and 19, we can see another factor which emerged in the evolution of the spinnaker: the tendency toward reducing the aspect ratio. This was followed for two reasons: at a high angle of incidence, a low aspect ratio sail is better, and the latter, being further outboard, is less blanketed by the mainsail. When running, when the main criterion of a sail is the area it presents to the wind, the diagonally cut balloon spinnaker is much superior to the old type. It is particularly so in light winds, when it can be swung far outboard and set high, away from the shade of the mainsail.

When running, the sail is at a large angle of incidence and is stalled, and the

Photo. 19

Fig. 117

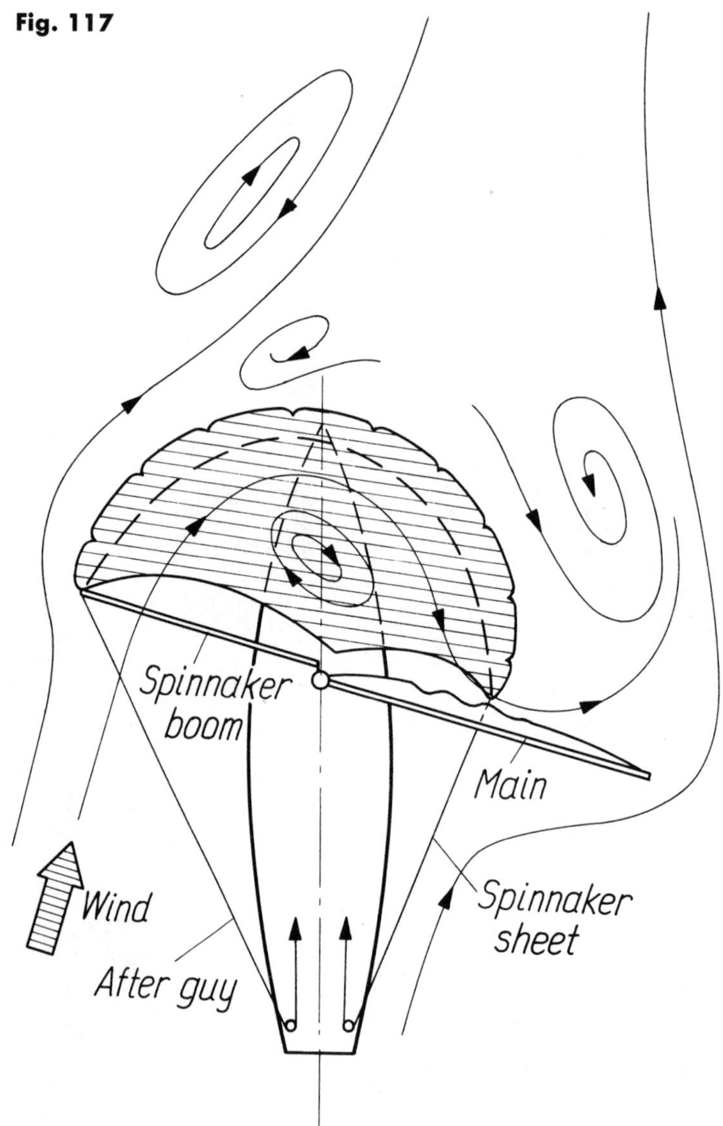

air flow on the leeward side is turbulent (Fig. 117). The air stream separates comparatively close to the edges of the sail, and hence the quality of the curved sail surface is not of prime importance except on aesthetic grounds. Any irregularities such as may occur at the seams have little aerodynamic significance. In any case, the roughly uniform distribution of pressures and suctions on the sail surfaces favors equal tensions throughout the fabric, producing few wrinkles.

The ductile, lightweight Nylon often used for these sails will easily stretch to accommodate errors in cutting, which introduce excessive local tensions. Handling and trimming the spinnaker when running presents few problems, and the leeches have no tendency to collapse. Only under certain circumstances can the fluctuating wake from the leeward side of the sail induce violent rolling, and this constitutes one of the few dangers to avoid when running.

Fig. 118

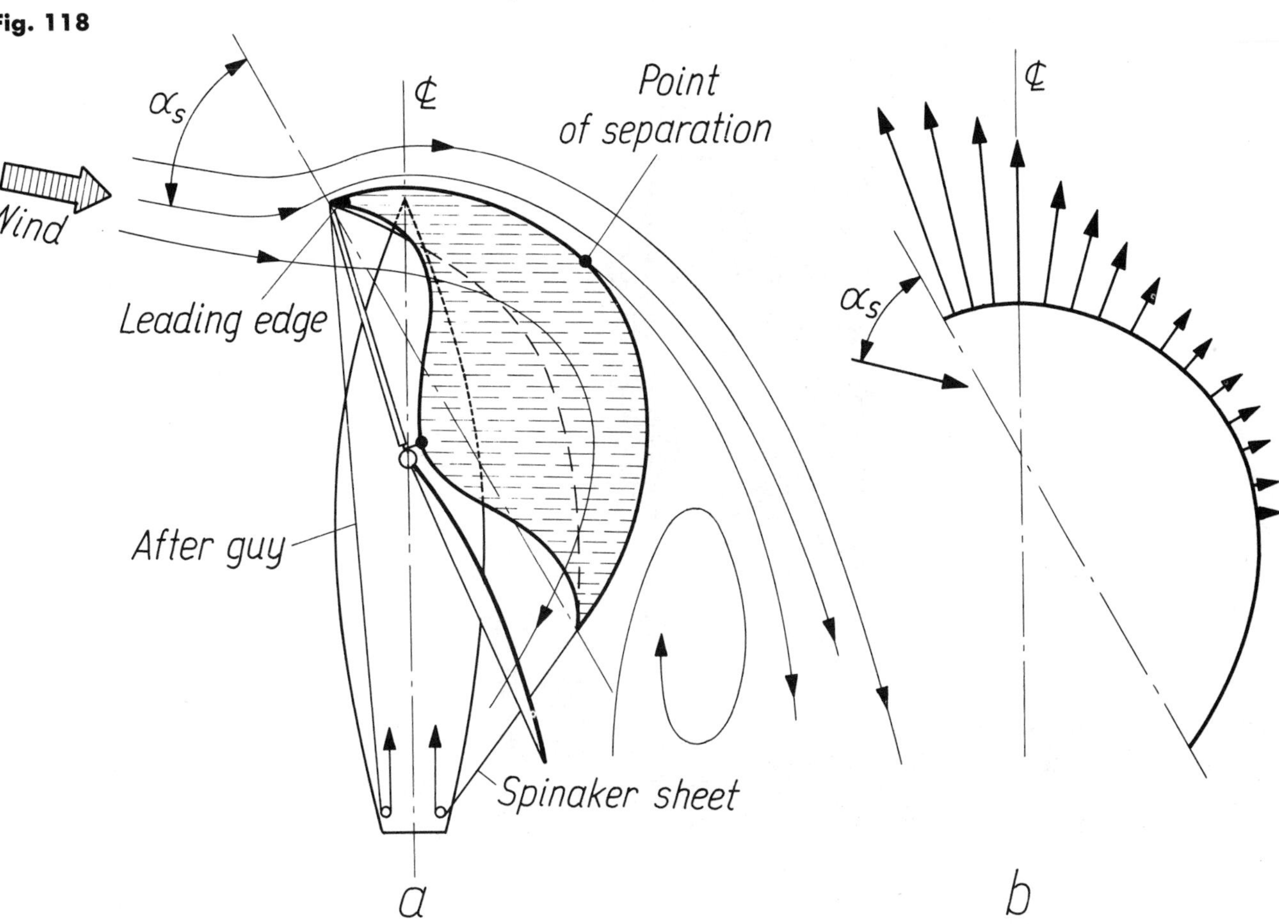

In sailing more on the wind (Fig. 118), the shape and set of the spinnaker become much more important. As the angle of incidence, α_S, of the spinnaker falls below 90° with the wind on the quarter right round to somewhere on a reach, when the luff of the sail collapses, considerable advantages can be obtained by changing the flow from that shown in Fig. 117 to something more like the flow over the foresail and mainsail when close-hauled. The ideal to strive for is a streamline flow, having as little separated flow as possible and developing a large suction at the luff. This results in an increased driving force and reduced heeling force, in spite of the major portion of the sail being well to leeward. Figure 118a, b shows the nature of the flow and distribution of suction on the leeward surface of a spinnaker when reaching. Its resemblance to the flow on a foresail, described in Chapter 2, is readily apparent. The outstanding feature of the pressure distribution is the large suction peak near the leading edge of the sail. As a result, a large tension is caused in this region, and if the fabric is laid diagonally, offering the least resistance to stretching, a large bulge will appear. This will be particularly prominent if the material is very light. Photograph 20 illustrates how the diagonally laid spinnaker falls down on a reach. It shows how *Sceptre's* Herbulot spinnaker develops a large bulge running the length of the luff, as a result of the

Photo. 20

sail fabric stretching considerably more than the reinforced leading edge. It is not difficult to visualize the detrimental effect of this on the flow over the sail. It could be likened to an enormous mast creating turbulent flow behind it, and is one of the most important factors which limit the minimum angle at which the sail can be set.

On a broad reach it is possible to keep such a sail filling by using it at too large an angle of incidence. Although this reduces the driving force and increases the angle of heel, it does allow one to work the sail. Coming more on the wind, the testing of the spinnaker's cut and trim becomes more severe. Then, the critical angle of incidence at which the luff collapses is of great importance, as it imposes a limit for sailing to windward using a spinnaker. It is logical to suggest that the limitations, in this respect, of the diagonally cut spinnaker could be improved by altering the cut so that the greatest tensions at the edges are along the line of greatest resistance of the cloth, i.e., along the weft. This led to the latest idea of the cross-cut spinnaker in which the panels are laid horizontally. With this it is easy to achieve exceptionally flat and smooth edges, favoring streamline flow, and hence a lower minimum setting angle. The horizontal lay of the seams also reduces their harmful effects to a minimum. Photographs 21 and 22 show *Columbia's* spinnaker "Little Harry" from two different viewpoints. Comparing this sail with that of *Sceptre* (Photo. 20), on the same point of sailing, one cannot but be struck by its flat, clean edges and smooth profile as against the latter's baggy, crinkled "Herbulot."

Photo. 21

Photo. 22

Undoubtedly in light winds, dead aft, when the criterion for a good spinnaker is frontal area, the diagonally cut balloon spinnaker is at least as good as any other. Under these conditions its large flow and nearly circular outline make it easy to fly, and keep setting, and hence a large area can be used. With the wind abeam, however, when the spinnaker begins to function partly as a headsail, its area is increasingly of less importance than its shape. Under these conditions the cross-cut spinnaker with its relatively small chord becomes superior. On balance, it is a better all-round sail, particularly in strong winds. Because of its smaller chord, it can be set flatter, and hence at a smaller angle of incidence, α_S, before it collapses. It can be used effectively up to a close reach, when it is then acting as a genoa. The genoa, on the other hand, begins to lose its efficiency when close reaching because of its limited sheeting base. Easing the sheets as one comes off the wind from close-hauled does not produce the expected and desired interaction of this sail with the mainsail because of the increased sail twist and camber causing backwinding. In the case of a spinnaker, under similar conditions, its wider sheeting base allows a better trim than a genoa. Perhaps, in time the spinnaker will evolve with the genoa into the "spinoa," a word culled for the author by an officer of the Royal Navy. Even at the present stage the cross-cut spinnaker goes a long way toward overcoming the weakest point in the design of most racing yachts—their limited sheeting base.

An essential consideration when making a spinnaker is the selection of the fabric weight and strength. If the material is too heavy, it will not set properly in light winds and will collapse in every lull, while if too light it will stretch and may even be damaged in stronger winds. The universal sail for all conditions does not exist, and it is true to say that the more universal it becomes, the less fitted it is for a specific use.

There is a strong body who opine that Nylon is the best available fabric for spinnakers. This is true in the case of the very deep parachute or balloon type spinnakers such as the Herbulot, where its large ductility has advantages, but is not so in the case of cross-cut reaching spinnakers, where it is imperative to prevent stretching to maintain the intended shape. Here Dacron, or any material having similar properties, is more suitable, as it stretches less.

Today, the spinnaker is not only a fair weather sail. One encounters storm spinnakers for heavy weather which are smaller and made of heavier fabric than the normal.

An interesting form of "twin spinnaker" intended for stronger winds was tried in one of the Atlantic Races. Figure 119 shows how this was made of two similar triangular sails. Since the point of application of the aerodynamic force is forward of that of the hull force, the yacht can be made "self-steering." If both sails are trimmed 20°–25° forward as in Fig. 119, this will be ensured. If the yacht shifts from the desired course before the wind, the leeward sail is blanketed by the other, and the resulting difference in the two sail forces produces a turning moment which corrects the yacht's course. This type of rig is easy to man and is particularly suitable for long-distance ocean sailing, as it saves a lot of work for the crew.

Fig. 119

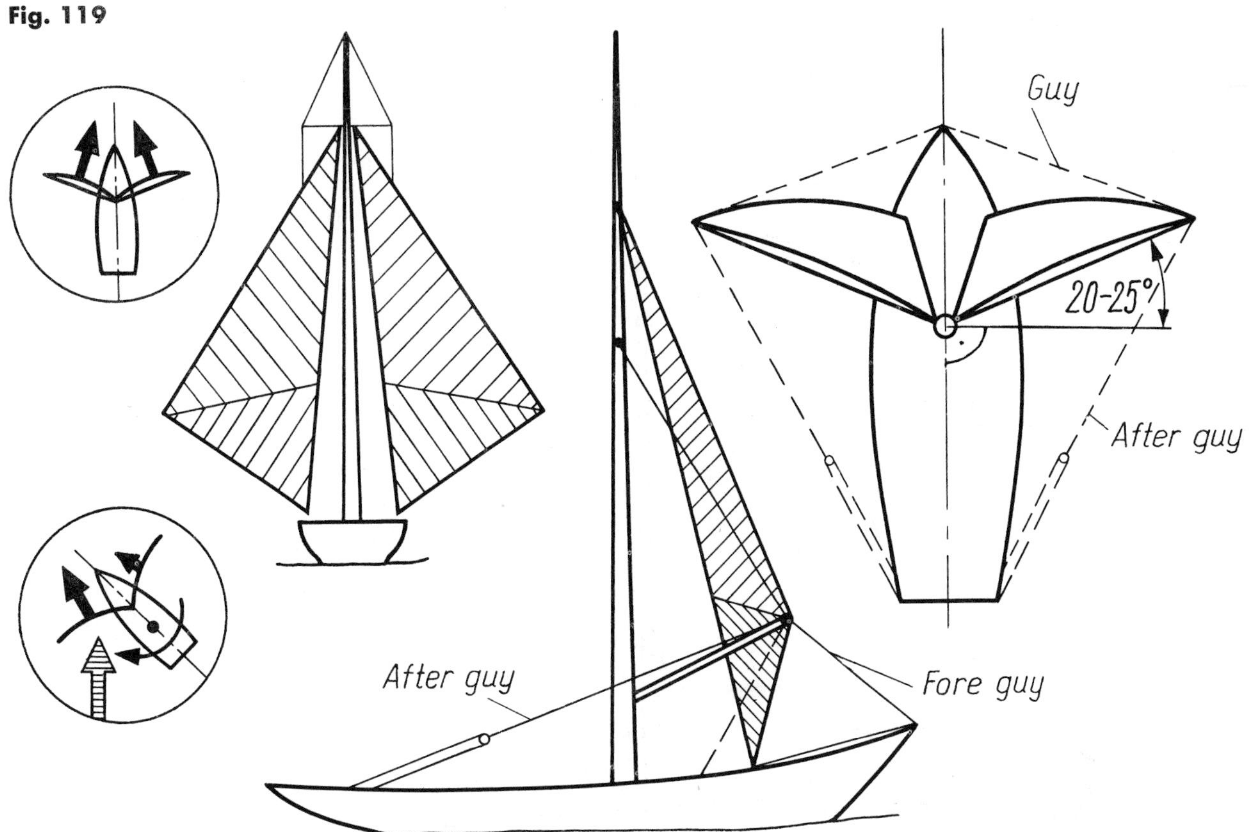

Cruising crews are, as a rule, not eager to use the spinnaker except on a dead run in light weather. The reason is easy to find. The main and fore sails, being suspended on the mast and forestay respectively, are easily controlled by a single sheet. On the other hand, the spinnaker, being freely suspended, is more difficult to control, particularly when reaching. It is enough to look at Fig. 120, showing the system for rigging a spinnaker, to appreciate the difference between handling it and a Bermudian mainsail. More so than other sails, it demands rapid and skillful cooperation between the spinnaker-man and the helmsman. In strong winds, when the sail can develop enormous forces, its handling may become a nightmare for an inexperienced crew. Working the spinnaker on the foredeck will be considerably simplified by having reliable, light and easily handled fittings enabling the boom to be handled with the minimum of fuss.

Trimming the spinnaker is effected by adjusting the positions of its head, tack, and clew, the last two of which interchange their names when jibing. The allowable clearance between the head of the spinnaker and the mast depends on the yacht's course, the cut of the sail, and the rolling characteristics of the yacht. When running, it is desirable to ease the halyard so that the sail can be set well forward to reduce the blanketing from the mainsail. The amount by which the halyard is eased is dictated by the lower parts of the sail, which should set roughly vertical. Excessive forward or backward slope is generally harmful.

If the yacht shows any tendency toward rolling, the clearance between the head of the sail and the mast becomes particularly important. It controls the way

Fig. 120

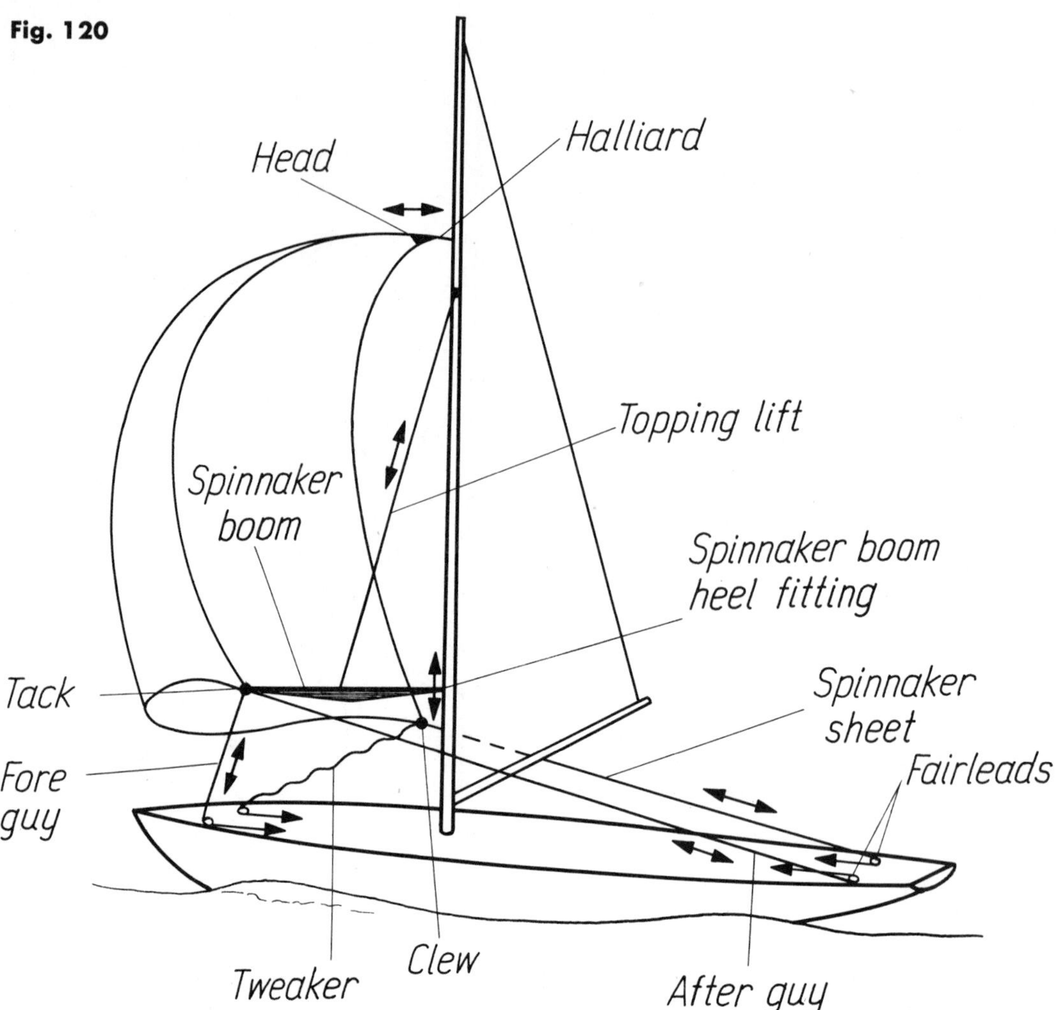

in which the sail swings relative to the mast. A critical distance can often be found, at which the swinging of the spinnaker magnifies the rolling of the yacht, and this, in turn, leads to collapse of the edges of the sail. In these circumstances one should depart from the critical condition by setting the sail either higher or lower.

The distance between the head of the spinnaker and the halyard sheave should be progressively reduced as one comes on the wind. The boom should be kept parallel to the water so that its full length is exploited. The slide fitting on the mast should be of ample length to allow the sail to be set high, improving its efficiency, since then the blanketing of the mainsail becomes less, the wind strength is greater, and the sneaker, or spinnaker staysail, works more effectively. In light winds lowering or dipping the boom will tauten the luff and prevent its collapsing. The fore- and after-guys and the topping lift together keep the boom steady and control its position in relation to the wind. It is usually set parallel to, or a little forward of, the line of the main boom (see Fig. 118). The best position for the tack of the spinnaker depends to a large extent on the way the sheets are arranged, which in turn fix the position of the clew. The positions of the tack and

Fig. 121

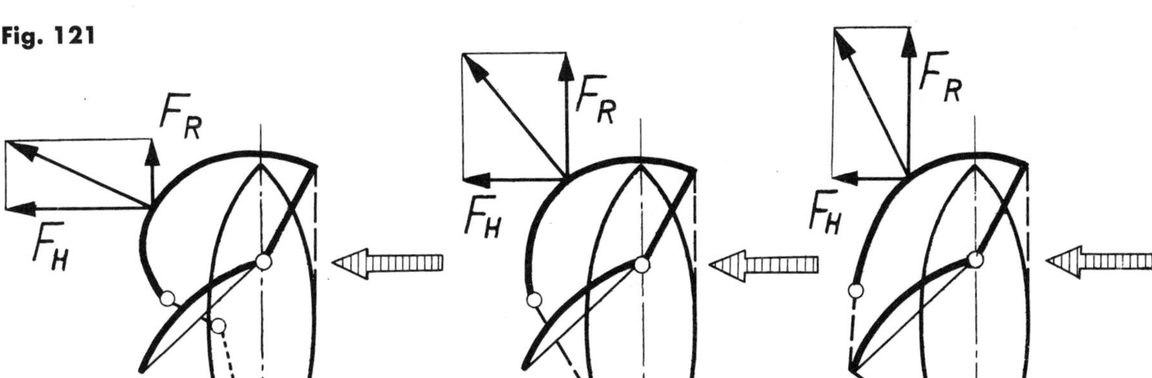

clew control the angle of incidence and, to some extent, the shape of the lower parts of the sail. Figure 121 shows some different ways of leading the sheets. A particularly effective way is to run the sheet through a block on the after end of the main boom, a method allowed under the R.O.R.C. Special Regulations. This arrangement gives the most effective combination of sail forces arising from the sail shape produced. A comparatively large driving force, F_R, is produced with a small heeling force, F_H.

Jibing a large spinnaker in a fresh breeze can be a dangerous undertaking. In extreme cases it is necessary to use the blanketing effect of a headsail or the mainsail. To obtain this one may have to bear away for a moment, taking care not to prematurely jibe the mainsail. Figure 122 shows how this is done on a cutter or a small yacht, using interchangeable guys and sheets. The spinnaker boom is double-ended so that either end can be fitted to the sail or the mast slider.

On larger yachts, where the loading on the spinnaker boom and therefore its weight are considerable, it is better to use a single-ended boom. In this case the topping lift is run to the end of the boom, rather than to the middle. When jibing, the boom is disconnected from the sail, passed under the forestay, and attached to the sail again, while the heel of the boom is secured all the time to the mast. This method can be applied to any yacht having sufficient distance from the mast to the forestay.

Fig. 122

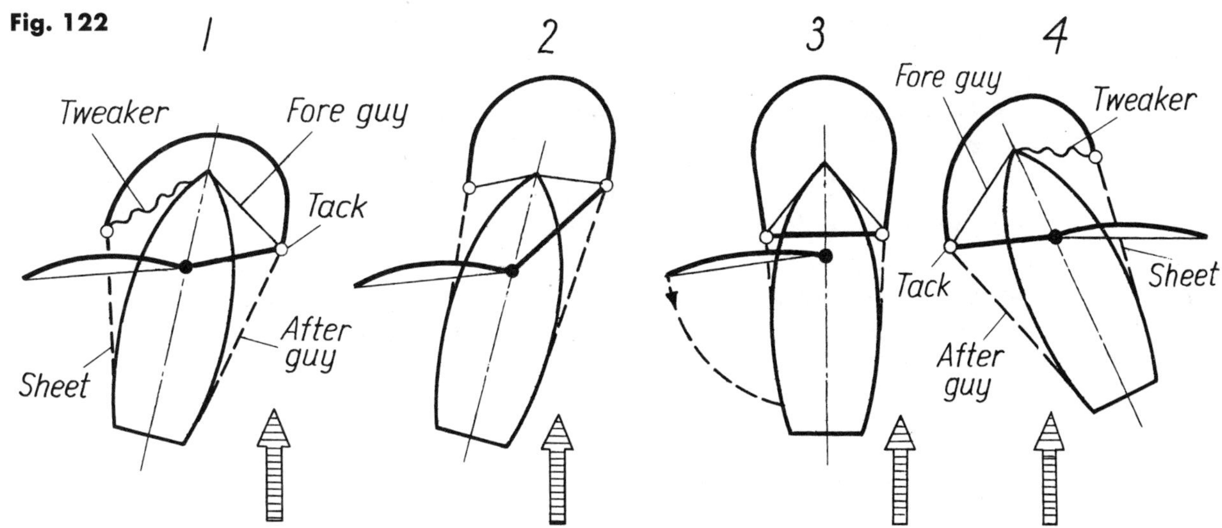

13. CENTER OF EFFORT

When discussing the suctions and pressures which are distributed over the leeward and windward sides of a sail in quite a complicated fashion, we found it convenient to assume that their effect could be represented by a single "total aerodynamic force, F_T" acting along a particular line. On Fig. 31b this line of action of the force F_T cut the sail at a point termed the "center of pressure." In sailing terminology this point is known as the "center of effort" (CE), and most books, when discussing this subject, assume that the CE remains stationary and lies at the geometrical center of area of the sail.

A typical method for determining the position of the CE is given in Fig. 123a, b. One first determines the geometric centers of area of the individual sails, CE_F and CE_M respectively for the foresail and mainsail (Fig. 123a). Then the line joining these two points is divided into two parts, by a simple geometrical construction, in proportion to the areas of each sail. Thus the common CE is found, being nearer the larger sail. In the Fig. 123b, the lengths CE_F-A and CE_M-B were drawn to scale representing the mainsail and foresail areas respectively. The line A-B then cut CE_F-CE_M at CE.

(a) Center of Effort and Its Relation to Directional Balance of a Yacht

The conventional method of finding the geometrical CE gives a point which does not, in fact, correspond with the true position of the "center of pressure." Nevertheless it has a certain practical value for yacht designers which helps them to evaluate the directional balance of a design. In reality the true CE changes its position within wide limits, and for the majority of courses is in front of the geometrical CE.

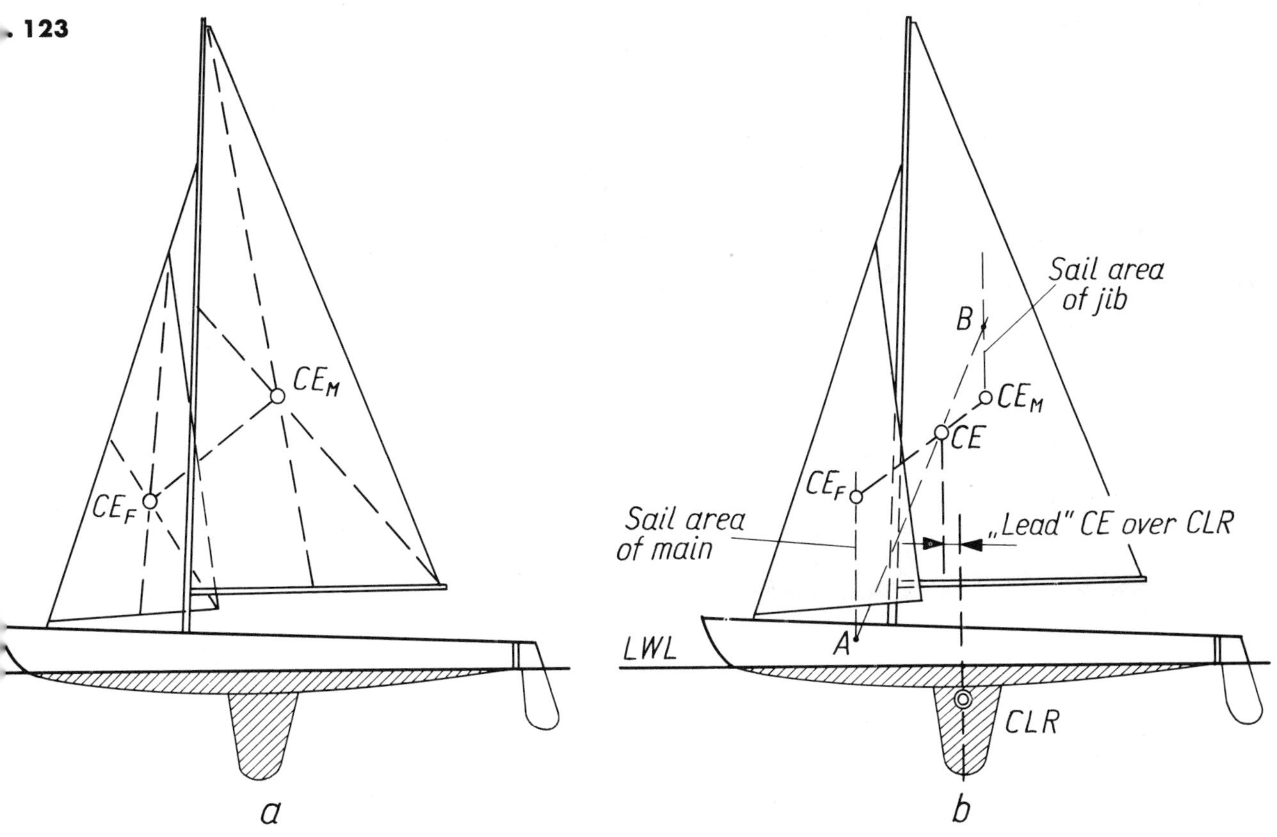

The effects due to errors in fixing the CE of the aerodynamic forces are partly compensated for by similar errors arising from the determination of the "center of lateral resistance," CLR. This point is taken as the geometrical center of area of the submerged hull and fin when viewed from the side, and does not usually include the rudder area (Fig. 123b). Once again, the CLR is not in reality a fixed point but moves about as the hull changes its attitude. The true CLR is forward of the geometrical CLR when close-hauled, and shifts aft as one bears away.

The method of finding the CE and the CLR (shown in Fig. 123) allows an approximate evaluation of the close-hauled directional balance of a yacht to be made. A balance is found when the total aerodynamic force F_T and the total hydrodynamic force R_T act along the same line. If they do not act in the same line, but are separated by some distance "a" known as the "unbalance arm" (Fig. 40a), then some steady compensation with the rudder will be necessary to keep a steady course. In other words, if F_T is aft of R_T by the distance "a," weather helm must be applied to react against the luffing moment $F_T \times a$ (equal to $R_T \times a$). The magnitude of the unbalance arm "a" determines whether the yacht is balanced and, to some extent, whether it is well tempered or hard mouthed. A yacht which is not well balanced is likely to be slow, since it requires constant rudder, with its resulting resistance, to keep on course and is difficult to steer as every wind change causes it to luff or bear away.

As a rule, designers' calculations of CE and CLR are made treating the wind and

Fig. 124

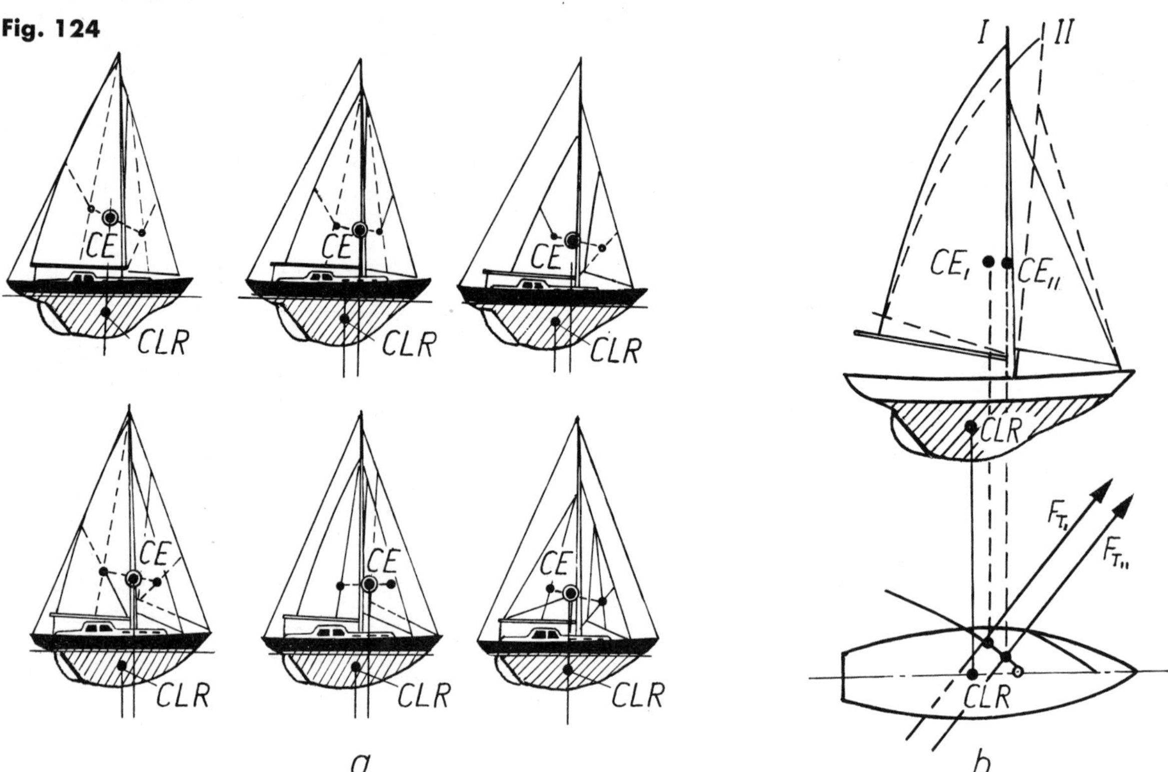

water forces as acting on the unheeled centerline plane. Figure 40 shows how the effect of heel and also the displacement of the sails from the yacht's centerline can give an unbalance arm "a" when the CE is vertically above the CLR, when the yacht is viewed from abeam. Designers compensate for this in a rule-of-thumb manner, by shifting their CE in front of the CLR by an amount termed the "lead." Many books express this "lead" as a proportion of the waterline length of the hull, but opinions among authors vary, the "lead" being given variously as anything from 0 per cent to 20 per cent of the waterline length. The success, or otherwise, of this somewhat arbitrary correction can be gauged by the number of ill-balanced boats one encounters.

Due to the shortcomings of design, it is often necessary to tune a yacht's balance. In practice it is not usually feasible to change the shape of the hull or keel, and so tuning becomes a matter of adjusting the position of the sailplan, or the sailplan itself, in relation to the hull. Shifting the mast in the appropriate direction or reapportioning the total sail area between main and fore sails can work wonders to the directional balance of a yacht.

Figure 124a illustrates how the geometrical CE shifts on a sloop and a cutter for different sail arrangements. When reefing or changing sails for different weather conditions, some attention should be paid to the effect on the yacht's balance. Selecting sails thoughtlessly can ruin the balance, which in bad weather can lead to getting in irons or broaching-to.

The effect of mast rake on the helm is shown in Fig. 124b. A yacht which originally carried weather helm can, after raking the mast forward, even carry lee helm. It should be emphasized, however, that when making any changes of this sort one must also ensure correct trim of the sails, as these also have a profound effect on the balance. As in most things, a compromise must be found. It is of little use balancing the boat perfectly if by so doing one seriously impairs the efficiency of the sails.

(b) Movement of the True CE

With the help of experiments on aerofoils of different aspect ratio and camber it was confirmed that the true CE (i.e., center of pressure) varies its position as the angle of incidence α is altered. For small angles α, the true CE lies near the leading edge, and as α is increased to 90°, it shifts toward the center of area, i.e., toward the geometrical CE.

Figure 125 demonstrates this phenomenon for an aerofoil of aspect ratio A.R. = 5 and 1/10 camber. For convenience, the position of the true CE is given as

Fig. 125

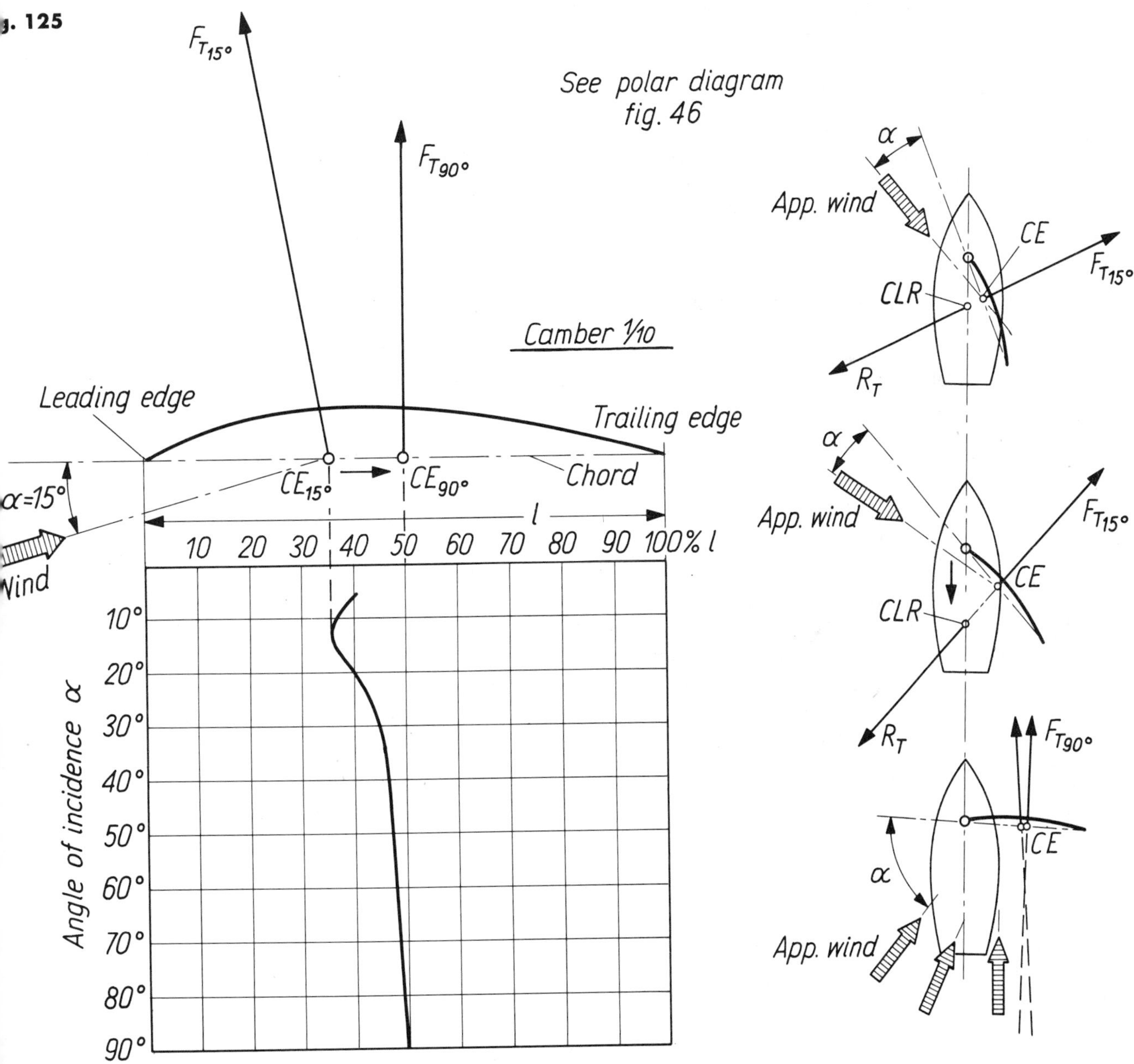

a percentage of the chord length, l, measured from the leading edge. It is easy, in general terms, to see why this occurs. At the smaller angles of incidence, the pressure distribution on the sail (see Figs. 31, 35, 38, 39) is characterized by a large suction near the luff, on the leeward side, and hence the resultant total force F_T is well forward. As the incidence increases and the sail stalls, the distribution of pressures and suctions becomes more uniform (see Fig. 39b) and the resultant total force tends to act nearer the center of area. On the graph (Fig. 125) are shown also two specific cases, forces F_{T15} and F_{T90}, for angles of incidence of 15° and 90°. The former would be appropriate for courses from close-hauled to a reach and the latter represents a dead run. The three sketches on Fig. 125 show how widely traveled is the intersection point of F_T on the yacht's centerline. When close-hauled, when the true CE is at about 35 per cent of the sail chord, the intersection point is a little aft, at about 50 per cent of the sail chord. This has the effect of making the designers' assumption about the geometrical CE being reasonable. As one comes off the wind, however, the intersection point moves aft rapidly until, on a run, F_T never intersects the hull centerline. Since the yacht, under the action of sail, hull, and rudder forces, must be in balance, it follows that the resultant force R_T of the hull and rudder must always exactly balance the sail force F_T. Thus in all cases R_T must pass through the true CE and the point of intersection of F_T with the hull centerline. How exactly it does this will be dealt with in Part III when we discuss the way in which hull and rudder contribute toward the resultant water force R_T.

The position of the CE will also depend on the camber of the sail. This has some practical significance, since a yacht will tend to have lee helm when a flat sail is changed for one with considerable camber. Figure 126 shows how the CE shifts for three aerofoils, all of aspect ratio A.R. = 5 but having cambers of $1/7$ (14.3 per cent), 1/13.5 (7.4 per cent), and $1/27$ (3.7 per cent). We can see that the resultant aerodynamic force F_T in the case of a fairly flat (camber $1/27$) sail, at a representative angle of incidence $\alpha = 14°$ is about 4 per cent of the sail chord forward of those with some curvature. The small inset to the figure shows how this must influence the position of the CLR, the shift in practice being accomplished by use of the rudder. Once again, on a run, when the sail incidence is near 90°, the CE's tend toward the center of area.

The general pattern of events shown in Fig. 125, for an aspect ratio A.R. = 5 is also true for sails of other aspect ratios. Since, however, the shifts were expressed as percentages of the chord l, it follows that sails with a low aspect ratio, and therefore a relatively large chord, will experience a larger shift in CE than those of high aspect ratio. In other words, shift in CE for a gaff-rigged yacht will be greater than for a Bermudian yacht. In the design stage, when one is assessing directional balance, this fact must be borne in mind. If the yacht is not to be hopelessly out of balance as one comes off the wind, one should give more lead for a sail rig of low aspect ratio, even though this may entail some slight out of balance when close-hauled.

Fig. 126

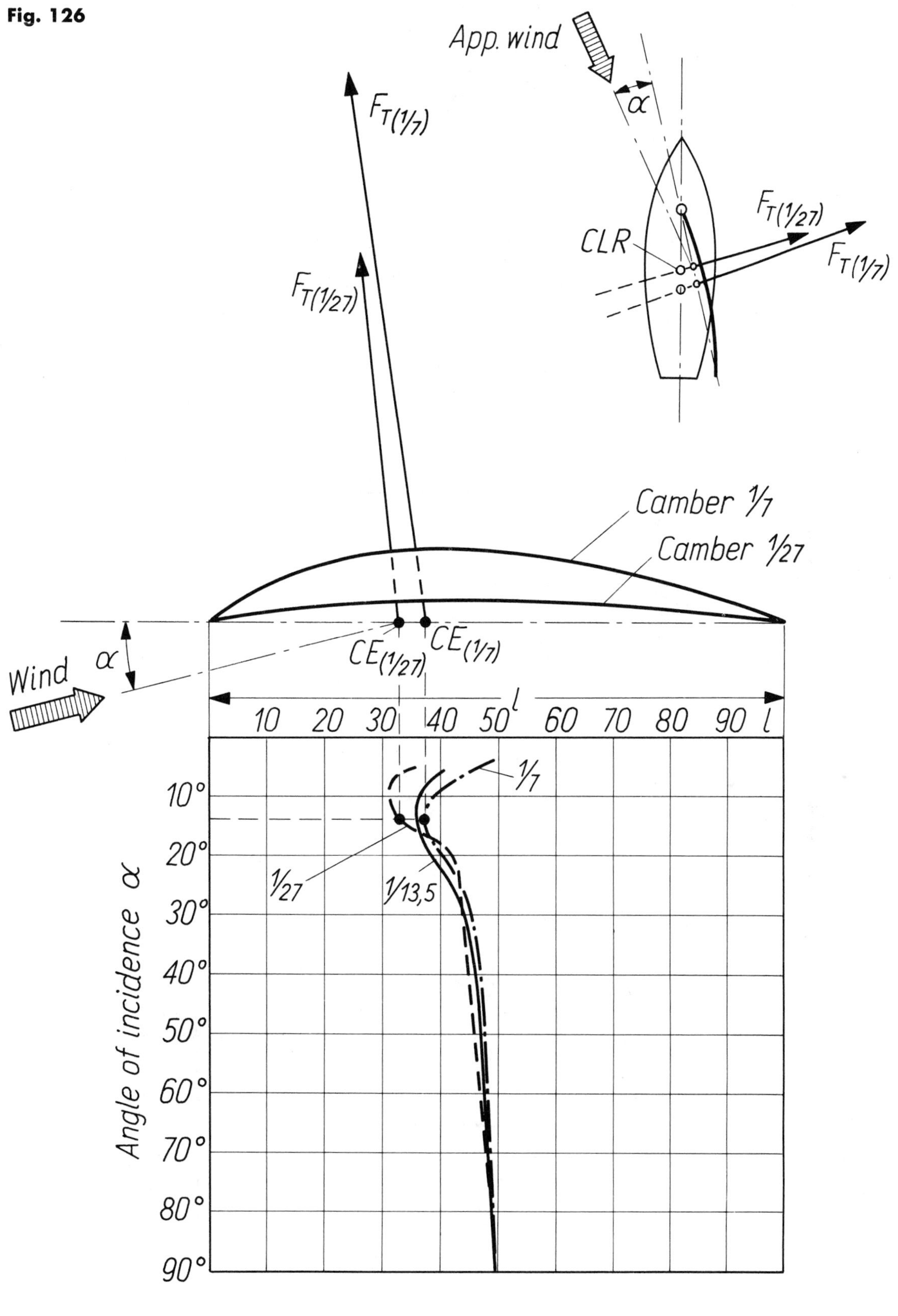

App. wind
α
$F_{T(1/7)}$
$F_{T(1/27)}$
CLR
$F_{T(1/27)}$
$F_{T(1/7)}$
Camber 1/7
Camber 1/27
Wind
α
$CE_{(1/27)}$
$CE_{(1/7)}$
l
10 20 30 40 50 60 70 80 90 l
1/7
1/27
1/13,5
10° 20° 30° 40° 50° 60° 70° 80° 90°
Angle of incidence α

Fig. 127

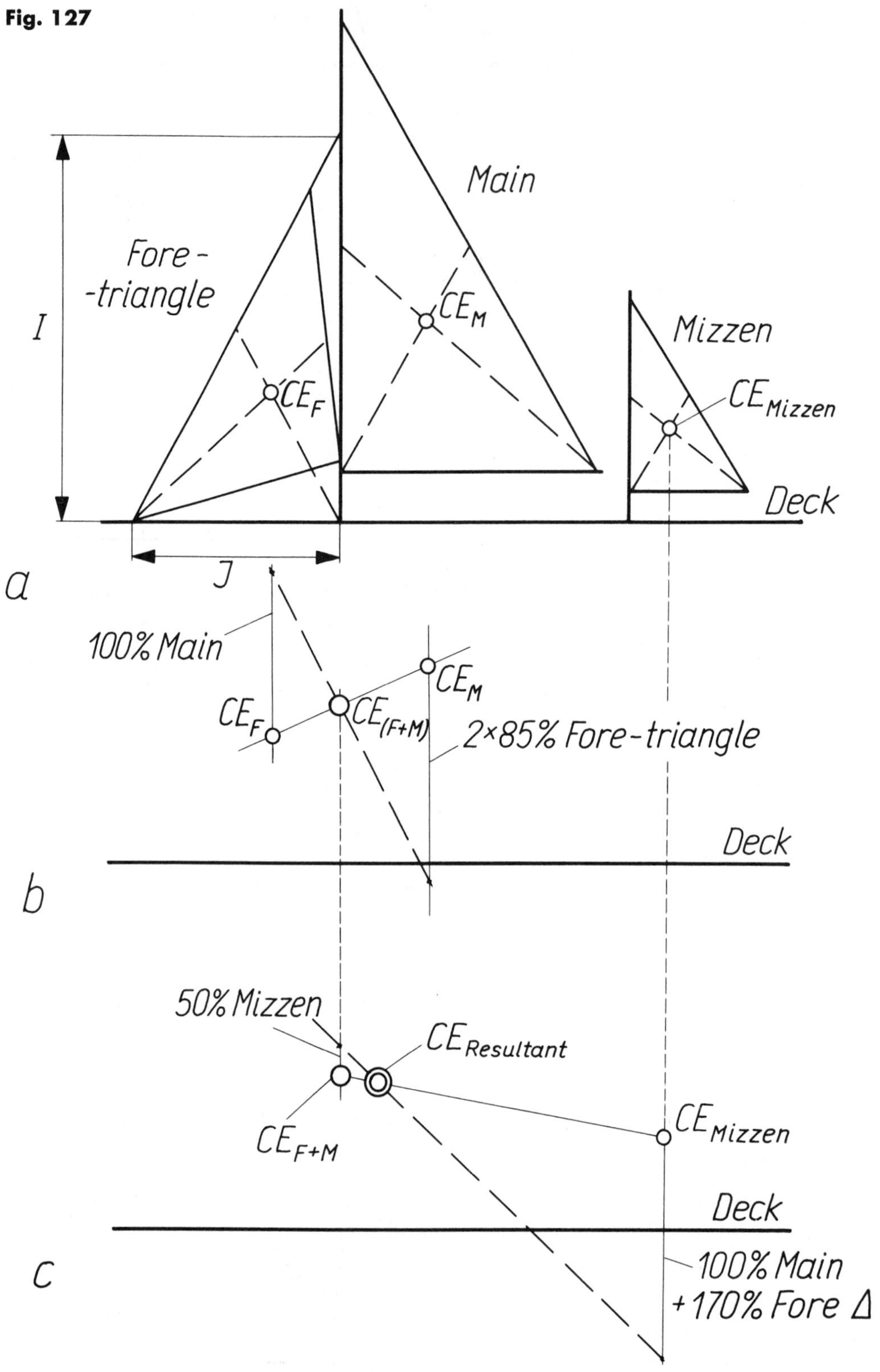

Main
Fore -
-triangle
I
CE_M
Mizzen
CE_F
CE_{Mizzen}
Deck
J
a
100% Main
CE_M
CE_F
$CE_{(F+M)}$
2×85% Fore-triangle
Deck
b
50% Mizzen
$CE_{Resultant}$
CE_{F+M}
CE_{Mizzen}
Deck
c
100% Main
+170% Fore Δ

(c) CE for the Combination of Main, Mizzen and Fore Sails

When considering the CE for the combination of several interacting sails it is necessary to bear in mind their relative aerodynamic efficiencies. From the analysis of the pressure distributions on the main and fore sails we learned that the mean pressure on the latter can be twice that of the mainsail, if it is permitted by the sheeting. The efficiency of the mainsail, because of the influence of the mast and possible backwinding, is generally lower than that of headsails. It would be incorrect therefore to assume that the resultant CE for these two sails is related directly to their separate areas, as was done in Fig. 123b. The question of what one can assume, however, is difficult to answer. Certainly it would be an unjustifiable simplification to assume a twofold efficiency for headsails.

A reasonable assumption is adopted by the Davidson Laboratory of the Stevens Institute of Technology, when balancing fore, main, and mizzen sails. Firstly they find the geometrical CE for each sail as in Fig. 127a. The mainsail is then rated at 100 per cent of its area and the foresail as $2 \times 0.85 \times (I \times J)/2$, i.e., as double the area $0.85 \times (I \times J)/2$ used in Rating Rules.

Figure 127b shows how these two "effective areas" are combined, at the true centers of area, to give the $CE_{(F+M)}$ for fore and main sails.

When the yacht has a mizzen, it is assessed at 50 per cent of its area, and this is again placed at its center of area. Its efficiency is assessed so low because of interference from the mainsail as well as its own mast. The final $CE_{Resultant}$ for all the sails is then determined as in Fig. 127c.

The prediction of directional balance, using these arbitrary simplifications, has been found in practice to be quite successful.

The dependence of the position of the CE on the aerodynamic efficiency of the separate sails is very often confirmed when tuning racing yachts. Merely by altering the trim of the sails one can make, or mar, the directional balance. At the risk of stating the obvious, it must be emphasized that before making radical changes to the sailplan or its position on the hull, one should ensure that the sails are properly trimmed. While performance and not balance should be the primary objective, yet at the same time, optimum performance will rarely be achieved where the balance is bad.

14. SOME REMARKS ABOUT CUT, SET, AND DEFECTS OF SAILS

This quiet sail is as a noiseless wing
To waft me from distraction;

BYRON, "Childe Harold's Pilgrimage"

Any helmsman who wants to improve the performance of his yacht should be capable of judging the quality of the sails, i.e., their curved shape, on which largely depends their aerodynamic efficiency.

Assuming that the sail is sewn of a good fabric, it should also possess:

1. A suitable profile (camber shape) at all heights
2. Freedom from irregularities such as creases, folds, bulky seams
3. The maximum dimensions allowed under the class rules or in the specification

Irrespective of what fabric the sail is made of (cotton, Nylon, Dacron/Terylene, etc.) its shape (1–3 above), predetermined by the cut, will also undergo to some extent changes in use. Cotton, of course, will be more affected than man-made fibers such as Dacron/Terylene. For these reasons it is up to the helmsman to watch for any changes and eventually to make some correction to the cut.

Even ordering a sail from a reputable sailmaker does not always ensure a perfect fit. Sailmaking is still largely a craft, and this means that to some extent the mistakes of their predecessors are perpetuated by the sailmakers, under the title of tradition. Only recently has science been allowed to help improve the art.

The best way to learn the importance of cut on sail performance would be by making one's own sail. Indeed, this is within the scope of owners of sailing dinghies, but as a rule, most people are afraid to try. They even prefer not to correct the obvious faults in their existing sails, relying rather on the help of a sailmaker. There must, inevitably, be some lack of rapport between the helmsman who knows his boat and sails intimately in varied conditions and the sailmaker who does not, and who even speaks a different "language." A fine example of the benefits of self-help can be found in Paul Elvstrom, many times world champion in the Finn class, who developed his well-known sailmaking business from being an amateur sewing his own sails. In any case, even if one is not interested in sewing one's own sails, it is useful to learn some fundamental facts about them to find a common language with the sailmaker, without which it is quite difficult to specify one's requirements when ordering a new sail or correcting an old one. The following factors will therefore be discussed in some detail:

1. The properties of the fabrics used in sailmaking
2. Fundamentals of sail cutting
3. How defects in sails are commonly caused
4. How to estimate the quality of a sail

(a) Properties of Sail Fabrics

A sail during its lifetime is subject to variable, and often very strong, forces from the wind, sheets and halyards. These forces produce a state of tension in the fabric under which the sail deforms, often to the detriment of its performance.

Because of the way fabrics are woven, they do not stretch equally in all directions under equal loadings. A woven fabric consists of straight threads called the weft, interwoven by perpendicular threads called the warp. Because the warp threads are not straight, but zigzag round the weft, they have less resistance to stretching than the latter. Hence if a fabric is loaded equally along the warp and weft, the strain, or extension expressed as a percentage of the original length, will be greater along the warp than the weft. Loading, however, need not be confined to these two directions, and it is found that if a sailcloth is loaded diagonally it stretches far more. Thus the strain in a cotton duck, after certain steady equal loadings (Fig. 128a), will be as follows:

	along warp	along weft	along diagonal
strain (stretch as percentage of length)	9%	7.5%	24%

A similar relationship is found for Dacron, but the values are only ⅓ to ⅒ of those for cotton.

Because of the very much more ductility along the diagonal than along the warp or weft, a loading in this direction will produce creases. A simple experiment with a handkerchief will show that when a uniform tension is applied along the warp or weft, the surface of the fabric remains smooth, while a similar tension along the diagonal will produce creases.

The diagonal stability will depend on the tightness of the weave—or in other words, the number of threads per inch—being best for a tightly woven cloth. For

Fig. 128

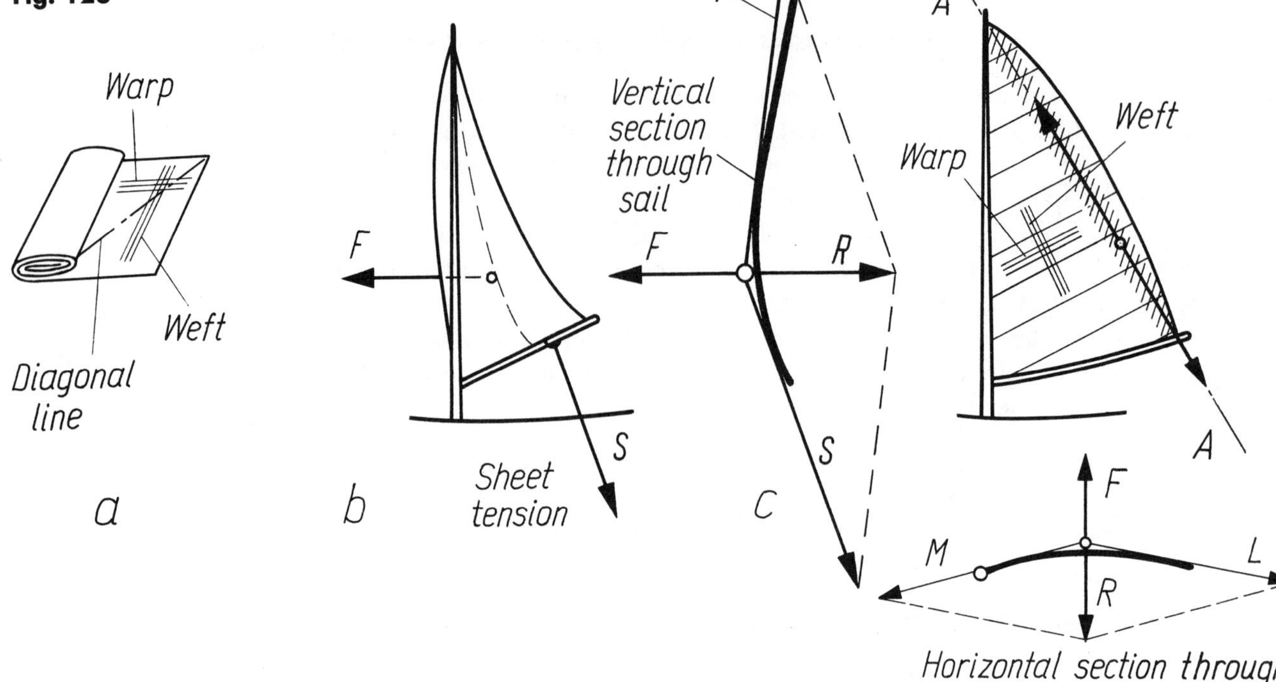

instance, a good sailcloth of 4 oz./sq. yd. weight should have more than 100 threads per inch for both warp and weft. This is particularly important for the synthetic fibers such as Dacron, which are too smooth to bind well, compared with cotton. The poor diagonal stability of Dacron for this reason is now improved by calendering, in which the fabric is passed through heated rollers so that the yarns fuse together and the surface becomes smooth and glossy. This process is itself not very effective if the initial weave is too loose. If this is so, in use, particularly in strong winds when tensions are large and the sail flaps frequently, the yarns tend to separate again. The material thus returns to its original state before calendering, and this is revealed by what was previously a well-cut sail suddenly going out of shape. It is therefore spoiled as a racing sail. The lighter fabrics, and particularly those with relatively few threads per inch, are very prone to spoiling through this cause.

Another reason for having a tight weave is that it reduces porosity, which in general is harmful in that it tends to equalize the pressures on the two sides of the sail.

One can therefore say that, for a cloth of given weight, the tighter the weave the better.

When making a sail the properties of the fabric should be borne in mind, so that the cloth is disposed in such a way that the warp and weft lie along the lines of greatest tension. For example, consider the Bermudian sail of Fig. 128b, c with the aerodynamic force F. This must be balanced by an equal and opposite force R from the sail. The force R can only be obtained from the tensions in the sail, and using the parallelogram of forces construction, it could be split into two components, S and T, in the line of the dotted sail section shown in the Fig. 128b, acting tangentially to the sail curvature. The "vertical" components of S and T (Fig. 128c) must be equal for balance. The force S must come from the tension in the mainsheet, and is balanced by the fabric tension T. It is clear that the tension forces in the fabric are considerably greater than the aerodynamic force F causing them.

In practice, of course, the problem of determining the tensions in the fabric is far more complex, as it has curvature in all directions and the aerodynamic force is distributed over its surface, but one can say that the magnitude of the tensions in the fabric will depend on the sail curvature, being greatest when sailing to windward, when the sail is fairly flat. When reaching, the boom lifts and the increased fullness of the sail lowers the tensions in it.

In a similar way we could consider the force F as being opposed by sail forces L and M acting along the warp (Fig. 128d). These forces eventually terminate at the mast and the very much less well supported leech. The latter can only be held in place by tension along A-A, from the mainsheet pull, and in strong winds will tend to sag forward and to leeward, deforming the sail, and shifting aft the point of maximum camber.

We can see that the maximum sail tensions are along the lines parallel to A-A, and therefore the cloths should be laid so as best to resist this loading. This is particularly true for cotton sails, nearly all of which are constructed as in Fig. 128d. Dacron's greater resistance to stretch allows more latitude in the way it is made, as, for example, in Fig. 142a, b, in which the warp carries the largest loadings.

Thus in order to sew a sail, one must first understand the forces within it and the nature of the fabric, and hence arrange the panels accordingly. Of course, the method of construction will not prevent its deformation in use if the fabric used is not strong enough. From many years experience, sailmakers have learned the best fabrics to use on different sized sails, for different purposes and weather conditions. In practice they describe the strength of the fabric by its weight, and have established such data as the graph shown in Fig. 129, giving the recommended weight of sailcloth (Dacron) for various sails for Ocean Racers. Lighter fabrics can be used for inshore work. A word of warning is necessary here. The horizontal scale of the graph in ounces per square yard is British usage, where a normal width of sailcloth is one yard. In the United States, fabric weight is quoted per yard run for a standard cloth width of 28½″. Since people often loosely refer to a cloth as of such a weight, in ounces only, one should check whether they mean the American cloth or the lighter British cloth. For example, a British 6-oz. cloth is equivalent to 4.8-oz. American cloth.

Many yachtsmen prefer to have heavier and thicker sails than strength considerations would dictate, for ease of handling and long life. This is the right approach if only one suit of sails is envisaged, but it must be remembered that there is no universal sail giving optimum performance in all conditions. Depending on the

Fig. 129

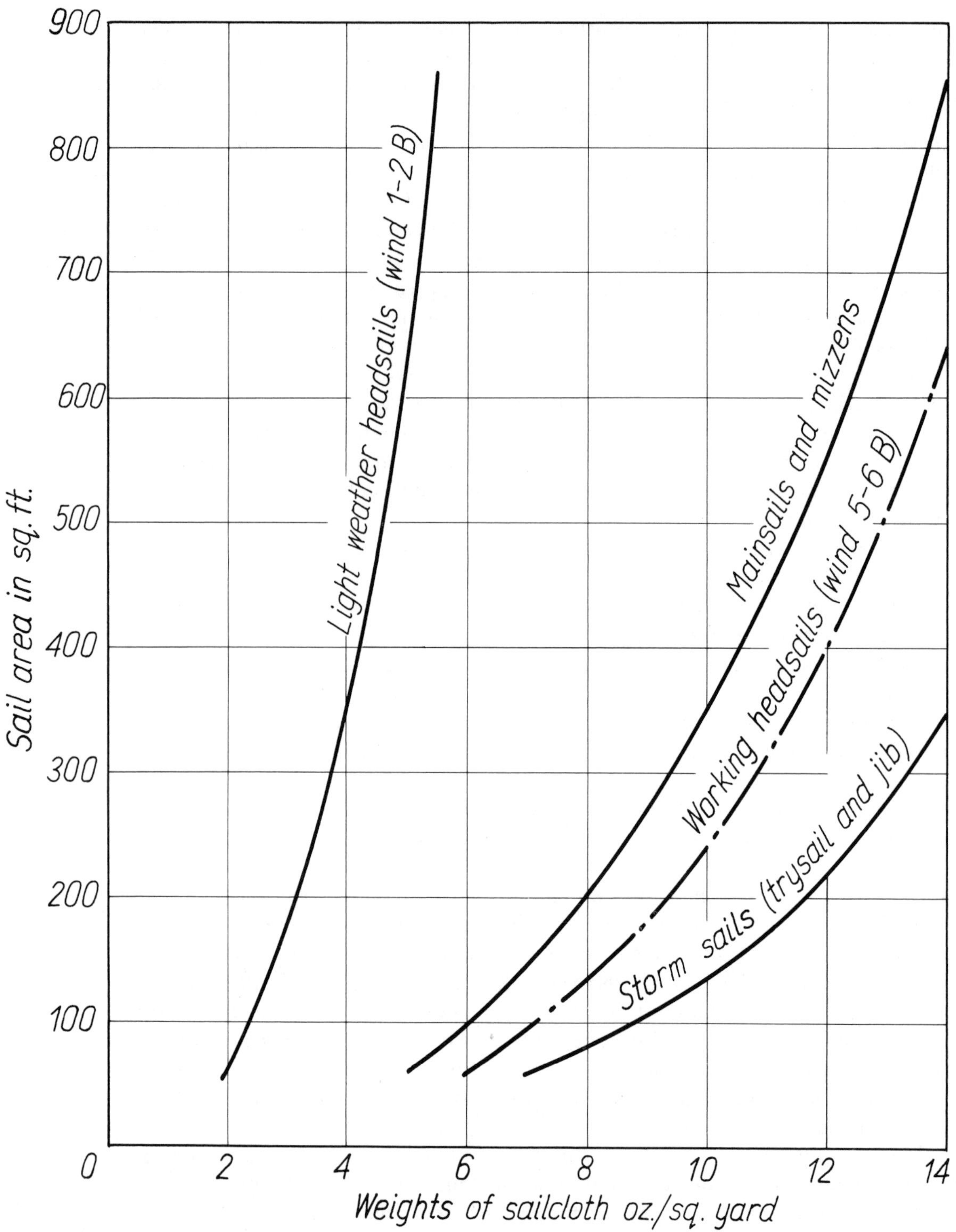

900
800
700
600
500
400
300
200
100
0
2
4
6
8
10
12
14
Sail area in sq. ft.
Weights of sailcloth oz./sq. yard
Light weather headsails (wind 1-2 B)
Mainsails and mizzens
Working headsails (wind 5-6 B)
Storm sails (trysail and jib)

weather, one requires sails of different fabric weights and cut for really serious racing.

Contrary to popular opinion, it does not pay to use the lightest sails possible in light airs, particularly if the water is choppy. Using a heavier fabric, the sail keeps its shape better as the mast swings, and does not hang down lifelessly like a curtain. For these reasons there is a growing tendency in racing circles to use somewhat heavier sails in light winds, in spite of them being too strong and the increased difficulty sailmakers have in successfully cutting the heavier-weight cloths. Particularly with such sails, one must be careful to avoid creasing them in storage, as a heavy synthetic material may hold a crease in a light wind. If necessary they should be pressed with a not too hot iron, and it is better to keep the mainsail on the boom than in a sail bag.

(b) Principles of Cutting the Mainsail

From old paintings we are quite familiar with the simple square sail (Fig. 130a). Under the action of the wind it attains a certain camber f, and in so doing, the free edges are pulled inward by an amount X. The original width AB is reduced by 2X, and if we wished to retain straight sides to the sail when set, it would be necessary to add some excess width to the sail (as shown in Fig. 130b). The amount of extra material required for this camber could be found by measuring the curved profile between the points 1 and 2 (equal to A-B) and subtracting the straight distance 1–2.

The above example gives the general idea behind the so-called surplus of sailcloth method which still forms the basis for cutting most sails of small or medium camber.

Let us now consider a cotton Bermudian sail set on a straight, rigid mast and boom. To obtain some camber one must add excess cloth along the luff and foot.

Fig. 130

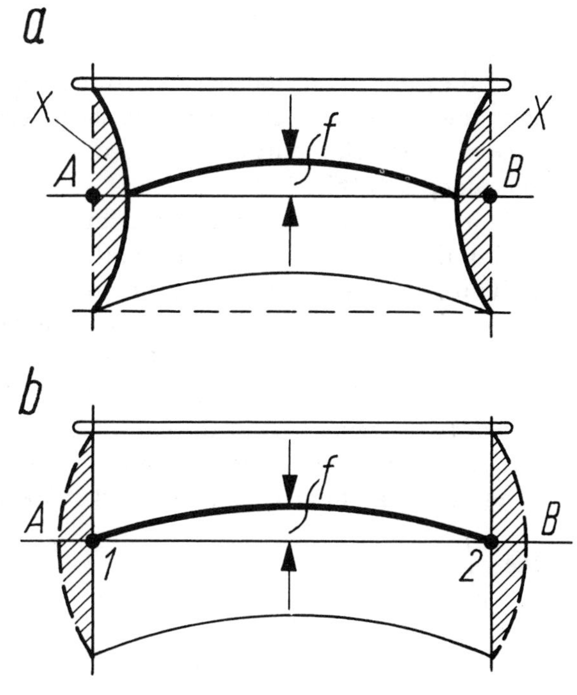

a

X X f A B

b

f A B 1 2

Fig. 131

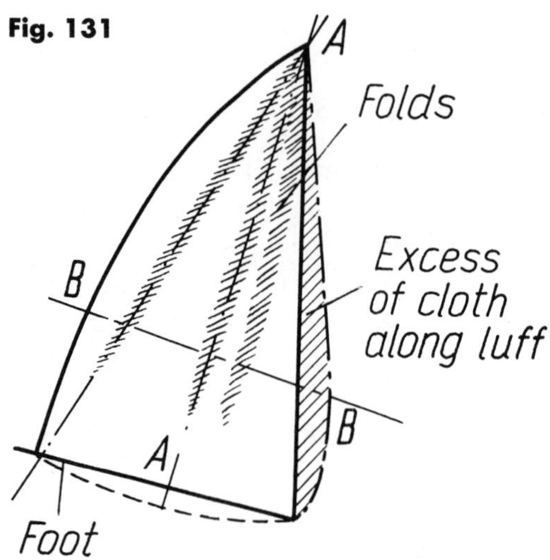

This is because the sail curves in all directions and thus, for example, excess length is required along both A-A and B-B (Fig. 131) to allow the point of intersection of these two lines to move out of the flat original plane of the sail. If these excess lengths are not in the correct proportion, creases will appear in the sail. If, say, no or insufficient allowance was made on the foot, the creases would be along lines approximately parallel to A-A, due to uneven loading of the warp and weft.

The appearance of such creases points to faulty cutting, and they can only satisfactorily be removed by recutting the sail such that the tensions within it are more evenly distributed. This is the primary aim of the sailmaker, and one which is not easy to fulfill, especially for a variety of weather conditions. Indeed, it is axiomatic that a sail has only a limited range of wind speed in which it will set well. Above or below this range, it will not be wholly satisfactory.

The second difficult problem which arises in sail cutting is the provision of the correct allowances to compensate for stretch, which depends on not only the shape of the sail in a given wind strength, and the pressure distribution on it, but also the type and quality of the sailcloth. The stretch in the vertical direction is in general greater than that parallel to the foot. This is because the forces along the mast due to the halyard and mainsheet tensions are larger than the horizontal forces from the clew outhaul, and also because the curvature along A-A is less than that along B-B (Fig. 131).

Bearing this fact in mind, the length h of the luff (Fig. 132a) is reduced when cutting the sail by Δh, and the length of the foot by Δl, where Δh is greater than Δl. Thus if the sail must fall on the points A, B, D to conform with the class rules, it must be cut as A, B_1, D_1, as in the figure. The length BC of the headboard suffers no change, i.e., $B_1C_1 = BC$, and also the amount and shape of the roach, which in most classes is controlled by limiting the dimension "m."

Nearly the whole art of the sailmaker lies in correctly estimating the amount and shape of excess material (shown shaded in Fig. 132b) to be added to the edges of the sail to give it its required shape after stretching.

The stretching allowance Δh on the luff, for a cotton sail, is about 2.5–4.0 per cent of the luff length h; for a heavy-weather sail the allowance is rather greater. Dacron stretches only ⅓ to ⅒ of that of cotton, the final amount depending largely on the degree of calendering, and hence the allowance Δh will be 0.25–1.3 per cent of h.

The percentage allowance Δl on the foot l should be close to, but not exceed, ½ of those given for the luff, for both cotton and Dacron.

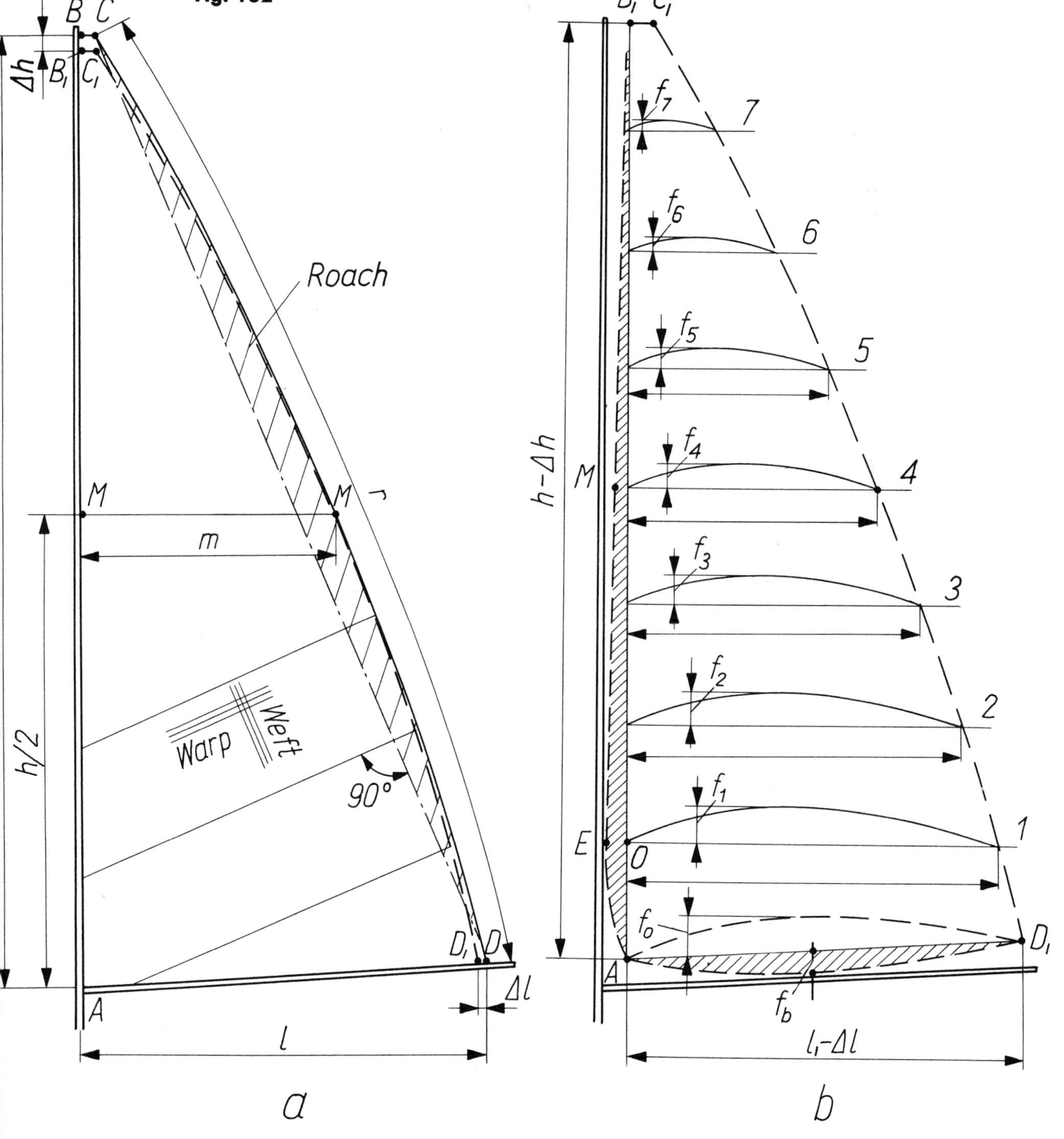

When a new cotton sail is used for the first few times, it suffers some permanent stretch along the luff and leech and as a result the dimension m (Fig. 132a), which is frequently taken as a measure of the roach, has a tendency to reduce. Therefore, when making the sail, the dimension M-M should not be reduced; on the contrary, it would be better to increase it a little and ensure that the sail is fully stretched before it is measured. This comment applies mainly to light-weather sails, where the maximum possible sail area is desired.

When cutting the leech to a measurement, once again some allowance should be made for stretch. If the fabric is badly chosen, the stretch on the leech can be as much as 10 per cent of its length. For a good quality cotton duck of the correct weight, the stretch should not exceed 2 per cent; for Dacron a figure of ⅓ to ⅒ of this should be expected.

Frequently sailmakers overestimate the stretch Δh and Δl, allowing for 4–6 per cent of the length, with the result that in use the sails do not pull out to the marks on mast-end boom fixed by the class rules. Some yachtsmen attempt to gain the full area by using excessive tension on the halyard and clew outhaul, but this is definitely the greater of the two evils. It is better to have somewhat less than maximum area than to obtain it by seriously distorting the sail. There is no real difficulty in recutting a sail if it is too large, and therefore it is better to make the sail too big rather than too small in the first place.

When sewing the bolt ropes to the sail the allowances Δh and Δl should be remembered when cutting the ropes to length.

Once the corrections Δh and Δl for stretching of the luff and foot have been decided, the next step will be to draw the curves defining the desired camber at various stations on the sail (Fig. 132b). If, say, the basic sail, allowing for stretch, is A, B, C, D, it can be divided into several sections 1, 2, etc. At these sections one draws the desired profile of, say, a circular arc of camber ⅒ of the chord, i.e., $f_1 = \frac{1}{10} L_1$, etc. If the mast is assumed rigid (reasonable for the majority of boats), one normally provides for the camber by allowing excess material in the luff, equal to the difference between the arc length and the chord length. Thus at section 1 the allowance EO is equal to the difference between 0 and 1 via the arc and the straight line l_1. If the camber is maintained at ⅒ for all sections, the excess cloth required will be 2.7 per cent of the local chord lengths. For other cambers, say, 1/20, 1/15, 1/13, 1/7, the allowances would be 0.7 per cent, 1.2 per cent, 1.6 per cent, and 5.4 per cent, respectively.

After fixing the curvature in the luff one should check and then alter the curve of the roach in such a way that the distance M-M falls within the class rules. In this connection it is worthwhile warning against the use of too much roach in an effort to gain sail area. This gives trouble in strong winds when the roach tends to move forward to give a straight leech (Fig. 133a). The basic reason for this behavior results from the increased camber as the wind strength increases, which is only resisted by the battens and the tensions of the mainsheet. Eventually the battens become ineffective, and folds appear on the sail at the inboard ends of the

Fig. 133

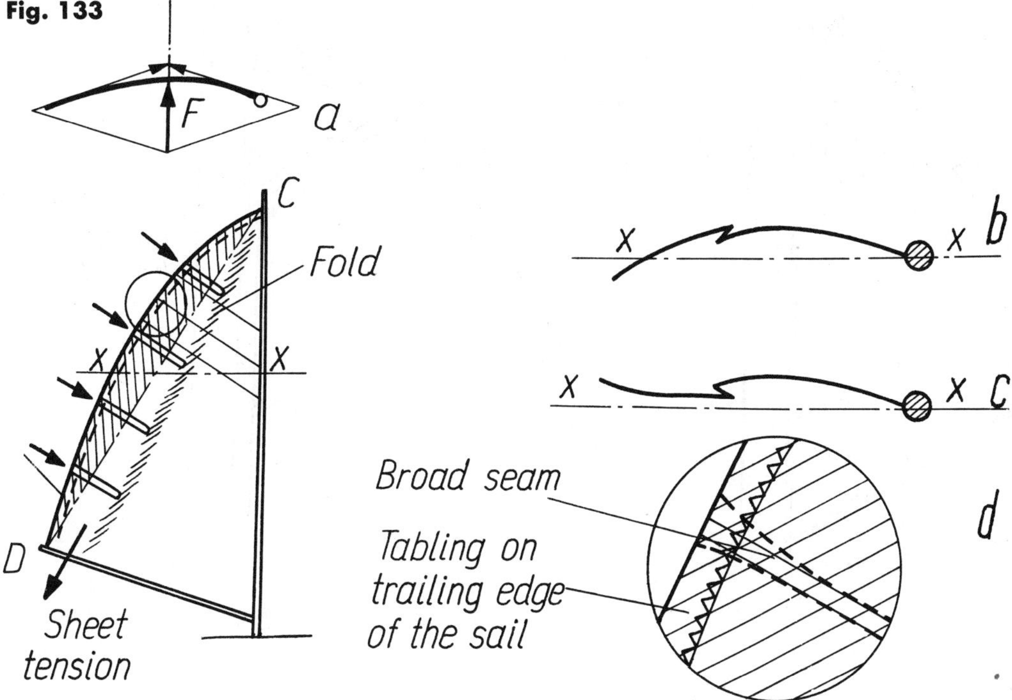

battens, and wrinkles throughout the roach. The creases can be of two types (shown in Fig. 133b, c). In the case b the portion of the sail, aft of the crease at the foot of the battens, curves to windward, continuing or exaggerating the curve of the sail. This is the more natural case, and can be attributed to the great resistance to stretch of the hem or tabling along the leech—a hard leech. Two remedies are available:

1. To reduce the strength of the leech by decreasing the width of the tabling or, in the case of Dacron, even to dispense with it altogether by heat sealing the cloth using a hot knife
2. To increase, if it is allowed, the length of the battens. In the eventuality of these being unsuccessful, one must reduce the area of the roach

The characteristic of case c is that the roach bends to leeward, and here one must decide whether this happens only in strong winds or also in weaker winds. In the former case, one must recut the foot of the sail, shifting the curve of the foot further aft, for reasons which will be apparent later in the discussion. If this defect occurs in both strong and light winds it points to the sail being overstretched in its afterparts, due to too weak a leech. This can be caused by initially stretching a cotton sail in too strong a breeze, the use of too light a sailcloth or insufficiently strong tabling on the leech or too large a roach. The stretch can be removed, and the roach tautened by introducing broad seams (Fig. 133d), which are tapered to accommodate the surplus material.

For heavy weather, it is usual to cut a mainsail with little or no roach. In these conditions one is not interested in having the maximum possible area, particularly if it severely reduces the efficiency of the sails, as indeed it does.

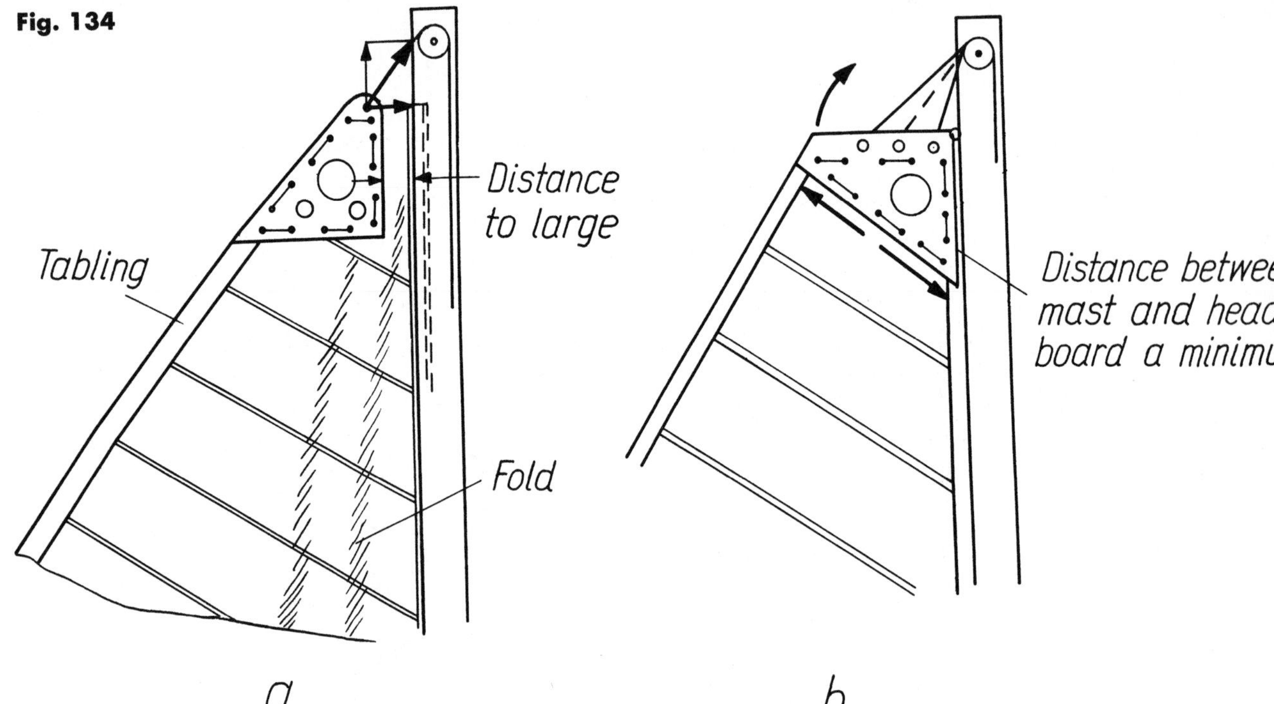

One frequently sees sails which have wrinkles around the headboard (Fig. 134a). They can be caused by the headboard being too far offset from the mast, so that the halyard pulls it forward, and also because the headboard transfers the halyard force into the sailcloth on the diagonal. The remedies are shown in Fig. 134b, which also shows how the halyard can be attached to the headboard on a bridle so that the tension in the roach can be regulated. If the wrinkles from the headboard are not local, but rather folds running to the foot of the sail, it indicates too little excess cloth in the foot, compared with the luff.

From the point of view of the air flow, it would be better if the curved foot of the sail did not suddenly have to become straight at the boom, but that the boom was shaped to the desired camber. Such a boom is, however, expensive and complicated and for these reasons has never found great popularity. In practice a relatively smooth transformation of the sail into the boom is obtained by allowing some surplus sailcloth in the foot (as shown in Fig. 132b).

The amount of excess cloth (f_b) in the foot is taken as 30–50 per cent of f_o, the desired camber height of the sail, just off the boom. Thus if the sail foot is 10 ft. long and the camber at station o is 1⁄10 of the foot, i.e., $f_o = 12$ in., then the foot of the sail should be cut with from $f_b = 3.6$ in. to 6 in. excess material in it. The lower value of 30 per cent is taken when the mast is straight and stiff, while the upper value applies to flexible masts such as for the Finn and Star classes.

The shape of the curved foot has a great influence on that of the whole sail, and therefore it is desirable to establish its final curve experimentally. This is particularly so if one is experimenting with a new sailcloth or mast. The sail should be firmly sewn to the luff bolt rope, but only tacked to that along the foot, and some spare material included here. On hoisting the sail, and preferably sailing with it, it will become evident what modifications are required.

The position of the maximum f_b of the curve affects the position of the maximum cambers (f_0, f_1, f_2) over the whole sail. The nearer is f_b to the mast, the more forward will be the camber of the sail. This is usually desirable if the mainsail is used with an overlapping foresail. On the other hand, one must not forget that if the roach of the sail is large, too forward a position of f_b will cause it to bend to leeward when reaching, even in moderate winds. This inclination will be aggravated if the portion of the curve aft of maximum f_b is too flat. For cat rigs and sloops without overlapping sails, maximum f_b is best positioned at the middle of the foot, if the mast is rigid. For flexible masts a position further aft is required, as bending of the mast flattens the afterparts of the sail very strongly, and may cause deformation. This will show up as a fold F (Fig. 137) running from the clew to the point of maximum curvature of the mast.

An interesting solution to the problem of smooth transformation of the sail into

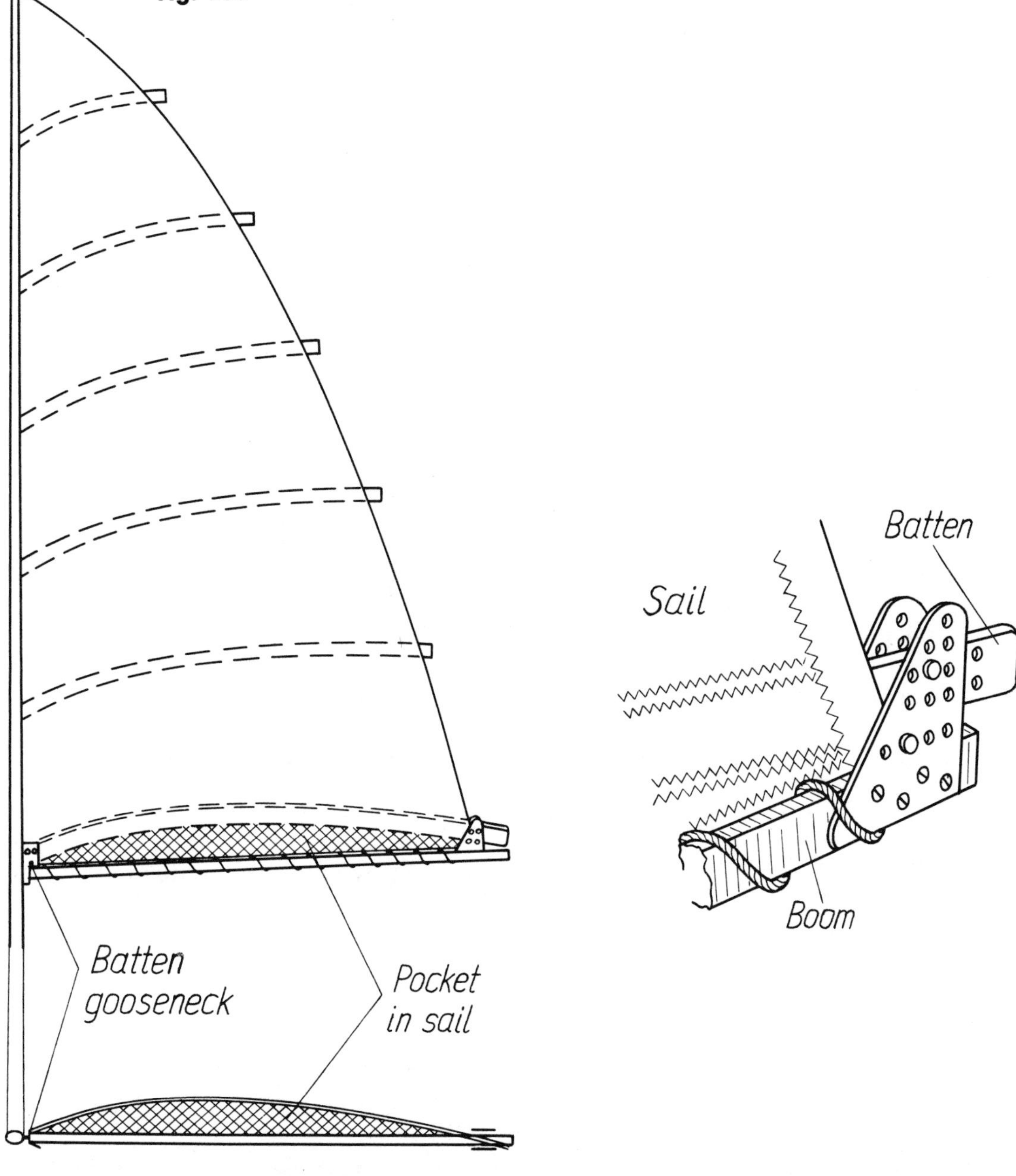

Fig. 135

the boom (see Fig. 135) was proposed by Wilson of New Zealand, and has recently become very popular, the majority of new catamarans using it. Its basic conception is rather similar to the Park Avenue boom (Photo. 3). The sail, fully battened, has at the foot a stronger batten which can be sprung beween the boom ends. Its curvature can be easily adjusted by altering the degree of compression. The sail, instead of flowing smoothly onto the boom, forms a sort of ledge, and thus not only is more of the sail of the desired shape, but also the ledge acts as a barrier to undesirable flow around the boom. The use of full-length battens confers advantages in that the required sail curve can be maintained more easily in different weather conditions, and the roach holds its shape. The camber of the sail is easily altered to suit different wind strengths by compressing the battens longitudinally so that they bow like the batten at the foot.

The final measure of how well the various allowances on luff, roach, and foot have been calculated and built into the final sail can only be taken when the sail is set. Normally one can only judge by eye, but in the case of the 12-Meter *Vim,* the two sails were separately hoisted, to avoid backwinding, and the profiles at various sections measured (Fig. 136). The table below gives the magnitudes of the cambers at each section, expressed as a percentage of the appropriate chord length, so that the figures can be directly compared.

MAINSAIL		FORESAIL	
Section	*Camber*	*Section*	*Camber*
1	1.2%	I	5.9%
2	9.1	II	11.8
3	11.4	III	17.0
4	12.7	IV	18.0
5	13.5	V	16.0
6	10.7		

On both sails the camber is considerably more at mid-height than near the foot. In particular the mainsail undergoes a striking deformation as it progresses from the boom to section 3. Even more surprising is the large amount of twist, over 40° from head to foot. Although it is not easy to say just what the ideal sail should look like, we can be quite certain that here we have a bad suit of sails. All sections should be at nearly the same angle of incidence to the apparent wind, and even allowing for the twist in apparent wind direction due to a wind gradient, this should only require a twist of about 7° over the height of the sail. In addition the camber of the sail should be maintained right down to the boom.

The ideal sail will only be so over a limited range of wind speeds, for a particular course, when the best compromise is obtained between:

1. The shape camber of the sail as predetermined by the original cut, and the stretch in the fabric
2. The twist in the sail, and in the apparent wind direction, due to the wind gradient, over the height of the mast.

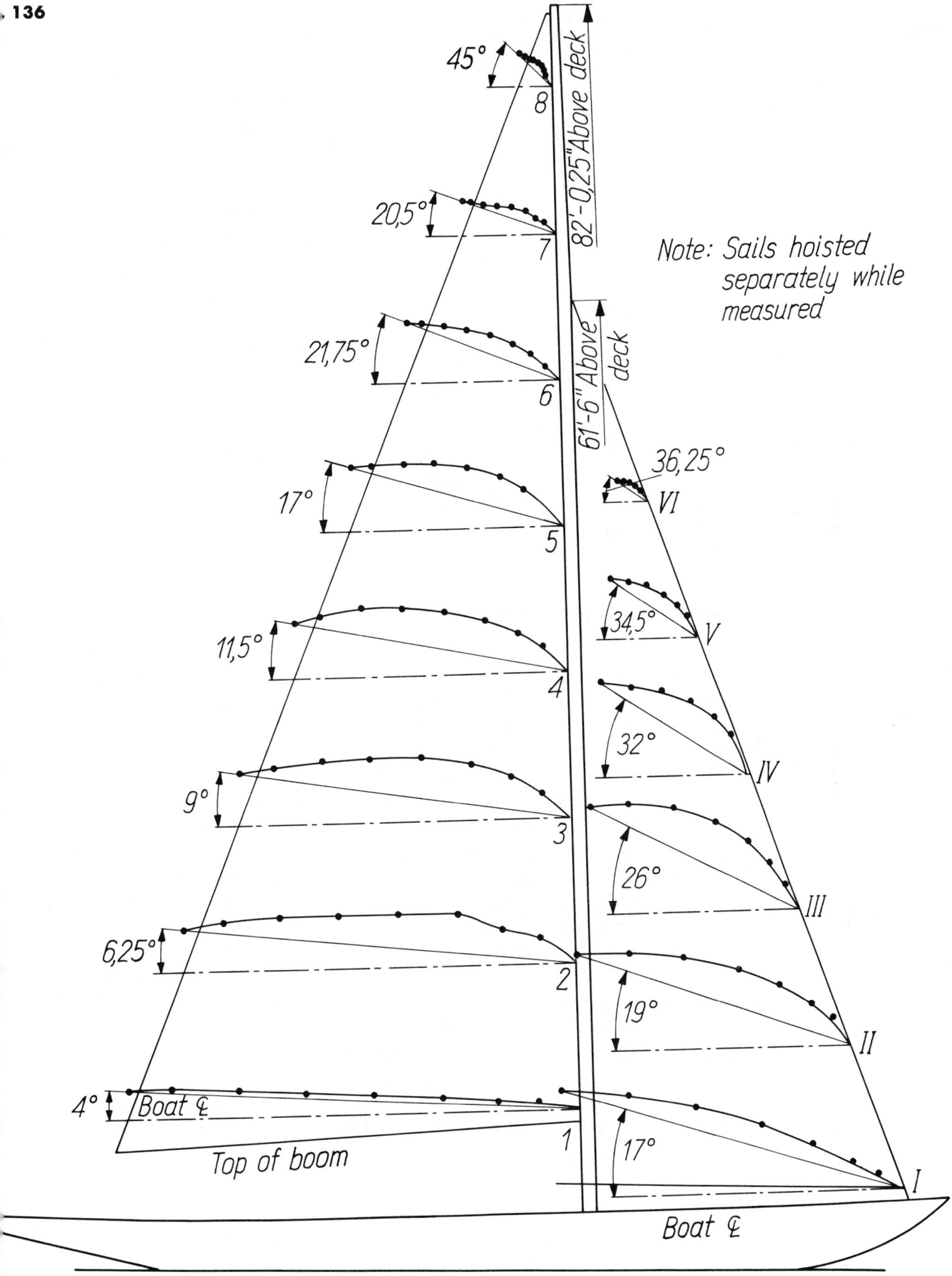

. 136

82'-0,25" Above deck

61'-6" Above deck

Note: Sails hoisted separately while measured

45°
8
20,5°
7
21,75°
6
17°
5
11,5°
4
9°
3
6,25°
2
4°
Boat ℄
1
Top of boom

36,25°
VI
34,5°
V
32°
IV
26°
III
19°
II
17°
I
Boat ℄

Fig. 137

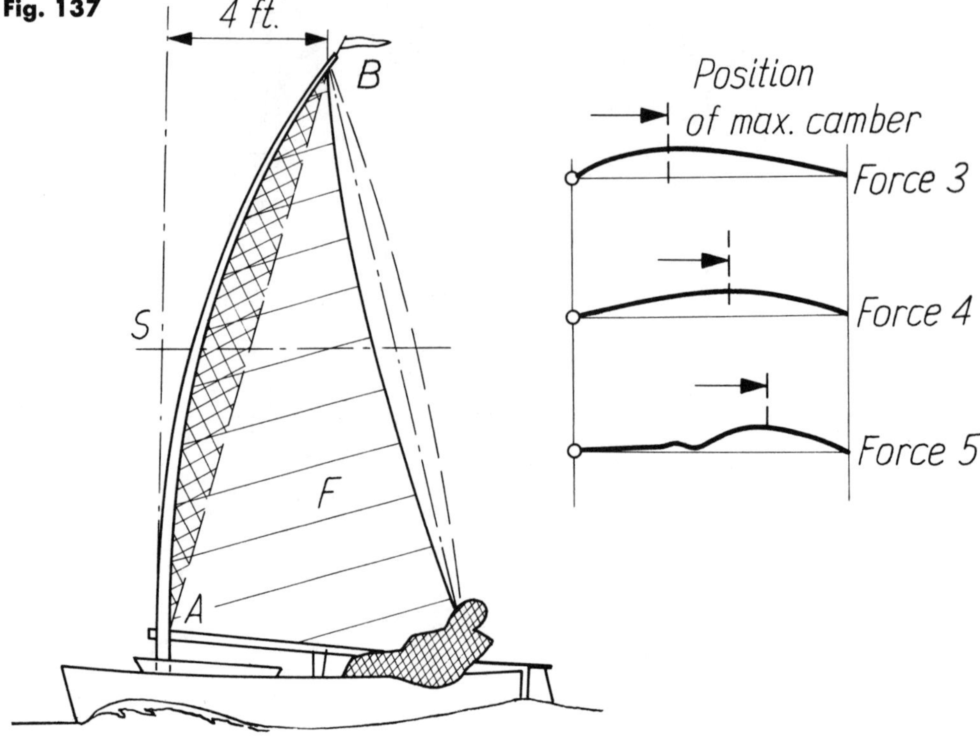

(c) The Problem of Flexible Spars

The method just described, using Fig. 132, for cutting sails of a desired camber can only be applied as it stands to sails working on rigid masts, well supported by standing rigging. When the mast bends appreciably, as in the Star and Finn classes, this must be taken into account.

Figure 137 shows a typical bent Finn mast when sailing to windward. The shaded area of the sail forward of the line A-B represents the material which will be "taken out forward" of the belly of the sail, so flattening certain parts of it. In general, the curve of this "deficit" of material due to mast bending will not be proportional to the surplus sailcloth worked into the luff to provide the camber for a sail designed for a straight mast. It is obvious, therefore, that when close-hauled, the surface will no longer be smooth and flowing, with the even camber distribution so desirable in a racing sail.

To avoid these obvious defects, one must allow for mast bending when cutting the sail. This is done (as in Fig. 138) by adding to the curve A of surplus material for a straight mast, the curve B, proportional to the shape of the bent mast. Thus the final curve C is obtained by adding together the offsets of curves A and B. The sail so obtained will have the desired camber when sailing close-hauled in a particular wind strength. On other courses, when the mast is not bent to any great extent, the camber will be greater. Even when close-hauled, the sail cut will only be correct for a particular wind strength and when set on a specific mast and rigging. For wind strengths greater than the design value, the shaded area forward of

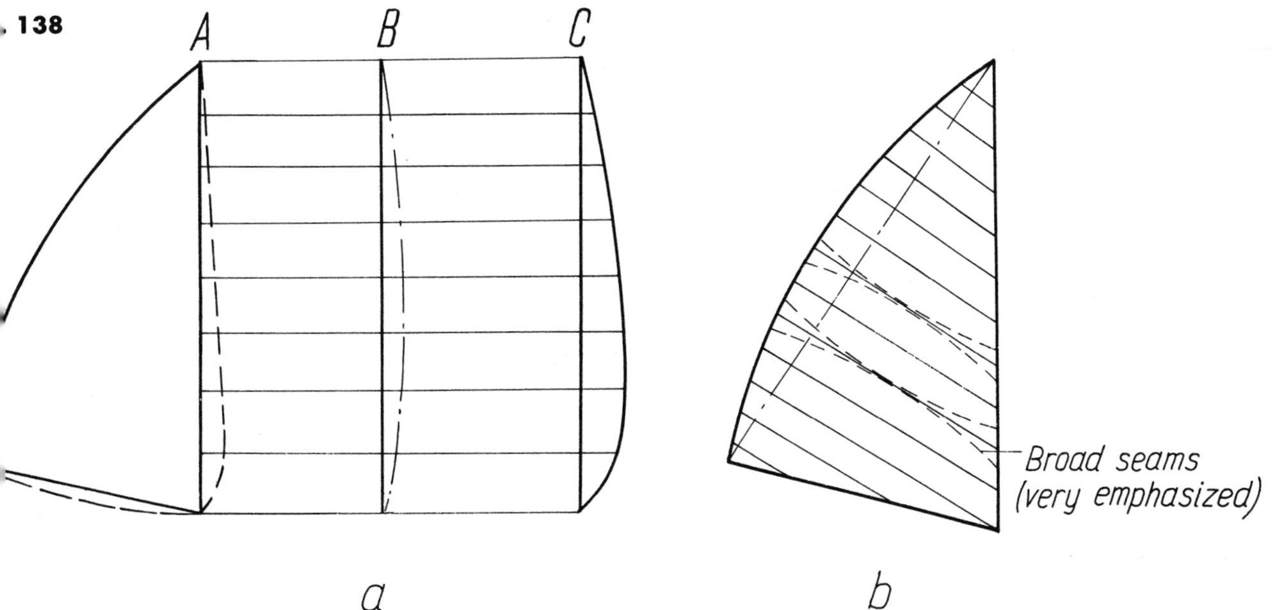

A-B in Fig. 137 will increase, and the uneven flattening of the sail so produced will cause folds, F, to appear radiating from the clew to near the point of maximum bow of the mast. Thus on a sail (Fig. 137) designed for a wind of Force 3 on the Beaufort Scale, the camber will move aft in a Force 4 breeze, and at Force 5, the forward parts will be very flat and separated from the highly curved afterparts by several creases. This phenomenon is particularly apparent on Dacron sails, and is known as "hard leech," as it would be alleviated if the leech could stretch. Even in cotton sails, with their greater elasticity, the tendency is still there, although to a lesser extent.

The flexible mast has therefore certain faults when it bends excessively. When the bending can be largely controlled, as in the Star, these disadvantages are more than outweighed by its advantages.

Remembering the formula for the aerodynamic sail force, $F = 0.00119 \times v^2 \times S_A \times C$, then if the wind strength requires it, we can either reduce our sail force F by reducing sail area S_A, or by altering the force coefficient C. On a rigid mast this means easing the sheets but on a bendy mast, a far better way is available to flatten the sail. This method was used for the first time by Heutschler in the Star class during the 1935 Olympic Games, with great success, and since then it has quietly revolutionized racing techniques in the smaller classes. At the present time it is rare for an Olympic class boat to be reefed, and this in turn has increased the importance of correctly tuning the sails on their flexible spars, i.e., fitting the sails to the spars—the sailmaker's job—or sometimes vice versa, i.e., fitting the spars to the sails—the crew's job.

To control the bending of the Finn's mast, which is freely pivoted and completely unstayed, is quite difficult. The shape of the curve it takes up depends entirely on the diameter of the mast at various heights. Since these are fixed the helmsman cannot control the character of the bend, only its amount. In other classes, such

Fig. 139

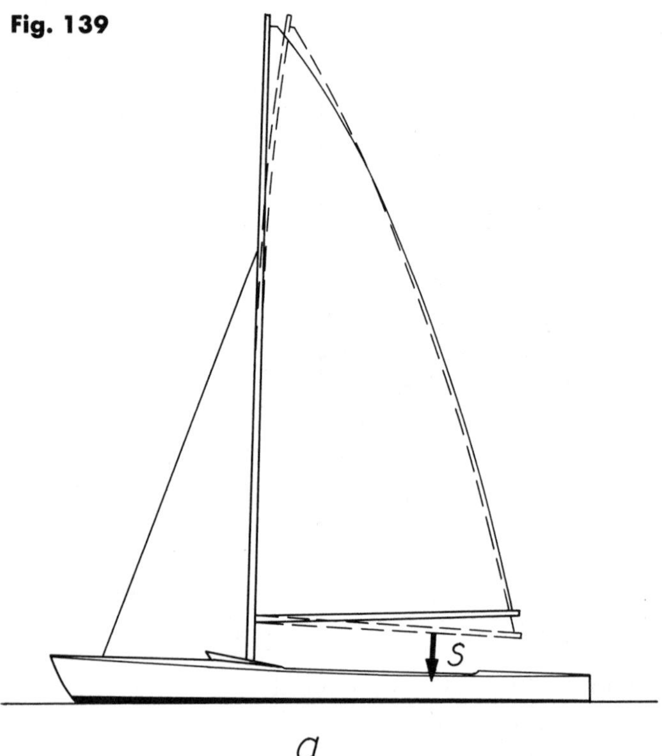

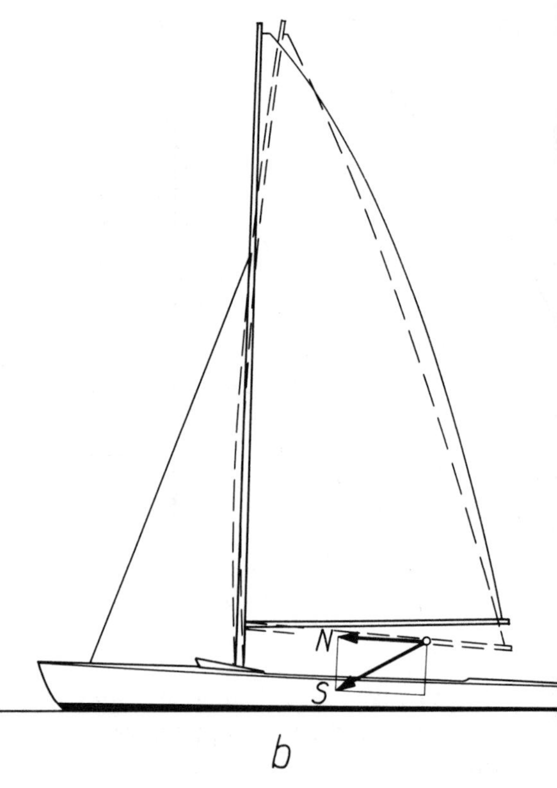

as the Star and Flying Dutchman, the crew can control the curve of the mast, using such tricks as that shown in Fig. 139. The mainsheet is attached to the boom on a track, and thus one can vary its line and point of application. In case a, the tension S is vertical and bending will be mostly above the forestay. In case b the sheet tension has a component N along the boom, which will push the lower part of the mast forward. For maximum effect the mast must be free at the deck, and only held loosely at the step. It follows that the curved masts in a and b will be of different shapes.

The problem of sailmaking has increased in complexity, for in addition to the considerations for rigid spars, one must now allow for mast material (wood, light alloy, glass fiber, etc.), mast shape and rigging, both standing and running, as well as the effects of wind strength.

Bending of the boom also has a considerable effect on the shape and set of the sail. As in the case of the mast it can either be controlled by the helmsman or be involuntary. The bending will depend on the construction of the boom (cross sections) and the way the mainsheet is attached.

There are three basic methods of attaching the mainsheet.

1. Mainsheet fixed to the end of the boom (Fig. 140a). With increasing wind strength the boom bends upward producing, for close-hauled sailing, an undesirable increase in sail camber. For reaching this need not be undesirable, if the increase in aerodynamic forces produced does not upset the lateral balance of the yacht.

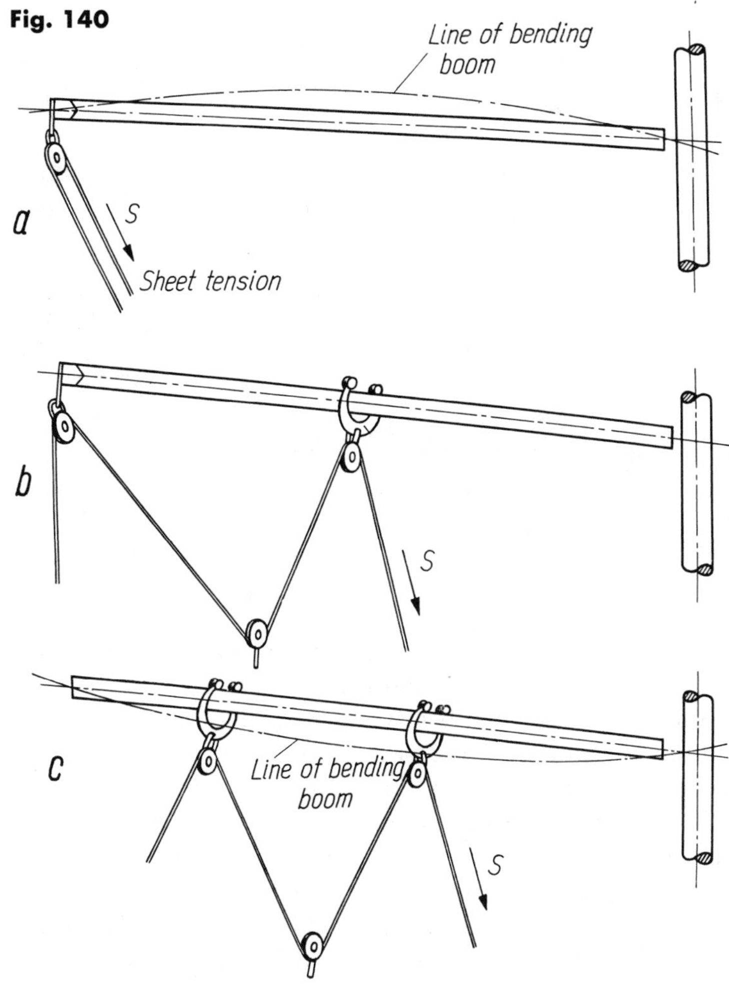

2. Mainsheet attached to the boom end and also roughly in the middle (Fig. 140b). This method ensures a straight boom on any course and in any wind.
3. Mainsheet fixed to the middle of the boom (Fig. 140c). This tends to flatten the sail as the wind rises and the mainsheet tension increases. By adjusting the fore and aft position of attachment, it is possible to regulate to some extent the boom bending and thus the sail flatness.

Flattening the mainsail can be achieved not only by means of the mast and boom, but also, within small limits, by shifting bodily the foot of the sail toward the outer end of the boom (Fig. 141a). It can be further improved by increasing the tensions in the foot and luff ropes. Sails made from synthetic materials are very sensitive on these tensions. If the halyard and clew outhaul are too tight, along the luff and foot of the sail appear characteristic folds—"tension pockets." If the sail is set properly, they should disappear when sailing to windward. On reaching, they may reappear, when the tensions in the sail are not sufficient to pull them out. It is advisable then to slacken the halyard and clew outhaul, until the sail attains its proper shape. Particularly when sailing in light airs, it is most im-

Fig. 141

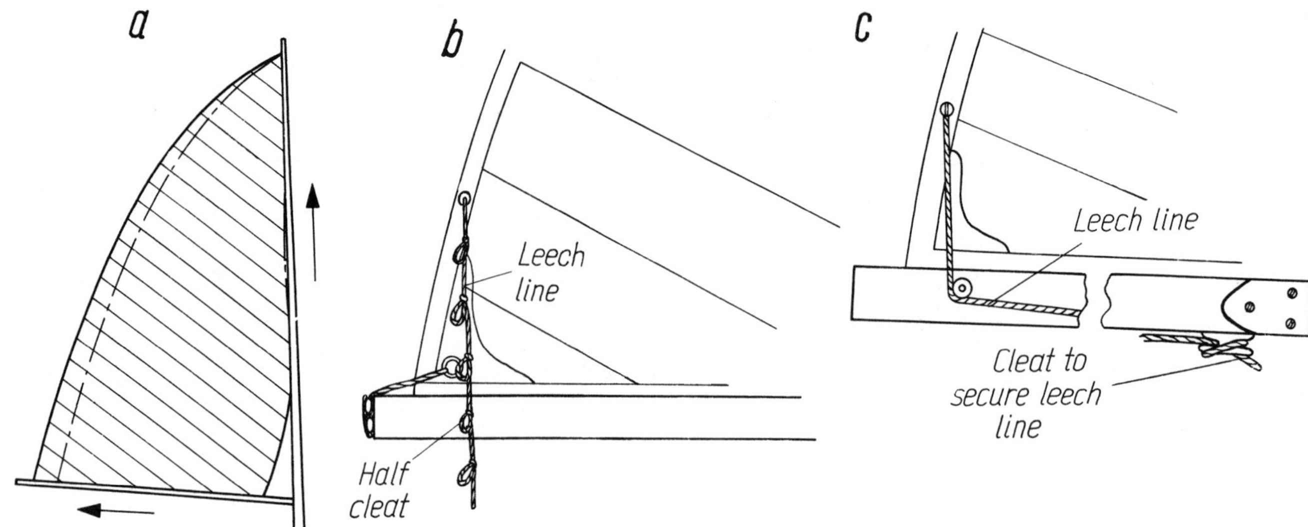

portant to have provision at the tack and clew of the mainsail for rapid adjustment of the tensions in the luff and foot.

Increase of sail camber when reaching can be achieved by hauling—in the leechline. Figure 141b, c shows methods how this can be done. In case b the leechline is adjusted by means of a special fitting at the end of the boom. This is inconvenient as one has to luff to reach the boom end, with attendant loss of time, and therefore a system such as case c is preferable, where the line is led well inboard.

When cutting highly cambered sails, it is not enough to shape them at the edges; they must also be shaped within the sail. This is done by the judicious use of broad seams (Fig. 138b). In the lower parts of the sail, particularly forward, the seams are made broad, while the upper and after parts have the conventional narrow seams. Thus there is comparatively more material in these latter regions, and the sail is free to take up a smooth profile. This procedure finds particular application on Dacron/Terylene sails.

Comparing Dacron and cotton, it could be said that the former often behaves more like thin sheet steel than an elastic cloth. This difference alone is enough to render ineffective many of the dodges learned over many years experience of working with cotton sails. In the case of cotton, the excess cloth cut into the luff and foot gradually works up and aft into the body of the sail without great difficulty as the sail is stretched. The material is permanently deformed to give the desired flow. In the case of the exceptionally flexible Finn mast, cotton sails can be still competitive, since their greater elasticity avoids the problems of a "hard leech," common with Dacron sails. In most other cases, Dacron is well superior, but it does mean that one cannot count on the elasticity of the material canceling errors in cutting. The sail must set properly the very first time it is hoisted.

New sail fabrics require, therefore, new methods of cutting and making up. The layout of the panels is still at the experimental stage, as some current types (Fig. 142) show. They all claim to produce a clean flat leech, which is usually

g. 142

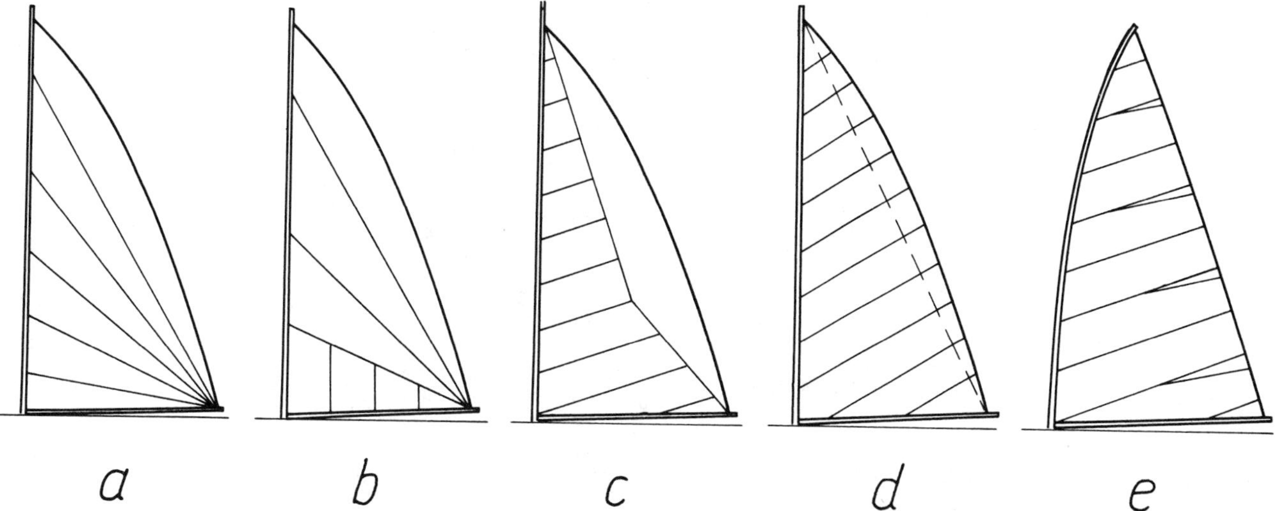

accepted as the criterion of a good sail. Examples a to d endeavor to introduce a little extra elasticity in the leech by an unconventional arrangement of panels. Example e, by Michael Auclair, uses triangular insertions in the roach, made of a more elastic material than the rest of the sail.

If we accept a flat leech as the criterion of a sail's quality, it is worth considering the function of the battens. Without doubt the best battens are those running the full width of the sail. To be fully efficient, whether full or partial length, a batten must have the correct stiffness and be unbreakable in use. The former condition requires that the thickness should not be uniform but should be greater within the roach to preserve a flat leech. It is not good enough to use one set of battens in all weathers. With increasing wind strength, the stiffness of the battens should be correspondingly increased to preserve the flat leech, and in general it is better to have them too stiff than too flexible. In all cases, however, they should have sufficient flexibility at their inner ends to avoid creases in the sail in this region.

Sails made from Dacron need stronger battens, especially at their outer ends. Photograph 23 shows as an example the fully battened sail of the catamaran Thai Mk.4, on which the undesirable tendency of the leech to curl to windward is very apparent. This could be cured by increasing the batten thickness at the outer ends.

(d) Cutting the Headsails

In principle headsails are three-sided sails, supported relatively freely only at the corners. In effect all edges are free to sag sideways and also in the plane of the sail by different amounts for each edge, depending on a variety of factors. For these reasons, the problem of cutting a headsail to a predetermined camber is more difficult than in the case of a mainsail, and explains why so many foresails in use are manifestly badly cut.

As an illustration we can consider the case of a typical foresail (as shown

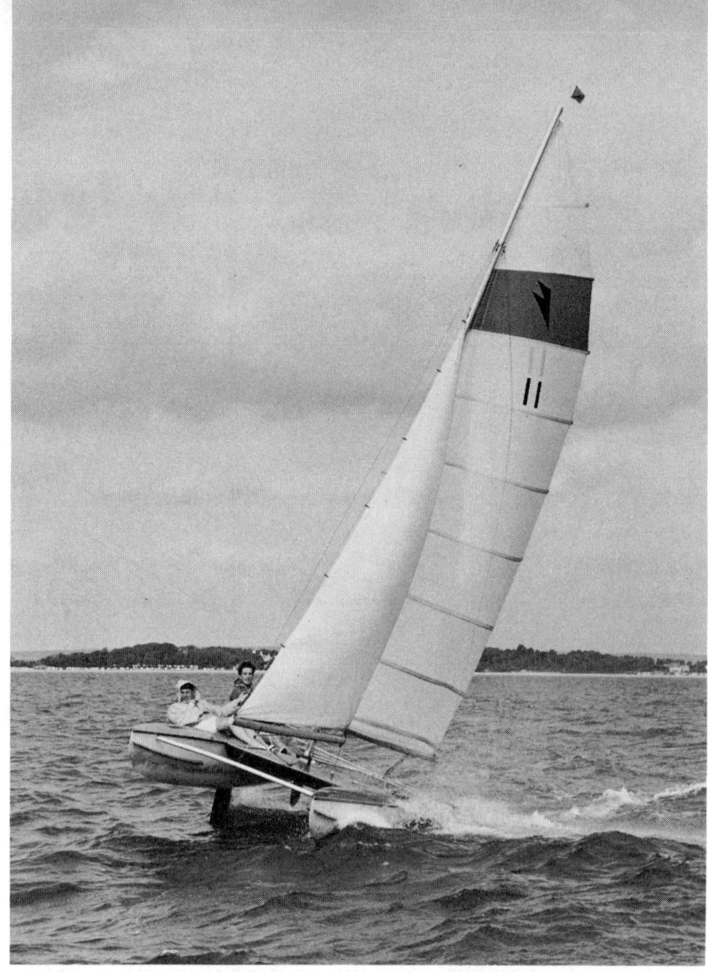

Photo. 23

in Fig. 143a). Initially cut with a straight luff (frequently recommended in textbooks on the subject) the sag aft of the forestay when sailing to windward will produce camber in the sail, even supposing the foot and leech remain straight. From the sketch it is clear that the camber at the various sections O_1, O_2, O_3 will be different, depending on the relative proportion of the material which works aft, to the local chord. The biggest camber will be produced somewhere close to section O_3, where the proportion of sag O_3C to the chord CC_1 is the greatest. Thus the camber of a sail cut in this fashion will generally increase toward the head, an un-

Fig. 143

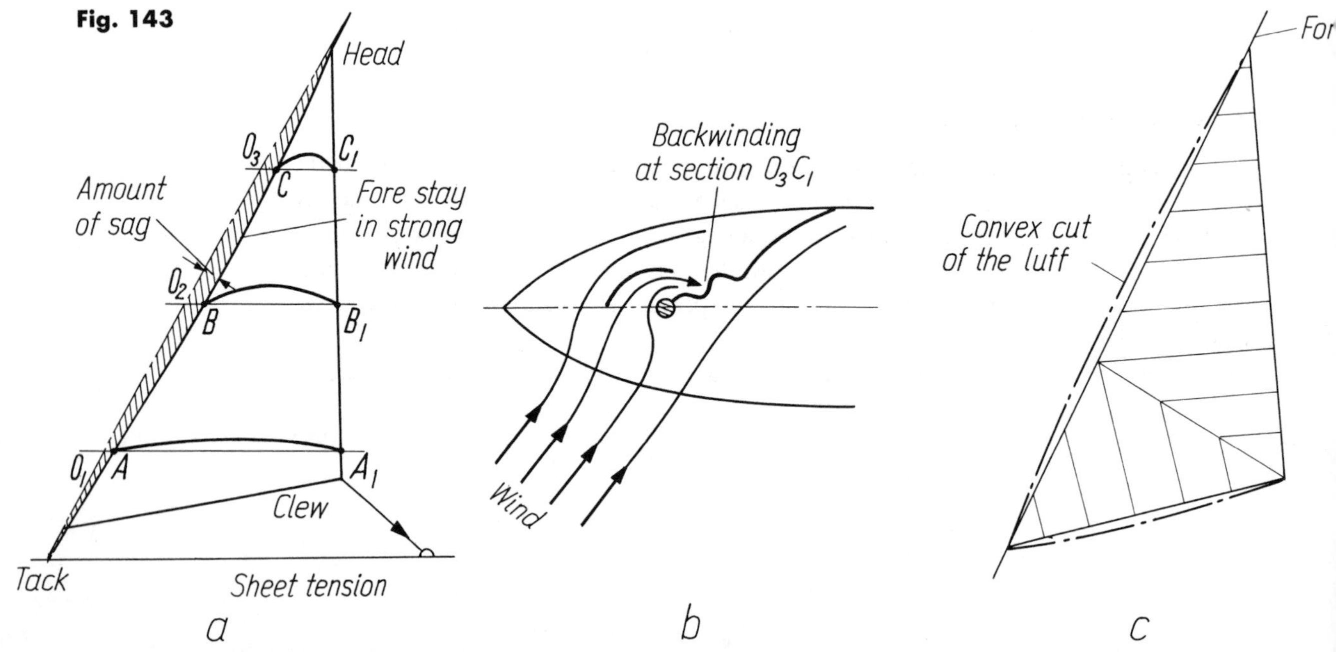

desirable but frequently encountered trait in headsails. As explained earlier, correct trimming of the foresheet will produce backwinding of the mainsail (Fig. 143b), while if the sheet is eased, the upper part of the foresail will probably flutter and so not be fully effective. Obviously, in a racing yacht, this will be regarded as a serious defect. It is not difficult to imagine how much more serious it will be if the headsail is cut with a convex luff (Fig. 143c), an idea which has even more supporters among the writers of sailing textbooks than that of cutting the luff straight.

We previously argued that the ideal close-hauled working condition for an overlapping headsail and mainsail was for the two sails to be sensibly parallel in the overlapping region and that the foresail should be relatively flat. When cutting the foresail this fact, as well as the sag in the forestay, must be born in mind. This sag is of particular importance when dealing with a sail of high aspect ratio, when the chord is relatively small. When the question of excess material on the luff of the mainsail was considered (in Fig. 132b), it was stated that to achieve a camber of $1/7$, it is necessary to allow 5 per cent excess material, based on the local sail chord. In the case of a high A.R. foresail, the sag in the stay can be more than 5 per cent of the chord, giving a large camber, which can produce backwinding even if there is no overlapping. This situation can be seen on Photo. 24 showing an International One Design sailing to windward.

Photo. 24

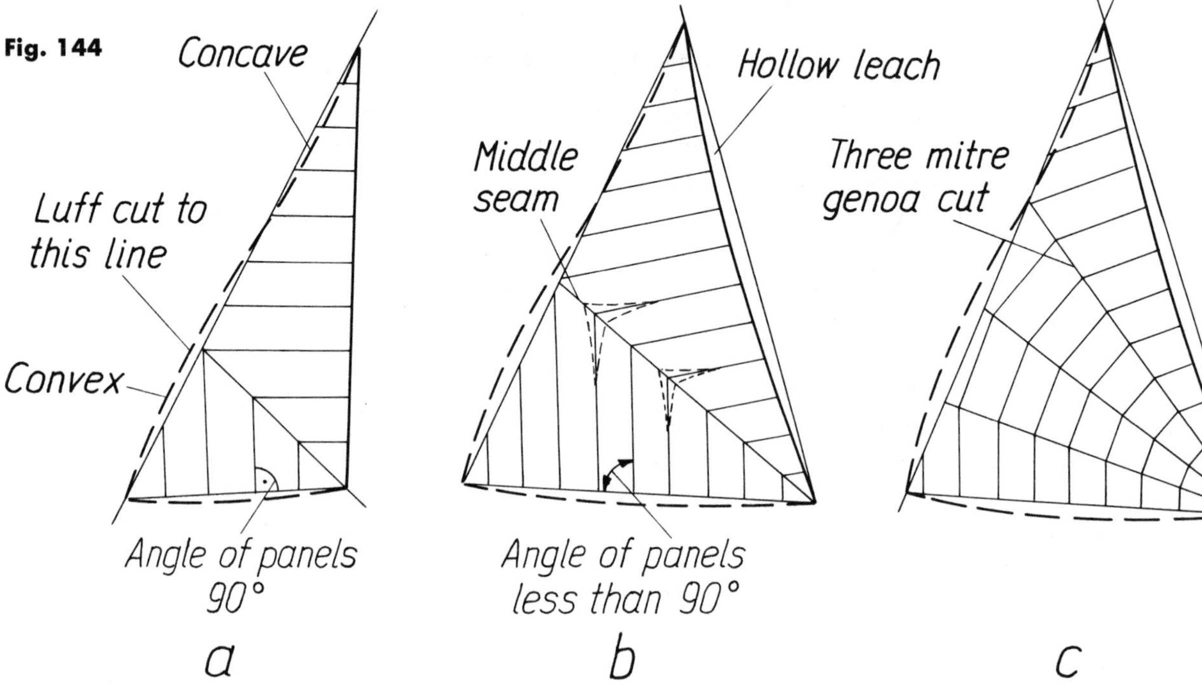

Attempts to counteract the effect of forestay sag frequently follow the old salts' advice of "keep the jib stay bar taut." Although like most such things, there is some sense in this saying, it should not be applied equally in all cases, as, particularly in small craft, excessive tension may only bend the hull and mast, and not reduce the forestay sag. Even in very strong yachts, where this dictum can be applied to the limit, it will be found impossible to eliminate the sag completely.

It is necessary therefore to introduce corrections when cutting the curved luff, having excess material near the foot but a deficit in the upper parts (as in Fig. 144a). In effect one is subtracting the sag of the forestay from the basic surplus allowance of cloth in a similar, though reverse, way to that which was used to compensate for mast bending on the mainsail. The best procedure to adopt is to guess at the sag and so make an approximate allowance, but defer cutting the sail finally until after it has been tried in actual windward sailing. The basic aim when making such adjustments as may be necessary is to produce a flat sail causing the minimum of backwinding.

For the same reasons, the camber of a headsail will be increased by sag in its leech, which should be counteracted by cutting the sail with a hollow leech (as in Photo. 14 and Fig. 144b). The tension from the sheet will produce horizontal tensions in the fabric near the leech, tending to flatten the sail and prevent the leech from curling—particularly useful when dealing with Dacron. On many racing yachts there are no restrictions on what shape of foresail one can set in heavy weather, when the normal working sail is changed for a smaller one. There are two main alternatives: to set either a sail short in the foot and long in the luff, or one which is relatively long in the foot compared to the luff length (like a windward genoa). To some extent the choice will depend on whether the mainsail is reefed, but experience on such boats as 12-Meters and the Flying Dutchman (which rarely or never reef when racing) indicates that the latter type of sail offers advantages, for a variety of reasons.

1. Using a short hoist windward genoa, which is almost as long on the foot as on the luff, the influence of sag in the luff is not so great as with a higher A.R. sail.
2. By decreasing the A.R. the center of effort, CE, is also lowered, hence reducing heeling moments, at a time when this is particularly important.
3. Such a sail will be cut with a low foot, which helps to seal the gap between sail and deck. By preventing flow around the foot of the sail, which would reduce the difference in pressure between the two sides, the induced drag of the sail is reduced. This was explained in the discussion of Figs. 50 and 51.

Such a low aspect ratio sail is the miter-cut genoa (Fig. 144b), which introduces a special problem of its own not usually significant in higher aspect ratio sails. This is the considerable stretching which can occur along the middle seam, running as it is diagonally to the cloths and giving rise to a large increase of camber in this region. In the case of a cotton sail this local stretch is largely transferred to other parts of the sail, but for Dacron this is not so. The problem, which is particularly marked if the fabric is light, can be overcome in one of three ways:

1. By arranging the panels such that they are not truly square to the foot and leech (Fig. 144b). This reduces the stiffness of the sail in these parts. Hence the sail stretches equally along the foot, leech, and along the middle seam.
2. By shortening the length of the middle seam using broad seams at the inner ends of the panels (Fig. 144b). This expedient can also be employed to correct the cut of existing sails.
3. By laying up the cloths in what is known as a "spider web" arrangement (Fig. 144c). This serves once again to allow the sail to stretch more evenly, but it has another advantage. As the seams converge toward the clew, the elasticity of the sail is reduced, and this leads to a flat leech and the position of maximum camber well forward.

For reaching, when more camber is required in the sails, the leech of the foresail is cut straight and more excess material allowed in the luff and foot.

(e) Adjusting the Rigging

Generally the views of yachtsmen on how to adjust the standing rigging are rather extreme; some say it should be very tight, others that very slack rigging is the answer. Usually these views are dogmatic, rather than based on any proof. In view of this, it would be best to emphasize now that there is nothing mystical about the influence of rigging on a yacht's performance.

The function of standing rigging is to support the mast and thus the sails, and the only way the tension in the rigging can influence performance is if it changes the shape or position of the sails. Such an example of how the tension can thus, indirectly, influence the yacht was given in Fig. 109 when discussing the genoa on the Flying Dutchman. Another example: when the tension in the jumper stays is reduced, the mast can bend aft a little under the force from the mainsheet—this flattens the sail, which is advantageous in a strong wind.

We can say then that tuning the standing rigging has some importance if thereby it affects the setting of the sails, their aerodynamic efficiency, or the directional balance of the yacht. It is difficult to give any general advice which can be applied to all boats in all conditions. Photographs 25 and 30 can be taken as an example. Undoubtedly the aerodynamic performance could be improved if it were possible to slacken the lee shroud when reaching. Then, the contour of the sail would not change abruptly at the wire, and the air flow would be smooth. The effects of improving the sails' efficiency will be more marked in light weather, when the boat is not sailing near its limiting speed. This particular problem, of how to slacken the shrouds, can be approached in two ways:

Photo. 25

Fig. 145

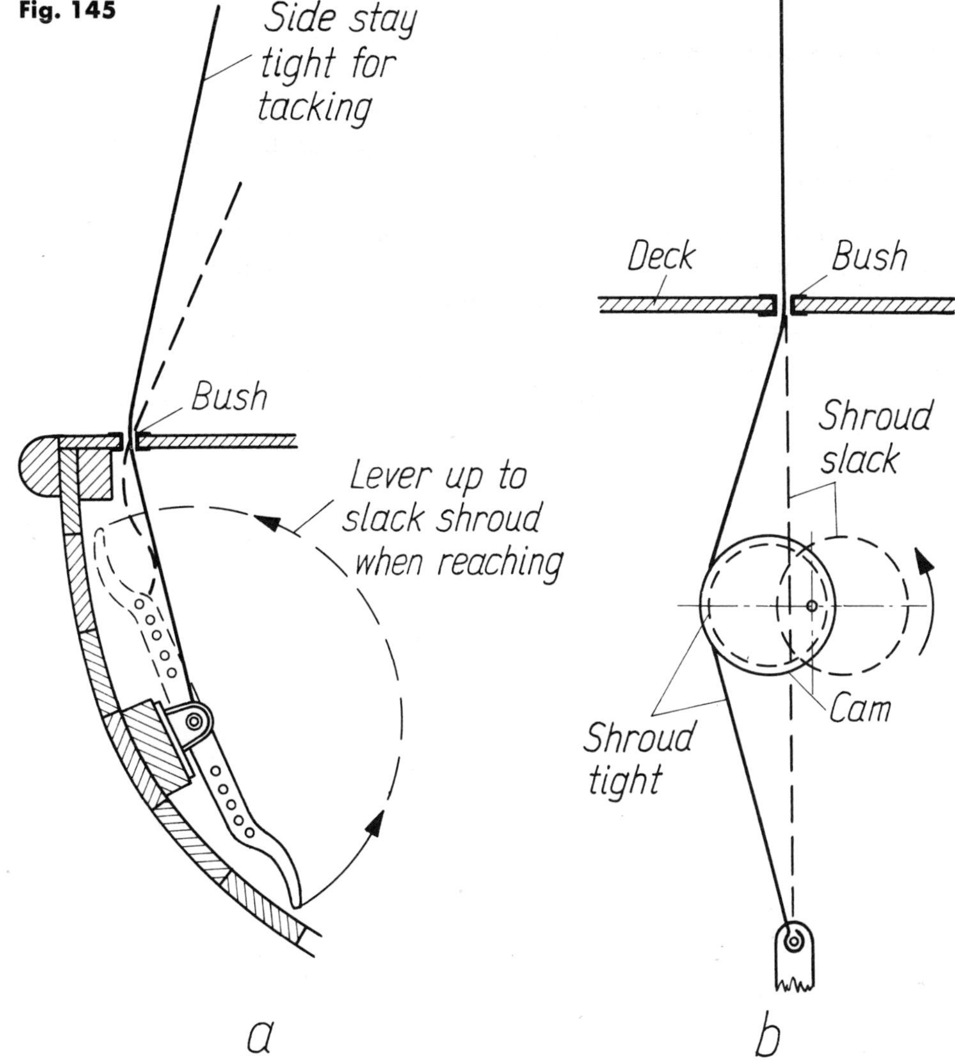

1. With all shrouds initially slack, the mast will lean to leeward, and with luck, or good judgment, the lee shroud will sag sufficiently not to foul the mast. This then is in accordance with the views of the slack rigging school.
2. An alternative is to have both shrouds initially tight, but to slacken the lee one when reaching: Fig. 145a, b shows two possible methods by which this might be done. This technique is a compromise between the two extremes. It allows one to have taut rigging for sailing close-hauled and slack rigging for sailing off the wind, and in this respect offers advantages over 1.

Many similar examples could be given, but there is little point, as each boat has its own specific problems which must be solved individually. In all cases, however, before regulating the standing rigging one should attempt to answer the following questions.

1. What is one trying to achieve by adjusting the rigging?
2. Is it likely to improve the efficiency of the sails or the directional balance of the yacht?

A few extremists like to tune their rigging like a fiddle, and for this there is no justification whatsoever, except in the case of the forestay previously mentioned. Once a wire is just taut, further tensioning serves only to stretch it or strain the mast or hull and in no way improves the supporting of the mast. Due to the small inclination to the vertical of most rigging, it often carries a load several times that of the force on the sail, and a high initial tension can only make matters worse.

PART III

THE MOTION OF A YACHT

1. THE HYDRODYNAMIC RESISTANCE OF THE HULL*

. . . Since we never reckon that we understand a thing till we can give an account of its "how and why," it is clear that we must look into the "how and why" of things coming into existence and passing out of it.

ARISTOTLE, *The Physics*

The speeds attainable by sailing yachts propelled by an aerodynamic driving force could be high, comparable with the speed of a sliding ice-yacht, but for the fact that water resistance increases very rapidly as speed increases. There are many reasons for this. Any water-borne craft, whether ploughing through the water, as a heavy displacement yacht does, or skimming (planing) over the surface, like a modern light dinghy, inevitably transfers some of the energy generated by the wind to the mass of water with which it is in contact.

Wave-making, for instance, is a particular form of energy dissipation which produces resistance to the forward motion of the hull, but though it is the most conspicuous, it is not the only hydrodynamic resistance a yacht must overcome at the expense of the energy developed by its sails. The movement of a hull produces several other, less obvious but equally harmful, effects, which in certain sailing conditions create a barrier of hydrodynamic resistance which limits the maximum speed attainable and also the weatherly ability of the boat.

The flow of water round the immersed part of the hull, and the resultant pressure changes which are the source of this resistance, are complex even in the

* Before starting this chapter, the reader is advised to refer again to Figs. 78, 79, and 80, and to remember that for *steady* sailing conditions the aerodynamic driving force F_R must be balanced by an equivalent hydrodynamic resistance R of the hull. Naturally, this balance of forces exists for different sailing speeds, according to the variations in the forces F_R and R.

simple case of a yacht sailing upright and without drift. This is due to the complicated shape of the hull and to the fact that a yacht moves at the boundary of two media, air and water, and this boundary is continually moving up and down.

Water flow becomes still more intricate when sailing to windward, when the yacht is heeled and making leeway.

The total hydrodynamic resistance is easier to understand and to evaluate when it is subdivided into:

1. Skin friction resistance, R_f.
2. Wave-making resistance, R_w.
3. Induced resistance, or resistance due to leeway, R_i.
4. Heeling resistance, or resistance due to heel, R_h.

Thus the total resistance $R = R_f + R_w + R_i + R_h$.

This subdivision of the total resistance is also valuable because it simplifies the carrying out of tests and the illustration of problems involved in the motion of a sailing yacht.

Eddy-making resistance, created by the afterpart of the hull, might also be added, but its contribution to the total is not easy to measure, since it is usually difficult to separate it from other types of resistance, such as wave-making and skin friction. Reference will, however, be made to eddy-making resistance wherever its importance makes this necessary.

The four resistances listed above vary in their relative importance according to the type of yacht, its speed, and its course relative to the wind. Each can have a considerable effect on the performance and behavior of a sailing craft.

The phenomena of water flow and hull resistance can best be studied by experiment. Direct observations, linked with measurements of the forces developed, can be made on a moving yacht or on accurate scale-model hulls in a test tank, such as the one at Southampton University. (Photo. 26 shows a scale model of a Dragon in this tank.) These two methods were first applied to yachts about 30 years ago by K. S. M. Davidson in the United States, and they have made it possible to forecast the behavior of a yacht with considerable accuracy. Towing tank experiments make it possible to gather information, and so improve the design of a yacht of any class, within a few weeks, whereas years might be needed to make the same observations of a yacht sailing on her normal business.

The methods first used by Davidson at the Stevens Institute to observe and measure the hydrodynamic resistances of a model are based on methods already in use among naval architects, and devised 80 years ago by William Froude.

Froude's suggestion—an ingeniously simple one—was that the total resistance of the hull could be conceived as the sum of two components: frictional resistance and residual resistance. The term "residual resistance," which occurs frequently in technical literature, means all resistances caused by the shape of the hull, but not skin friction resistance. Thus of the three resistances listed above, $R_w + R_i + R_h$

Photo. 26. The towing tank at Southampton University, 88 ft. long, 8 ft. wide and 4 ft. deep. A one-sixth scale of a Dragon class yacht is attached to the balance system and the attainable speed of the model is up to 5 ft./sec.

(2,3,4) form the residual resistance. This apparently elementary, but actually significant, idea enables us to study and calculate the frictional and residual components of the total resistance separately from the data obtained in the towing tank. The method used is, in principle, as follows.

The total resistance is measured experimentally, and the frictional resistance can easily be calculated. The residual resistance of the model is then obtained by subtraction, and from this the residual resistance of the full-scale hull can be worked out, using Froude's law of similarity, which will be explained below. Skin friction for the model can also be converted, by another law, into skin friction resistance for a full-scale hull. Then by adding the residual and frictional resistances so obtained, the total resistance for the full-scale hull is found.

It is now known that skin friction itself affects residual resistance, and so the final calculation includes an inevitable but approximately calculable error.

However, without this simplifying assumption introduced by Froude, many practical and theoretical problems in naval architecture would be exceedingly difficult, if not impossible, to solve. This unavoidable error is in any case not very significant, and the results based on towing tank tests were quite satisfactory when compared with the results obtained on full-scale hulls.

(a) Skin Friction Resistance—R_f

The basic characteristics of frictional resistance were described in the section on the aerodynamic skin friction resistance of sails. They apply in the same way to a hull moving through the water. However, while the mechanics involved are similar in both cases, the significance of skin friction for a hull moving in water is much greater, since the density of water is approximately 835 times that of air. If the speed of the water flow past a yacht were to be measured at two points, one very close to the yacht's skin, the other further away, it would be found that the former would show a much lower speed than the latter.

The particles of water which are closest to the immersed surface of the hull adhere to it, and so travel at the speed of the yacht itself. Their motion is transferred to other particles, and so, as a result of the viscosity of the water, the hull is surrounded by a kind of coating of calculable thickness, called the boundary layer. Experiments have shown that it is in this layer that frictional resistance acts. In the boundary layer the speed of the water particles rises from zero to the speed of the hull. Its thickness increases gradually toward the stern, reaching 1–2 per cent of the LWL. Thus, if the LWL is 20 ft. the thickness of the boundary layer will be 2½–5 inches at the stern. The thickness of the boundary layer of a small boat with a short wetted area is relatively greater than of a large boat with a long wetted area.

The existence of the boundary layer can easily be proved by dropping a small floating object close to the hull. For a while it will move in the same direction as the boat, against the flow of water past the hull, until some accidental vortex whirls it outside the boundary layer.

Clearly, the thicker the boundary layer, the greater the mass of water receiving this momentum from the hull, and the greater will be the energy loss, or skin friction resistance.

Skin friction may be calculated according to the following formula:

$$R_f = C_f \times \frac{\rho}{2} \times v_s^2 \times A$$

where C_f = skin friction coefficient

ρ = mass density of water

$= \frac{\gamma}{g}$ where γ weight of unit of volume (62.3 lb./cu. ft.—fresh water
64.0 lb./cu. ft.—salt water)

g = gravity acceleration of 32.2 ft./sec.^{2}
v_s = velocity of yacht in ft./sec.
A = wetted area in ft.^{2}

Therefore for fresh water

$$R_f = 0.97 \times C_f \times v_s^2 \times A$$

and for salt water

$$R_f = 0.995 \times C_f \times v_s^2 \times A$$

The friction coefficient C_f is not a constant but varies according to the character of flow in the boundary layer, the length of the hull L, the velocity v_s, and the smoothness of the wetted area.

The section on Friction Drag (5b in Part II) discussed the significance of Reynold's number, Re, on which depends the characteristics of the flow within the boundary layer, and the associated friction coefficient. It was shown that the size of Reynolds' number is determined by the three factors which describe the flow—i.e., the velocity of the flow, the length of the body, and the viscosity of the fluid.

For the flow of water round an immersed hull, Reynolds' number will be:

$$Re = \frac{v_s \times L}{\nu}$$

where v_s = velocity of yacht in ft./sec.
L = length of immersed area in feet.
ν = kinematic viscosity of water at normal temperature (15°C, 59°F)

For fresh water $\nu = \frac{1.23}{10^5}$ ft.^{2}/sec. and so

$$Re = \frac{v_s \times L}{1.23} \times 10^5$$

Sea water has a kinematic viscosity about 5 per cent higher than that of fresh water.

We can now consider the importance of Reynolds' number and the associated frictional coefficient C_f in an actual case. Figure 146b shows schematically the flow of water around the hull of an International Canoe at the waterline (see Fig. 25). For clarity the flow is shown on one side only, and the proportions of the boundary layer are much enlarged. The drawing shows the probable pattern of flow when the velocity v_s = 2 knots. The corresponding values of Re at several points along the waterline are marked above the flow lines. Note that for a little over 3 ft. from the bow (i.e., approximately 20 per cent of the boat's over-all length) laminar flow occurs, until, at a critical value of Re below 10^6 (1,000,000), a transition point is reached, and the flow changes its character and becomes turbulent. This change from the smooth laminar flow to the turbulent flow is due to the appearance

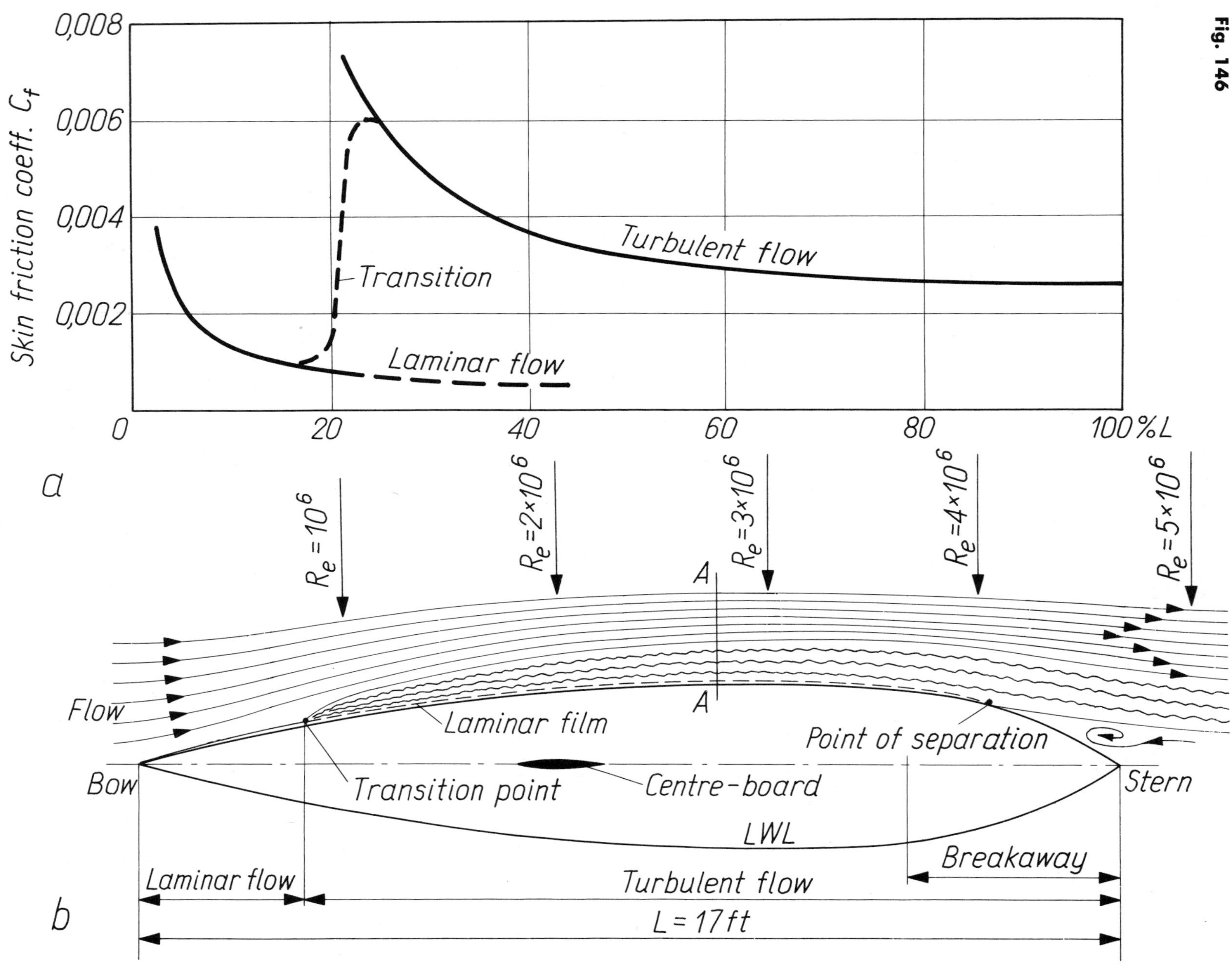

Skin friction coeff. C_f
0,008
0,006
0,004
0,002
0
20
40
60
80
100%L
Turbulent flow
Transition
Laminar flow
a
$R_e = 10^6$
$R_e = 2 \times 10^6$
$R_e = 3 \times 10^6$
$R_e = 4 \times 10^6$
$R_e = 5 \times 10^6$
A
A
Flow
Laminar film
Point of separation
Bow
Transition point
Centre-board
Stern
LWL
Breakaway
Laminar flow
Turbulent flow
b
L = 17 ft

Fig. 146

of fluctuations in the boundary layer at right angles to the direction of motion. In the boundary layer waves are generated with a frequency of approximately 100 cycles per second, and these in turn are responsible for the transfer of irregular motion into further layers of water. This increases the thickness of the boundary layer and also losses due to friction.

An examination of the values of the friction coefficient just before and just behind the transition point (see Fig. 146a) shows that the C_f value jumps from below 0.001 to above 0.006. Boundary layer waves are responsible for the transition from laminar to turbulent flow, and this occurs only when the height of these waves exceeds a critical level. When the values of Reynolds' number are small (i.e., when the boat's speed is low) the viscosity of the water will automatically damp most of these transverse oscillations, thus preventing the formation of turbulent flow.

The critical value of Reynolds' number at which turbulent flow appears, lies between 5×10^5 and 5×10^6. The actual point depends largely on the shape and smoothness of the immersed surface. Surface imperfections can cause turbulent flow even for lower values of Reynolds' number; for example, if the forebody of the immersed part of the hull is carefully smoothed, turbulent flow may be postponed until $Re = 5 \times 10^6$. The smoothness needed to maintain laminar flow means that "no roughness detectable to the finger-tips should be allowed." In theory it would be possible, in the case of the International Canoe shown in Fig. 146b, for laminar flow to be preserved along the whole length of the hull. It is clear from the drawing that the point at which $Re = 5 \times 10^6$ is reached lies behind the stern.

In practice laminar flow can only be maintained to the separation point, which is situated in the afterbody of the hull. Beyond that point, toward the stern, the separation of the boundary layer occurs, and a new type of resistance appears, which may be called eddy-making resistance. As this latter resistance cannot easily be distinguished from friction resistance when taking readings, an unavoidable error is introduced here. If the underwater part of the hull is spindle-shaped, the gradual contraction of the flow along this section will help to maintain laminar flow artificially in the boundary layer, for a greater proportion of the total length and for higher values of Re. Figure 146b demonstrates that from the bow to section A-A the flow contracts, but thereafter the situation is reversed and the flow section starts to expand, which favors the formation of turbulent flow. This knowledge could be used to advantage when designing, or improving, the shape of a keel. Experiments with yachts of the Dragon class have revealed that performance can be improved by sharpening the blunt leading edge of the keel, within the limits allowed by the class rules, and by shifting aft its maximum thickness.

The shape of the hull at the waterline shown in Fig. 146b may be taken as a suitable, if slightly exaggerated, horizontal section of a keel which will facilitate "laminarization" of the flow and reduce frictional resistance. The leading edge of a keel should, however, be somewhat rounded and its width reduced aft of the sec-

Photo. 27

Fig. 147

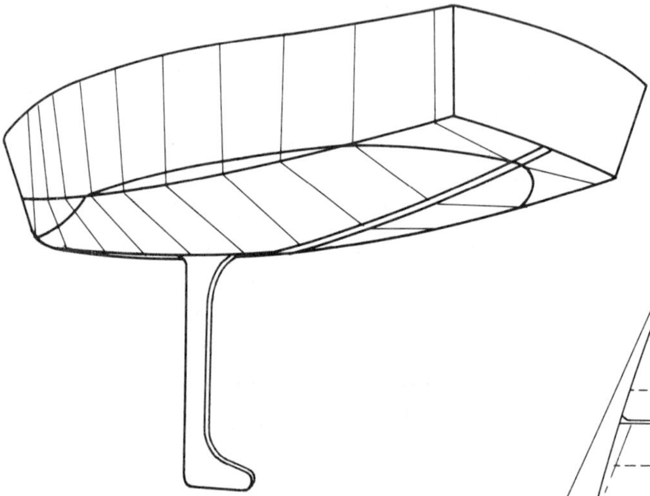

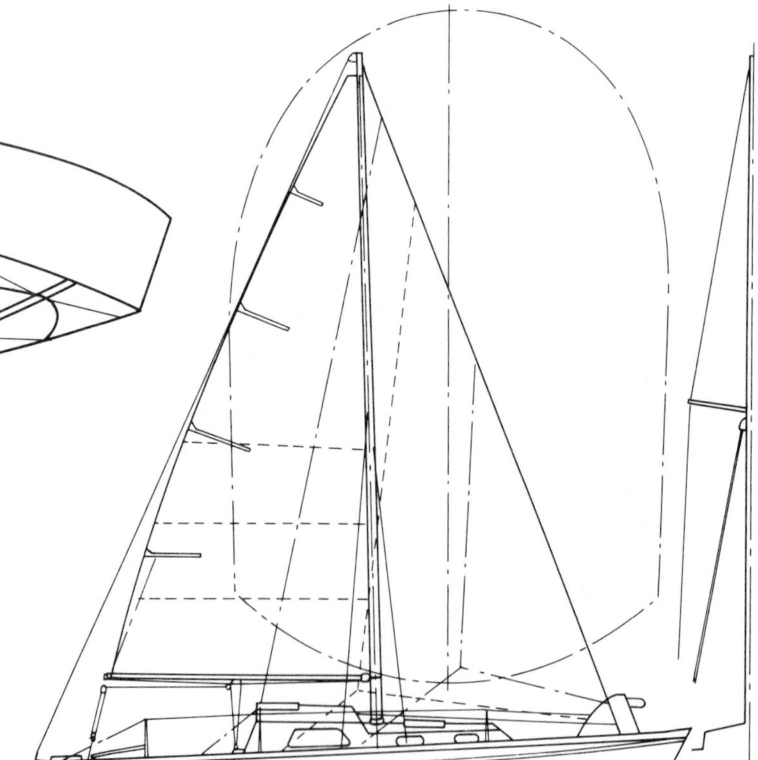

tion of maximum thickness A-A. An analysis of the slim forward sections of *Columbia's* keel is also instructive (Photo. 27).

It is easier to reduce skin friction and so gain these advantages on hulls with a relatively narrow separate fin and keel (see Figs. 147 and 11).

When the velocity $v_s = 2$ knots (as shown on Fig. 146), the values of Re rise toward the stern, and the "best" critical value, $Re = 5 \times 10^6$, lies behind the stern. Now if the boat speed is increased to, say, 10 knots, the magnitude of Re will also increase. In other words, the Re scale will move towards the bow and with it the critical $Re = 5 \times 10^6$. To find the point at which the transition from laminar to turbulent flow occurs for a hydrodynamically smooth hull (i.e. in which no roughnesses are detectable to the finger-tips) the formula used is:

$$Re = \frac{V_s \times L}{\nu}$$

where $V_s = 10$ knots $\simeq 16.9$ ft. per sec.

$$\nu = \frac{1.23}{10^5} \text{ ft.}^2\text{/sec.}$$

critical $Re = 5 \times 10^6$.

Thus the critical distance from bow Lcr at which turbulent flow begins to develop is:

$$Lcr = \frac{Re \times \nu}{V_s} = \frac{5 \times 10^6 \times (1.23/10^5)}{16.9} = 3.6 \text{ ft.}$$

This is about 20 per cent of the length of the hull, the maximum distance for which the flow inside the boundary layer can be laminar. The remaining 80 per cent of the length, and of course more than 80 per cent of the wetted area will be in the turbulent flow zone. Obviously then, if the velocity and the length of the hull are certain to produce a high Re value, it is impossible to obtain laminar flow with its small friction coefficient, even if the surface of the hull were mirror smooth. In the example calculated for $V_s = 10$ knots, the maximum distance for which laminar flow could be preserved in perfect conditions is only 3.6 feet. From this it is easy to deduce that it pays to spend time polishing in particular the centerboard, rudder (or fins), and the hull from the stern to the after-end of the centerboard.

The full-scale experiments carried out on the International Canoe by T. Tanner at the National Physical Laboratory (U.K.) confirmed that laminar flow exists over 80 per cent of the centerboard's area.

To preserve laminar flow and minimum frictional resistance it is particularly important for the leading edge to be smooth. Even slight roughnesses on the bow or leading edge of the centerboard or rudder may cause turbulent flow, while some roughness away from these edges is less damaging. Since, however, it is the forward portions of hull or centerboard that most frequently suffer damage, it is necessary to give special attention to them when overhauling the boat.

The next point to consider is the influence of surface imperfections or roughness in the turbulent flow zone, normally created when sailing at average speeds. Although turbulent flow is characterized by velocity fluctuation in all directions inside the boundary layer, there always remains a sublayer at the very surface of the hull (see Fig. 146b) in the form of a thin laminar film. This covers slight roughnesses and makes the wetted area hydrodynamically smooth as long as the protuberances of the rough areas are sufficiently encased within the laminar film. The thickness of this sublayer decreases with the rise in the value of Re, and a speed is reached at which the grain of the roughness begins to emerge from the laminar film, with a consequent increase in resistance.

Figure 148 gives the curves, prepared by Schlichting, of the skin friction coefficients, C_f at different values of Re for surfaces with various degrees of roughness. Curve A shows the change in C_f for a hydrodynamically smooth surface in turbulent flow. Although this curve actually relates to a flat surface, it can be applied to

Fig. 148

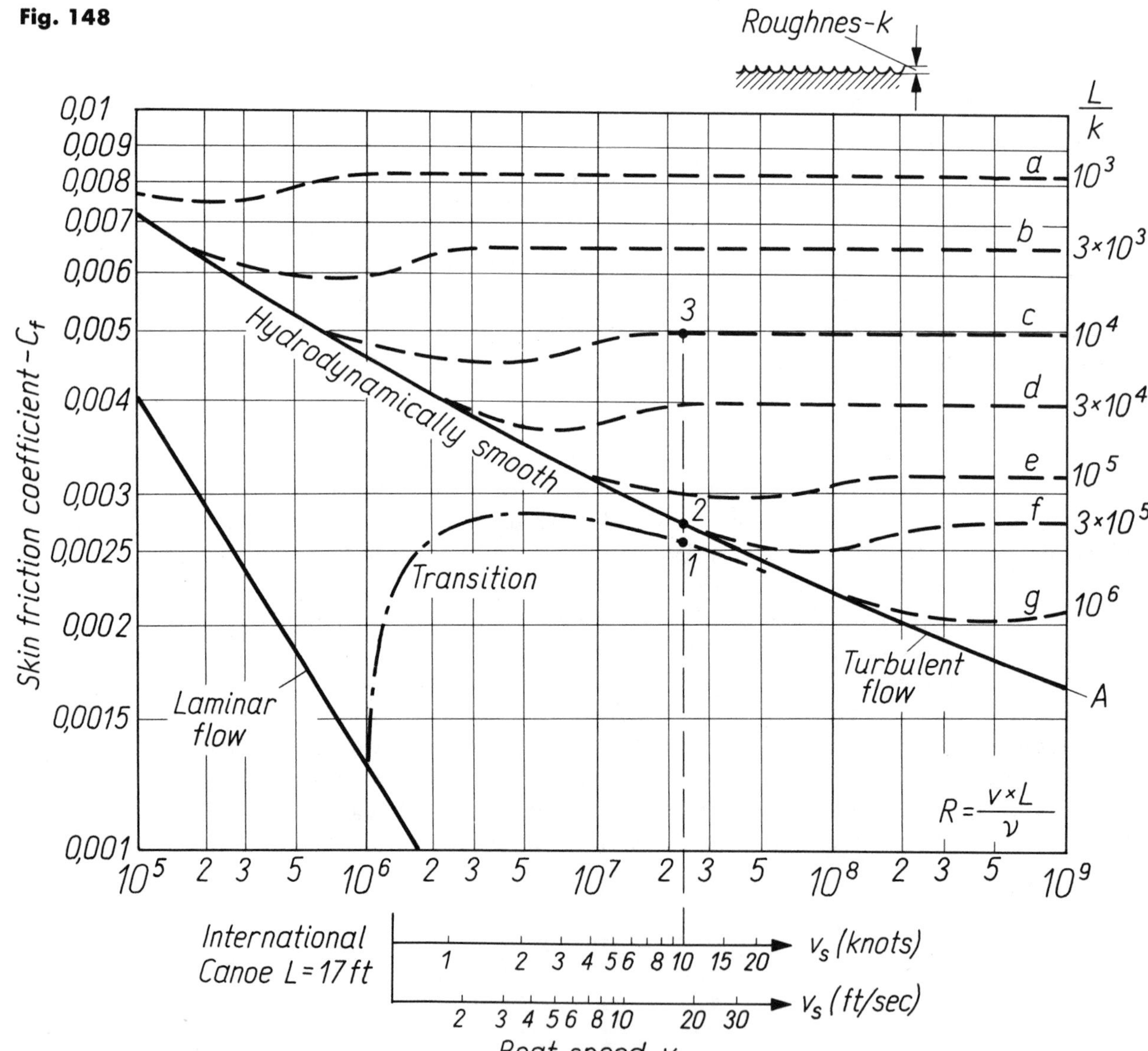

surfaces with a slight curvature and gives a close approximation to the actual values. In the range of Re values which have to be reckoned with in yachting, it differs very little from the I.T.T.C. (International Towing Tank Conference, 1957) Correlation Line used in naval architects' practice for the calculation of skin friction.

It is now necessary to define the term "a hydrodynamically smooth surface" in relation to turbulent flow. Above curve A are drawn curves a, b, c, d, e, f, and g, representing the coefficients of friction, C_f, for different grain sizes (or degrees of roughness). Numbers beside these curves give the ratio L/k, i.e., length of wetted area, L, to the height of the grains, k, which enables us to apply the results from this graph to yachts of different lengths. For example, taking the International Canoe, and assuming L = 17 ft., v_s = 10 knots (16.9 ft./sec.), the appropriate Reynolds' number can be calculated:

$$Re = \frac{v_s L}{\nu} = \frac{16.9 \times 17 \times 10^5}{1.23} = 2.34 \times 10^7$$

For convenience, in Fig. 148 the scales of speeds, in knots and ft./sec., were drawn so that they would correspond to the appropriate Re. Now, taking the roughness of the immersed hull (or the grain size) as 20 mils (.02″), then $L/k = (17 \times 12)/.02 \cong 10.2 \times 10^3 \cong 10^4$. Thus from the graph the skin friction coefficient, when $Re = 2.34 \times 10^7$ (10 knots), and $L/k = 10^4$ (point 3), is $C_f = 0.005$.

The table below gives the degree of roughness k in mils for different types of surface.

Finished and polished surface	0.02 mils	0.00002″
"Smooth" marine paint	2.0 ″	0.002″
Galvanized metal (average)	6.0 ″	0.006″
Ordinary wood	20.0 ″	0.02″
Barnacle growth (average)	200.0 ″	0.2″

In the example shown, the coefficient C_f is calculated for "smooth" bare wood. By covering it with marine paint, k will be reduced to 2.0 mils, and then, by a similar calculation, curve e will produce a coefficient of skin friction $C_f = 0.003$. Yet such a surface is still not hydrodynamically smooth, and the coefficient C_f could be brought down to the point 2 on curve A by polishing to reduce the roughness to the permissible level. This may be easily calculated from the formula:

$$k = \frac{8}{v_s \text{ knots}} = \frac{14}{v_s \text{ ft./sec.}}$$

This means that for a speed of boat v_s = 10 knots k should not exceed 0.8 mils if the surface is to be hydrodynamically smooth.

Permissible roughness for point 2 can be interpolated from curves e and f which approach curve A tangentially above and below point 2.

Point 1 on the "transition curve" below curve A indicates that laminar flow can occur on certain parts of the hull.

Basically then, the permissible roughness depends on the boat's speed. As the speed increases, so the required standard of smoothness becomes more stringent, especially for planing and skimming boats. For nonplaning boats the required smoothness is about 2.0 mils, and this is not very difficult to achieve using marine paints or varnishes.

Two questions may now need an answer: what proportion of the total hydrodynamic resistance is provided by friction resistance, and to what extent can changes in skin friction resistance influence the speed of a yacht?

Figure 149 gives the answer to the first question. It records the results of full-scale measurements carried out on an International Canoe hull in the towing tank at the National Physical Laboratory (U.K.). In fact, this was one of the first attempts to measure the resistance of a full-size hull instead of a model. The lower

Fig. 149

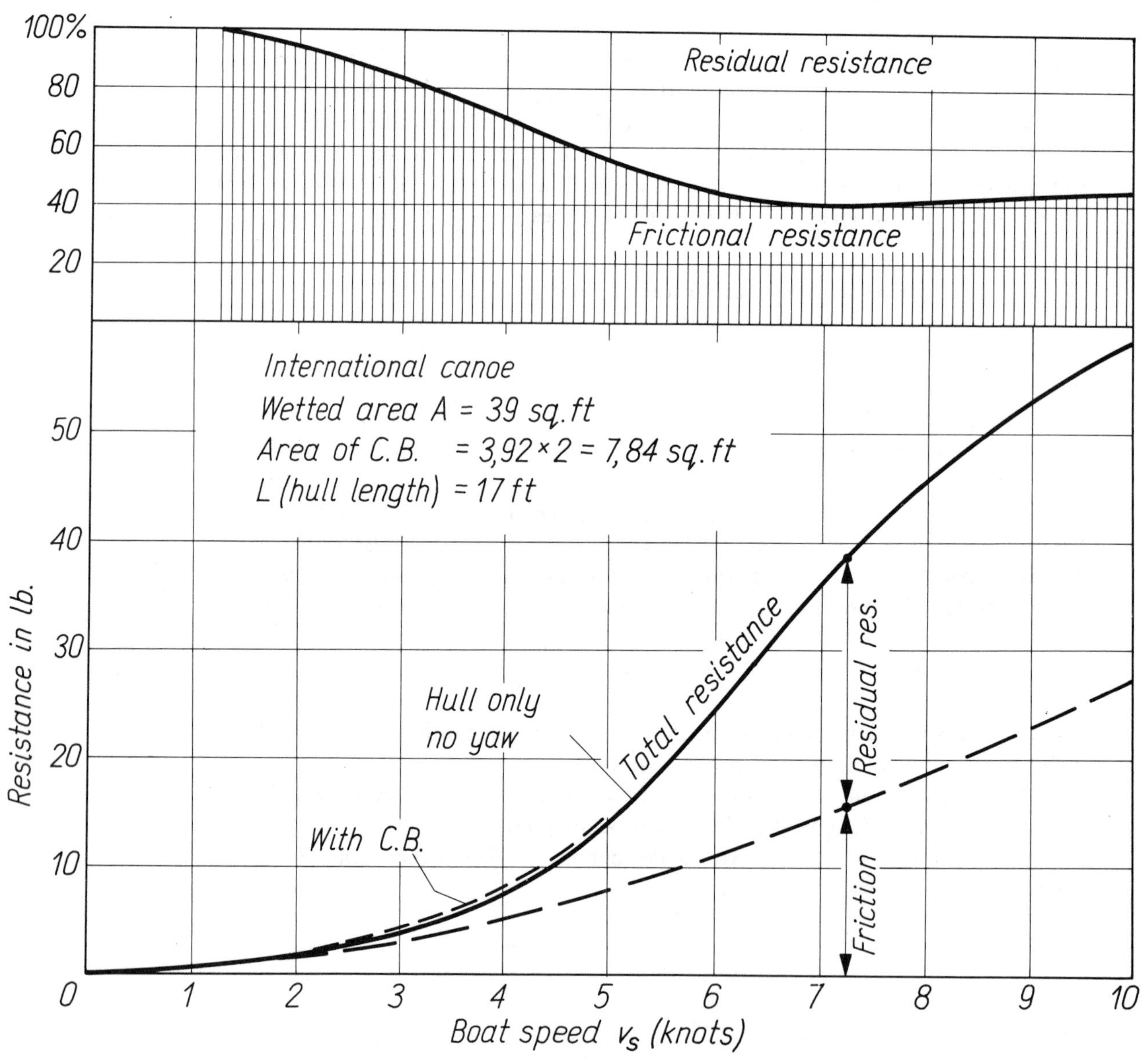

graph gives the total resistance for the hull upright with no yawing and without rudder or centerboard for speeds from 0 to 10 knots, and with the centerboard for speeds from 2 to 5 knots. Below this line, a dotted line gives the curve for the friction resistance of the hull alone for comparison. In this upright position—that is, as though running or broad reaching—residual resistance is virtually limited to wave-making resistance. The upper graph shows the relation between skin friction and residual resistance. At low speeds the predominant factor is friction resistance. As speed increases, wave-making resistance becomes of greater consequence and reaches approximately 60 per cent of the total resistance. Then, for fast planing boats, the importance of frictional resistance again increases slowly. The picture we have given to show the relation between the two kinds of resistance is that of a light craft, sailing with wind astern and without heeling or leeway.

Conditions are not the same on a course to windward, for then two other kinds of hydrodynamic resistance are added—resistance due to leeway and resistance caused by heeling. Residual resistance is then the major factor. This problem will be analyzed in detail later.

The answer to the second question—to what extent can changes in skin friction resistance influence the speed of a yacht—can be found in Fig. 150.

Two curves, relating resistance to speed, are shown for the famous yacht *Gimcrack,* on which the first trials were performed for measuring the aerodynamic coefficients of rigging, now known as "Gimcrack coefficients." One curve represents her total resistance variation with a foul bottom and one with a clean bottom.

If these curves had been taken for two competing yachts of the same class and with the same rigging, then for a driving force on the sails equal to 40 lb. (i.e., a light wind), the yacht with a foul bottom would sail at a speed of 4 knots, while the other's speed would be greater by $\Delta v_s' = 0.27$ knots (i.e., it would sail at 4.27 knots). This obviously means that on a course 1 nautical mile long the gap would be about 385 feet, or about 13 lengths. This, of course, assumes both helmsmen handle their craft with equal skill. In stronger winds, when the driving force on the sails may reach 200 lb., the difference in speed will only be $\Delta v_s'' = 0.14$ knots, since the contribution of friction resistance to total resistance is relatively lower at higher speeds, or, in other words, for greater values of Re.

Skin friction resistance is also involved in another current yachting controversy: to what extent does waxing or oiling the bottom of the hull influence friction resistance? Experiments in the towing tank have proved that the use of these remedies has no measurable effect on resistance. In fact, the widely recommended silicone polish rather surprisingly causes a slight increase in resistance.

However, there is another possible way of reducing skin friction. The transition from laminar flow to a turbulent boundary layer, with its drastic increase in resistance, is connected with the appearance of oscillations, that is, instability of flow within the boundary layer. It is the rigid surface of the hull which promotes this. Max Kramer developed a method for repressing this dynamic instability for greater Re values by imitating the structure of a dolphin's skin. The wetted area is

Fig. 150

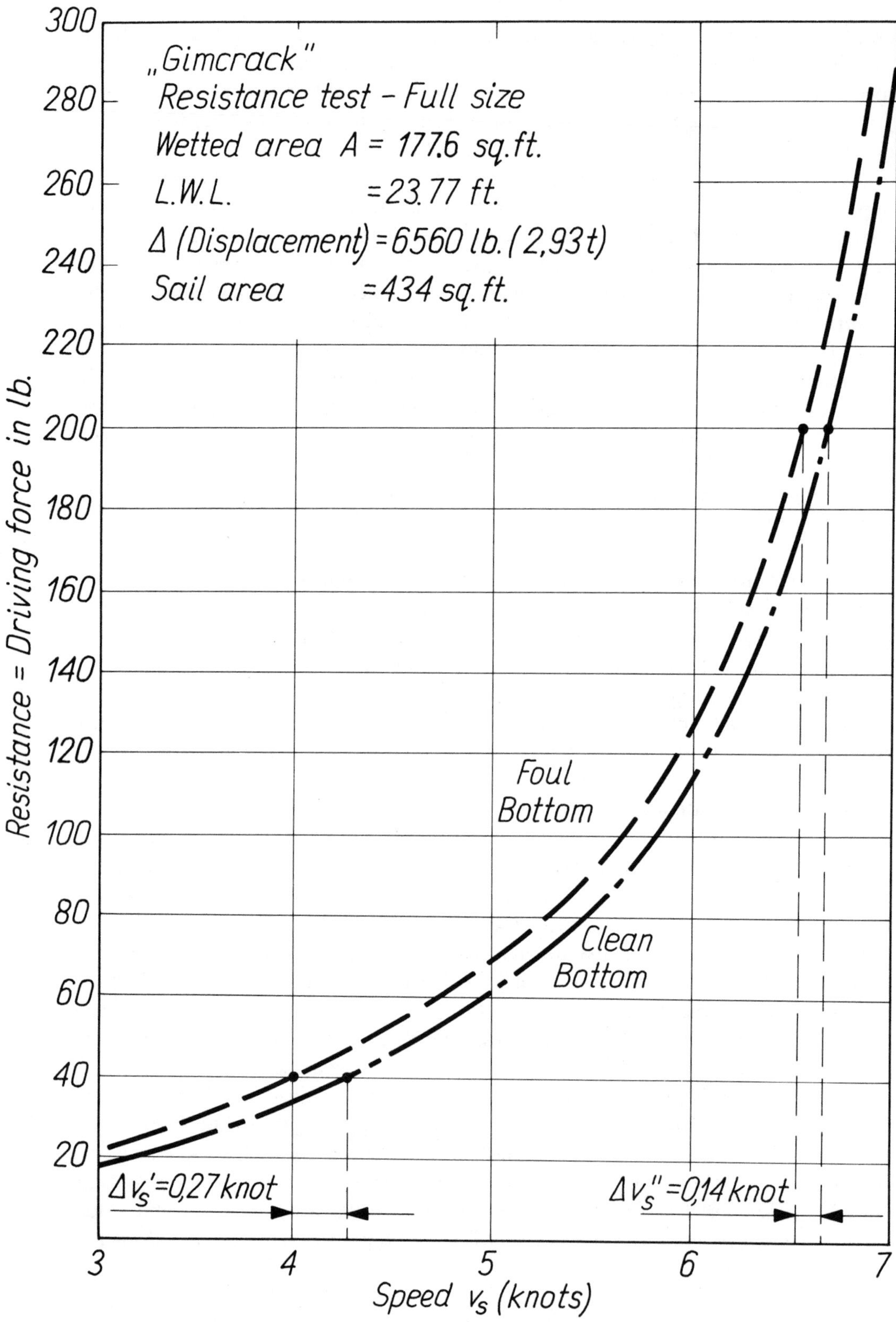

„Gimcrack"
Resistance test - Full size
Wetted area A = 177.6 sq.ft.
L.W.L. = 23.77 ft.
Δ (Displacement) = 6560 lb. (2,93 t)
Sail area = 434 sq. ft.
Foul Bottom
Clean Bottom
Δvs' = 0,27 knot
Δvs'' = 0,14 knot
Resistance = Driving force in lb.
Speed vs (knots)
300
280
260
240
220
200
180
160
140
120
100
80
60
40
20
3
4
5
6
7

covered with a rubberized elastic material called "Laminflo," whose flexible surface, an artificial dolphin's skin, exercises some damping effect and can absorb some of the energy imparted by the vibration of the water particles in a turbulent boundary layer. It was found experimentally that such a stabilization of the boundary layer can reduce friction resistance by almost 50 per cent. It opens new and promising prospects of improving the speed of water-borne craft.

(b) Wave-making Resistance—Rw

Before considering the effects of wave-making resistance on a yacht's performance we must first discover how and why waves are formed around a sailing yacht. The problem can be simplified by assuming that it is the water which moves and that the hull is anchored in a flowing river or tidal current. The flow around the hull will then be the same as if the hull were moving across still water, and measuring the forces on the anchored hull will give the size of the hydrodynamic resistance.

The principle of wave formation can be explained in terms of the well-known physical law that energy is indestructible and can be converted from one form to another. A classical example of this is the stone of mass m thrown upward with an initial speed v. The kinetic energy imparted to the stone causes it to rise, gaining height but at the same time losing this energy. At the point at which the stone pauses and then begins to fall, the kinetic energy ($Ek = mv^2/2$) equals zero. It has changed into the potential energy of displacement or position $Ep = m \times g \times h$ (where g = the acceleration due to gravity) whose measure is the attained height, h. As the stone begins to fall the process is reversed, the potential energy is converted into kinetic energy, and if there were no friction resistance from the air the stone would gain the same kinetic energy—speed—as it had when it was thrown up.

The undulation, no matter whether caused by the motion of the hull or by the wind, consists of a periodic rising and falling of water particles. A certain amount of energy must be used to cause and maintain this oscillating motion. The principle of the conservation of energy, as applied to fluids, has already been treated in Part II under Bernoulli's equation.

Although Bernoulli's equation refers to ideal fluids where there is no friction, approximately correct results are obtained when it is applied to water, which has viscosity. This kind of simplification, already encountered when the flow of air around a sail was considered, makes it easier to understand the formation of waves.

Bernoulli's equation as applied to wave motion is:

$$\frac{\gamma v_1^2}{2g} + \gamma h_1 = \frac{\gamma v_2^2}{2g} + \gamma h_2 = \text{const.}$$

and means that the sum of the kinetic and potential energy of a moving fluid in motion is constant.

Fig. 151

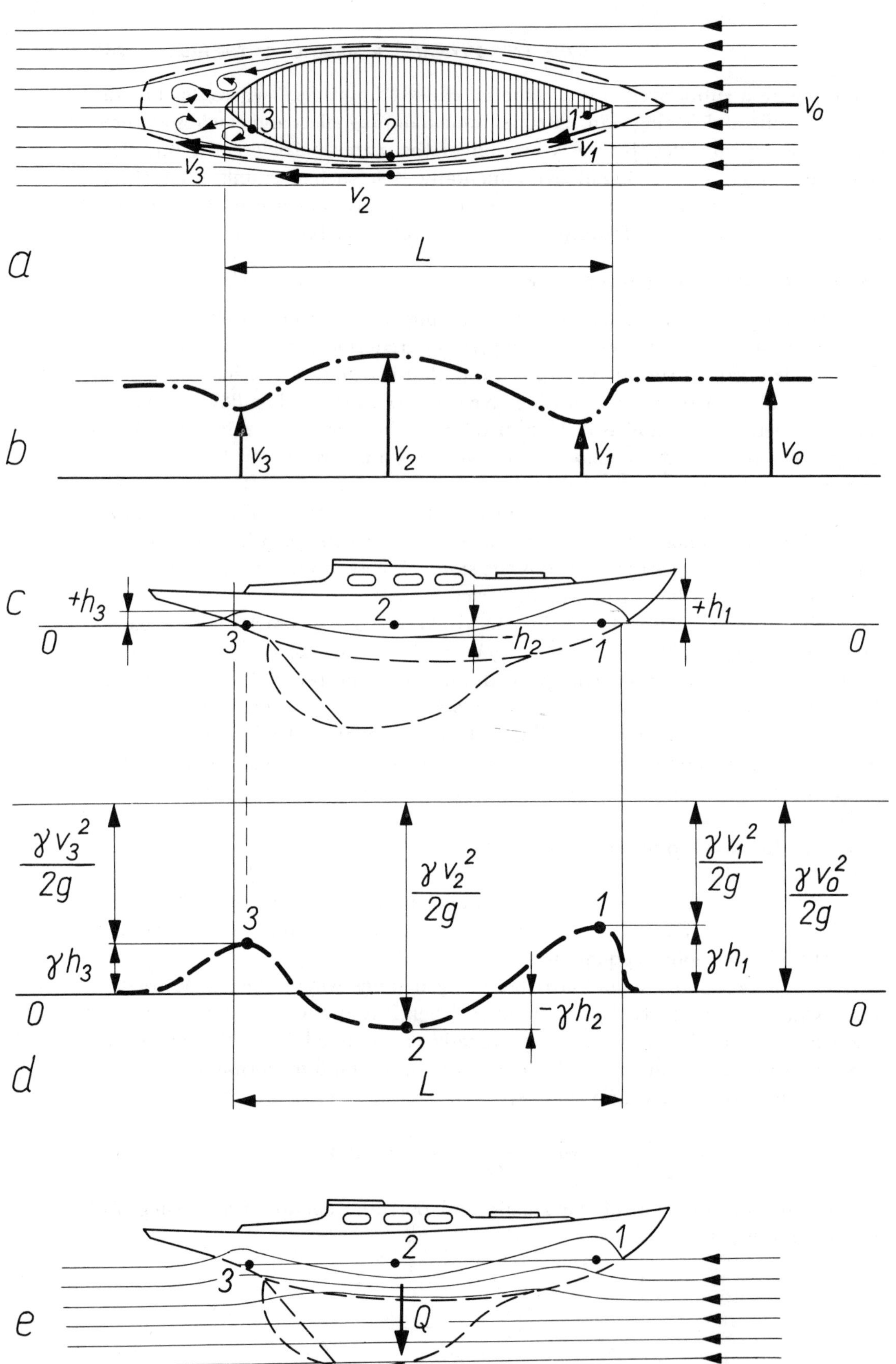

a
b
c
d
e
L
v_0
v_1
v_2
v_3
1
2
3
0
$+h_1$
$-h_2$
$+h_3$
$\frac{\gamma v_0^2}{2g}$
$\frac{\gamma v_1^2}{2g}$
$\frac{\gamma v_2^2}{2g}$
$\frac{\gamma v_3^2}{2g}$
γh_1
$-\gamma h_2$
γh_3
Q

where γ = weight of a unit of volume of 1 cu. ft.

g = gravity acceleration

$\frac{\gamma v^2}{2g}$ is the expression for the kinetic energy

and γh is the expression for the potential energy

If the velocity of the water particles before reaching the hull is v_0 (see Fig. 151a), then at the point 1 of contact with the hull, which is an obstruction, they will be slowed down to velocity v_1, so that $v_1 < v_0$. At point 2 the velocity of the water particles will increase, because the flow contracts, and becomes v_2, and $v_2 > v_0$. In the vicinity of the stern the flow expands, and so the velocity of the particles will fall again to v_3. Thus in the neighborhood of the hull the velocity of the water particles will vary, as shown in Fig. 151b, and so their kinetic energy K.E. must vary also.

At the point 1 the K.E. will fall, but, as the sum of K.E. and the potential energy, P.E., cannot change, the P.E. of the water particles in that position must change correspondingly. The water particles at point 1 will be lifted to the higher level h_1, piling up (as shown in Fig. 151c). The energy equation at this moment will be:

$$\frac{\gamma v_0^2}{2g} = \frac{\gamma v_1^2}{2g} + \gamma h_1$$

At point 2 however the K.E. of the water particles is greater, and their P.E. (γh_2) must therefore be reduced. As they fall below the level 0–0, the energy equation becomes:

$$\frac{\gamma v_0^2}{2g} = \frac{\gamma v_2^2}{2g} - \gamma h_2$$

The variation in these two forms of water particle energy is shown by the curve in Fig. 151d.

In addition to these factors, suction, caused by the contraction of the flow below the bottom of the hull, especially at the section through point 2, will suck the hull below its normal waterline (see Figs. 151e and 152). The magnitude of this sinkage force Q, as will be explained below, varies with the speed of the yacht.

Fig. 152

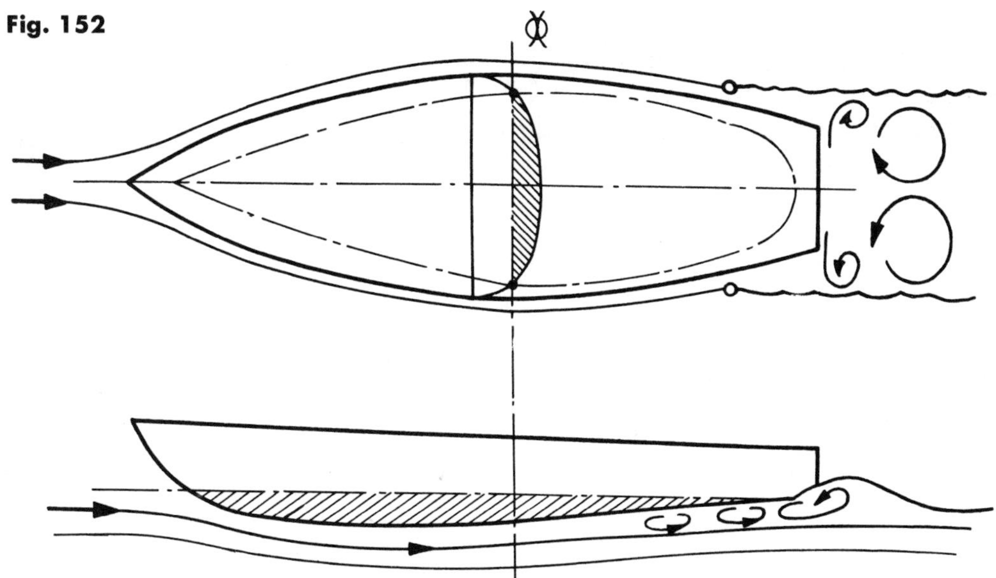

At those points where the K.E. of the water particles decreases, the water will rise, and as the hull passes, the water falls again, setting up the wave motions. The bow and the stern are thus responsible for the two systems of wave-making, bow wave and stern wave. The size of the wave is greater where the changes in the K.E. of the water particles around the hull are greater, that is, where the speed and immersed volume of the hull are greater.

The graphs in Fig. 151d, e make it clear that bow waves are higher than stern waves. The diagrams in Figs. 151a and 152 show also the effects of the viscosity of water. This makes the water unable to follow the lines of the hull, and the flow separates from it at a point well abaft midships. The resultant eddies complicate the problem of the stern wave-making and make the intensity of the stern wave less than its theoretical value, i.e., what it would be but for the viscosity of water.

The wave system around the immersed portion of a moving hull is developed at the expense of energy which would otherwise produce motion. This system is shown schematically in Fig. 153a. It may be divided into two groups, divergent waves and transverse waves, and both types are being constantly generated, near the bow and stern, and move forward with the hull. The divergent waves consist of a series of separate short waves, whose centers lie almost on a straight line running at an angle of 18°–20° to the direction of the motion of the hull. The height of the divergent stern waves is relatively lower than that of the corresponding bow waves. The transverse waves have their crests at right angles to the direction in which the hull is moving, and develop within the space enclosed by the divergent waves. As they get nearer the stern, the length of the crests of the transverse bow waves increases while their height diminishes.

Bow and stern divergent wave systems are propagated separately, cannot combine, and do not interfere with each other. Their significance is relatively slight. The bow transverse waves, however, can be superimposed on to the transverse stern waves, as their length is variable and depends on the velocity of the hull. It is this type of wave which is of fundamental importance in the development of wave-making resistance (see Fig. 153b, c, d, and e).

The length of the transverse waves λ(ft.), measured from one crest to the next, can be calculated, if the speed of the boat v_s is known, from this formula:

$$\lambda(\text{ft.}) = \frac{2\pi\, v_s^2}{g} \quad \text{where } g = 32.17 \text{ ft./sec.}^2$$
$$= 0.195\, v_s^2 \text{ when } v_s \text{ is in ft./sec.}$$
$$= 0.557\, v_s^2 \text{ when } v_s \text{ is in knots}$$

The table below gives the length of the transverse waves formed by a moving body at speeds of from 1 to 10 knots.

v_s in knots	1	2	3	4	5	6	7	8	9	10
λ in ft.	0.557	2.23	5.01	8.91	13.93	20.06	27.30	35.65	45.13	55.71

Fig. 153

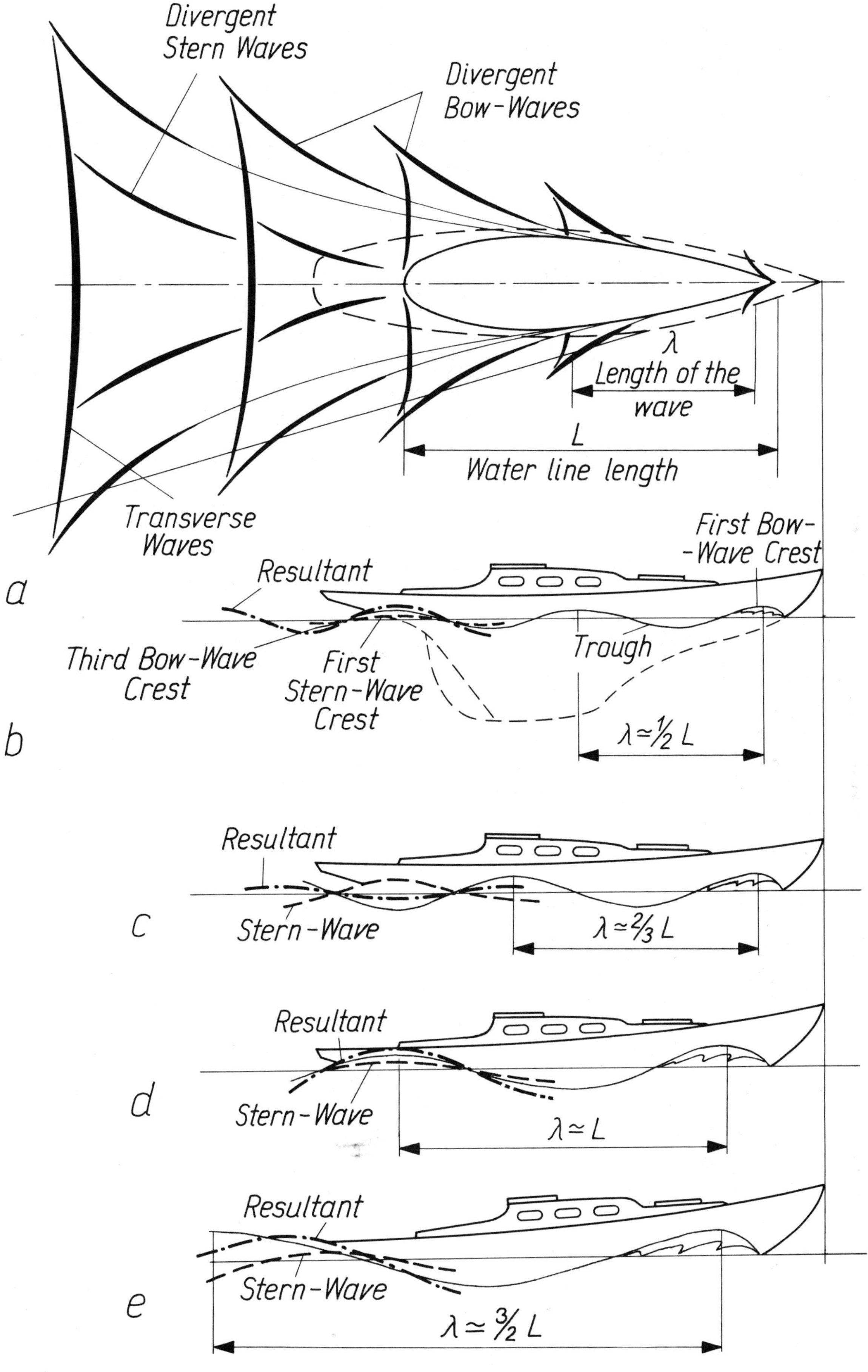

Divergent Stern Waves
Divergent Bow-Waves
λ
Length of the wave
L
Water line length
Transverse Waves
First Bow-Wave Crest
a
Resultant
Third Bow-Wave Crest
First Stern-Wave Crest
Trough
b
λ≃½ L
Resultant
c
Stern-Wave
λ≃⅔ L
Resultant
d
Stern-Wave
λ≃L
Resultant
e
Stern-Wave
λ≃3/2 L

The transverse wave system becomes longer with every increase in speed. Thus, a boat with a LWL of 20 ft., sailing at a v_s of 2 knots, would have nearly 8 waves along the waterline; at 3 knots there would be about 4 waves; and at 6 knots, one wave. From this one can deduce a boat's speed v_s, if the length of a transverse wave is known:

$$v_s \text{ (knots)} = 1.34\sqrt{\lambda}, \text{ if } \lambda \text{ is in feet}$$

Equally, the length of the wave λ produced by the speed of the yacht and the length of the hull are related. When $\lambda = L$, then $v_s/\sqrt{L} = 1.34$. If this is checked against an example where $L = 36$ ft., then, as $v_s/\sqrt{L} = 1.34$:

$$v_s = 1.34\sqrt{36} = 1.34 \times 6 = 8.05 \text{ knots.}$$

At $v_s = 8.05$ knots, the length of the wave is found:

$$\lambda = 0.557 \times v_s^2 = 0.557 \times 8.05^2 = 36 \text{ ft.}$$

This relationship between the length of the wave λ, produced by the velocity v_s, and the length of the hull L (at the waterline) are of fundamental importance in predicting the behavior of all types of boats. It was discovered by William Froude (1810–1870) when he was observing the waves produced by models of similarly shaped hulls. He stated that the hydrodynamic resistance depends on the wave pattern formed around the hull, that is, on the ratio $v_s/\sqrt{L}$, known today to naval architects as the speed–length ratio.

The relationship between the number of waves along a hull of length L and the speed/length ratio $v_s/\sqrt{L}$ is shown in Fig. 154.

When $\dfrac{v_s}{\sqrt{L}} = 0.6$ there are 5 waves along L

When $\dfrac{v_s}{\sqrt{L}} = 0.95$ there are 2 waves along L

When $\dfrac{v_s}{\sqrt{L}} = 1.34$ there is 1 wave along L

In his "Law of Comparison" Froude also laid down the principles by which full-scale resistance may be predicted from experiments with models. The law states that the ratio of wave resistance to displacement is the same for geometrically similar hulls, when the speed/length ratios $v_s/\sqrt{L}$ are the same.

Strictly speaking, the speed/length ratio is a modification of the so-called Froude number $v_s/\sqrt{gL}$, where g is the acceleration due to gravity, but nowadays this number is very seldom used, since g is a constant (32.2 ft./sec.^{2}) and can be omitted.

Froude number: $$\frac{v_s}{\sqrt{gL}} = \frac{v_s/\sqrt{L}}{3.36}$$

The significance of wave patterns and the corresponding speed/length ratio $v_s/\sqrt{L}$ on the degree of wave resistance can be better understood by analyzing

Fig. 154

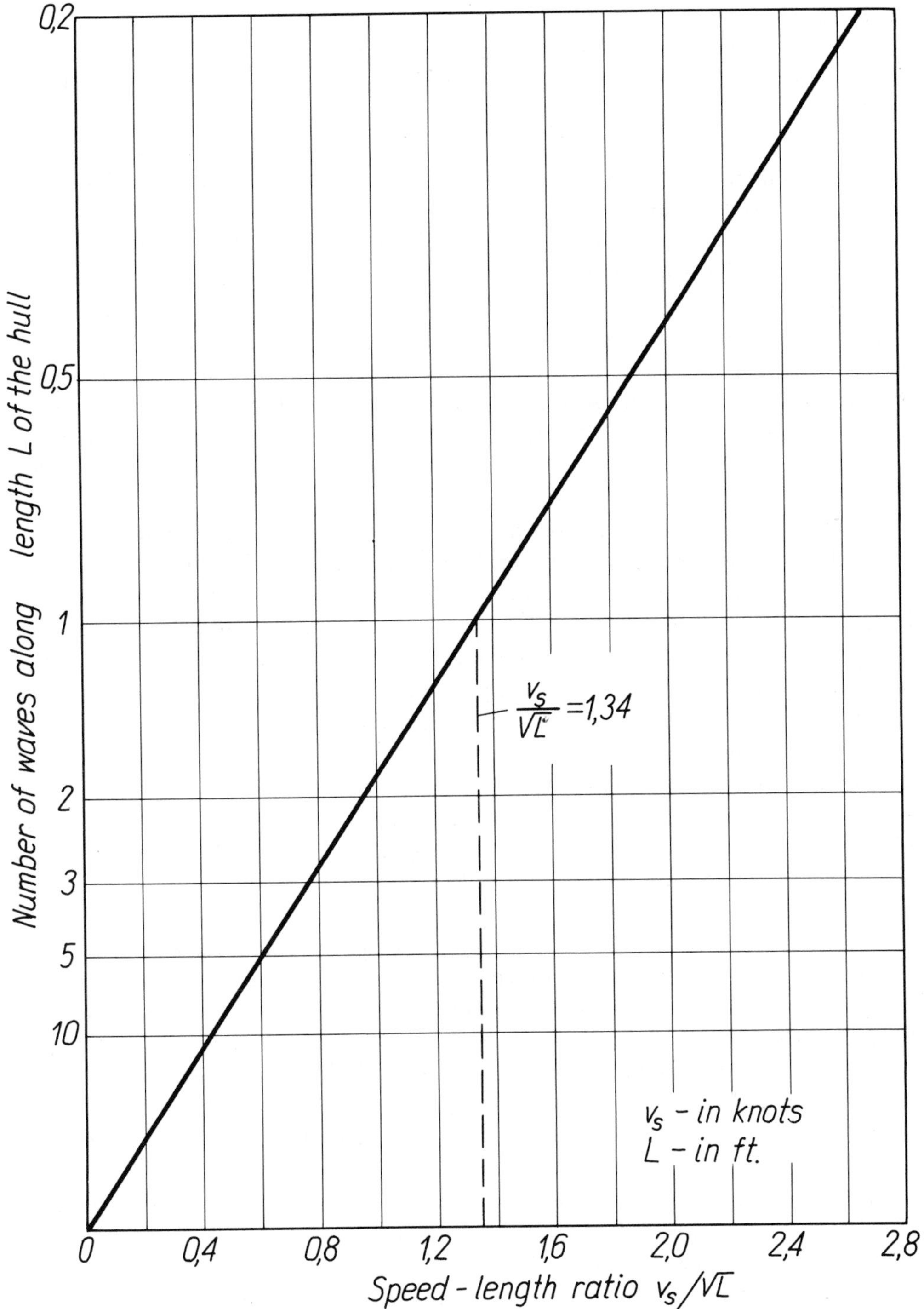

0,2
0,5
1
2
3
5
10
Number of waves along length L of the hull
$\frac{v_s}{\sqrt{L}} = 1,34$
v_s – in knots
L – in ft.
0
0,4
0,8
1,2
1,6
2,0
2,4
2,8
Speed - length ratio $v_s/\sqrt{L}$

Fig. 153. Sketches a and b show what happens when there are two bow waves on a hull of length L, so that the bow and stern transverse wave systems interfere with each other.

The crest of the third bow wave is added to the first stern wave, making the final wave higher. In fact, the wave system which can be observed behind the hull, is a result of the mutual interference between the two wave systems. However, it is possible for the trough of the bow wave to overlap the crest of the stern wave (as is shown in Fig. 153c), and when the two systems are thus in opposition they partly cancel each other.

Figure 153d, e shows a particularly disadvantageous type of interference when the two systems combine to intensify the final wave system. In the case shown in Fig. 153d, where the speed/length ratio $v_s/\sqrt{L} = 1.34$, the yacht is sailing on its own single wave. There is a large crest at the bow, another at the stern, and a trough amidships. Longitudinal trim changes at the same time, the bow rising. If $v_s/\sqrt{L}$ is increased, the stern will "squat" excessively, because the trough of the wave is shifted to the after-body of the hull. As the distribution of displacement along L depends on the wave profile, the hull at this speed is being sucked down below its designed waterline.

Taken together, all these factors have a tremendous effect on the magnitude of the hydrodynamic resistance, limiting the maximum attainable speed, particularly for heavy displacement vessels of deep draft. Thus the system of waves produced by speed becomes a trap from which "displacement types" cannot escape. The total energy lost by a sailing craft in making and maintaining its waves is proportional to the second power of the wave height h and to the length of the wave: $R\alpha(h^2\lambda)$. The resistance to motion increases at the same rate.

Analytical calculation of wave resistance is made difficult by the number of different hull shapes available, and so in practice resistance is deduced indirectly by means of model tests in the towing tank. Figure 155 gives the results of measuring the hydrodynamic resistance created by a model at the Stevens Institute of Technology, United States, converted to full-scale.

The resistance curves relate to a fast cruising yacht of modern design, intermediate between pure racer and pure cruiser, sailing in an upright position with no heel or drift. The total resistance comprises skin friction and wave-making resistance only. The resistance of the hull in an upright position is its basic characteristic, besides being a useful criterion of the running and reaching performance of the yacht. Heavy-displacement yachts of considerable displacement in relation to their length always produce resistance curves which take a sharp turn upward when $v_s/\sqrt{L}$ reaches approximately 1.1. The shape of the total resistance curve in Fig. 155 shows that for a speed/length ratio $v_s/\sqrt{L}$ ranging from 0 to 0.7 the rate at which the resistance increases is relatively slow, roughly according to the square of the speed, so that when the speed v_s is doubled, the resistance is increased four times. So, for a yacht to be able to sail twice as fast, the aerodynamic driving force must be increased four times. In Fig. 155 the resistance

Fig. 155

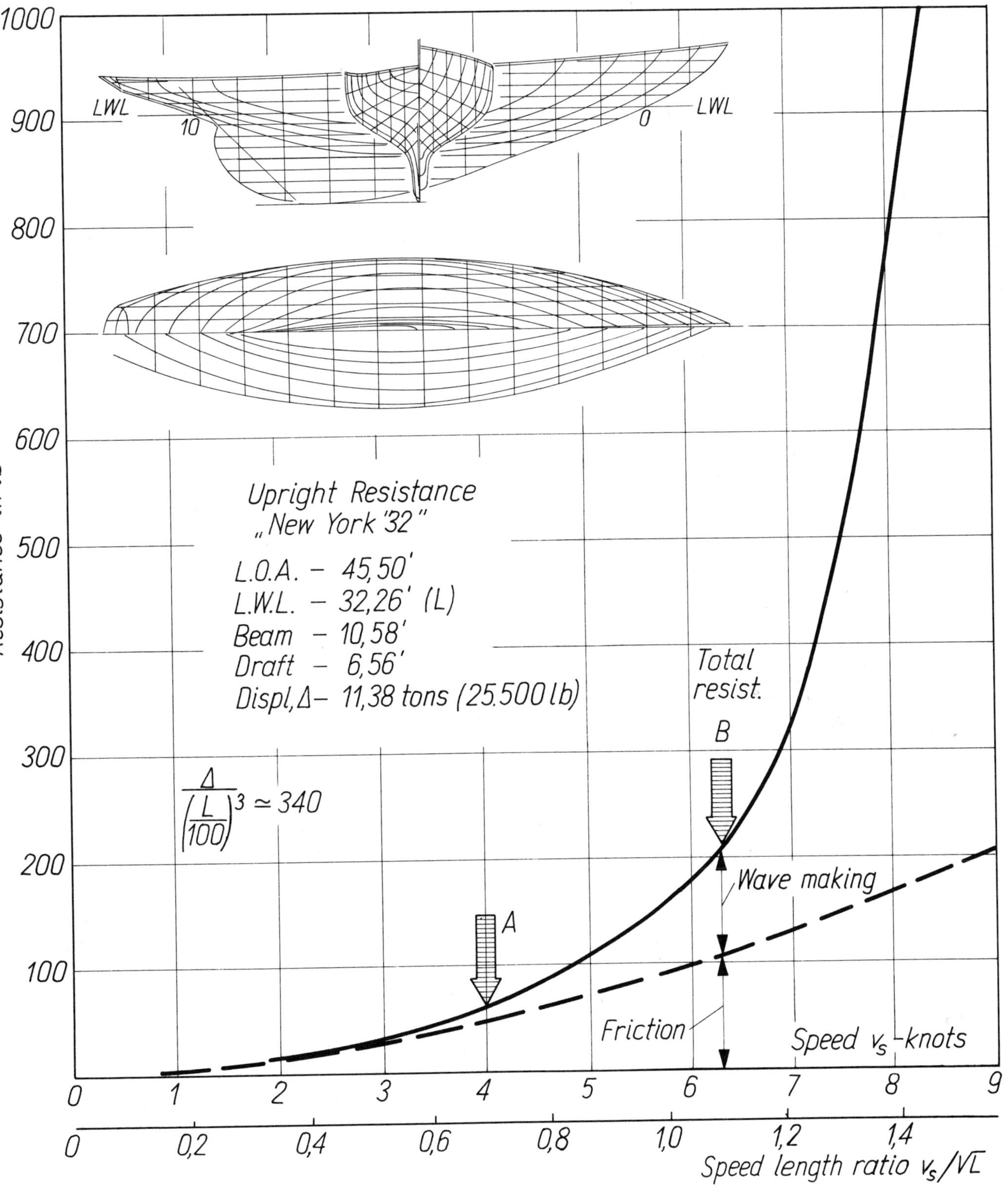

LWL
10
0
LWL
Upright Resistance
„New York '32"
L.O.A. – 45,50'
L.W.L. – 32,26' (L)
Beam – 10,58'
Draft – 6,56'
Displ, Δ – 11,38 tons (25.500 lb)
$\frac{\Delta}{\left(\frac{L}{100}\right)^3} \simeq 340$
Total resist.
B
A
Wave making
Friction
Speed v_s – knots
Speed length ratio $v_s/\sqrt{L}$
1000
900
800
700
600
500
400
300
200
100
0
1
2
3
4
5
6
7
8
9
0,2
0,4
0,6
0,8
1,0
1,2
1,4

at 2 knots is 15 lb., but at 4 knots it is 60 lb. Wave-making in this speed range is not very important, and speed depends mainly on the amount of friction resistance, as reflected by the wetted area and its smoothness.

When the value of $v_s/\sqrt{L} \cong 0.7$ is reached, wave-making begins to have a certain effect, and resistance increases at a higher rate in section A-B than it did in section O-A. From point B, where $v_s/\sqrt{L} = 1.1$, the resistance rate increases very sharply, and can rise to the third, fourth, fifth, or even sixth power of the velocity, especially for heavy-displacement keel boats. Again, Fig. 155 shows that if a speed v_s of 7 knots is to be raised to 8 knots (by 14.3 per cent) the driving force of 340 lb. must be increased to 830 lb. (by 145 per cent). Greater speeds make this situation worse, while at the same time the possibilities of increasing the driving force are limited either by the stability of the yacht, its "power to carry sail," or by the strength of the hull and rigging.

Limitations enforced by the strength of the hull structure and rigging apply particularly to racing keel boats like the 5.5 and Dragon which can easily be overstrained on a reaching course when the crew drives through without reducing sail.

In the most advantageous conditions, the finest heavy-displacement keel boats can achieve a speed/length ratio $v_s/\sqrt{L} = 1.4$; in other terms, a yacht has a maximum speed $v_s = 1.4\sqrt{L}$. J-class boats, which raced for the America's Cup, "the fastest all-round sailing vessels ever built," could reach a speed equal to 1.45 $\sqrt{L}$ in ideal conditions. The famous *Stormy Weather* made her best passage in a big following sea, at 8.8 knots for about 48 hours, a relative speed of $1.42\sqrt{L}$. In the Bermuda regattas, racing yachts sail at an average rate of $0.8\sqrt{L}$ to $1.1\sqrt{L}$. The small, and also famous, *Sopranino* (see Fig. 13) crossed the Atlantic in 1951 from the Canary Islands to Barbados, 2800 miles, in 28½ days, which with her LWL of 16 ft. gives her a relative speed of $1.03\sqrt{L}$.

It may now be instructive to compare the relative speeds of yachts with those of ships which are driven by the mechanical power of their turbines and not by the wind. Destroyers can reach $v = 2\sqrt{L}$ by using turbines that develop 36,000 h.p. The fast passenger liner, *Queen Mary*, can reach a speed of about 30.5 knots, which, with her LWL of 1000 feet, gives:

$$\frac{v}{\sqrt{L}} = \frac{30.5}{\sqrt{1000}} = 0.96, \text{ or } v = 0.96\sqrt{L}$$

From Fig. 154 it can be seen that she sails with two self-generated waves along her waterline length, and so below the critical speed/length ratio of 1.1 where wave-making resistance becomes considerable. Typical cargo vessels seldom exceed $v = 0.5\sqrt{L}$, and their turbines are mainly occupied in overcoming friction resistance.

These facts prove convincingly that keel yachts compare favorably with transport vessels using power. In fact, sail is quite superior in relative attainable speed, the only true criterion for comparing boats of different LWL. For most of the time, however, yachts sail at an average relative speed $v_s = 0.9\sqrt{L}$, and at this speed skin friction is the principal source of resistance.

We already know that the resistance of the yacht increases as the square of the height of the waves that this motion creates. Now if the displacement (or the immersed volume of the hull, which corresponds to it) is reduced, the character of the resistance will also be changed, and with it, the maximum attainable speed. A very useful criterion for comparing the ability of boats to attain high sailing speeds is the displacement/length ratio:

$$\frac{\Delta}{(L/100)^3}$$

where Δ is the displacement in tons (1 ton = 2240 lb.)
L = waterline length in feet

In using this ratio one must bear in mind that whereas displacement Δ is a speed-reducing factor, the length L, taken with it, is the speed-producing factor. Figure 156 demonstrates the importance of this ratio by comparing the resistance curves for two yachts, a 6-Meter and a 5.5-Meter, sailing upright. Both yachts have a similar LWL of 23 ft., but the 6-Meter has almost twice the displacement of the 5.5. The appropriate values for the displacement/length ratio are given in Fig. 156. The 6-Meter, a typical heavy-displacement boat, is similar to the *New York 32* previously described (Fig. 155), for which

$$\frac{\Delta}{(L/100)^3} = 340.$$

Fig. 156

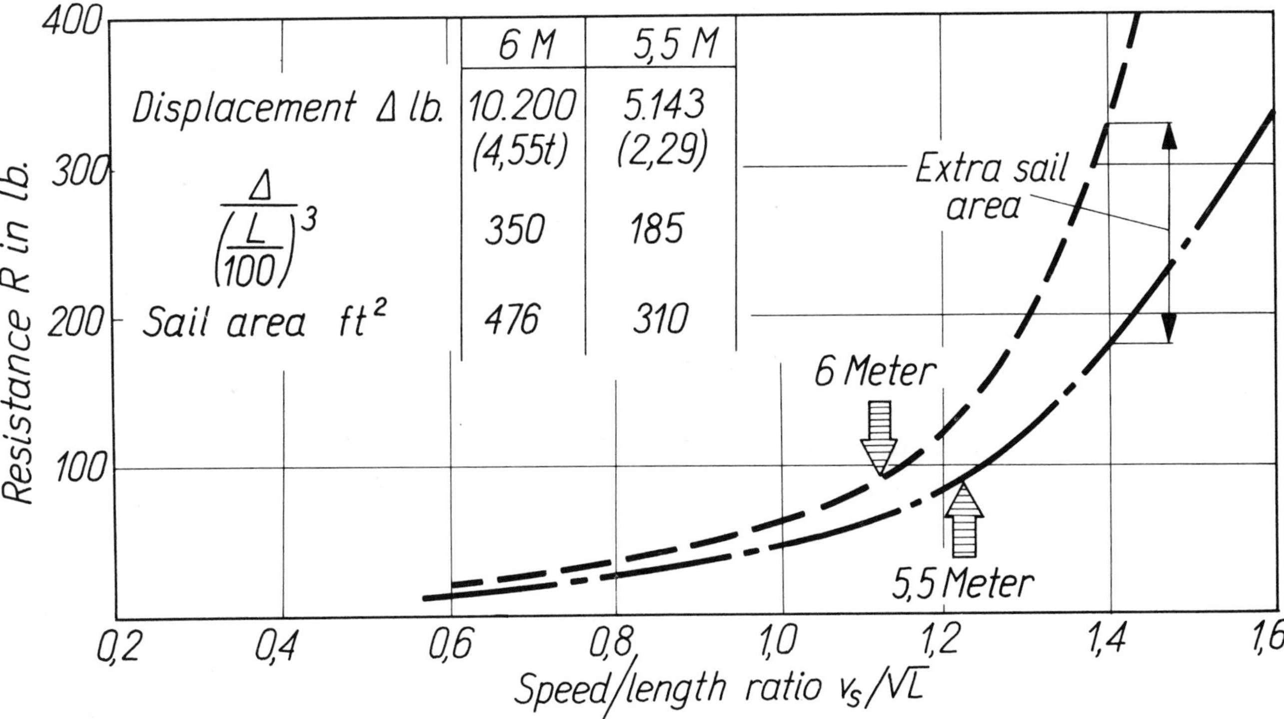

The 5.5, however, represents rather the light-displacement type. The difference gives the lighter craft the advantage in stronger winds (i.e., for a greater speed/length ratio). Both yachts could reach a relative speed $v_s = 1.4\sqrt{L}$, but for this the driving force needed by the 5.5-Meter will be about 180 lb., and for the 6-Meter about 325 lb. If the driving force is assumed to be approximately proportional to sail area, then a 6-Meter would need to carry about 83 per cent more sail area than a 5.5 to balance the negative effect of its greater displacement. In fact, the 6-Meter's sail area is only about 54 per cent greater, and it is therefore bound to be defeated by the faster 5.5.

In Fig. 156, it can be seen that both the curves for the 5.5-Meter and the 6-Meter turn upward suddenly, indicating increased wave-making. Beyond this point, however, the angle of the curve for the 5.5-Meter is not so steep as that of the 6-Meter: this shows that its resistance barrier to speed is not so great. Compared with the 6-Meter, the 5.5-Meter is a low wave-making type.

A reduction in the rate of increase of hydrodynamic resistance by using a lower displacement/length ratio can be comparatively easily obtained with the smaller boats, not exceeding 30 ft. LWL. For a longer boat, like the ocean cruiser, it is difficult to devise an adequately strong, seaworthy and comfortable hull, and yet employ a sufficiently low displacement/length ratio.

However, the 5.5-Meter has, of course, no chance of reaching "planing speeds," as her displacement/length ratio is still too high. Planing is a form of high speed sailing which can only be achieved by drastic reduction of hull fullness, that is, cutting down the space within the hull. Equally, sea-keeping ability must be lowered below that of a "normal" yacht. Froude defined sea-keeping ability as "the combination of habitability and speed." In a cruising yacht, habitability comes first because it is no use having a fast boat if she exhausts her crew. For those seeking the thrill of planing on sheltered water a happy combination of displacement, length, and sail area might be found in the Flying fleet designed by Uffa Fox (cf. Photo. 28, which shows the *Flying Twenty-five*).

The *Flying Fifteen*, a typical representative of the family, has a displacement/length ratio:

$$\frac{\Delta}{(L/100)^3} = \frac{0.447}{(15/100)^3} = 132$$

and can reach a maximum speed of 12 knots, i.e., the speed/length ratio

$$\frac{v_s}{\sqrt{L}} = \frac{12}{\sqrt{15}} = 3.1$$

Although the yacht is actually a keel boat, it deviates considerably from the classical keel boat concept which is the product of the I.Y.R.U. policy on habitability and speed (cf. Part I, Yachts and Rating Formulas).

Figure 157a, b shows the *Flying Fifteen* and the 5.5-meter, a typical I.Y.R.U. class. A comparison of the wetted area and waterline of both boats, aft of the midships section, is particularly instructive.

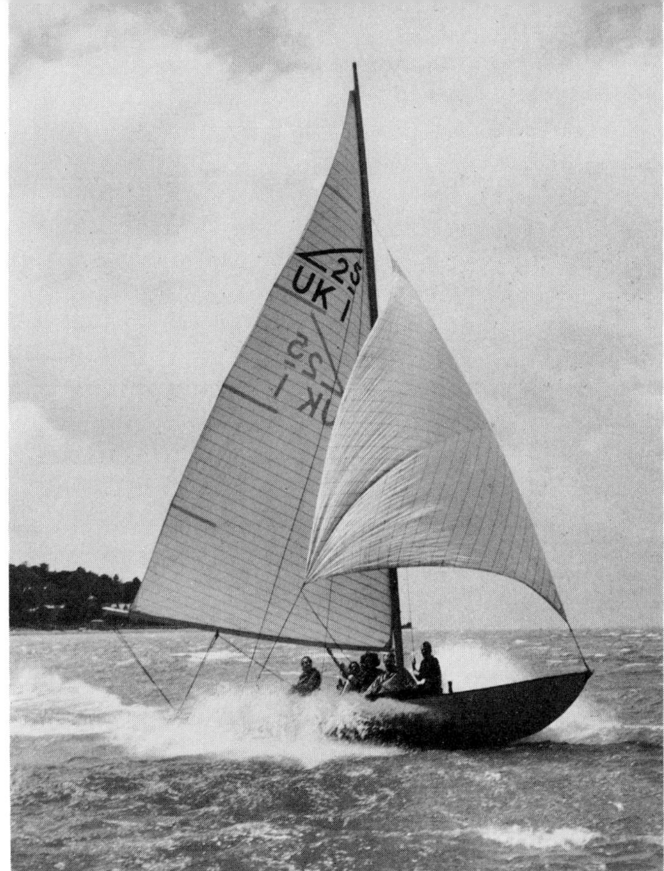

Photo. 28

It is known from experiments that a value of

$$\frac{\Delta}{(L/100)^3} = 150$$

is about the upper limit for a planing boat, but it is not a sufficient criterion in itself, as other factors have to be considered. To discover these, however, we must define "high-speed sailing" and analyze the behavior of water-borne craft at higher speeds.

(c) Basic Stages in Yacht Motion

It is known both from experience of sailing in the normal way and also from towing tank tests that the longitudinal trim of a hull under sail is not stable as speed increases. Every sailing craft changes her fore and aft trim according to the wave pattern generated along the hull and the size of the dynamic forces of water pressure on the bottom of the hull. Whatever the length and displacement, there is a typical way in which trim changes with the increase in speed. As an example, the results obtained at the National Physical Laboratory (U.K.) in full-scale tests of an International Sailing Canoe (displacement 435 lb.; cf. Fig. 25) can be considered. While the measurements were being made, the Canoe was allowed to take up its natural fore and aft trim, and the towing force was applied at approximately water level. These results can be extended and other craft included so that our basic knowledge of the factors which influence the behavior of a yacht sailing upright could be improved.

Fig. 157

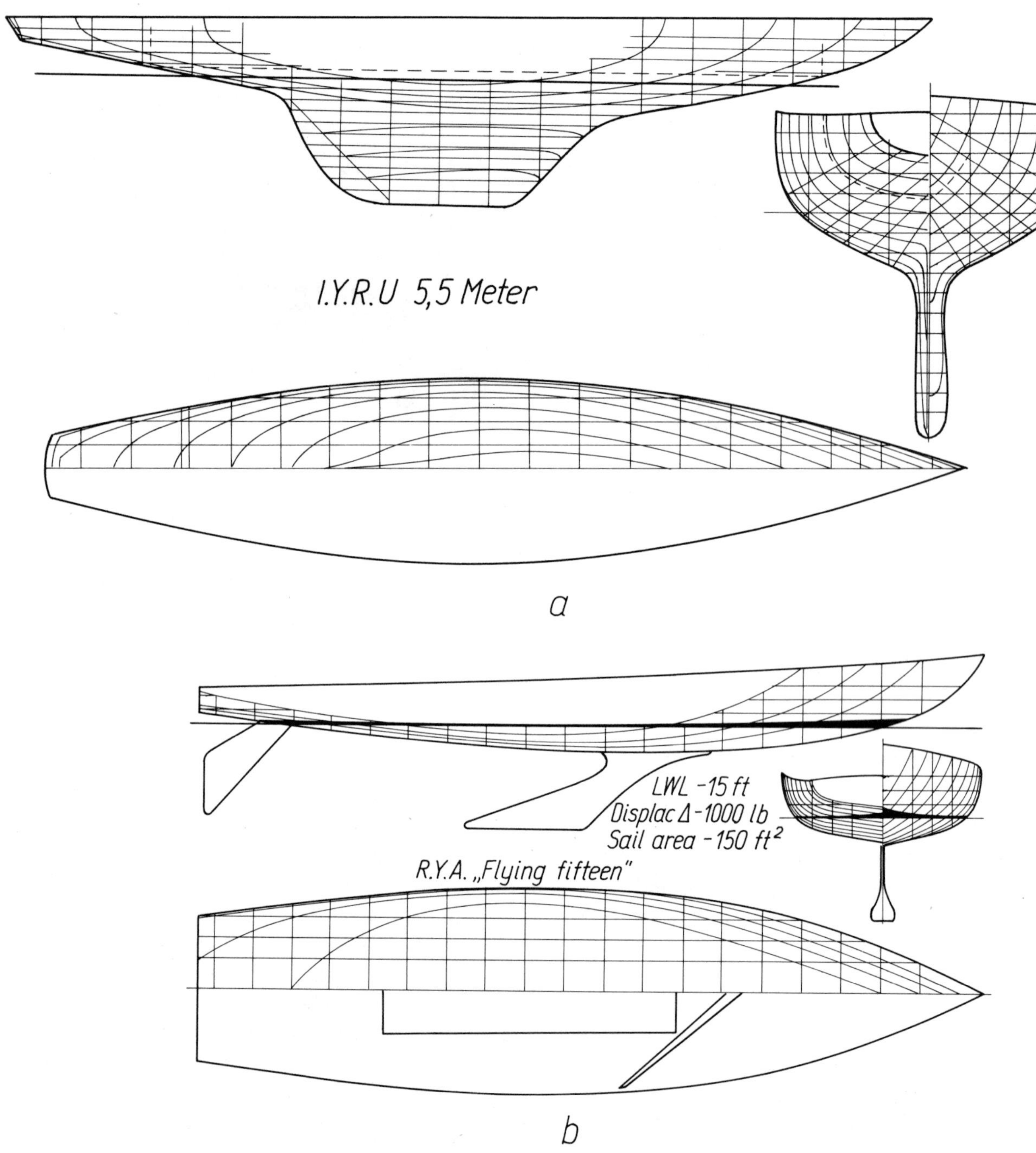
I.Y.R.U 5,5 Meter
a
LWL -15 ft
Displac Δ-1000 lb
Sail area -150 ft²
R.Y.A. „Flying fifteen"
b

Figure 158 deals with trim and resistance for the Canoe sailing upright and is in three sections, 1, 2, and 3. The lower graph shows total resistance for boat speeds v_s from 0 to 9.5 knots. At the top are given the corresponding changes in bow, stern, and midship positions compared to normal level trim (that is, to DWL, designed water line). The scale of the speed/length ratio is inserted between the two graphs, and applies to both. The curves on the top graph above v_s = 9.5 knots have been interpolated from different data.

Fig. 158

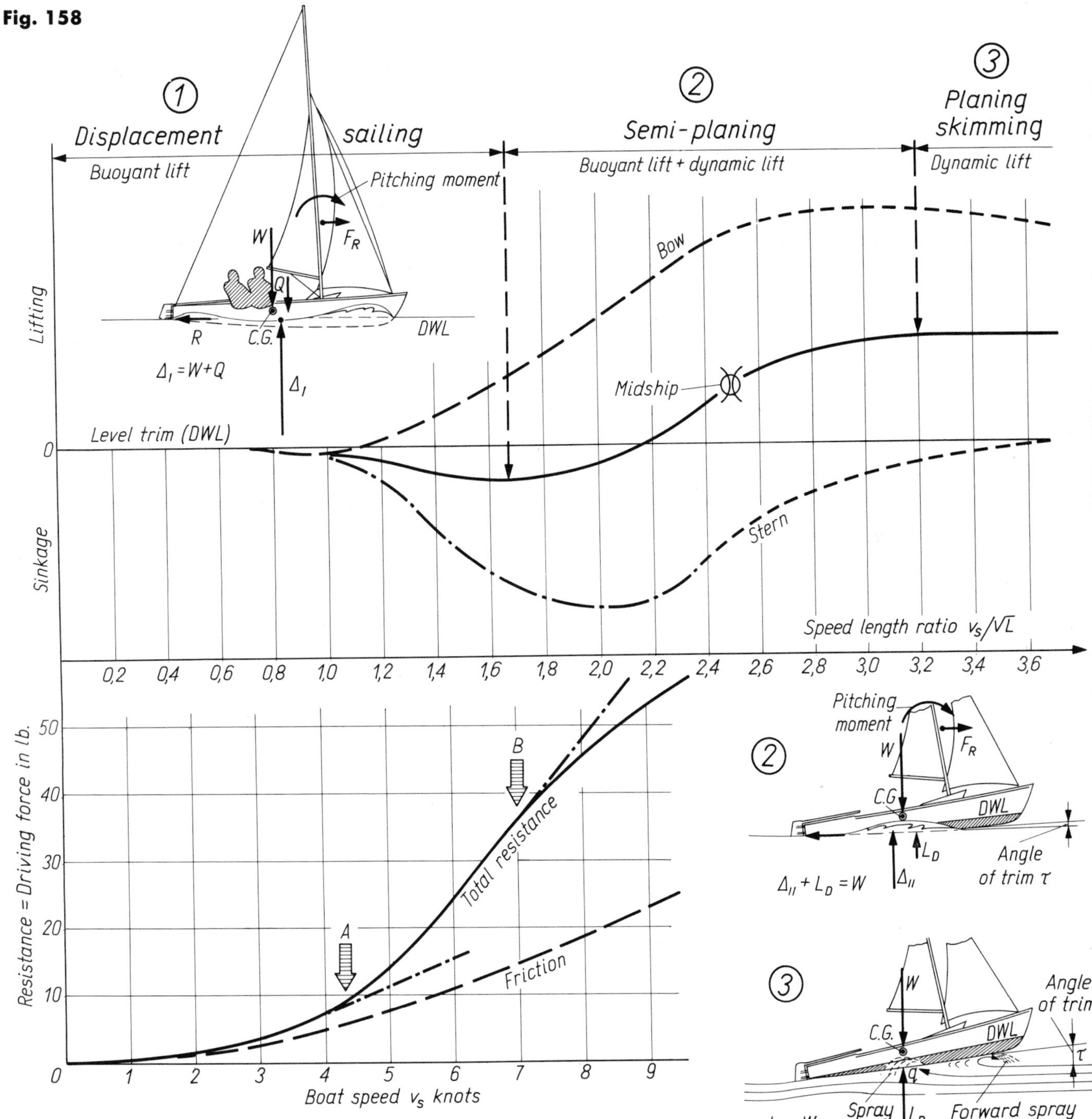

Within a speed range of 0 to 3 knots, corresponding to $v_s/\sqrt{L}$ of 0 to 0.7, the boat maintains the same trim as when at rest. The pitching moment of the aerodynamic driving component F_R, which might tend to depress the bow and raise the stern, is slight at low speeds. Its effect depends on the weight W of the boat. For heavy-keel boats it is negligible, and for the *New York 32,* for instance, at $v_s/\sqrt{L} = 0.7$, the driving force (which equals the resistance) is only $60/(11.38 \times 2240)$ approximately .23 per cent of the displacement (Δ). In practice a relatively small driving force like this cannot produce a visible change in the longitudinal trim of the hull.

For the Canoe, too, the magnitude of the driving force $F_R = R$ with respect to weight W at $v_s = 3$ knots is almost 1 per cent and also negligible. The boat sails with about four waves along her length, and her total weight W is supported by a lift that is equivalent to the mass of water displaced by the volume ∇ of the immersed hull. From the time the speed/length ratio $v_s/\sqrt{L}$ passes 0.7, however, the Canoe's hull tends to sink lower in the water, because the dynamic force of suction Q appears. Hydrodynamic resistance then increases as well, partly because the hull has sunk lower, but chiefly because of the increased importance of wave-making. Buoyant lift, equivalent to the displacement Δ_1, has now to balance the sum of the forces W and Q.

When $v_s/\sqrt{L}$ exceeds 1.0 the stern will begin to squat, and the bow to lift, an effect particularly marked in boats with a sharp stern. This condition will continue to develop as speed increases until a specific limit is reached. Sinking of the hull continues progressively until $v_s/\sqrt{L} \cong 1.7$. As the speed/length ratio, or the driving force, increases, there is a tendency for longitudinal trim to change due to the wave pattern generated along the hull. This tendency is opposed by the aerodynamic pitching moment (see Fig. 158, section 2). These phenomena are not important for heavy-keel boats, but for light craft, such as the Finn and F.D., their significance cannot be ignored. In fact, it is often necessary for the crew to shift their weight aft to counter this downward pressure from the sail. This problem will be discussed fully later.

Dynamic lift is of little consequence with $v_s/\sqrt{L}$ ranging from 0 to 1.7. The boat floats on the water, as it must while governed by the Law of Archimedes. It is supported entirely by the buoyant lift of the water. This stage is commonly called "displacement sailing." The majority of sailing boats and, of course, all deep-draft keel boats (the displacement types) never pass beyond this form of motion (Fig. 158, section 1). It is interesting to notice that a boat's displacement Δ, or the immersed volume ∇ which corresponds to it, changes when the vessel is moving, and is exactly equal to the boat's weight only when she is at rest or moving very slowly.

When the ratio of driving force to weight F_R/W approaches 0.1, the speed is high enough to drive the boat up the slope of its bow wave. The hull is inclined to the water surface at the angle τ (cf. Fig. 158, section 2), and forces of dynamic pressure, i.e., dynamic lift L_D, begin to have an effect on the bottom of the hull. At a speed marked on the lower diagram by the arrow B, the effect of the dynamic lift

L_D becomes stronger than that of dynamic suction Q, and the hull begins to emerge slowly from the water. This can be seen on the upper graph, where the middle curve represents the degree of immersion of the midship section in relation to normal trim at rest.

As the hull ceases to sink, so resistance to motion decreases, and the slope of the hydrodynamic resistance curve falls. This critical moment, very important for high-speed sailing, can be seen on the total resistance curve in Fig. 158 below the arrow B. The International Canoe reached this transition point when the ratio of driving force to boat's weight $F_R/W = 37/453 \cong 0.08$, i.e., about 8 per cent, and when the speed/length ratio was approximately 1.7. The value of $v_s/\sqrt{L}$ at which the dynamic lift L_D takes effect depends primarily on the displacement/length ratio and on hull shape. For the International Canoe

$$\frac{\Delta}{(L/100)^3} = \frac{0.203 \text{ ton}}{(17/100)^3} = 41.5,$$

which is particularly low and makes high speeds possible.

The other factors which have a major influence on a boat's ability to attain a high speed are stability and sail area. Of these, stability, which regulates the effective driving force in stronger winds, is achieved in the case of the International Canoe in a somewhat unusual way. A scrutiny of Photo. 29 will explain better than any description the extent to which the combination of the major factors such as sail area, stability, length, and displacement differs from that of the traditional "normal" yacht.

Photo. 29

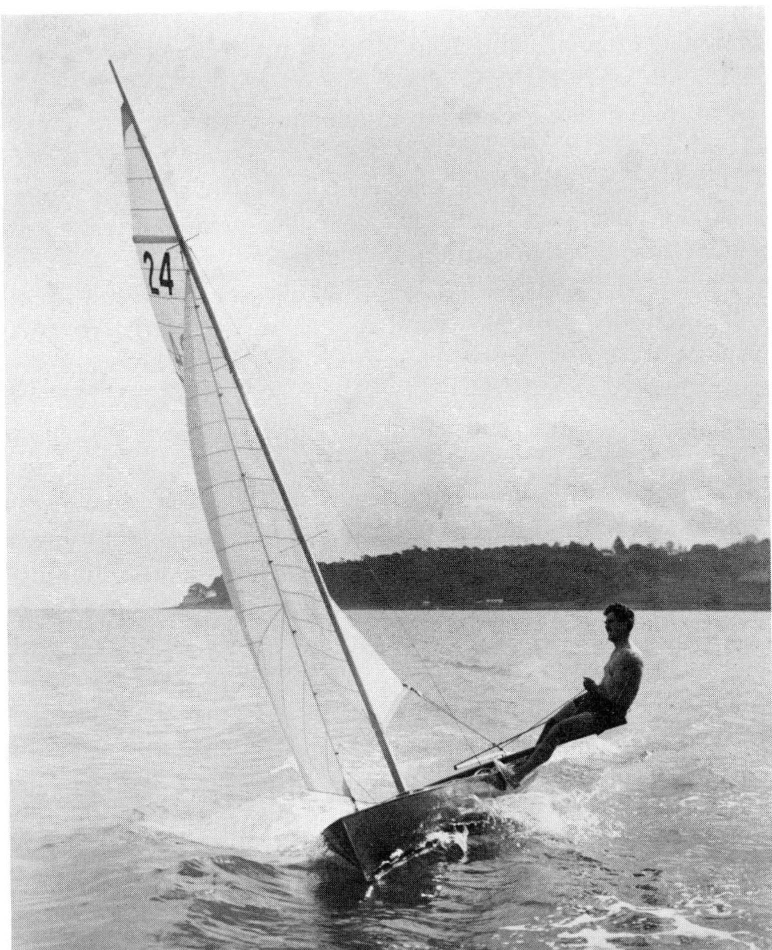

The table below, which compares the displacement/length ratio of the Canoe with other well-known and fast boats may justify this description by her builder Uffa Fox: "... no other singlehanded boat can match them in speed or movement as they slip along with the grace of an ocean bird. . . ."

International Canoe:	41.5
International Finn:	92
International Flying Dutchman:	54
International 5-0-5:	79
International 14 ft.:	98
National Merlin–Rocket:	105
Class A (Inland Lake Scow):	70

A further glance at Photo. 29, and especially at the helmsman, however, reveals the price to be paid for this pleasure. The basis of high-speed sailing can be summarily defined as drastic sacrifice of space within the hull.

The canoe's maximum speed of about 16 knots gives her a speed/length ratio

$$\frac{v_S}{\sqrt{L}} = \frac{16}{\sqrt{17}} \cong 4$$

and thus a relative speed of $v_S = 4\sqrt{L}$. An analysis of Fig. 159 may make even clearer the importance of the displacement/length ratio on attainable speed. This graph gives resistance curves for the "Narrow Finn" model, in an upright position and at different loadings, as obtained by Professor Ata Nutku of Istanbul University. Curves A, B, C, and D relate to the hull without appendages (centerboard or rudder). The curve on the left, included for comparison, relates to the same model fitted with a ballast keel and rudder. Form lines for the Narrow Finn were derived from the original Finn (Fig. 19) by multiplying width measurements by 0.8 and depth measurements by 1.2.

The figure shows that the attainable relative speeds for a driving force of 3 lb. will be $v_S = 1.69\sqrt{L}$, $1.79\sqrt{L}$, $1.82\sqrt{L}$, and $1.94\sqrt{L}$ for models A, B, C, and D, respectively, so that the difference in relative speed between the light A and the heavy D model is about 15 per cent. For greater driving forces (i.e., in stronger winds) these differences are more marked.

Deductions of the same kind can be made for full-scale boats, and results will correspond to those found for the models if the proportions between their displacements are known. Hence we may draw the conclusion that for the one-design classes such as the Flying Dutchman, 5-0-5 and Finn nothing will reduce resistance so much as cutting the boat's weight down to the lowest permitted level. This is why in many racing classes there is a trend toward reducing the weight of the crew, while simultaneously trying to use to the utmost advantage this human "movable ballast." Efficient toe-straps, sliding seats, and trapezes allow the crew to sit out as far as possible. The problem is in fact that of finding the optimum crew weight which gives the best compromise between keeping the boat upright and re-

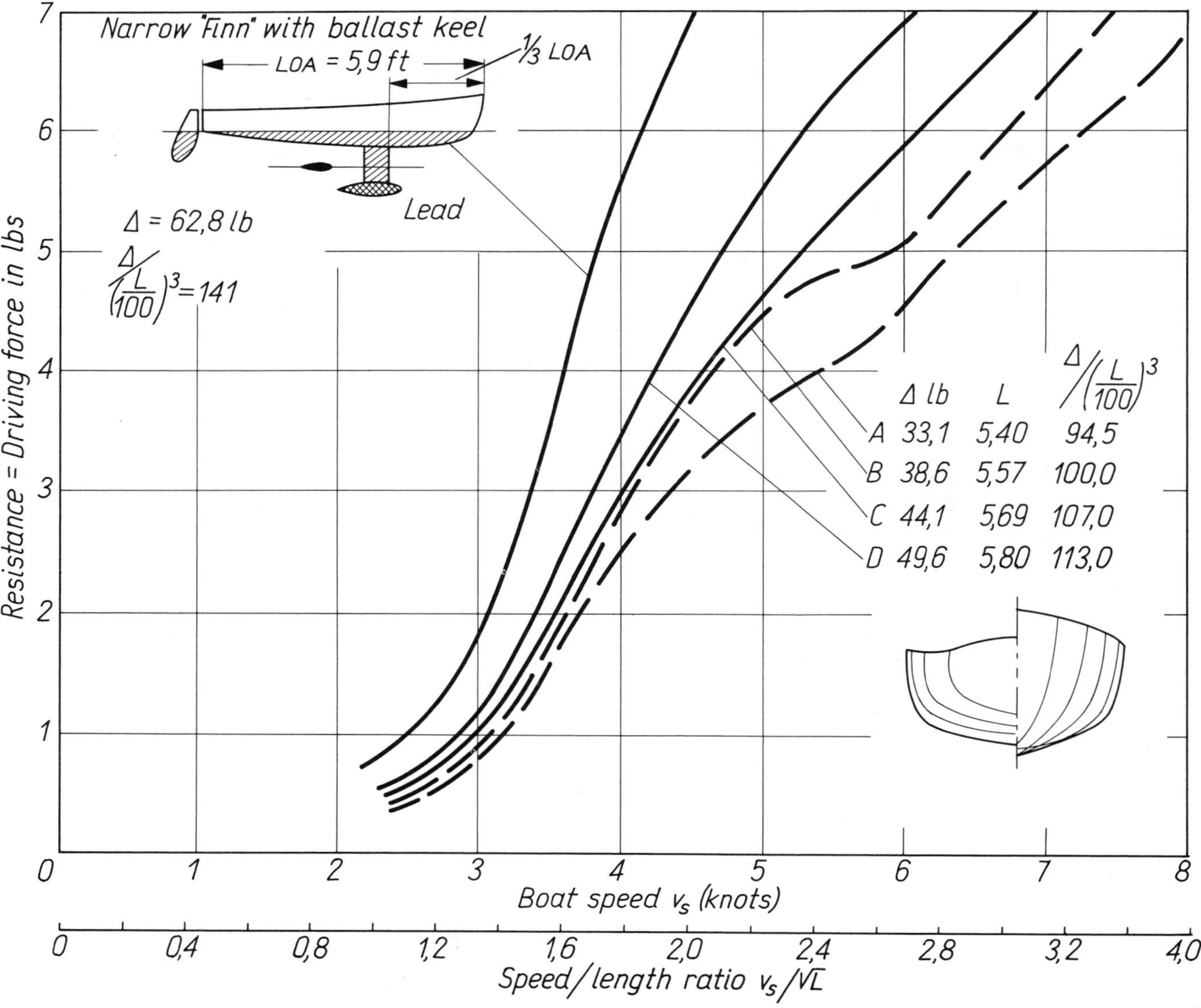

Narrow "Finn" with ballast keel
LOA = 5,9 ft
1/3 LOA
Lead
Δ = 62,8 lb
Δ/(L/100)³ = 141
Δ lb L Δ/(L/100)³
A 33,1 5,40 94,5
B 38,6 5,57 100,0
C 44,1 5,69 107,0
D 49,6 5,80 113,0
Resistance = Driving force in lbs
0 1 2 3 4 5 6 7
0 1 2 3 4 5 6 7 8
Boat speed vs (knots)
0 0,4 0,8 1,2 1,6 2,0 2,4 2,8 3,2 4,0
Speed/length ratio vs/√L

Fig. 159

Photo. 30

ducing its total weight. Efficient self-bailing equipment sees to it that the boat is dry, and so lighter, especially when racing in heavy weather.

Further consideration of Fig. 158 is now necessary. If the driving force is sufficiently large (about 0.1 of the boat's weight) the hull will start to rise under the influence of dynamic lift, and the mid-section returns to level trim. As speed continues to increase, the wetted area is again reduced, and therefore the rate of the rise of hydrodynamic resistance decreases. (Hydrodynamic resistance does still increase, but at a lower rate.) Now the bow wave shifts toward the midship section and the bow rises above the water, and the impression given is that the boat is beginning to plane (cf. Fig. 158, section 2; Photo. 30). However, this stage is not yet "planing" in the hydrodynamic sense. The boat, partly immersed, is floating on the surface of the water supported on its buoyant lift plus dynamic lift, which together balance the weight of the boat. This stage of motion, when the boat floats supported by both hydrostatic and hydrodynamic forces, may be called *semi-planing.* The term planing or skimming should properly be reserved for describing pure hydrodynamic planing. Semi-planing (Fig. 158, section 2), then, starts at the moment when the dynamic forces created by the speedy passage of the hull through the water begin to make their influence felt. At the same time, there is good reason for accepting the view that high-speed sailing may be defined as beginning at this point. Semi-planing ends when pure planing begins, that is, when the boat rises above the surface of the water and is supported entirely by dynamic lift, so that the hull has emerged almost completely from the water and is skimming over its surface. For the International Canoe the semi-planing range lies within speed/length ratios of 1.7 to 3.2. These values, of course, vary from boat to boat, and depend on the chosen combination of the main factors: sail area, displacement, length, and stability.

It is important to understand two terms used by yachtsmen: "displacement form" and "planing form." The first group will be represented by such classical heavy-keel yachts as *New York* (Fig. 155), the 6-Meter, and the Dragon (Fig. 17)—all yachts with a displacement/length ratio above 150. As they never exceed the maximum displacement speed of $1.7\sqrt{L}$ and always float supported by the buoyant lift of the water, the shape of their hulls has to be adjusted, in the main, to those phenomena of wave-making resistance which are important in this speed range.

The characteristic feature of the "displacement forms" is their relatively great length/beam ratio, their deep draft, the lack of fullness at the ends of the hull, in relation to the midship section, and the somewhat sharp stern.

Among "planing forms" can be included all boats designed to exploit fully the dynamic lift generated by a flat underwater surface running over the water at a high speed. Their characteristic feature is a small length/beam ratio, shallow draft, and the transition of the waterlines from a V-shaped section at the bow to a broad, flat-bottomed transom. The shape of the cross sections aft of amidships is particularly important, and so, of course, is the displacement/length ratio. The importance of the shape of the bottom of the hull can be appreciated by studying the graph in Fig. 160, obtained in the Turkish Ship Building Research Institute by

Fig. 160

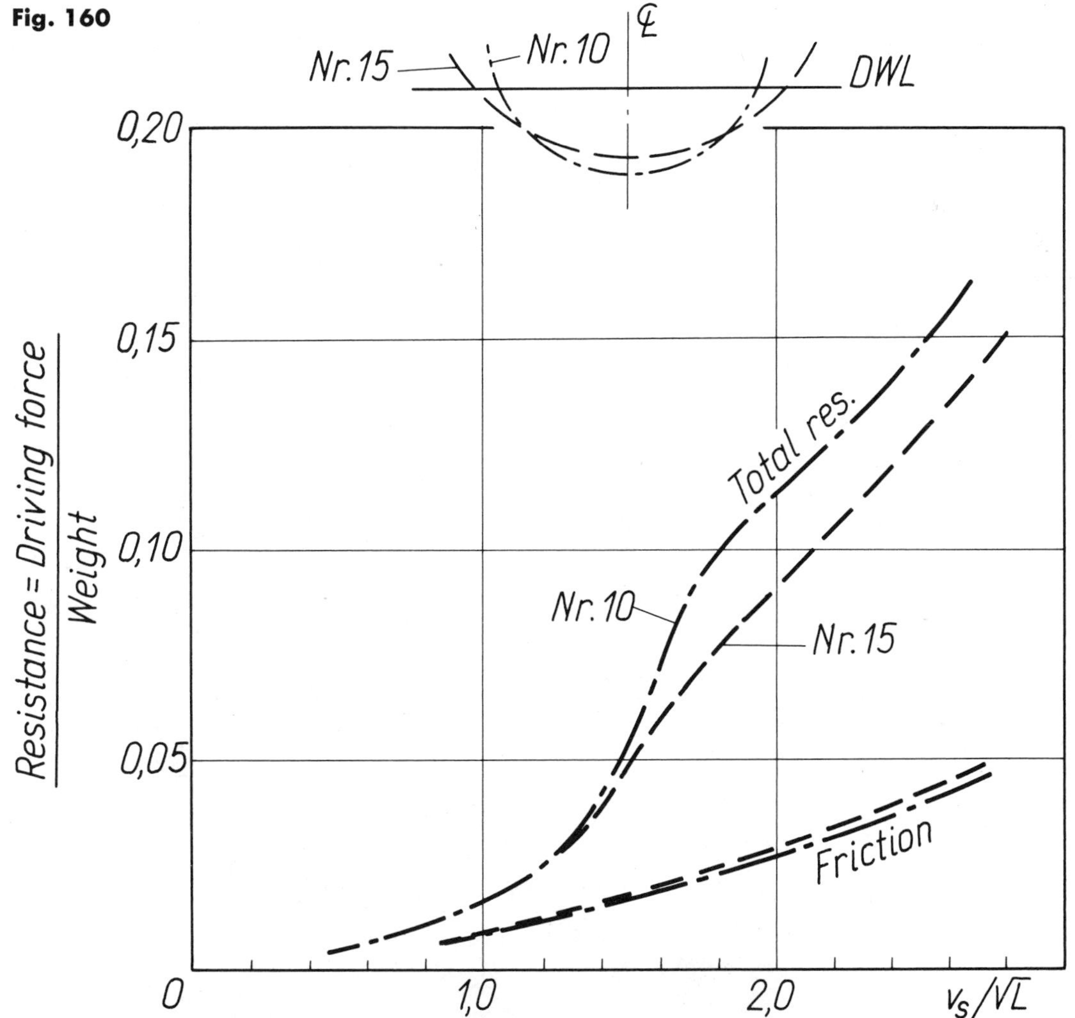

Professor Ata Nutku. Curves 10 and 15 relate to geometrically similar models, but different in semi-circular section. Displacement/length ratio was about 140. For the flat-bottomed model, No. 15, the characteristic inflection of the resistance curve which marks the beginning of semi-planing occurs when the ratio of

$$\frac{\text{driving force}}{\text{weight}} \cong 0.065 \text{ (6.5 per cent)},$$

and the speed/length ratio $v_S/\sqrt{L} = 1.6$. For model No. 10, however, semi-planing does not begin until

$$\frac{\text{driving force}}{\text{weight}} \cong 0.095 \text{ (9.5 per cent)}$$

and the speed/length ratio $v_S/\sqrt{L} = 1.7$. Model No. 15, therefore, is capable of high-speed sailing in much lighter winds.

Interesting results can also be obtained by comparing the cross sections of one of the Flying Fleet (Fig. 157), which planes readily, with that of the Narrow Finn with ballast keel (Fig. 159). An analysis of the Narrow Finn's hydrodynamic resistance curve shows a very restricted capacity for high-speed sailing.

Clearly, therefore, a hull cannot be designed which satisfies the requirements both for a good planing performance and for displacement sailing as well. The actual shape of any hull is bound to be a compromise between contradictory requirements, as yachts sail in all sorts of weather conditions. A boat designed solely for high-speed sailing will have an inferior performance in lighter winds to boats designed for such conditions, and vice versa. The scow shown in Fig. 18 is an example of the uncompromising high-speed design; it is a flat-bottomed "skimming dish." Within a certain speed range, her performance improves if she is sailed slightly heeled, as mentioned earlier.

The dynamic lift needed for that state of motion called pure planing or skimming can be better understood by studying Fig. 158, section 3; Fig. 161; and Photo. 31.

Photo. 31

Fig. 161

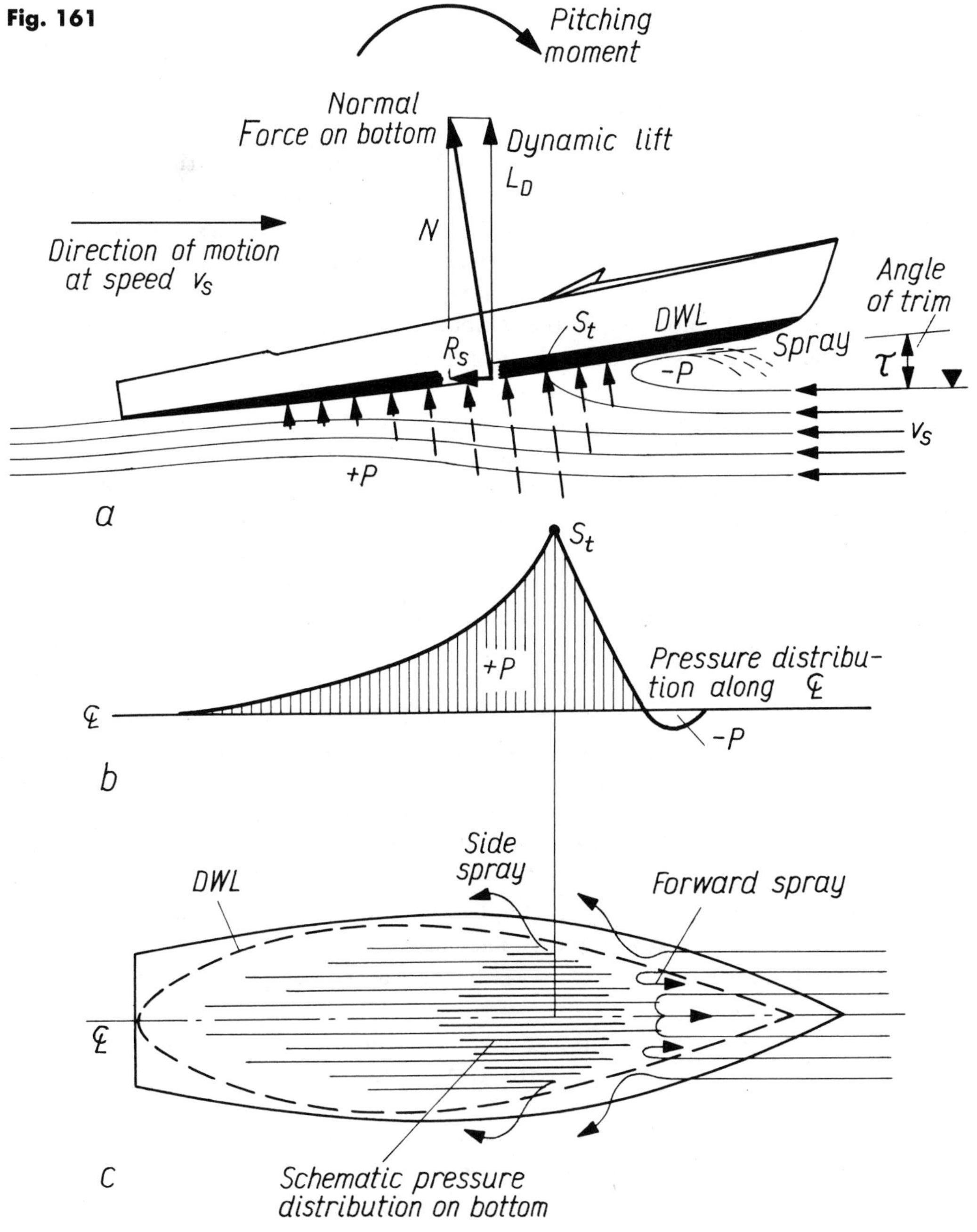

The flow under the flat bottom of the boat as it skims over the surface at the angle of trim τ is in some ways similar to that occurring on the windward side of a sail. Due to the slowing of the water flow under the hull, the kinetic energy of flow in any one area is converted to pressure p, which is exerted perpendicularly to the bottom (Fig. 161a). The over-all effect of these partial pressures p can be represented as a "resultant normal force" N. The highest pressure will be at the stagnation point St, where the water flow is completely arrested and the magnitude of its velocity is zero. This is shown in Fig. 161b, which represents the pressure distribution along the centerline. Ahead of the stagnation point a small amount of water is thrown forward as spray. The schematic pressure distribution on the bottom is traced in Fig. 161c, where the lines, which record the magnitude of the pressure, are less concentrated toward the DWL. There appears to be some sort of leakage of pressure here, revealed externally as spray thrown out sideways. This leakage will be greater in the case of a narrow hull. Both side and forward sprays show up well in Photo. 31, of the planing hull of a 5-0-5. This remarkable foam around the hull is undoubtedly a sign of dissipated energy or a form of resistance to motion.

The magnitude of this resistance is found in Fig. 161a by resolving the normal force N into its two components L_D and R_S. Dynamic lift L_D balances the boat's weight W (Fig. 158, section 3). The resistance component R_S, created in the generation of the lift is the price to be paid for eliminating wave-making resistance by lifting the hull (Fig. 161a). Calculations indicate that this new form of resistance R_S, which may be called spray resistance, can be almost as large as wave-making resistance. The reduction in total resistance when planing must therefore be attributed mainly to the reduction in skin friction, which is a result of the decrease in wetted area.

Experiments made by the author in the Finn class, in planing weather conditions, have shown how sensitively the boat reacts to changes in the size of the wetted area. Lowering the centerboard more than the necessary amount can suddenly interrupt the planing, with a prompt deceleration and excessive "squatting." The angle of trim τ can also have a decisive effect upon the boat's planing characteristics, for it governs the relationship between L_D and R_S. The deciding factor affecting the longitudinal trim τ is the distribution of live ballast along the gunwale, especially in the case of light displacement craft. Trim is also affected by the shape of the hull, the position of the center of gravity, the pitching moment, and the speed.

If the crew sit too near the mast it may be impossible to reach the preliminary stage of semi-planing. The shorter the DWL, and the greater the ratio of crew weight to total weight, the more sensitive the boat will be to the trim τ.

Many yachtsmen seem convinced that once the boat has reached the planing state, hydrodynamic resistance does not increase any further. For example, a well-known yachting magazine has suggested: "In the case of true planers, like hydroplanes and scows, planing is easy to understand because the planing hulls are skimming over the surface, displacing very little water, if any, and the resistance of the water is practically nil." The resistance curve of the Class A Inland Lake Scow (Fig. 162) shows at once that this view is wrong. The resistance curve, found by measurements of the forces affecting the model in an upright position, demonstrates that resistance to motion increases all the time throughout the speed/length ratio from 0 to 4.4. This is obvious, since it is never possible to eliminate friction resistance, which rises as the square of the speed, nor the resistance involved in generating the lift.

As we already know from the analysis of the resistance curve for the International

Fig. 162

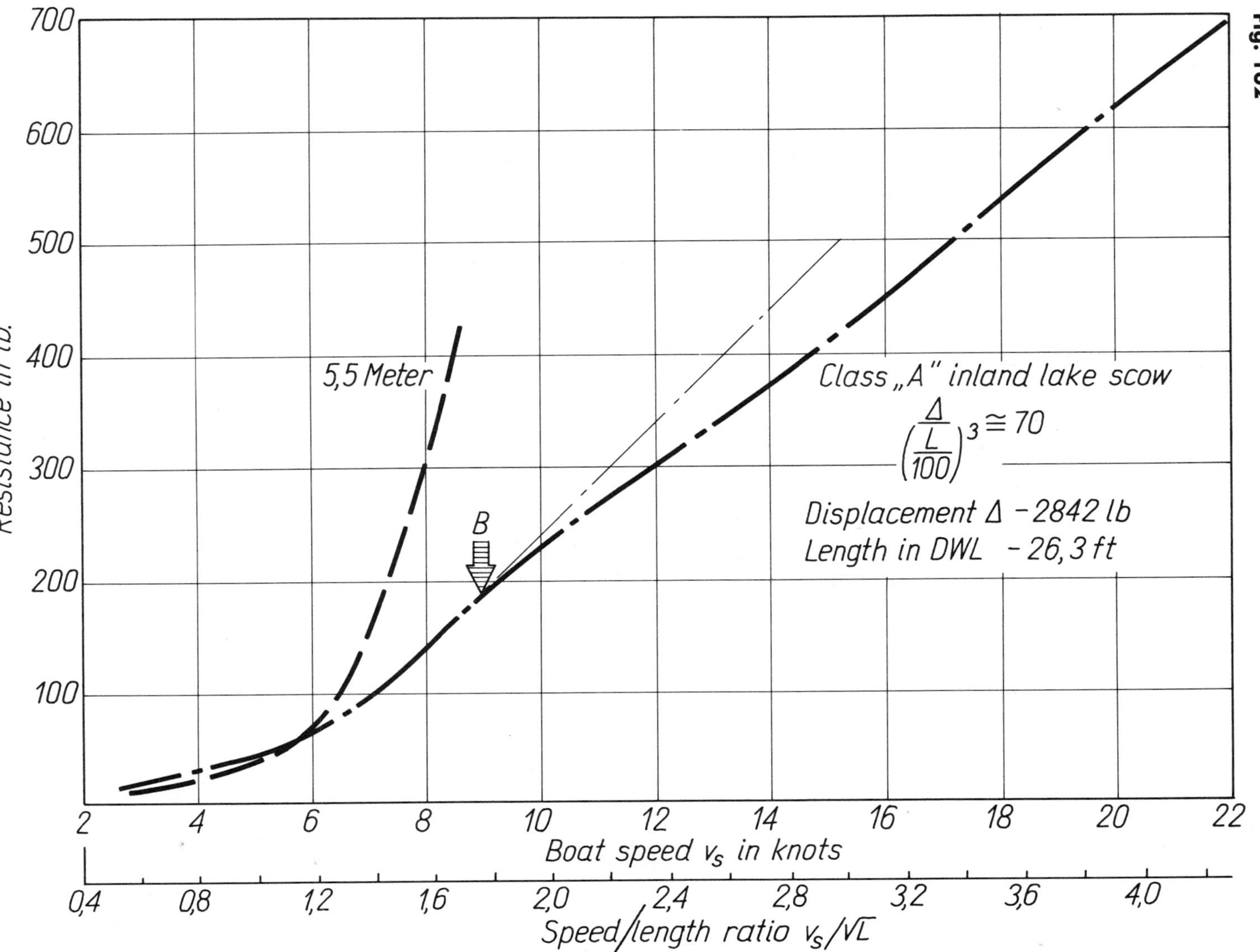
Class „A" inland lake scow
$\frac{\Delta}{\left(\frac{L}{100}\right)^3} \cong 70$
Displacement Δ – 2842 lb
Length in DWL – 26,3 ft
5,5 Meter
B
Boat speed v_s in knots
2 4 6 8 10 12 14 16 18 20 22
Speed/length ratio $v_s/\sqrt{L}$
0,4 0,8 1,2 1,6 2,0 2,4 2,8 3,2 3,6 4,0
Resistance in lb.
100 200 300 400 500 600 700

Canoe, the only characteristic of the semi-planing state is a relatively sudden lowering in the rate of increase in hydrodynamic resistance, apparent at $v_s/\sqrt{L} \cong 1.7$ (i.e., point B). It is therefore probable that the acceleration felt by the crew at the moment of transition from displacement sailing to semi-planing is responsible for the illusion that resistance has become "practically nil."

Figure 162 also includes a resistance curve for the light displacement 5.5-Meter, which emphasizes how much the attainable speed is influenced by the reduction in the rate of increase of hydrodynamic resistance. When the driving force increases twofold, from 200 lb. to 400 lb., the speed of a 5.5-Meter will increase from 7.3 knots to about 8.5 knots, i.e., by 16.5 per cent. In similar conditions the increase in speed for a scow would be from 9.3 knots to 14.7 knots, i.e., 58 per cent.

All the examples above relate to states of motion for a yacht sailing in an upright position, as it would on a reaching or running course, when the main resistance factors are wave-making and skin friction. New hydrodynamic resistances appear, however, as the yacht heads closer to the wind, and their importance increases gradually as the angle between boat's centerline and wind gets smaller.

(d) Resistance due to Leeway (Induced Resistance)—R_i

From an analysis of the aerodynamic and hydrodynamic forces on a yacht sailing to windward, as given in Figs. 40 and 80, the following deductions can be made: the aerodynamic driving force F_R is achieved at the cost of developing a harmful but unavoidable force F_H, which causes undesirable drift and heeling. The hull counters these effects of the force F_H by:

(a) Having enough lateral stability to support the sail plan and prevent a capsize

(b) Generating a sufficiently powerful hydrodynamic side force F_s, as the underwater portion of the hull, moving crabwise, cuts the water at a certain angle of attack, or leeway.

Later it will be shown that the hull can only do this by developing a resistance additional to those of wave-making and skin friction. It, too, should be kept as small as possible.

The requirements for the hull are in some measure the opposite of those for the sails. The aerodynamic efficiency of a sail will be greatest if it develops simultaneously the maximum driving force F_R with the minimum heeling force F_H. The aerodynamic drag angle ϵ_A, which measures the ability of a yacht to sail to windward, will then be smaller, and the smaller it is the better.

The hydrodynamic efficiency of the immersed part of the hull, which acts as a hydrofoil for the generation of side force F_s, will be greater when a large force F_s is achieved by means of the smallest possible additional resistance R, that is, for the smallest possible value of the hydrodynamic drag angle ϵ_H. Now, the fundamental relationship between aero-hydrodynamic efficiency and the capacity to sail close-hauled can be expressed quite simply as:

Apparent course $\beta = \epsilon_A + \epsilon_H$ (cf. Fig. 80)

The factors affecting the hydrodynamic efficiency of the hull below the waterline must now be examined to discover the most desirable shape. The hydrodynamic side force F_s is the sum of the effects produced by fin keel, hull, and rudder.

The action of the fin keel (Fig. 163) may be taken first. When leeway $\lambda = 0$ (as in Fig. 163b) and the yacht is upright, only the hydrodynamic resistance could be measured on a symmetrically streamlined fin keel, and this would consist mainly of skin friction, plus the small contribution of profile drag or profile resistance. (Naval architects use the term resistance rather than drag, which is popular in aerodynamics; the terms are interchangeable.) However, when the fin keel is set at a particular angle λ to the course being sailed (Fig. 163c), the characteristic flow and pressure distribution on the two sides will develop, similar to those already described for the aerodynamics of a sail. The sum of pressure and suction produces the resultant hydrodynamic force R_T. This is made up of the side force F_s, perpendicular to the direction of motion, and resistance R to the motion, and this last is greater now than in example b. Since within the small range of the angle of attack $\lambda = 0°–10°$ the resistances due to friction and profile do not increase, the appearance of this additional resistance can only be due to "end leakage," which is the flow of water under the bottom of the fin keel from the region of pressure to that of suction. This leads to the formation of vortices, such as those clearly visible in Photo. 32, which shows the water flow lines around a model of a Dragon's hull. As with the sails, this kind of resistance is called induced resistance R_i, as it is inseparably connected with the formation of the side force F_s. Nearly everything said earlier about induced drag for the sails applies equally to the induced resistance of the hull. Figure 163a shows how the induced resistance, R_i, varies as the leeway angle, λ, increases from $\lambda = 0$ to λ_1, when the resultant hydrodynamic force on the fin keel increases. The polar diagram drawn there does not differ in any respect from that used to express the magnitude and direction of action of the total aerodynamic force when a sail is changing its angle of attack to the wind. This angle of attack is leeway in the case of the fin keel.

Induced resistance R_i depends largely on the magnitude of the side force, F_s, and the aspect ratio, A.R., of the fin keel, and may be expressed as:

$$R_i = k \frac{F_s^2}{A.R.}$$

where k is a constant based on the shape, cross section, etc., of the fin keel.

Photo. 32

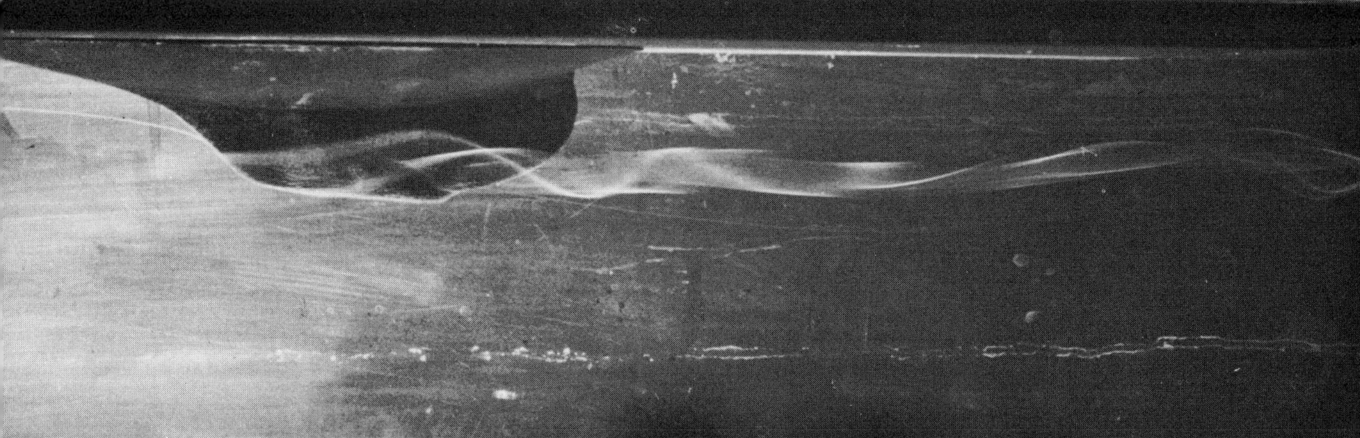

Fig. 163

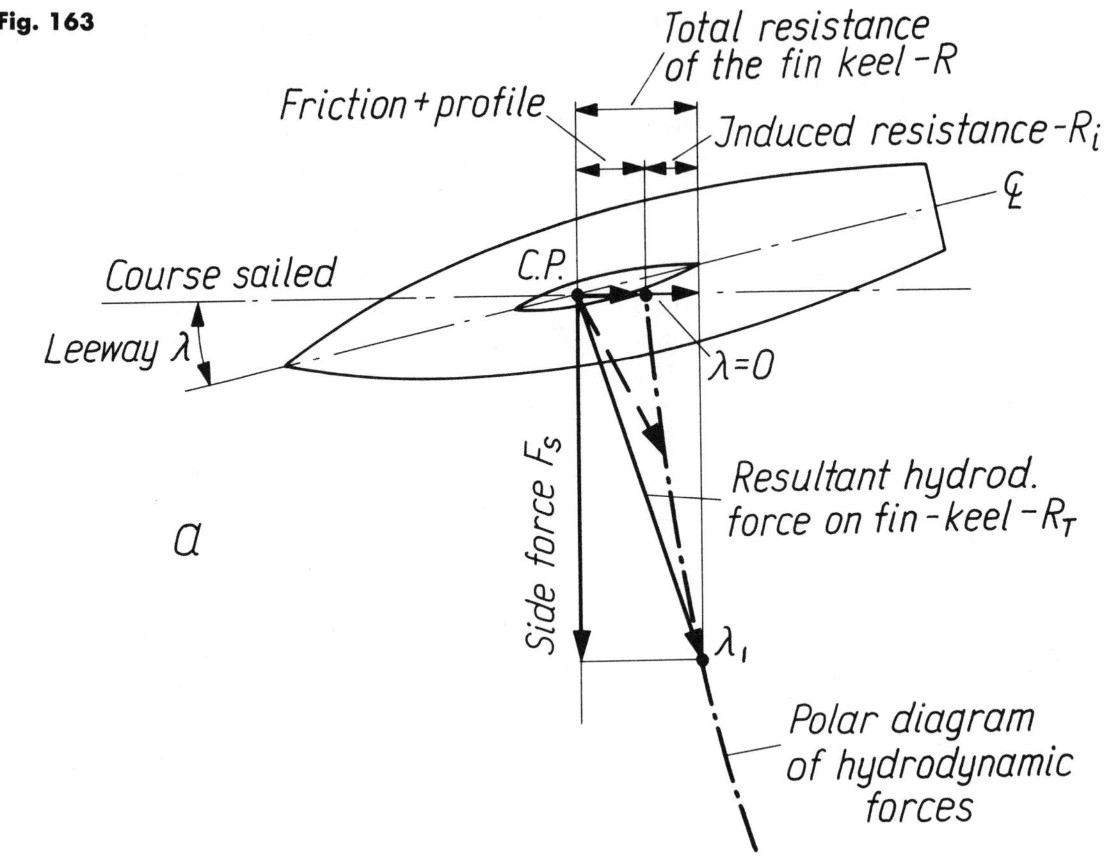
Total resistance
of the fin keel - R
Friction + profile
Jnduced resistance - R_i
℄
Course sailed
C.P.
Leeway λ
λ=0
Side force F_s
Resultant hydrod.
force on fin-keel - R_T
a
λ_1
Polar diagram
of hydrodynamic
forces

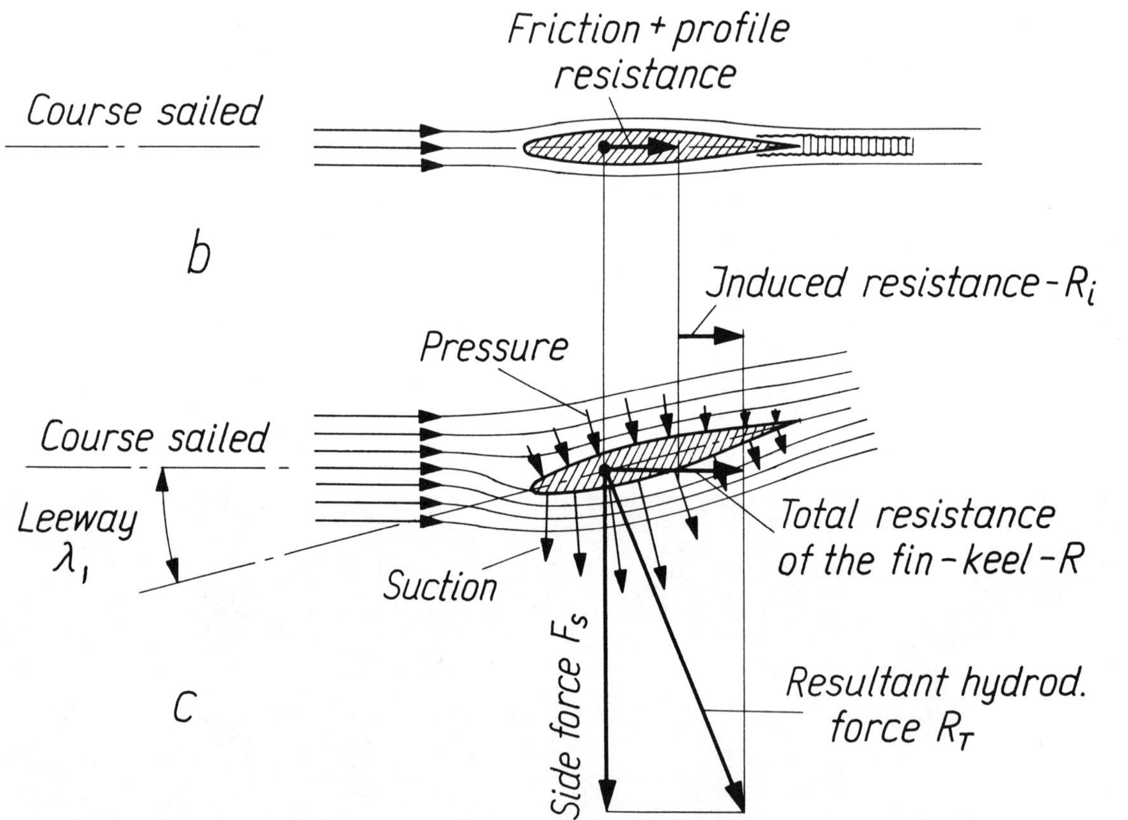
Friction + profile
resistance
Course sailed
b
Jnduced resistance - R_i
Pressure
Course sailed
Leeway
λ_1
Total resistance
of the fin-keel - R
Suction
Side force F_s
c
Resultant hydrod.
force R_T

The resistance curves for a full-scale International Canoe (Fig. 164) demonstrate the contribution induced resistance makes compared to the basic hydrodynamic resistances (i.e., wave-making and skin friction) when sailing in an upright position. The lowest curve shows the variation in total hydrodynamic resistance for the hull alone and without leeway. The next curve is for the resistance of the hull plus centerboard when $\lambda = 0$. The extra resistance due to lowering the centerboard is about 10 per cent of the total resistance. The other two curves relate to the resistance variation for leeway angle $\lambda = 5°$ and $\lambda = 7°$. This shows that at a speed of 4 knots, when the speed/length ratio is about 1.0, and the angle of drift $\lambda = 5°$, the increase in hydrodynamic resistance is about 45 per cent, while when $\lambda = 7°$ it is almost 90 per cent greater than the original basic resistance without leeway. This increase relates only to the hull with the centerboard lowered but without the rudder. The rudder can make an equally important contribution, especially if the directional balance of the boat is bad, and she carries, for example, a considerable weather helm.

164

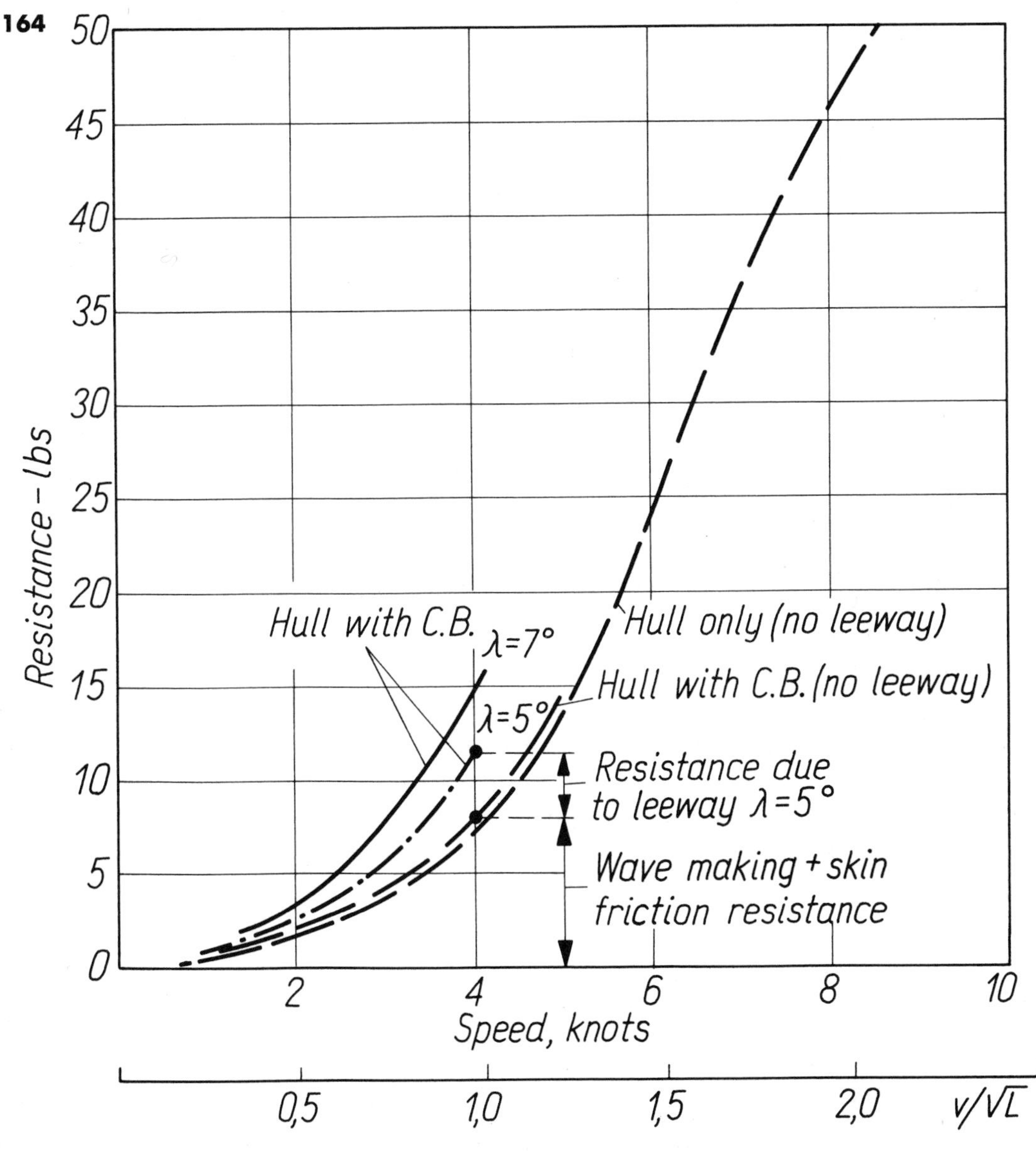

Fig. 165

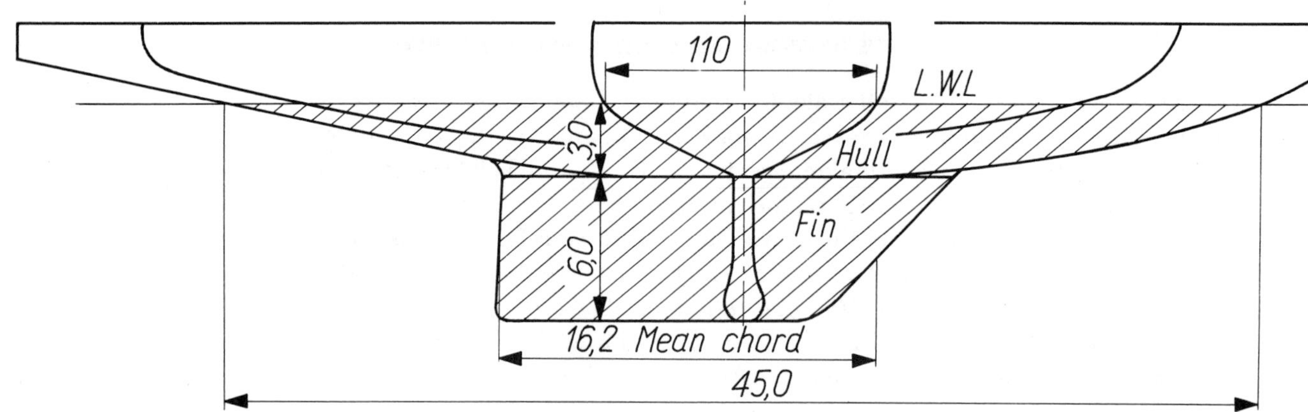

Measurements during the test proved that the Canoe's shallow draft hull can only contribute about 2.5 per cent toward the side force, and the hull proper may therefore be described as a very ineffective hydrofoil. This has been confirmed by the interesting results obtained by Pierre de Saix in the Davidson Laboratory in 1962. His experiments were carried out on a model 5.5-Meter racing sloop, which is of the fin-keel type, having the hull distinct from the fin keel attached below it (see Fig. 165). New instrumentation and experimental techniques had to be worked out to measure the side force, F_s, of:

1. The isolated fin (in the presence of the flat plate)
2. The fin in the presence of the hull
3. The isolated hull
4. The hull in the presence of the fin
5. The complete model

The model can be studied in detail in Photo. 33.

The table below shows, in percentages, the results of these measurements of the side forces for the different angles of heel at a speed of 4 ft./sec. ($v_s/\sqrt{L} = 1.2$) and the drift angle $\lambda = 4°$

Angle of heel	0°	10°	20°	30°
1. Isolated fin force (in the presence of flat plate)	52%	51%	49%	56%
2. Additional fin force	28%	23%	20%	6%
3. Isolated hull force	6%	6%	6%	7%
4. Additional hull force	14%	20%	25%	31%
5. Complete model	100%	100%	100%	100%

In lines 2 and 4 the additional forces are given for the fin and hull respectively when they are connected, which produces an advantageous interaction for both. Thus when the angle of heel is 0°, the hull in isolation only contributes 6 per cent of the generated side force. With the fin added, the contribution of the hull is in-

Photo. 33

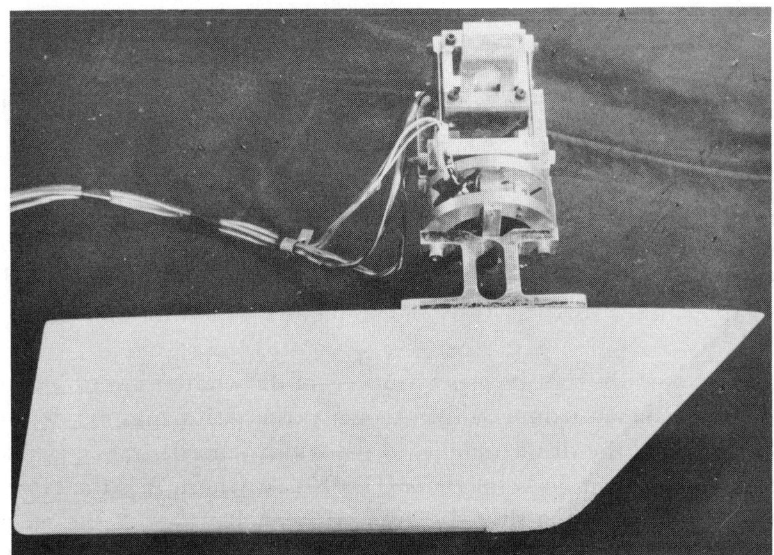

Fin and balance

Isolated fin

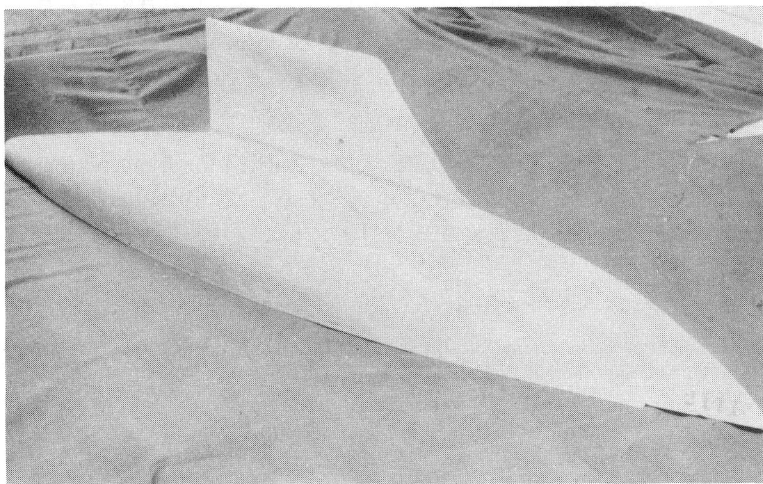

Complete model

creased by 14 per cent. The efficiency of the fin keel is improved in the same way. At this angle, however, 80 per cent of the force is generated by the fin and only 20 per cent by the hull.

As the angle of heel increases, the immersed section of the hull becomes asymmetrical in form (cf. Fig. 78), and the asymmetrical flow slightly improves its performance as a hydrofoil generating side force. This will be discussed again in the next chapter, after further study of the factors which influence the action of the fin.

There is no doubt that its aspect ratio is of the highest importance for achieving maximum efficiency from the fin. Aspect ratio, A.R., may be defined, as for the sails, as a ratio of the draft (height) to the width (chord). When the keel is not rectangular, its aspect ratio is taken as $(\text{Draft})^2/A$, where A is the lateral area of the fin keel. It is also known that the greater the A.R. (that is, the narrower the fin) the less will be the resistance due to "end leakage" and the greater its hydrodynamic efficiency. As the fin keel is suspended below the hull, the equalization of the pressure on one side and the suction on the other can only proceed under the bottom of the fin (as shown in Photo. 32). The losses that can be attributed to induced drag, therefore, are smaller than those which occur when "end leakage" can appear at both ends, as happens with the normal air stream flow around sails (Photo. 2). The hull, then, by its effect on the water flow round the fin, has the effect of doubling the aspect ratio of the fin. In comparison with the geometrical A.R. $= (\text{Draft})^2/A$, the effective A.R. may be expressed roughly as $2 \times (\text{Draft})^2/A$. This definition is based on the assumption that the water surface is a limited plane, so that around the hull and partly submerged fin only two-dimensional flow can occur. This assumption may be sufficiently accurate at very slow speeds when the surface waves are relatively small. At greater speeds, however, the marked influence of large surface waves complicates the flow and the effective aspect ratio is decreased. The empirical value found from experiments is given as $1.7 \times (\text{Draft})^2/A$.

Figure 166 illustrates the problem of A.R. in a somewhat simplified form. The efficiency of four hydrofoils of different A.R., but the same streamlined sections, is expressed in terms of side force coefficients C_s for variable leeway angles λ. By taking the angle of incidence (the leeway) as, for example, $\lambda = 5°$, then the coefficients C_s when A.R. = 5, 2, 1 and 0.5 will be $C_s \cong 0.3, 0.2, 0.13$, and 0.09, respectively. Now if this is applied to a keel of lateral area $A = 10$ sq. ft., when the speed $v_s = 10$ ft./sec. (5.9 knots), the side force produced by fin keels can be calculated for the A.R. stated:

$$F_s{}^* = 0.97 \times C_s \times v_s^2 \times A \text{ (lb.) for fresh water}$$
$$F_s = 0.995 \times C_s \times v_s^2 \times A \text{ (lb.) for salt water}$$

For fresh water, $F_s = 0.97 \times 10^2 \times 10 \times C_s$.

$$^*F_s = \frac{\rho}{2} \times C_s \times V_s^2 \times A, \text{ but } \rho = \frac{\gamma}{g}$$

where γ = weight of a unit volume of fresh water (62.3 lb./cu. ft.) or salt water (64.0 lb./cu. ft.)
$g = 32.2$ ft./sec.^{2} (acceleration due to gravity)

Fig. 166

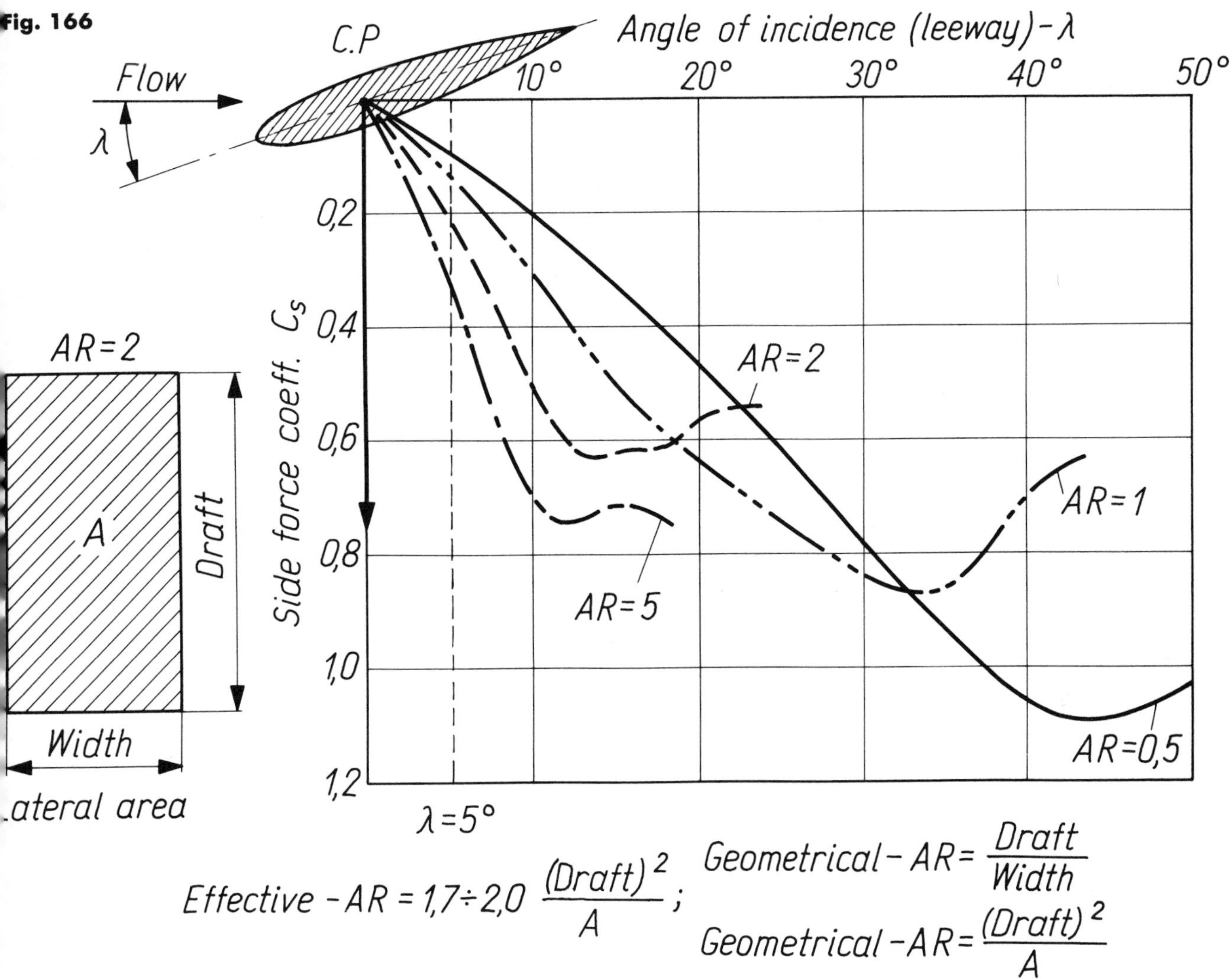

Then for		5	2	1	0.5
	A.R. =	5	2	1	0.5
	C_s =	0.3	0.2	0.13	0.09
	F_s (lb.) =	291	194	126	87

This makes it clear that the side force produced per unit area of keel can vary considerably, depending on the way the lateral area of the hull below the waterline is distributed between the draft and width of the keel. Two conclusions may be drawn from this:

(a) By increasing the draft, and so the A.R., the desired side force can be obtained with a smaller lateral area of hull. This reduction in wetted area reduces both skin friction and induced resistance.

(b) By increasing the draft but retaining the same total lateral area, the desired side force can be obtained with less leeway.

In both cases, it is possible to improve the sailing performance to windward. There are, however, certain reasons which check the general increase of the A.R. of the hull below the waterline:

1. The class rules often limit the maximum draft. For instance, the R.O.R.C. formula allows without penalty only a certain depth proportional to the other measurements.
2. Tradition and the boat designer's adherence to certain aesthetic criteria in appraising the shape of the hull are very powerful.
3. The dynamic lateral stability of the yacht deteriorates when the keel's A.R. is increased, as it simultaneously lowers the center of lateral resistance. When under way, the yacht will heel more when the same aerodynamic force is applied to the sails. This is undesirable from many points of view, and will be discussed in a later chapter.

Traditionalists tend to overexaggerate these limitations, though they are extremely important. Increasing the aspect ratio of a fin keel will often improve the performance of a yacht, especially a light-displacement cruiser, whose stabilizing moment is produced not only by heavy ballast but also by a shallow, beamy hull (form stability). This applies equally to flat-bottomed boats like scows and beamy dinghies.

The aspect ratio of the fin keel can be greatly increased in the two-hulled craft where lateral stability is obtained by the wider form. Another example of a daring, nontraditional approach to the problem of the fin-keel's A.R. is *Black Soo,* designed by E. G. Van de Stadt, shown in Fig. 147. This planing, light-displacement cruiser whose length is 29½ ft. and whose displacement is 1.57 tons has an exceptionally narrow deep fin of high A.R. Her displacement/length ratio

$$\frac{\Delta}{(L/100)^3} = 90$$

and her maximum speed may reach 22 knots.

Shoal draft centerboarders achieve a high A.R. by lowering the plate when close-hauled, and this explains to some degree their racing successes over the classic heavy and narrow keel boats. Centerboarders have an additional advantage, for they can reduce their wetted area by lifting their plates when sailing courses on which a large lateral area of hull is not needed.

Figure 167 shows two different centerboards used in light dinghies. The elliptical shape of a, with its higher aspect ratio will undoubtedly be more effective than the quadrant-shaped b. Changing the shape of the centerboard may also reduce the angle of drift. If, for example, in a certain restricted class the leeway can be reduced by 1° by improving the A.R. of a keel or CB (Fig. 168) then when sailing close-hauled over a distance of one nautical mile, Yacht A would be able to make good to windward about 106 ft. more than Yacht B, whose drift angle is 1° more. Over a typical triangular regatta course 10 miles long, some half of it the windward leg,

Fig. 167

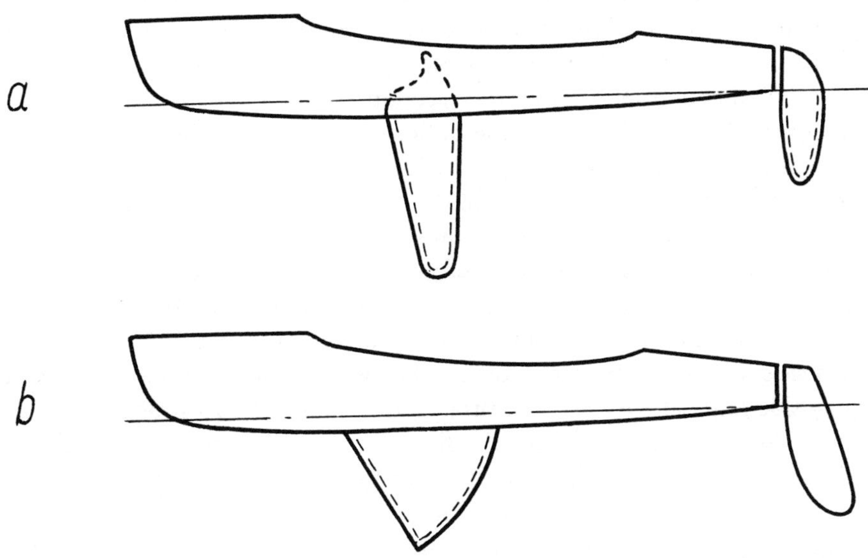

Fig. 168

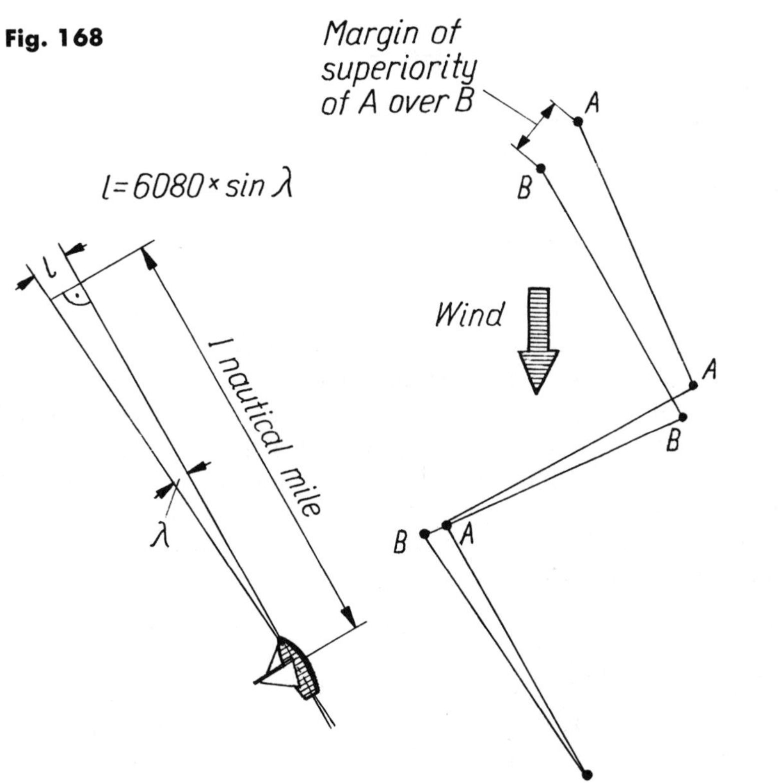

the gap between the two yachts will be over 500 ft. An advantage of this sort cannot be ignored, especially as, when the helmsmen are equally matched, races can be won or lost by a margin of a few seconds. These hypothetical calculations assume, of course, that other conditions remain unaltered.

The shape of the fin in cross section also has considerable influence on its efficiency. A streamlined section is better than a flat plate, as an analysis of Fig. 169 will prove. The graph shows two polar curves, one for a hydrofoil of symmetrical cross section and one for a flat plate, both with the same A.R. = 5.

The two sketches at the side show that although both are set at the same angle of attack $\lambda = 10°$, the direction of action of the resultant hydrodynamic forces is different. Resolving these forces into their components, side force and resistance, demonstrates that the resistance of the flat plate is greater when the magnitudes of both side forces are the same, or in other words, the streamlined plate develops the same side force at the cost of a smaller drag angle ϵ_H. In practice, for example, this means that the hydrofoil and the flat plate could be used as rudders, and in certain sailing conditions they might have to be kept at an angle of attack $\lambda = 10°$, to compensate for weather helm. The graph gives their respective coefficients of resistance as $C_D = 0.05$ for the streamlined, and $C_D = 0.14$ for the flat plate. If the area of each rudder $A = 5$ ft.^{2}, and both boats are sailing at a speed of 10 ft./sec. (5.9 knots) then for fresh water the corresponding resistances will be:

$$\begin{aligned} R &= 0.97 \times C_D \times v_s^2 \times A \text{ (lb.)} \\ &= 0.97 \times C_D \times 10^2 \times 5 \\ &= 485\, C_D \end{aligned}$$

Then for the streamlined section $R = 24.2$ lb.
and for the flat plate $R = 67.9$ lb.

Naturally, if both boats are to sail at a speed of 10 ft./sec., the boat with the flat rudder must have a greater sail area to compensate for the additional resistance to its motion. This inferiority of the flat plate is even more marked at greater angles of attack. This is because the flow of water breaks away immediately behind the leading edge of the flat plate, creating turbulent flow and increasing the resistance. However, the flow can follow the contour of the streamlined hydrofoil more easily, and the breakaway occurs considerably further from the leading edge.

The shape of the leading edge also has an influence on the flow and on the magnitude of the resistance of the fin keel or rudder. Figure 170 gives the results of experiments to find the resistances for four centerboards, all of the same shape, typical of those used in the International Canoe, all of geometric A.R. = 2.75 and area A = 3.92 sq. ft., but of different cross section. Sections a, b, c, and d in Fig. 170 are exact copies of those tested.

The first curve on the left represents the changes in the resistance of the hull alone, for different angles of drift from 0° to 7°. Curves a, b, c, and d are for the hull plus the respective centerboard whose cross section is shown. Even in the range

Fig. 169

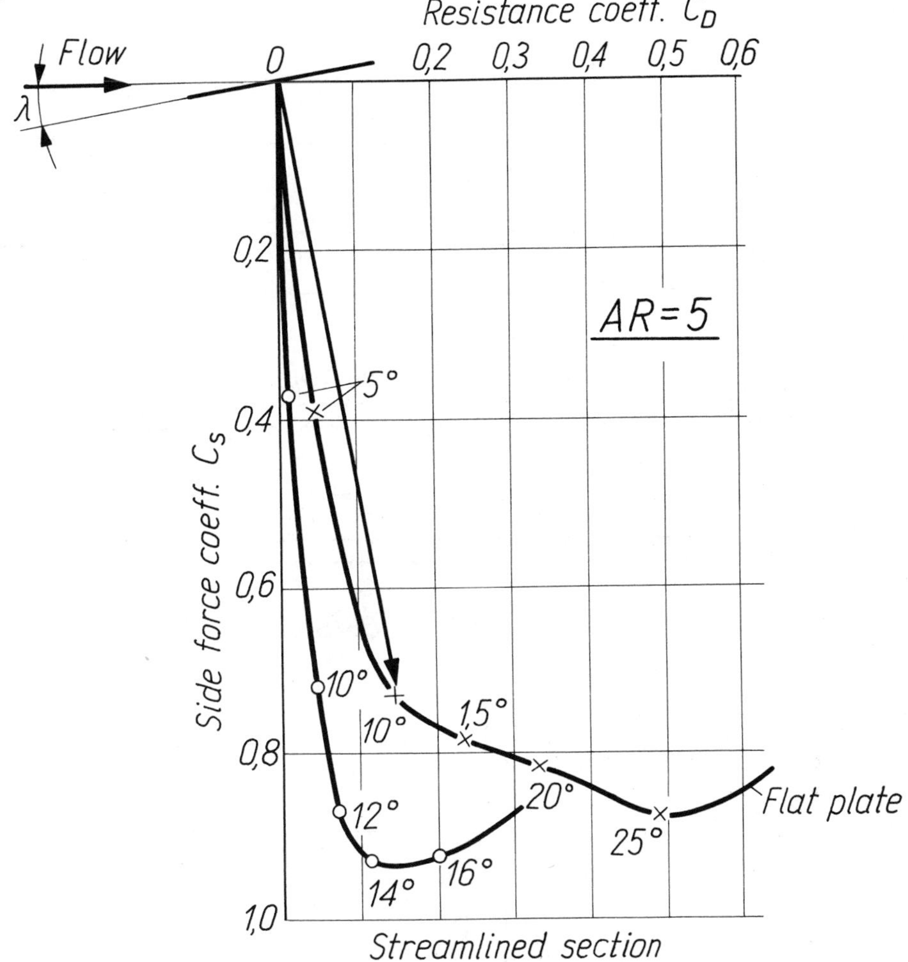

Resistance coeff. C_D
Flow
λ
0
0,2
0,3
0,4
0,5
0,6
0,2
0,4
0,6
0,8
1,0
Side force coeff. C_S
AR=5
5°
10°
10°
15°
20°
25°
12°
14°
16°
Flat plate
Streamlined section

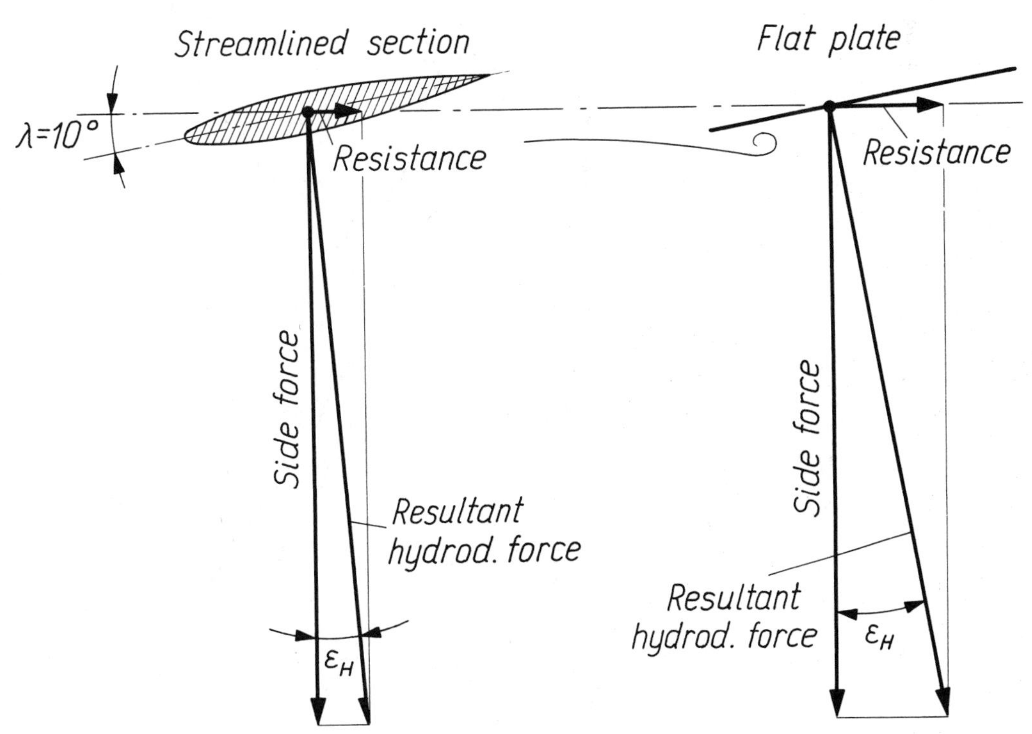

Streamlined section
Flat plate
λ=10°
Resistance
Resistance
Side force
Side force
Resultant hydrod. force
Resultant hydrod. force
ε_H
ε_H

Fig. 170

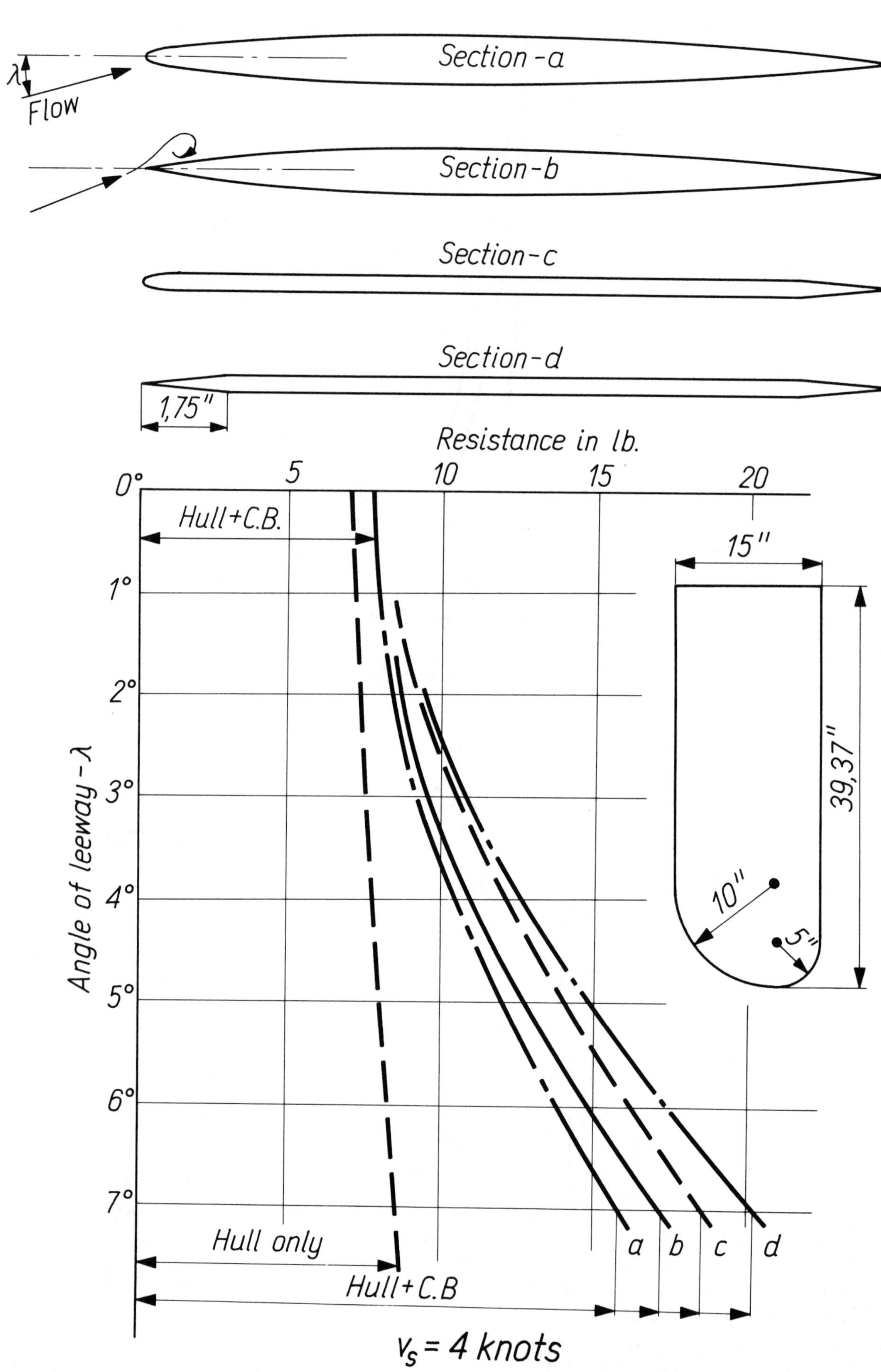

Section-a
λ
Flow
Section-b
Section-c
Section-d
1,75"
Resistance in lb.
0°
5
10
15
20
Hull+C.B.
15"
1°
2°
3°
4°
5°
6°
7°
Angle of leeway-λ
39,37"
10"
5"
a
b
c
d
Hull only
Hull+C.B
v_s = 4 knots

Fig. 171

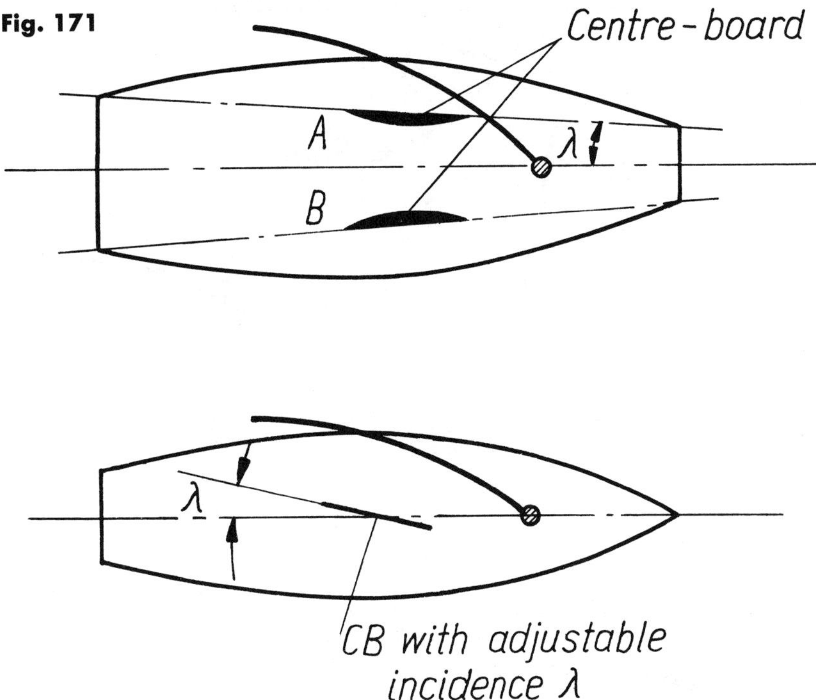

of leeway angles encountered in practice with the International Canoe, i.e. $\lambda = 2°–5°$, the difference in resistance between sections a, b, c, and d can reach 15 per cent to 20 per cent. Most advantage is derived from a centerboard having cross-section a, and this is confirmed by racing experience.

The hull itself contributes about 90 per cent of the resistance when side force is zero ($\lambda = 0°$) but only about 50 per cent at 7° of yaw, its actual increase in resistance at this degree of leeway being about 20 per cent. This would suggest that by suitably varying the angle of attack of the centerboard in relation to the centerline of the hull, so that the hull moved exactly along the course sailed, the total resistance of the boat could be reduced by the amount contributed by the drift of the hull.

Yacht designers are indeed attempting to reduce resistance by using centerboards of unusual form. Figure 171 shows one example. The flat-bottomed hull has two asymmetrical centerboards, set at such an angle that they converge toward the centerline. When sailing to windward the board on the windward side is raised. The remaining leeward board, set at the angle λ, generates sufficient side force for the hull to move without making leeway.

A single centerboard can produce a similar effect if it is set at an angle of attack λ about 3°–5° to the centerline of the hull. This will eliminate the crabwise motion of the hull, which is anyway very inefficient as a hydrofoil for producing side force.

To return to the problem of the correct shape for the leading edge of the fin keel: thorough tests indicate that the most efficient section for the leading edge of fin

Fig. 172

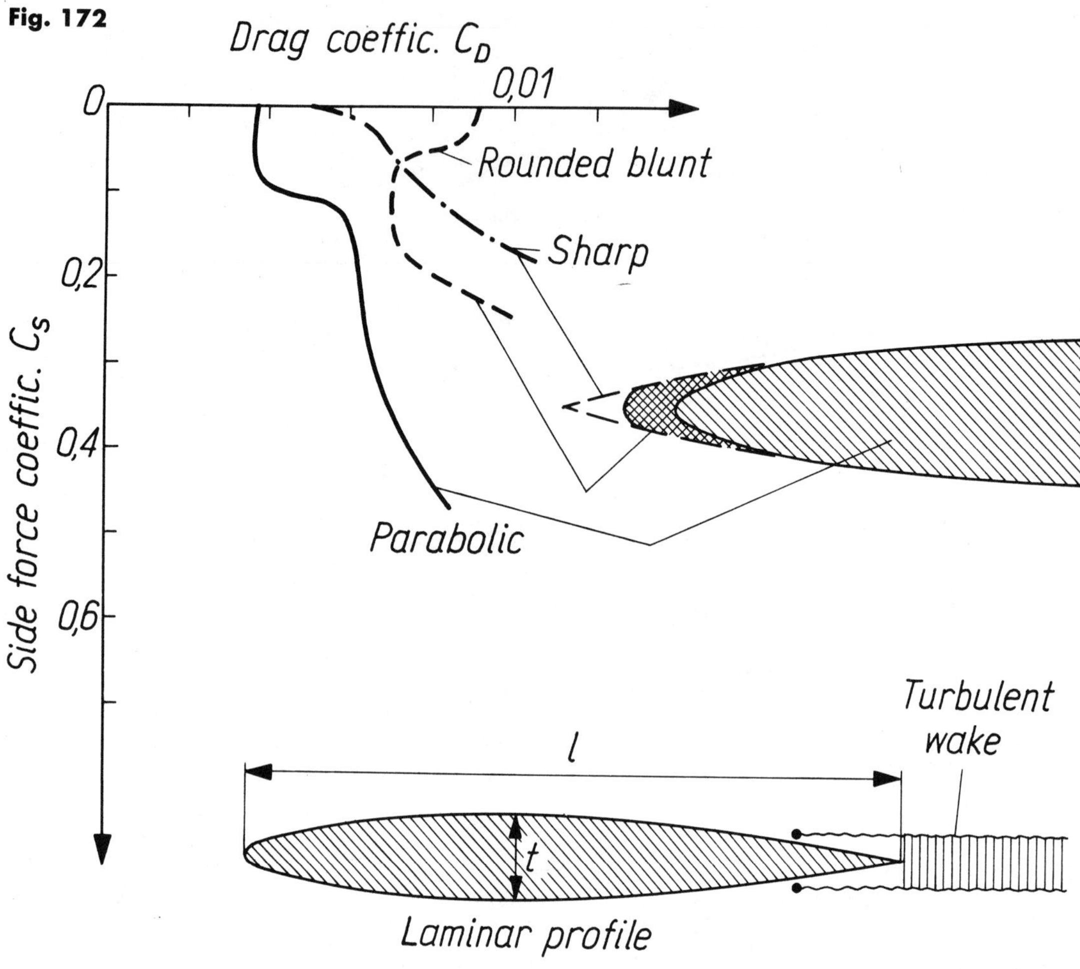

keel or rudder is parabolic (see Fig. 172). A sharp leading edge gives particularly poor results, except when side force is near zero, when the angle of incidence is lower than that met in practice. A rounded blunt edge is not so good as a parabolic one. Inset at the bottom of Fig. 172 is the laminar profile of a fin whose shape is the most desirable from the hydrodynamic point of view. The point of maximum thickness should be at least 50 per cent, if not more, of the total length of the keel, aft of the leading edge.

A comparison of the blunt leading edge of *Sceptre's* keel, shown in Photo. 34, with the sharper shape of *Columbia's* (Photo. 27) suggests that these were among the differences between the challengers that led to the results in the America's Cup Races in 1958.

The trailing edge is of relatively little importance, as it lies in the area of turbulent wake. There is no scientific foundation for the popular belief that the centerboard or fin must taper as sharply as a razor. Experiments have proved that cutting the trailing edge off blunt for up to 5 per cent of the profile length l does not influence resistance, and is undoubtedly more practical.

The hydrodynamic side force needed to balance the aerodynamic heeling force depends almost entirely on the yacht's speed v_S. As the square of this appears in

Photo. 34

the formula for calculating hydrodynamic reaction (used in the analysis of Fig. 169 when the generation of side force was discussed), surely the greater the speed of the boat, the smaller the drift needed to achieve adequate side force.

Figure 173 illustrates the relationship between the speed v_d at which the yacht is drifting sideways, its forward speed v_f along the centerline of the hull, and the angle of drift λ during the period in which the yacht accelerates from a standstill to full speed, when sailing to windward. This period is naturally longer for a

Fig. 173

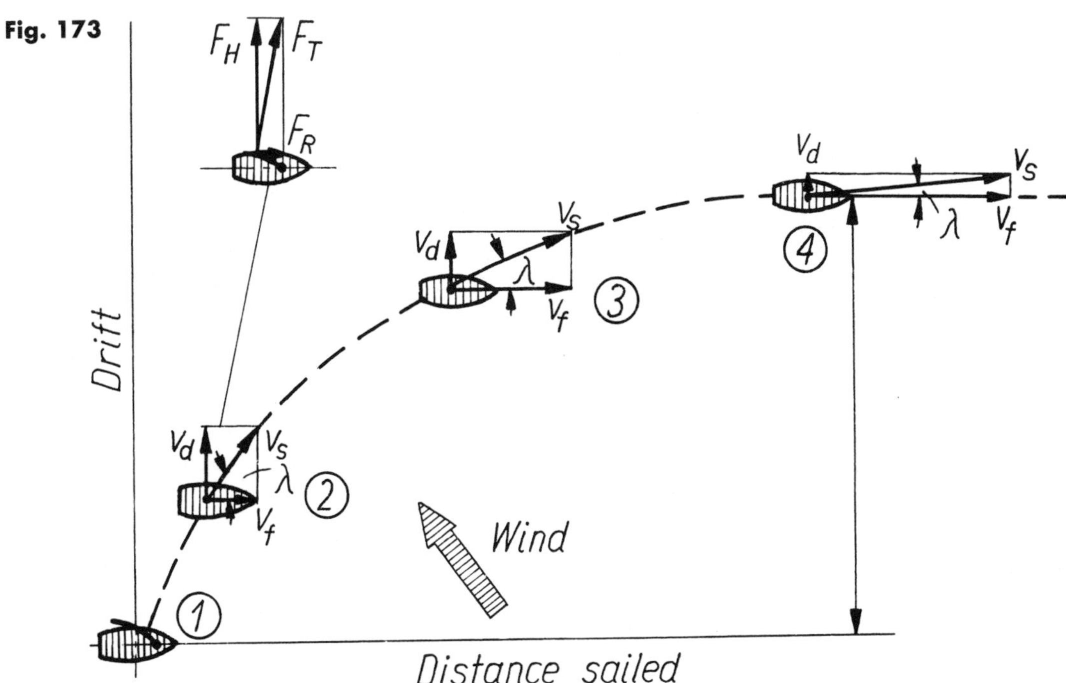

Fig. 174

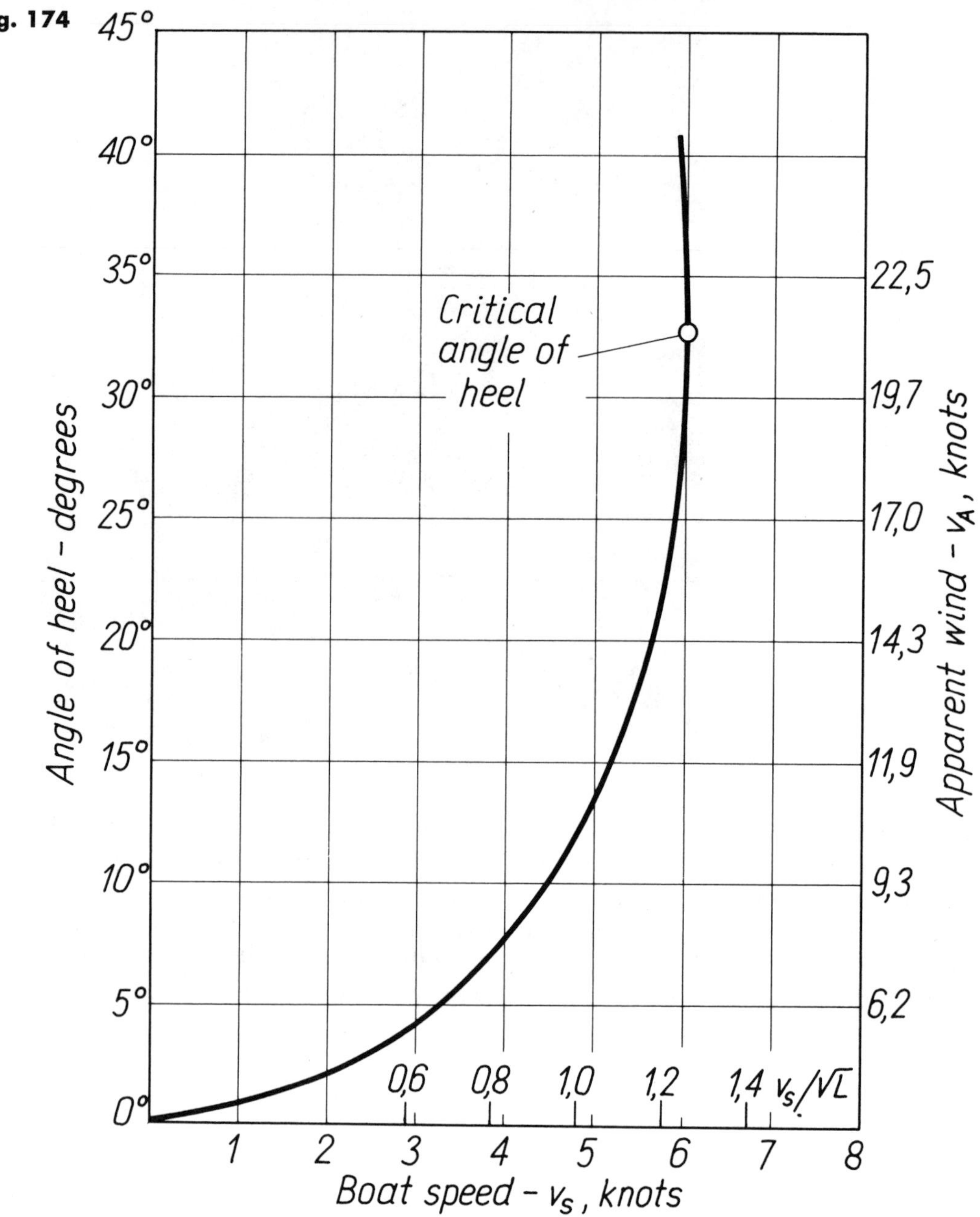

ballast-keel yacht, with its greater mass (i.e., inertia), than the acceleration time for a light dinghy. However, it always takes some time to reach full speed, and this is connected with loss of "weather gauge," when, at the windward mark before the start of a race, a helmsman trying to keep his position to weather loses speed. The period of acceleration can be unconsciously delayed by a helmsman who hauls in the sheets too much, a very common habit of inexperienced crews starting to windward in a tight pack of boats.

For the yachts whose speed v_s is low (Fig. 173, cases 1 and 2), the apparent wind will be relatively full. Excessive hauling in on the mainsheet will produce a large amount of F_H, which causes drift, with simultaneously a small amount of driving force, F_R. A yacht with its sails sheeted like this would go on drifting, until, with the slow increase of boat speed v_s, and consequent change in the direction of the apparent wind, the general hydro-aerodynamic efficiency of the yacht improves.

(e) Resistance due to Heel: R_h

Behavior typical of a ballast-keel yacht when sailing to windward is shown in Fig. 174. The data for the graph were obtained from tests on *Gimcrack,* already mentioned during the discussion on skin friction (Fig. 150).

For low apparent wind speeds, which involve only small angles of heel up to 10°, an increase in wind speed will cause a considerable rise in the speed, v_s, of a yacht. Beyond this point, however, when the wind strength increases the angle of heel, the rate of increase in v_s shows a marked decline. When the apparent wind $v_A \cong 20$ knots, which corresponds to a true wind speed $v_T \cong 15$ knots, the yacht reaches its maximum speed $v_s \cong 6$ knots and the critical angle of heel, which is just above 30°. If there is a further increase in the wind, so that aerodynamic forces increase the angle of heel beyond 35°, sailing speed v_s begins to fall below the attainable maximum. This proves that the power of the aerodynamic driving force F_R in certain conditions can be frustrated by the retarding effect of the force F_H, already shown to be the cause of drift and heel.

This means in fact that the increase in the driving force created by a rising wind is not proportional to the much greater increase in resistance created by the heeling force. The results obtained on the yacht *Gimcrack,* and from a model of her in the towing tank, are interpreted in Fig. 175. They demonstrate how enormous can be this rise in the hydrodynamic resistances caused by the heeling force. The con-

Fig. 175

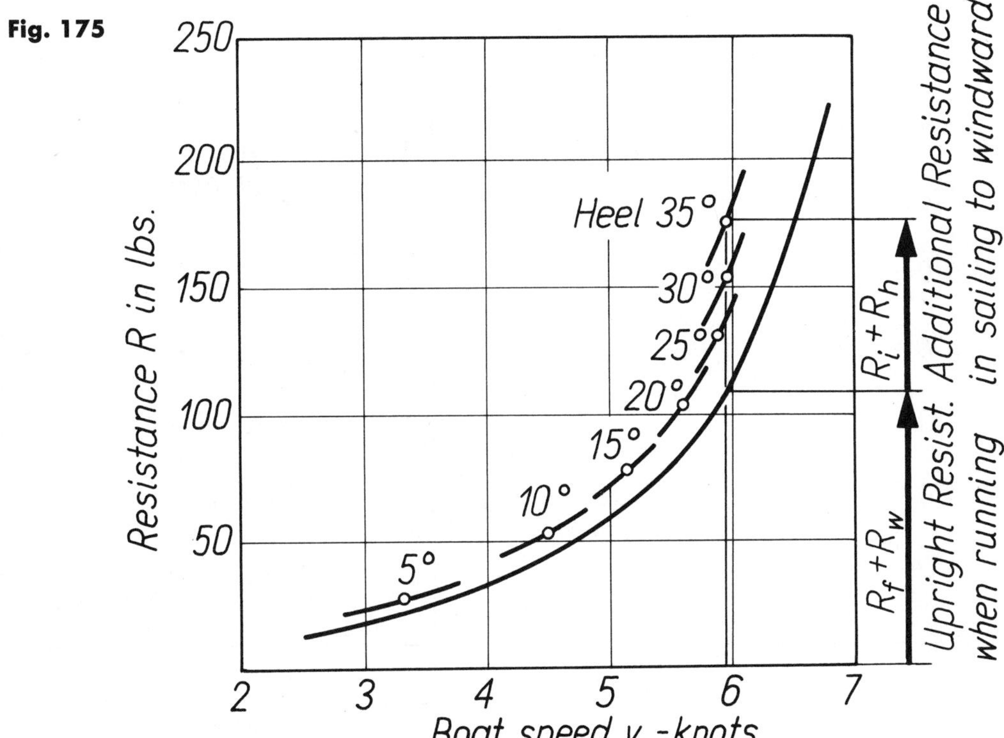

tinuous curve traces the variation of the hydrodynamic resistance, R, to the boat's speed, v_s, when she is sailing upright before the wind. The various shorter curves relate to changes in the hydrodynamic resistance at different angles of heel, including the induced resistance due to leeway. For example, the values of the resistances at $v_s \cong 6$ knots show that the resistance when sailing to windward at an angle of heel of 35° is almost 40 per cent greater than when in an upright position on a run.

The total resistance of a yacht can be divided into two sections, each of which has its special influence in accordance with the course being sailed. When running before the wind, the hull will mainly develop skin friction resistance, R_f, and wave-making resistance, R_w. In Fig. 175 this is marked by the vector $R_f + R_w$. As the boat comes closer to the wind, two other forms of resistance at once become of greater importance: resistance due to leeway, R_i, and resistance due to heeling, R_h. At small angles of heel, the induced resistance, R_i, is the more important of these, but at greater angles of heel the resistance due to heeling, R_h, takes precedence. Their relative magnitudes (shown in Fig. 176) relate to a keel yacht, the 6-Meter *Jill,* which in the shape of its hull resembles *Gimcrack,* and whose L.W.L. is 23.5 ft. For clarity, the scale of the resistance R is 5 times greater than that for

Fig. 176

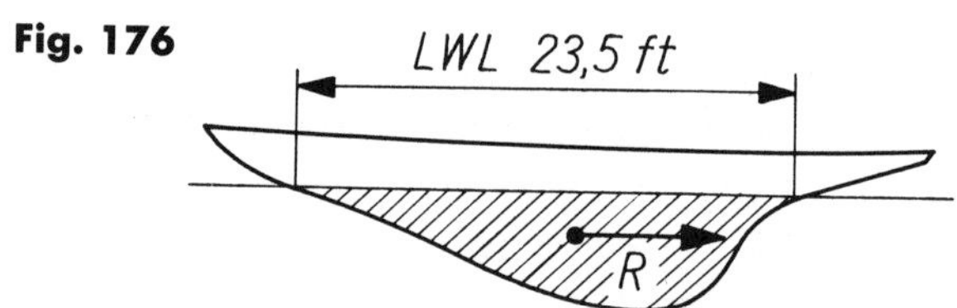

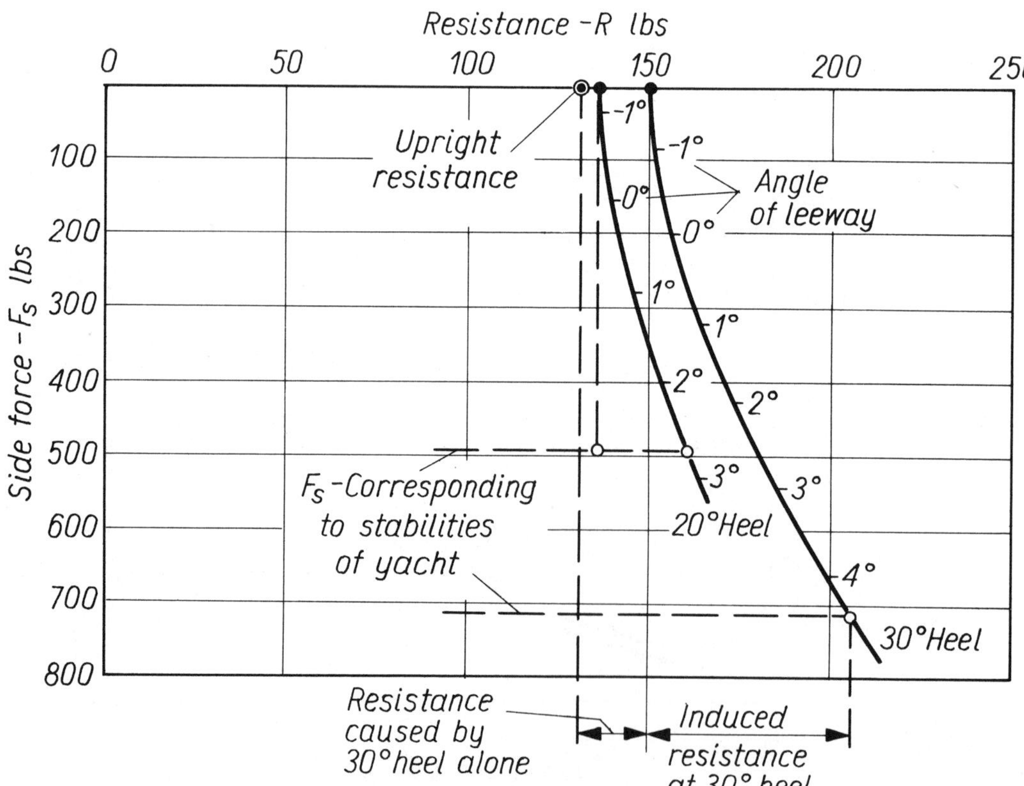

the side force F_S. Two curves show in the form of a polar diagram how resistance R and side force F_S vary for angles of heel of 20° and 30°, and for different angles of drift, when $v_S = 6$ knots. The increase in resistance caused by an angle of heel of 20° is still relatively small when compared with resistances in an upright position. It should be noted that the hull when heeled develops side force even when leeway is negative. When the angle of leeway is zero, but the heel is 20°, the side force is quite considerable, nearly 30 per cent of the value of F_S. In such a case the heeled hull functions in effect as a hydrofoil, and somehow reduces the drift necessary to achieve sufficient side force F_S. Up to certain limits, then, the negative effects of heeling, which appear as an additional resistance, are compensated for by the reduced leeway. Here it may be appropriate to endorse this interesting judgment by quoting Professor K. S. M. Davidson, of the Stevens Institute, United States: "Insofar as it is correct, however, it invalidates the old impression that 'lengthened sailing lines,' or some other supposed peculiarity of conventional yacht form, reduces the heeled resistances. What seems more probable is that the yacht form is relatively successful in avoiding large additions to the wave-making resistance as the heel increases."

Resistance caused by a 30° heel increases upright resistance by about 15 per cent, and contains already about 25 per cent of the resistance caused by the heeling force. To quote Professor Davidson again: "The extra resistance caused by heeling alone is primarily the result of having altered the wave-making characteristics of the form. This interference is strengthened by the rapidly growing importance of resistance as the heel angle exceeds 20°." Experience with dinghies supports this statement, for it is known that for a given wind speed a boat can be sailed closer to the wind the more upright she is kept. Moreover, it is confirmed by the knowledge that a keel boat's performance to windward in strong winds is at its best if the heeling is allowed to reach but not to exceed the critical angle.

These are convincing reasons for reefing a boat in a stiff breeze, to prevent the situation shown in Fig. 174, where, due to the excessive increase of the aerodynamic forces developed by full sail, the actual speed of the yacht decreases. Speedometer tests carried out on the boat *Victory* have shown that in a strong breeze and carrying full sail, her speed to windward was 2.5 knots. When the sails were reefed, a step the crew did not think necessary, the speed increased to 3.5 knots. Many yachtsmen, particularly the novice helmsmen of light dinghies, do not appreciate the real losses that heeling can cause. Sailing with the sails sheeted in hard heeling over, sometimes to a dangerous degree, as a result of this rather than of the wind's strength, all this gives the inexperienced helmsman an impression of great speed coupled with a feeling of risks and thrills. It is magnificent, but it is not efficient.

Excessive heeling affects not only speed but also the ability to beat to windward. It was shown earlier (in Figs. 78 and 80) that the angle to the wind at which a boat can sail, β, is the sum of two drag angles: ϵ_A—aerodynamic drag angle, and ϵ_H—hydrodynamic drag angle. Now if any factors cause an increase in either ϵ_A or ϵ_H, at once the performance of the yacht is affected. A heeling force F_H allowed to produce excessive heeling can cause this. The influence of heeling on the aerodynamic efficiency of the rigging was mentioned in the analysis of Fig. 82. This is definitely bad, as it increases the value of ϵ_A.

Useful inferences can be drawn from the table below, the data in which relate to *Gimcrack* sailing close-hauled.

Angle of heel Θ degrees	5.0°	10.0°	15.0°	20.0°	25.0°	30.0°	35.0°
App. wind v_A knots	6.2	9.3	11.9	14.3	17.0	19.7	22.5
Boat speed v_s knots	3.3	4.5	5.2	5.6	5.9	6.0	6.0
Side force F_s lbs.	87.6	172.0	248.0	317.0	383.0	444.0	496.0
Resistance R lbs.	26.0	53.4	78.5	103.0	130.0	154.0	175.0
Hydrodyn. angle of drag ε_H, degrees	16.6	17.5	18.1	19.1	20.5	21.8	23.3
Course β degrees	26.1	26.5	27.0	27.6	28.6	29.7	31.0

The hydrodynamic angle of drag, ϵ_H, increases steadily as the yacht's speed rises. This is because resistance, R, develops at a rate greater than the square of the speed, and at the same time side force, F_s, varies in relation to the square of the speed. The helmsman can have no influence on this phenomenon, except that when the yacht has reached her maximum close-hauled speed, $v_s \cong 6$ knots at $v_A \cong 19.7$ knots, it is possible to prevent any deterioration in her performance by reefing. A crew which does not reef at this stage may eventually notice that while the speedometer is recording the same speed, $v_s \cong 6$ knots, the yacht is making 1.5° less to windward, this being the difference in the values of ϵ_H when heeled at 30° and 35°.

These remarks on heeling apply especially to heavy-displacement boats. For a flat-bottomed, light-displacement boat such as the Scow, whose resistance curve was given in Fig. 162, a moderate amount of artificially induced heel, within the limits of 20°–30°, can improve performance. When sailing in a light wind it is actually advisable to shift the crew to leeward of the centerline to reduce the wetted area and the friction resistance.

The table below proves this from data based on a report from the Davidson Laboratory, United States, on the Class A Inland Lake Scow.

	Heel 0°		10°		20°		30°	
V_s knots	*Total Resistance*	*Friction*	*T.R.*	*Frict.*	*T.R.*	*Frict.*	*T.R.*	*Frict.*
7.8	111.0	108.0	106.0	74.2	89.8	56.0	83.1	50.1
9.4	181.0	144.0	170.0	106.0	149.0	80.7	136.0	72.1
14.6	374.0	293.0	382.0	191.0	305.0	200.0	274.0	179.0
Wetted area	199.4 sq. ft.		193.9 sq. ft.		155.0 sq. ft.		142.8 sq. ft.	

Thus, for example, moving a crew of 650 lb. to lee so that an angle of heel of 20° is achieved will reduce the hydrodynamic resistance by about 19 per cent, and this in turn will improve the close-hauled performance by about 5 per cent.

It is, however, obvious that if the boat is allowed to heel too far, her aerohydrodynamic efficiency will be so far affected that the advantages accruing from the reduction of the wetted area will be too small to compensate for the other negative effects.

Another harmful result of excessive heel is that it can change the yacht's directional balance by increasing the weather helm. A comparison of the array of forces acting on a dinghy shown in Fig. 177a and b reveals that more weather helm is carried in a, at a greater angle of heel, than in b, where the angle of heel is smaller. Weather helm, which appears and increases almost automatically as the boat heels, is defined as the yawing couple $F_{T_{II}} \times a$, which tends to produce

Fig. 177

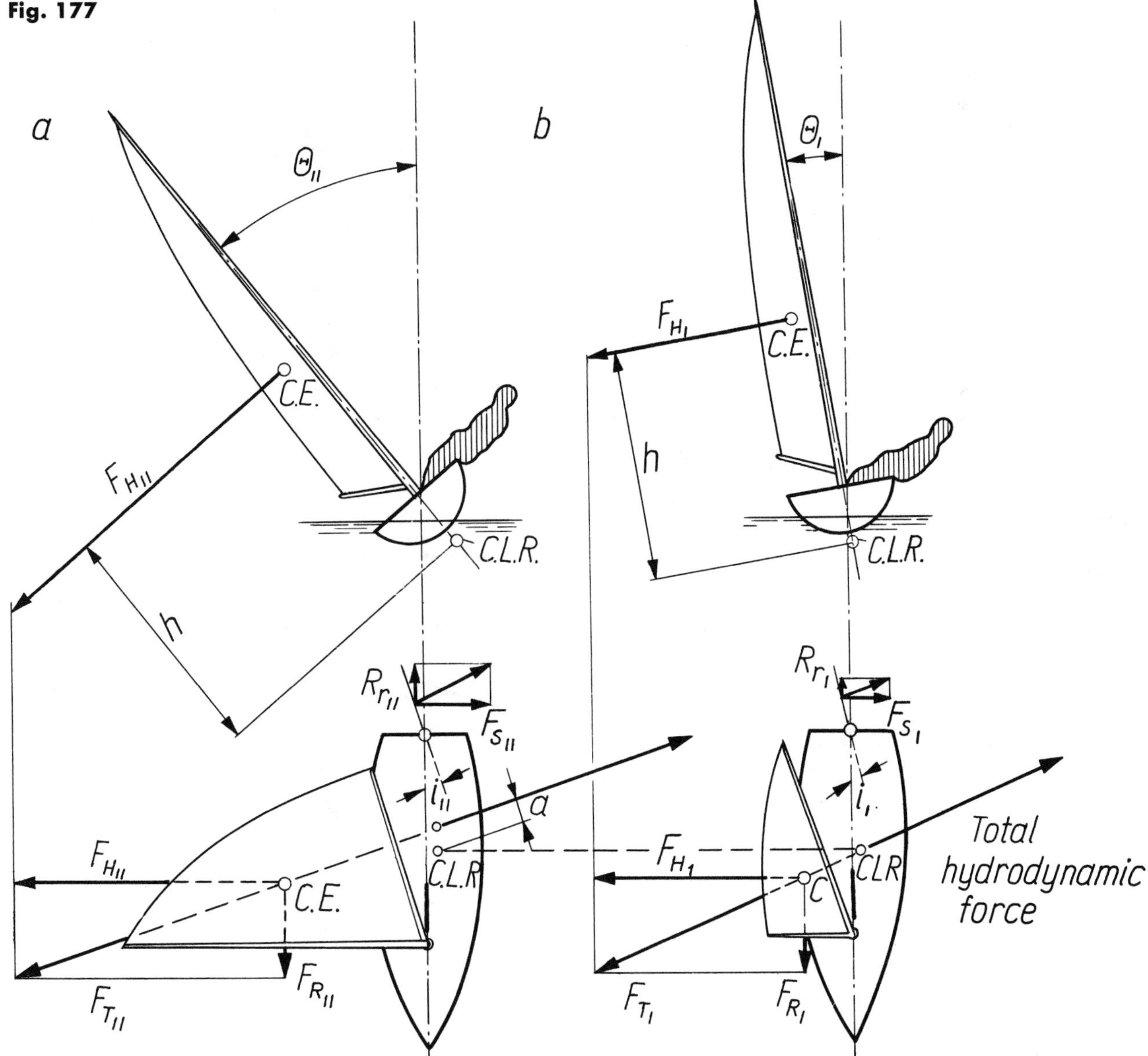

a change of course. The unbalanced arm "a" appears when the boat heels. The weather-acting couple, or in other words, the yawing moment, can in certain circumstances be so strong that the rudder cannot correct it, and the yacht will luff suddenly into the wind with her sails shaking, in spite of the helmsman's efforts. However, to keep the boat on her course the effect of the weather-acting couple must be corrected by suitable adjustments of the helm, even though increasing the angle of the rudder from $i_{,}$ to $i_{,,}$ inevitably leads to a rise in the hydrodynamic resistance of the rudder from $R_{r,}$ to $R_{r,,}$, which reduces the speed of the yacht. This extra resistance to the yawing moment can become as much as 40 per cent of the total resistance. Yet how often we watch a helmsman struggling at the helm, a particularly exhausting task in a long race. There are no grounds for carrying full sail simply for the pleasure of feeling a mighty force acting on the rudder.

Fig. 178

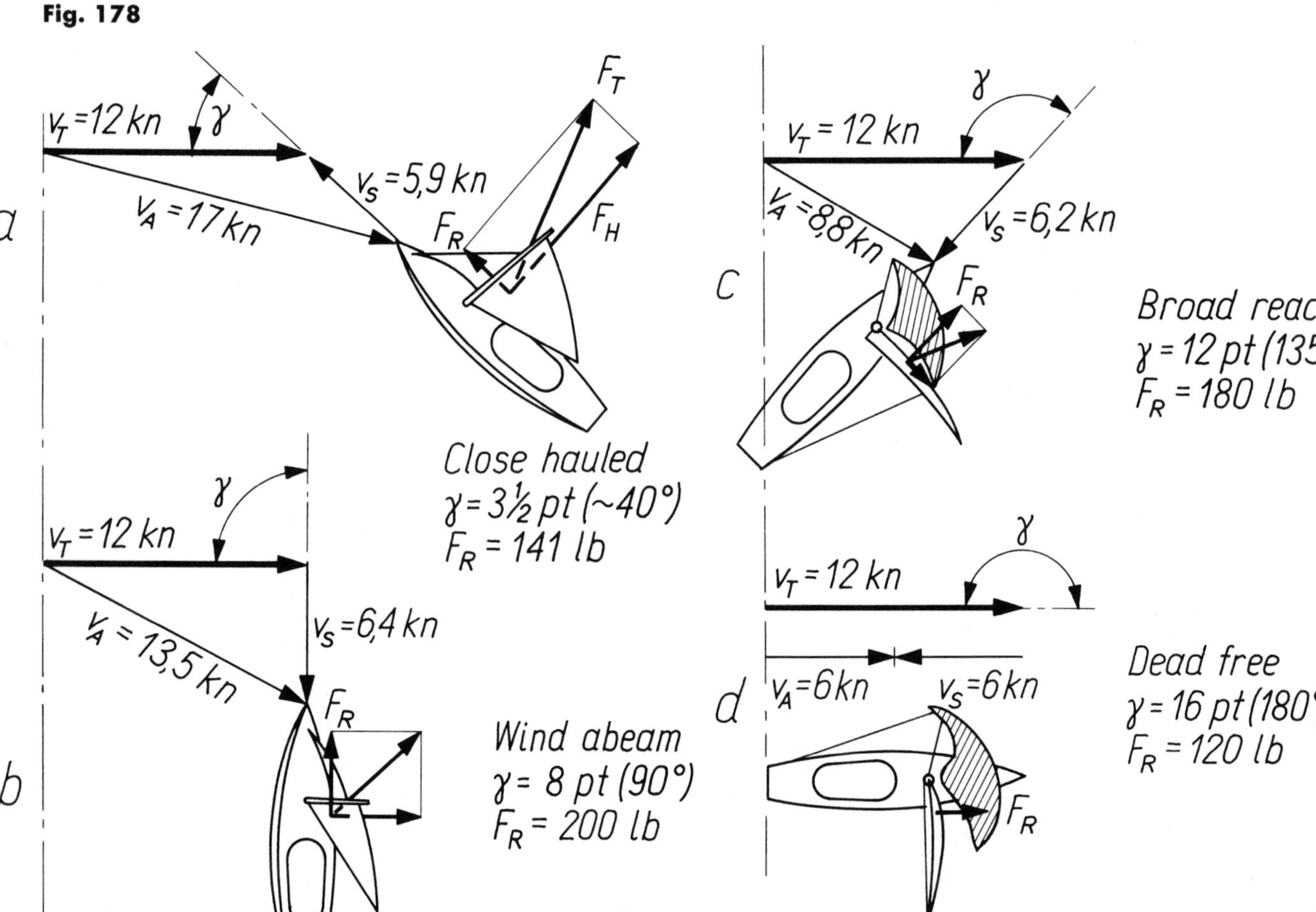

2. YACHT PERFORMANCE

It is not what your ship will *not* do that you want to know to get on terms of successful partnership with her; it is, rather, that you ought to have a precise knowledge of what she will do for you when called upon to put forth what is in her by a sympathetic touch.

J. CONRAD, *The Mirror of the Sea*

(a) All-round Performance

Variations in sailing angle have relatively little effect on the speed of heavy-displacement yachts. Figure 178, for example, shows the behavior of a 6-Meter (23.5 ft. in LWL) in a 12-knot true wind. The drawings were prepared from data obtained by Professor K. S. M. Davidson and deal with four basic sailing courses: close-hauled, wind abeam, broad reach, and dead run. Changes in the speed of the yacht were less than 10 per cent whatever the point of sailing. There are two reasons for this. The first can be found by comparing the velocity vectors v_A of the apparent wind, for on these depend the magnitude of the aerodynamic forces, especially the driving force component, F_R. When a close-hauled yacht bears away from the wind, the apparent wind velocity falls rapidly, thus reducing the magnitude of the total aerodynamic force. Initially the effect of this reduction in F_T is more than compensated for by the increase in the driving force, F_R. This is a direct result of the geometric relation of the vectors that represent the arrangement of forces on the sail (cf. cases a and b).

Later, when the course passes through broad reaching to running free, the magnitude of the driving force F_R decreases steadily until a certain minimum level is reached. Breaking out a spinnaker or an increase in the sails' camber can increase the speed at this point. Nevertheless, the drop in v_A from 17 knots when close-hauled to 6 knots on a dead run, to about a third of its original power, has much more influence on the aerodynamic forces, since these are proportional to v_A^2, than sail area or aerodynamic coefficient.

The other reason why variation in the driving force, F_R, only produces slight changes in the boat's speed, v_s, is the fact that in this range of sailing speeds the curve of hydrodynamic resistance is very steep (cf. Fig. 156). It has already been shown that the effect of driving force variations on the speed of motion is small when the speed/length ratio $v_s/\sqrt{L} \cong 1.2$.

The speed polar diagram (Fig. 179) represents the performance of the yacht for different true course angles, γ. In it the sailing speed, v_s, plotted on the sailing angles, γ, at $v_T = 12$ knots produces an almost circular diagram. Inside this curve is drawn a hypothetical curve for the lower wind speed which would let the yacht sail at a speed/length ratio, $v_s/\sqrt{L}$, of about 1.0. Here the changes in driving force, whether caused by S_A or by the aerodynamic coefficient (camber) or by v_A, would be more marked, and the speed polar diagram is therefore flatter for running courses.

A knowledge of a yacht's speed polar diagram can be very helpful when tackling a number of the tactical problems encountered when cruising or racing. Figure 180 illustrates two examples of its use. Three yachts—A, B, and C—are racing toward the finishing line, G'-G'', and the correct choice of the course which will enable one of them to reach the line first is vital. Few helmsmen can in fact choose correctly. However, by constructing a line parallel to G'-G'' and at the same time tangential to the speed polar diagram, the right course γ opt is found on the line OB where this passes through the tangential point. Sailing closer to the wind along OA or, with the wind freer, along OC, will not be so profitable. In general helmsmen do tend to sail too close to the wind when approaching the finishing line. The decision may at times be governed by psychological factors. For instance a competitor likes to be spotted as early as possible, and may think he will record a better time by crossing the line at the point nearest the committee boat, whether this is near G' or G''.

The second example relates to downwind sailing, when a sloop would use her spinnaker. From the speed polar diagram it is clear that on a dead run it would be better to tack along OX or OY to cross the line M'-M'' first. The gains due to sailing faster, with the spinnaker out of the mainsail's blanketing zone, coupled with the simultaneous development of a stronger apparent wind, will compensate for the longer distance that has to be covered.

"Tacking to leeward" can also offer tactical advantages, for by it one may avoid being blanketed by a rival's sails, or approach the next mark in a favorable position for rounding the buoy unimpeded (cf. Fig. 181). During trials with 5.5-Meters it was agreed that in light winds unexpected gains might be made, even by a very considerable deflection $\Delta\gamma$ from the shortest course D_k. By bearing away from a dead run by $\Delta\gamma = 40°$, a speed 60 per cent greater than that possible on D_k was

Fig. 179

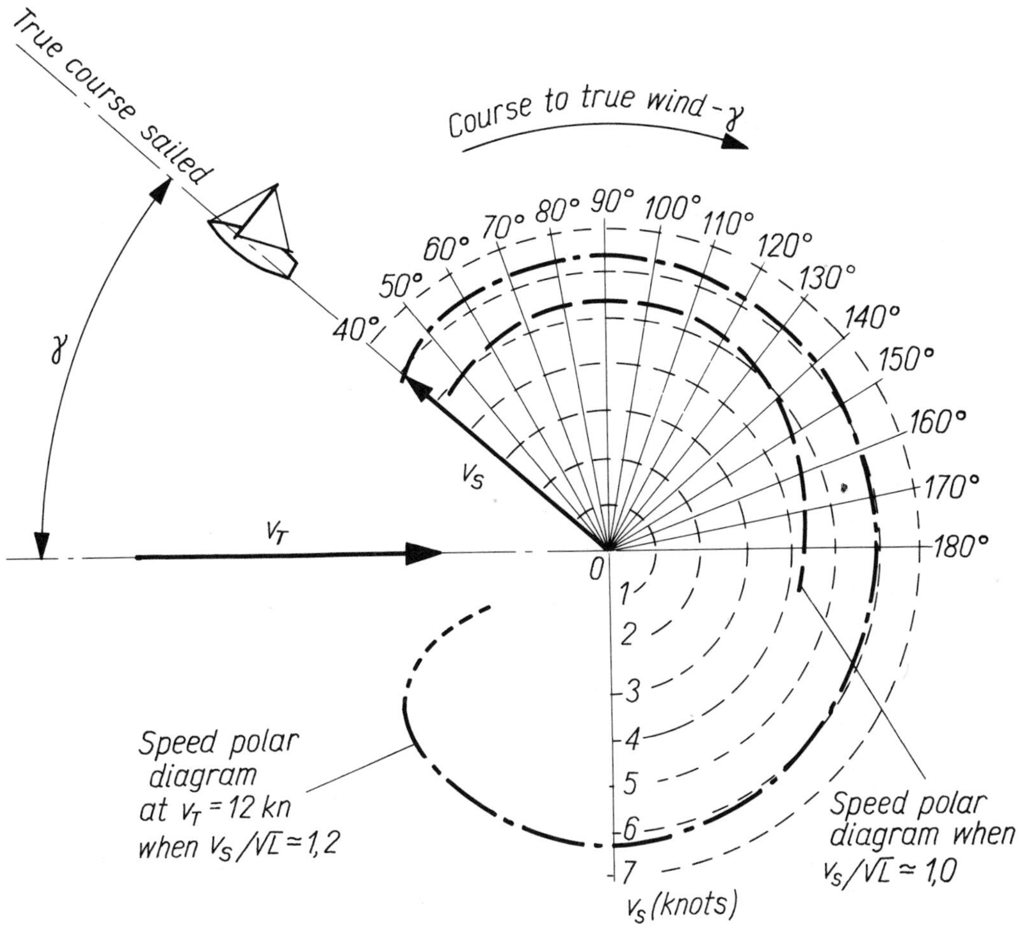

True course sailed

Course to true wind – γ

40° 50° 60° 70° 80° 90° 100° 110° 120° 130° 140° 150° 160° 170° 180°

γ

v_S

v_T

0

1 2 3 4 5 6 7

v_S (knots)

Speed polar diagram at $v_T = 12$ kn when $v_S/\sqrt{L} \simeq 1{,}2$

Speed polar diagram when $v_S/\sqrt{L} \simeq 1{,}0$

Fig. 180

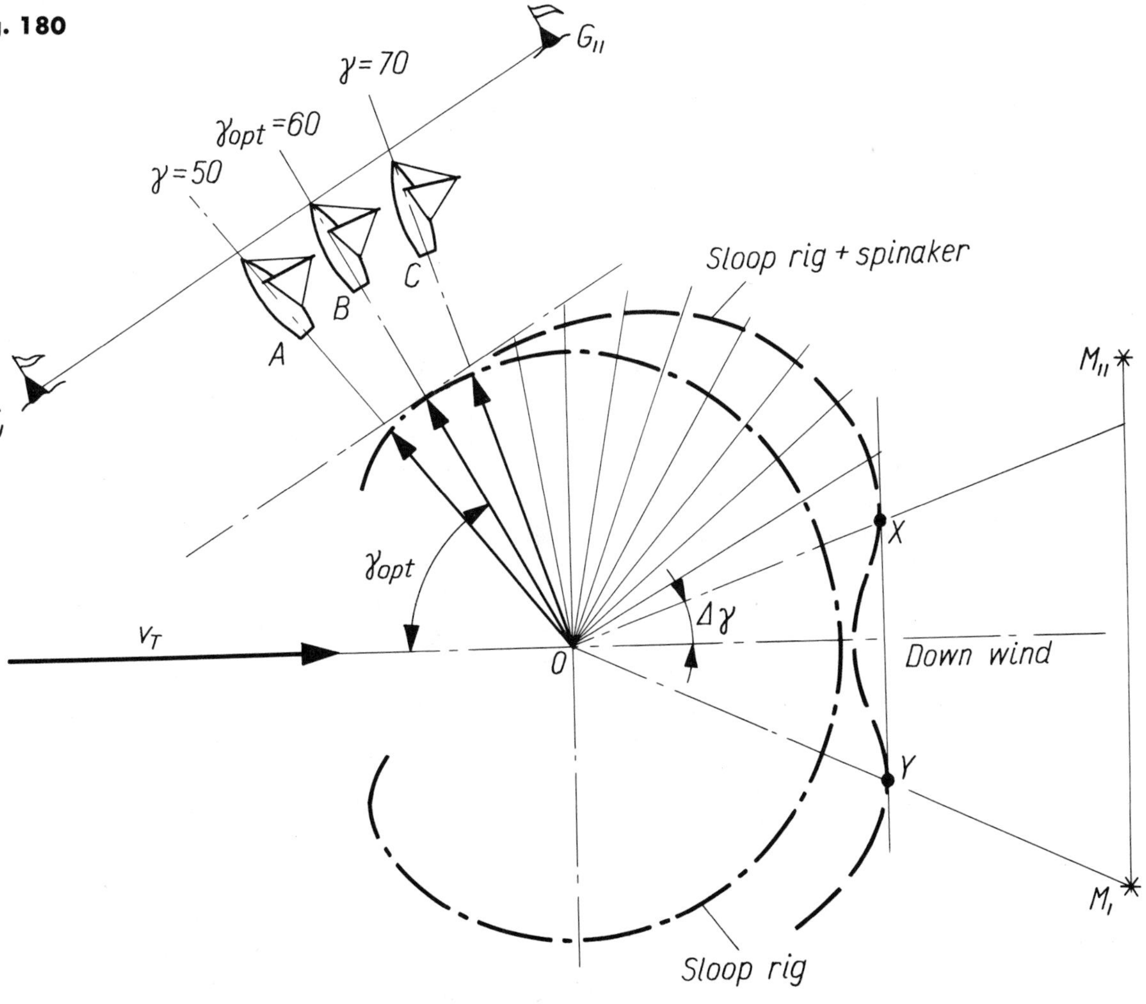

G_{II}

$\gamma = 70$

$\gamma_{opt} = 60$

$\gamma = 50$

A B C

G_I

Sloop rig + spinaker

M_{II}

X

γ_{opt}

$\Delta\gamma$

v_T

0

Down wind

Y

M_I

Sloop rig

Fig. 181

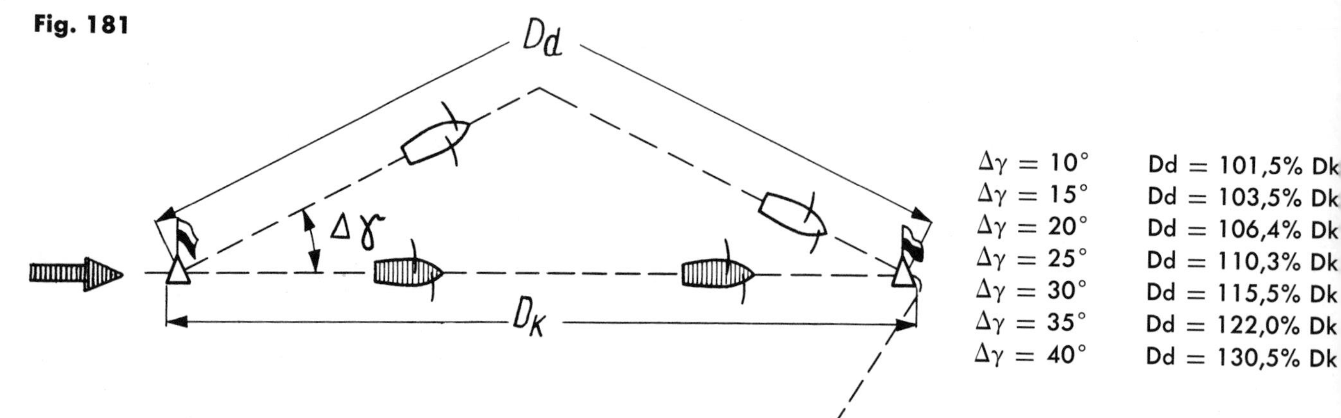

achieved. As the track D_d proved to be 30 per cent longer than D_k, the net gain in time was about 19 per cent. In stronger winds, however, when $\Delta\gamma = 30°$ from dead before the wind, the speed increase was only 10 per cent, while the distance was greater by 15.5 per cent, the resultant loss in time being 5 per cent. The difference in these results is accounted for by the sharp upturn in the hydrodynamic resistance curve (cf. Figs. 155, 156) when a keel boat is sailing in a strong wind at almost the maximum attainable "displacement speed," and then v_s variations are negligible, even though "tacking downwind" increases the aerodynamic force considerably. These trials also showed that sea conditions affect the advantages that may be gained from this technique. In a choppy sea the gains were lower, while in calm water with light winds the best results were achieved when $\Delta\gamma$ was between 30° and 40°. Generally speaking, selection of a suitable deflection angle depends on the qualities of the individual yacht.

A further interesting comparison can be seen in Fig. 182, where a 6-Meter, a conventional heavy keel boat, is contrasted with the fast-cruising catamaran *Symmetry*. The information was taken from a publication by the latter's designer, Hugo Mayers. Both the speed polar diagrams for different courses, γ, are plotted

Fig. 182

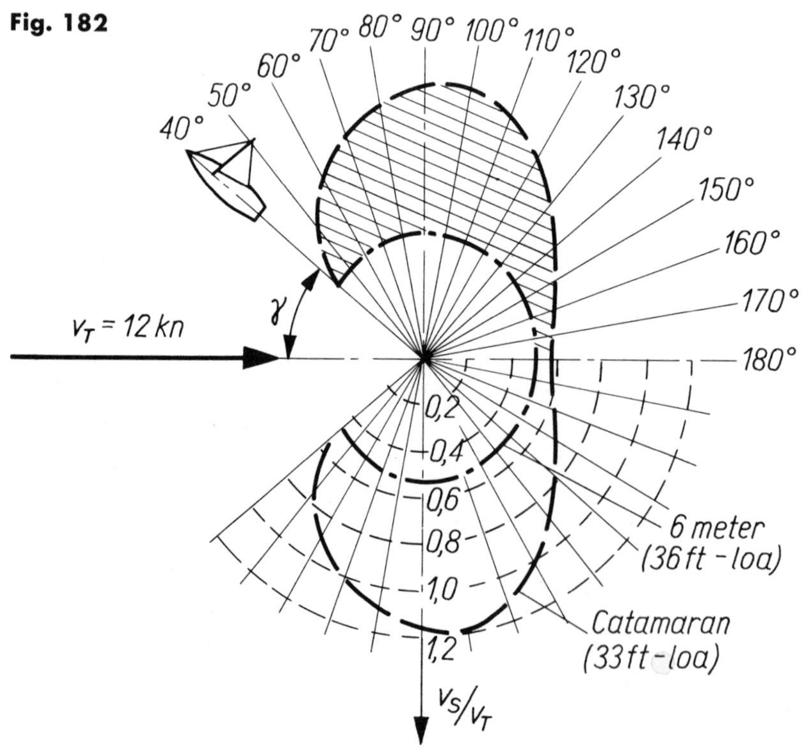

for a true wind speed $v_T = 12$ knots, but instead of the actual boat speed, v_S, the related ratio v_S/v_T is used. On courses very close to the wind and on a dead run, the difference in speed between the 6-Meter and the catamaran is small. On a reach, however, the catamaran's speed is about twice that of the 6-Meter. These curves could be taken as representing two different basic tendencies in present-day boat building. The 6-Meter is a typical keel yacht, and preserves the well-tried traditional combination of sail area, displacement, and length with the most appropriate hull shape for sailing at relative speeds $v_S < 1.4\sqrt{L}$. In the keel boat classes there is no practical way of producing a radical improvement in all-round speed, or in other words, of raising the ratio v_S/v_T above 0.6.

Catamarans are capable of attaining much higher speeds (i.e., a higher v_S/v_T ratio) than a single-hulled sailing craft. In Fig. 182 the area between the two curves is shaded, and in this area the speed polar diagrams of all fast, light-displacement boats, racing dinghies like the Flying Dutchman, Finn, and Scow, could be drawn. The all-round performance of any sailing boat will resemble one or other of these two basic speed polar curves, dependent on its displacement/length ratio

$$\frac{\Delta}{(L/100)^3} \text{ and its sail area/displacement ratio } \frac{S_A}{\Delta}.$$

The catamaran achieves a ratio $v_S/v_T = 1.2$, which means that she can sail faster than the true wind speed, v_T. This can be improved, and progress is still being made.

Today's concept of the fast, light-displacement boat and catamaran, revolutionary and even offensive though it is, is not new. As often happens, it was rediscovered and spontaneously accepted, because the contemporary psychological climate favors this kind of concept. The speed at which a human being can move does not increase his happiness, and yet he would experience profound unhappiness if his hopes of increasing his speed were taken from him.

In fact, light-displacement "skimming dishes" were sailing in the nineteenth century on American and even on English waters, causing outraged feelings among respectable yachtsmen. Centuries ago, moreover, it was in the light catamarans and trimarans, built without a single metal nail, that men of primitive tribes found and colonized countless Pacific islands.

The basic conditions needed for a sailing craft to attain high speeds are minimum weight, maximum sail area, and the stability to carry that sail area. Satisfying the first two conditions is largely governed by the lateral stability of the hull. This is the problem explained in Fig. 183, where a ballast-keel boat and a catamaran are contrasted on a high-speed sailing course, with the wind abeam. A simple deduction from a study of the hulls alone proves that sailing speed will be higher if the hull is able to counter a high heeling force, F_H, while maintaining a small angle of heel and the minimum of hydrodynamic resistance R. Since resistance, R, is a function of the weight, W, of the boat, the heeling ratio F_H/W can thus be a criterion of the ability of a boat to reach high speeds. A comparison of the upper drawings in Fig. 183, which show the forces acting on the keel boat and the cat when the true course $\gamma = 90°$ and $v_T = 12$ knots, shows that the faster catamaran is really close reaching, whereas the keel boat is broad reaching, simply because the apparent wind vector, v_A, is drawn out ahead by the higher sailing speed, v_S. As a result, the heeling force, F_H, has become proportionately greater than the driving force, F_R, and thus the requirements for lateral stability are increased by any increase in the ratio of v_S/v_T. As we cannot expect any radical changes in the efficiency and driving power of the sails, inevitably the driving component, F_R, will always remain a fraction of the heeling component, F_H. Therefore to increase the driving force, F_R, demands the discovery of some means of countering the negative effects of the heeling force, F_H. This can only be achieved by changing the principles employed in lateral stability. Despite the concentration of over 70 per cent of the total weight of the 6-Meter in the lead ballast at the bottom of the keel, the lateral stability, which controls her ability to carry a large area of sail, is relatively limited. It may be expressed as the ratio F_H/W, approximately $1/15$ to $1/20$, which is typical for any keel yacht.

Now if the heeling force $F_H = 465$ lb., i.e., $1/20$ of the total weight $W = 9400$ lb., then the 6-Meter responds to the F_H by heeling to an angle of 20°. This is almost the critical angle for maximum speed, and so there is no prospect of improving on this relationship. This principle of ballast distribution in relation to the hull form, as can be seen in the lower drawing in Fig. 183, is not very effective. The righting arm, RA, of a ballast yacht is zero when she is in an upright position, and so her initial stability is small. The increase in RA develops relatively slowly and it is impossible for any really great aerodynamic force to be attained on the sail without seriously upsetting her lateral stability, which in its turn determines the yacht's hydro-aerodynamic efficiency. This leads to the paradox that a heavy ballast keel is most effective when the angle of heel reaches 90°. This is a most desirable characteristic from a safety point of view, but is hardly the best for high-speed sailing. External or internal ballast forms some 35–45 per cent of the total displacement of a cruising boat, and may reach as much as 80 per cent in a racing boat. It therefore increases the displacement, adds considerably to the resistance, and requires a strong, heavily built structure. Heavy ballast beneath a single hull is, then, a very expensive way of attaining the capacity to carry a large sail area.

For the catamaran the position is almost completely different, since its initial stability is relatively great. The righting arm increases very sharply at small angles of heel until it reaches its maximum when the weather hull lifts just clear of the water. The value of the RA will then be about half the beam of the craft. At the same time the hydrodynamic efficiency of the catamaran is at its best, as the resistance to motion is reduced.

It must be emphasized that the catamaran's great lateral stability is achieved by having two widely spaced light hulls. Stability "due to spread" can be improved by filling and emptying ballast tanks in the windward hull, and, of course, by moving the crew.

Fig. 183

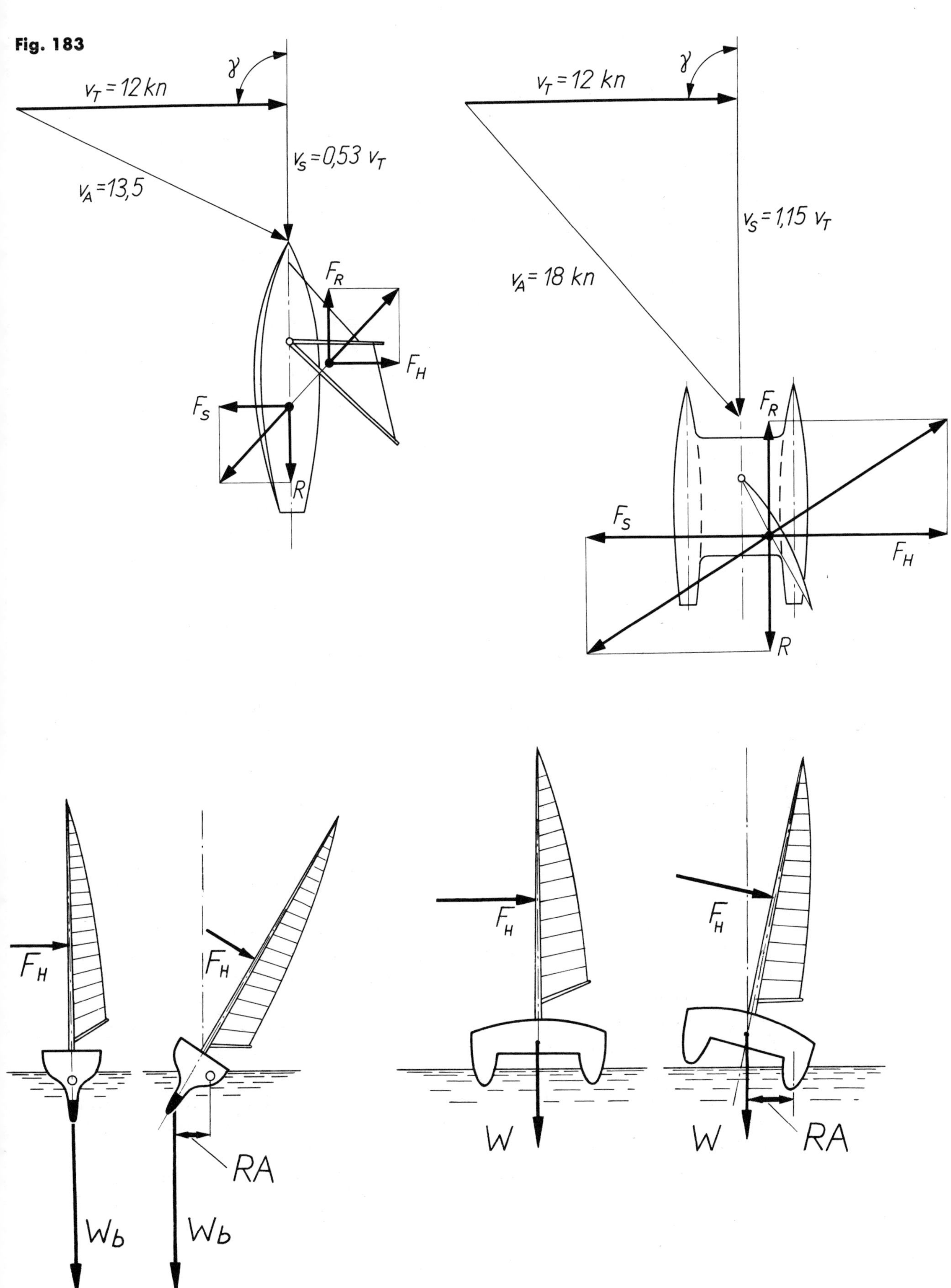

γ
$v_T = 12\,kn$
$v_S = 0{,}53\ v_T$
$v_A = 13{,}5$
F_R
F_H
F_S
R
γ
$v_T = 12\ kn$
$v_S = 1{,}15\ v_T$
$v_A = 18\ kn$
F_R
F_S
F_H
R
F_H
F_H
RA
Wb
Wb
F_H
F_H
W
W
RA

A catamaran's sail area/displacement (S_A/Δ) can be increased beyond what is possible in a single-hulled ballast yacht. The average ballast yacht carries some 100–150 sq. ft. of canvas for each ton of displacement. A racing 6-Meter has approximately 110 sq. ft./ton, while the racing catamaran *Hellcat* has 640 sq. ft./ton. The S_A/Δ ratio is equally great for the planing dinghies, whose stability depends on the proper distribution of the crew on the weather rail, sliding seat, or trapeze. Typical ratios are

F.D. $\cong$ 610 sq. ft./ton
5-0-5 $\cong$ 650 sq. ft./ton
Finn $\cong$ 540 sq. ft./ton
18 ft. Australian skiff above 600 sq. ft./ton
International 10 sq. m. Canoe $\cong$ 540 sq. ft./ton

A ratio of over 400 sq. ft./ton appears to be indispensable if a boat is to be able to plane.

Figure 184 gives the results of experiments by Professor Ata Nutku on models of a similar length but different displacement, Δ, and of different shape amidships. These were (1) the Narrow Finn with ballast keel, L = 5.83 ft.; (2) the Finn, L = 5.45 ft.; (3) a catamaran, L = 5.22 ft. By contrasting the data for the light racing dinghy hull with those for the catamaran, it can be seen that the latter has a lower hydrodynamic resistance in spite of its greater displacement/length ratio $\Delta/(L/100)^3$. The catamaran's resistance curve has shifted bodily in the direction of a greater speed/length ratio, $v_s/\sqrt{L}$, mainly because of the reduction in wave-making resistance due to the narrow hulls. These diagrams show that twin hulls can prove superior to a single hull if their displacement/length ratio is reduced, and this can be done fairly easily. *Hellcat,* for example, which won the 1961 International Catamaran Challenge Trophy, has a ratio

$$\frac{\Delta}{(L/100)^3} \cong 38$$

while for most planing dinghies it is twice this figure, and there is no hope of reducing it.

The resistance curve for the light-displacement Narrow Finn, with ballast, illustrates fairly well the cost of stability through weight. In comparison with the hull of the normal Finn, the "narrow" Finn shows a marked increase in resistance due to its greater displacement.

The resistance curve of a catamaran has characteristic humps and hollows related to the coupled wave system of the two hulls. The high ratio of driving force to displacement, so easily achieved on a catamaran, suggests that there are good prospects for the future of this type of yacht. Relative speeds attainable on a twin-hull can exceed $4.5\sqrt{LWL}$, even in the case of a cruising cat where safety requirements put some restrictions on the builder.

Naturally, sailing at these speeds demands a change in the psychological adjust-

Fig. 184

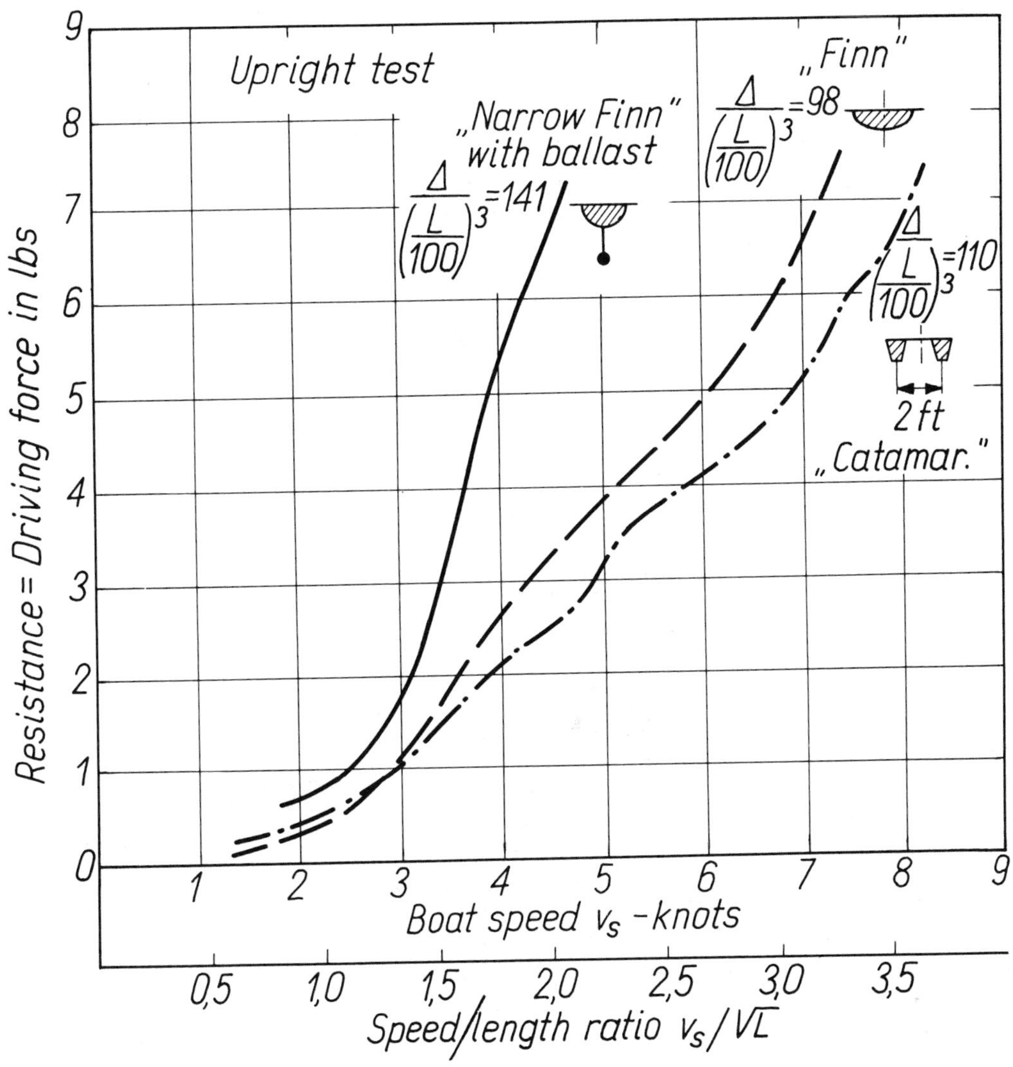

ment of the crew, as can be appreciated by reading the impressions of Dave Rochlen (from *Yachts and Yachting*), who had charge of a watch on *Waikiki Surf* during the Honolulu Race.

We sailed and raced in winds up to 40 knots with seas no greater than 15 to 18 feet with perhaps 50 foot of slope on the wave. At times 5, 6, or 8 feet of the wave tops would flip over and run down the face. We were running with most of the stuff and did a great deal of *surfing*. During one siege of line squalls, when the ocean seemed to be blown flat by what I guess was about 40 knots we were "schussing" down long endless grey valleys of water—sometimes riding the same wave for five minutes—until, in order to avoid certain *shelving out* spots we would come up wind and let the wave go by. Other times we would outrun one wave and rush up the back of the next wave, finally catching its "face." As you can imagine there can be quite a bit of skill involved in manoeuvring in and out of the "wave situations" to the best advantage of speed—and safety. Three of us in the crew were well orientated around this surfing technique and were able to get amazing speeds out of the "cat" while riding waves. The *Waikiki Surf* performed excel-

Fig. 185

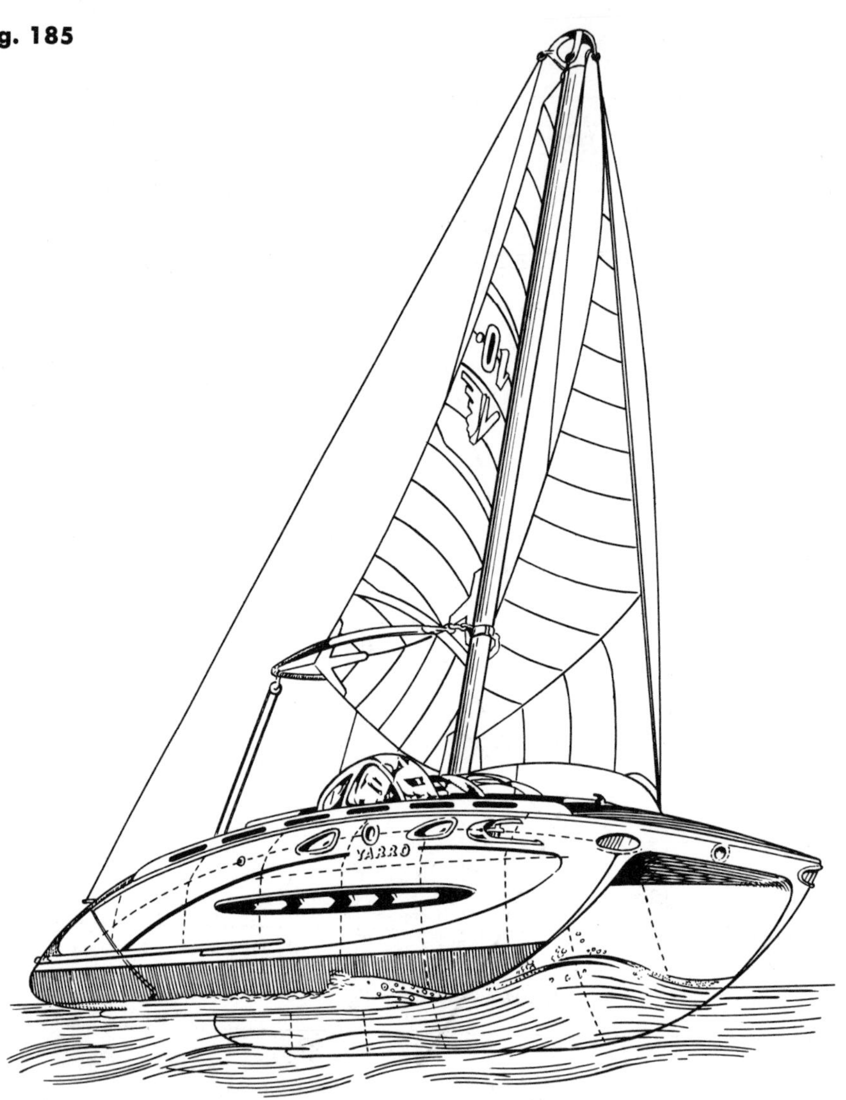

lently at all times in all conditions at sea, but crew skill is essential. We experienced a small hull failure which was unfortunate, but not crucial. By that I mean that it can be and has been remedied easily. I am convinced that the "cat" we raced is a sound seagoing craft able to withstand the same conditions any conventional boat of its same length could stand. There comes a time in all ocean sailing when it is necessary to shorten sail, also a time to "heave to." The catamaran is no exception.

Lightness means speed and, automatically, speed means danger and I don't see how we will ever be able to "cruise comfortably" at 25–30 knots. Racing is not comfortable, its a *thrill,* an adventure, as you well know. There is no package answer to safety. We had a man on the tiller bar and a man standing right by on the main sheet going to windward and with beam winds. This was in anticipation of capsizing, just playing it safe, but we could have shortened sail and played it safe that way.

The number of types of biscaphs and triscaphs built for high-speed sailing is uncountable, matched by the unlimited ingenuity of enthusiasts in search of new and original designs, many of which can be found in the publications of the

"Amateur Yacht Research Society," New York City. Two designs for offshore cruising catamarans are given here as examples.

Figure 185 shows the Australian *Yarro,* designed by J. Szabo:

Dimensions	
LOA	28 ft. 6 in.
LWL	23 ft. 5 in.
Extreme beam	13 ft. 9 in.
Displacement	2866 lb.
Draft	1 ft. 10 ins.
Sail area (max.)	589 sq. ft.

The maximum speed developed is above 20 knots. The characteristic of *Yarro's* hulls is the complete lack of centerboards or fins below the hull. As in the old Polynesian designs, asymmetrical hulls are sufficient to produce the side force F_S (Fig. 186) mainly on the leeward hull. The steering is particularly interesting. In the original version (Fig. 186b) the rudders were completely faired into the hulls. In the designer's opinion:

Fig. 186

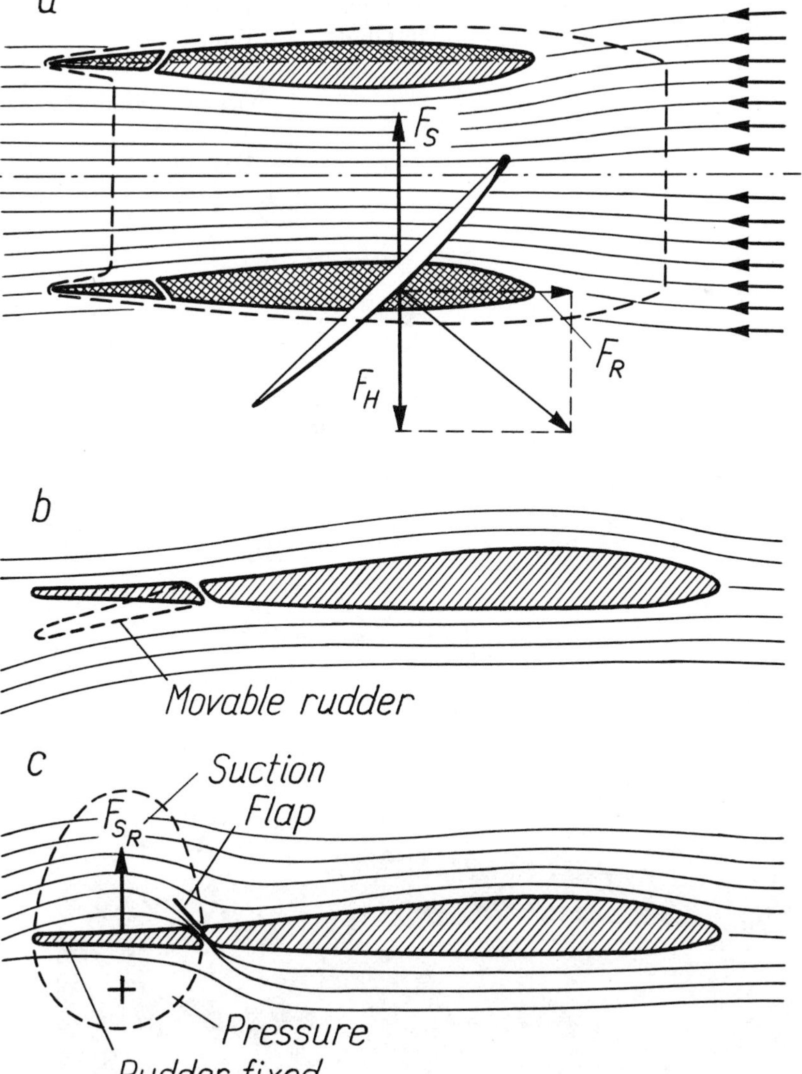

. . . this arrangement proved a great improvement where resistance at different helm angles was concerned, the increased resistance due to rudders being less than a fifth of that of the conventional type hung on the stern. The faired-in version was more effective at 1 degree angle than the hung-on-stern version at 5 degrees.

In the second version, the steering arrangement is altered (Fig. 186c) and the rudder now

does not move at all. It is a fixed portion of the hull, and steering is accomplished partly by boundary layer control, partly by a small flap which controls the flow through the slot, a practice well known to aircraft designers, but never before used in the design of sailing boats. The arrangement shown develops turning moments that force the reluctant catamaran to turn on sixpence like a lively dinghy.

Photograph 35 and Fig. 187 show the English narrow cruising catamaran, *Golden Miller,* designed by Michael Henderson.

Dimensions		*Sail Area*	
LOA	20 ft. 9 ins.	Main	75 sq. ft.
LWL	18 ft.	Genoa	195 sq. ft.
Hull beam	3 ft. 6 ins.	Yankee 1	100 sq. ft.
Displacement	2780 lb.	Yankee 2	75 sq. ft.
Max. speed	10–12 knots	Yankee 3	40 sq. ft.
		Genoa staysail	60 sq. ft.
		Staysail 1	40 sq. ft.
		Staysail 2	25 sq. ft.

Photo. 35

. 187

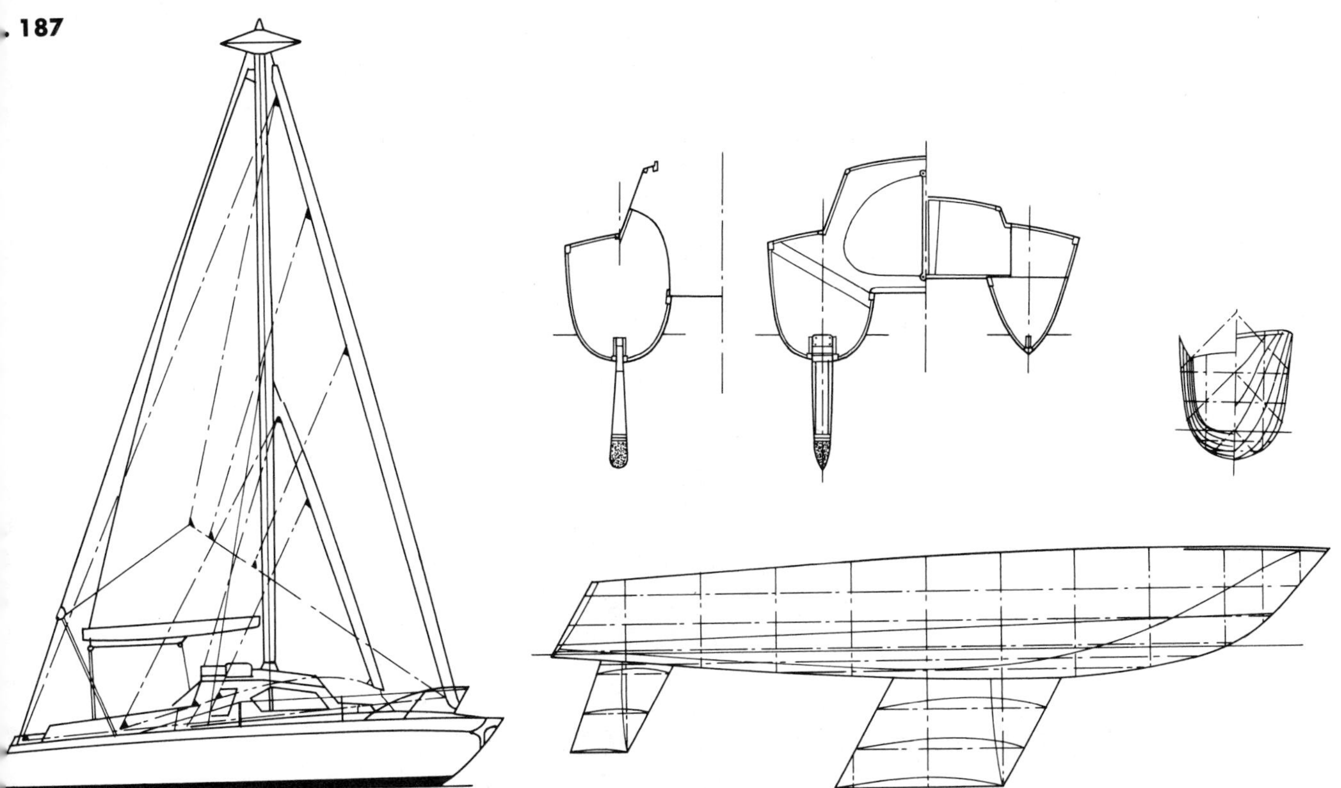

Unlike *Yarro,* she has symmetrical hulls and efficient profiled fins and rudders. Practical experience and tests in towing tanks suggest that symmetrical hulls are better in the low and high speed ranges, when the $v_s/\sqrt{L}$ ratio is below 1.5 or above 3.0. In the intermediate range there is no real difference. Most recent fast-racing catamarans have symmetrical hulls. For safety, *Golden Miller* has masthead buoyancy and a moderate amount of iron ballast, twice 300 lb. in her fin keels. The amazing stability of this catamaran was admired by the author on a film. Easily controlled, she even returned smoothly to normal after heeling almost to the point of "no return."

Recently "sailing creatures" have begun to appear which in certain conditions break completely with the traditional method of floating supported buoyantly on the water (see Photo. 36). They almost seem as absurd as the vessel described by Edward Lear:

> They went to sea in a sieve, they did
> In a sieve they went to sea:
> In spite of all their friends could say,
> On a winter's morn, on a stormy day,
> In a sieve they sailed so fast.

This type of craft uses buoyant lift only when at rest or sailing very slowly. As soon as a certain speed is reached, the hull rises up above the water surface, and is supported entirely on hydrofoils. In this way the friction resistance of the hull's

Photo. 36

wetted surface and the spray resistance are eliminated, and the only resistance left to overcome is the small hydrodynamic resistance of the hydrofoils themselves.

Hydrodynamic lift develops in a similar manner to aerodynamic lift on sails or on the wing of an airplane. Figure 188 shows four alternative hydrofoil arrangements.

Hydrofoils were introduced with great success in the construction of fast motorboats. Any attempt to apply them to sailing craft, however, runs into difficulties over preserving stability. The hydrofoils must be kept at a constant depth below the surface of the water, and at a constant angle of attack (incidence), no matter

Fig. 188

a b

c d

what the sailing conditions. Since the amount of lift in the hydrofoils varies with the boat's speed and her angle to the water level, variations in these may make the upper portion of the hydrofoils emerge from the water. The lifting force then decreases rapidly, the hydrofoils dive under again, and as a result the boat may start to pitch heavily. There is a further difficulty in obtaining the hydrodynamic force needed to prevent drift and heel. Sea waves in strong winds are another complication, and require some form of automatic control for setting the hydrofoils at a suitable angle to each wave. This sudden rapid pitching can be very dangerous. In Switzerland a member of the crew of a hydrofoil sailing boat was thrown through the cabin roof in one accident.

However, despite all these difficulties experimental yachts are sailing on hydrofoils at 30 knots. Figure 189 shows a sketch of an American yacht whose hydrofoils are arranged like a ladder, so that as speed increases they gradually emerge from the water. This satisfactory system affords some protection against pitching and jolting. The inclined setting of the hydrofoils develops enough side force, F_S, to prevent drift. Lateral stability is obtained in the same way as with twin hulls, and the line of action of the resultant of F_H and W must pass through the hydrodynamic center of pressure, CP, of the immersed hydrofoils or hydrofoil (cf. Fig. 190).

Figure 191 shows a hydrofoil arrangement designed by Grunberg* in which skis ahead of the bows control the angle of incidence on hydrofoils fixed amidships.

Fig. 189

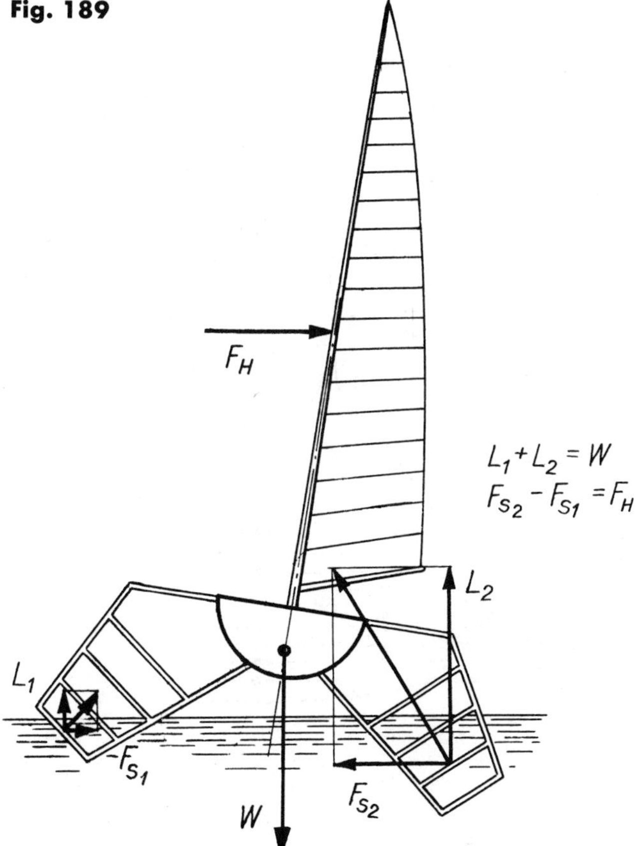

* Very promising seems to be Christopher Hook's arrangement, which is essentially a hydraulic analogue computer to give the hull minimum acceleration.

Fig. 190

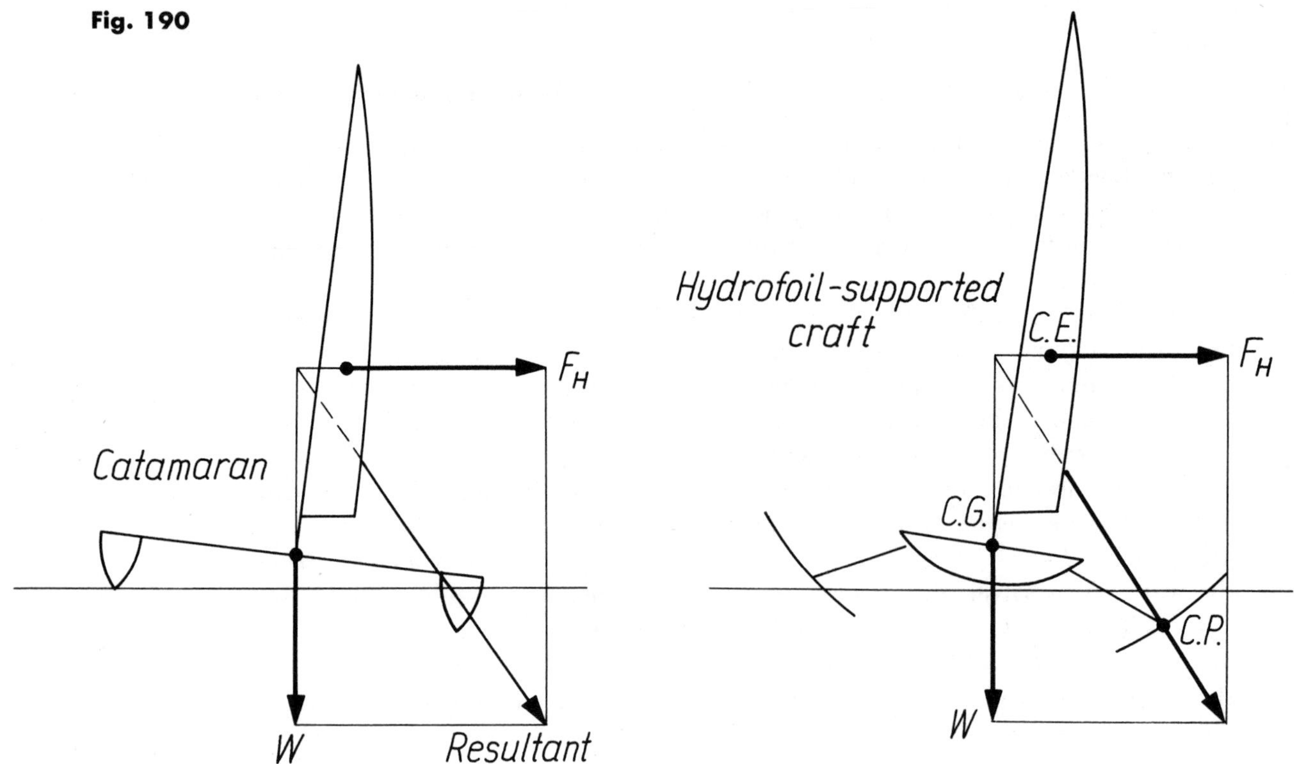

Fig. 191

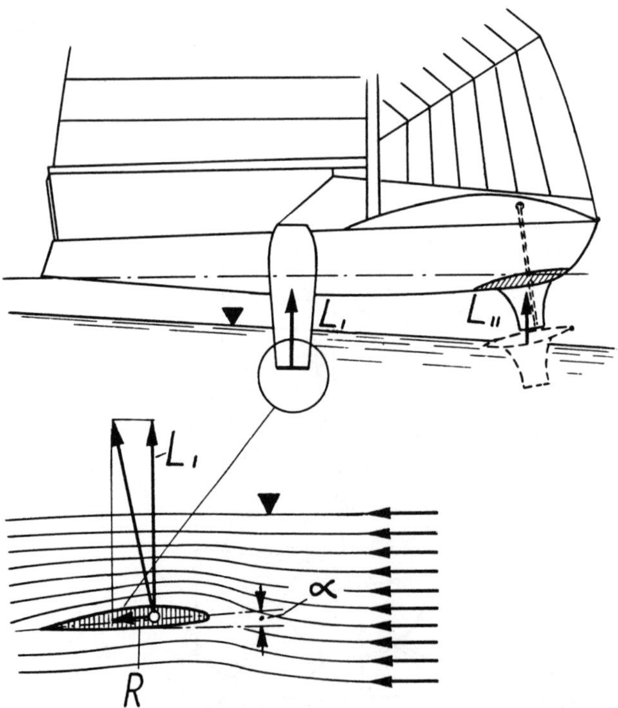

The magnitude of the hydrodynamic lift for a fully submerged hydrofoil can be calculated from the following formulas:

$$\text{Lift } L = 0.97 \times C_L \times v_s^2 \times A \text{ lb. (fresh water)}$$

and

$$\text{Lift } L = 0.995 \times C_L \times v_s^2 \times A \text{ lb. (sea water)}$$

where C_L is the hydrodynamic lift coefficient
v_s is the speed of the yacht in ft./sec.
A is the hydrofoil's area in sq. ft.

The curve of coefficients C_L and C_D is shown in Fig. 192. It concerns the hydrofoil whose profile is shown, which has an aspect ratio of 5. The ratio of lift L to resistance R is at its best when the angle of attack α is within 1°–5°. If $\alpha = 3°$, then the coefficient $C_L = 0.4$. For $v_s = 20$ knots (33.8 ft./sec.) and $A = 1$ sq. ft.:

$$L = 0.97 \times 0.4 \times 33.8^2 \times 1 = 445 \text{ lb.}$$

At the same time the resistance to motion, R, is only 1/20 of the lift, i.e., $R = 445/20 = 22.25$ lb. To this must be added the resistances of the supports by which the hydrofoils are attached, which have to incorporate the automatic adjustments for controlling the angle of incidence and the resistance of the rudder, etc.

However, there can be no doubt that these water skating craft have demonstrated that, in theory at least, new possibilities have been created of increasing

Fig. 192

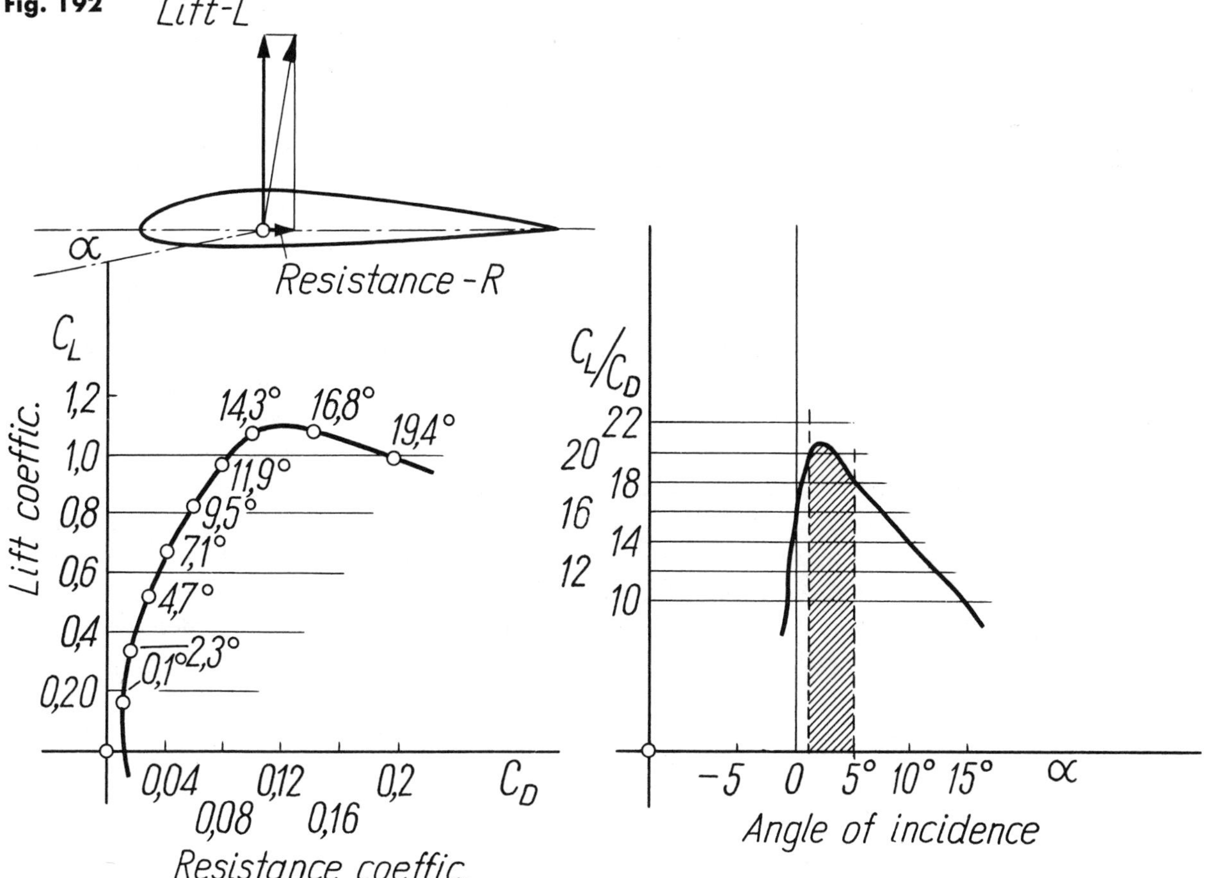

sailing speed even when driving force values are relatively small. This makes them attractive in spite of the enormous practical difficulties involved in their construction, and in automatic control in a choppy sea.

(b) Optimum Performance to Windward

Since it has been shown that for a given course to windward and a given true wind speed v_T there is a particular sheeting angle and angle of incidence at which a boat will attain its best speed, it follows that there must be a course (γ opt) on which one can sail fastest upwind (Fig. 193a). When sailing on that course, the boat's speed dead to windward or "speed made good to windward," v_{mg}, will be at its maximum. Yacht B in Fig. 193a has the greatest v_{mg}. Although her speed is less than that of C and she is not as close to the wind as A, obviously she will make the greatest distance to windward in a given time. Speed made good, then, is the composite product of the boat's speed v_s and the true sailing course γ; where

$$v_{mg} = v_s \times \cos \gamma$$

Speed made good, v_{mg}, is just as important a criterion of the yacht's performance for the helmsman as it is for the designer. Undoubtedly v_{mg} is most significant in yacht racing, where windward performance is of primary importance. In an Olympic triangular course, 55 per cent of the distance would be beating, 26 per cent reaching, and only 19 per cent running. The organizers of most sailing races round buoys make sure that there is more sailing to windward than on any other course, as it is generally agreed that sailing close-hauled is the best test of helmsmanship.

Figure 193b gives the velocity vector diagram for a yacht sailing to windward. Since the speed of the true wind v_T cannot be influenced by a helmsman, it follows that the geometric relations among v_s, v_A, γ, β, and v_{mg} will depend, directly or indirectly, on the helmsman's judgment, though this, of course, is limited to some extent by what is the best possible windward performance for that yacht. The problem is how to coax the yacht into her best performance.

From the practical sailing point of view, it is important to know how speed made good, v_{mg}, changes in relation to true wind speed, v_T. Direct measurements of v_T and v_{mg} from the deck of a sailing yacht are impossible, but it should be possible on a moving yacht to record apparent wind v_A, boat's speed v_s, drift angle λ, and heading angle β-λ. From these data, it is a simple matter to calculate v_T, v_{mg}, and γ. It was on this principle that full-scale tests were carried out on the 5.5-Meter *Yeoman* at the National Physical Laboratory in Great Britain (Fig. 194). The data and results attached are taken from a Yacht Research Council Report. The instrumentation and the technique used for taking measurements merit special attention. A wind anemometer of the rotating-cup type recorded the mean speed of the apparent wind (v_A) and the heading angle β-λ. It was erected on a

Fig. 193

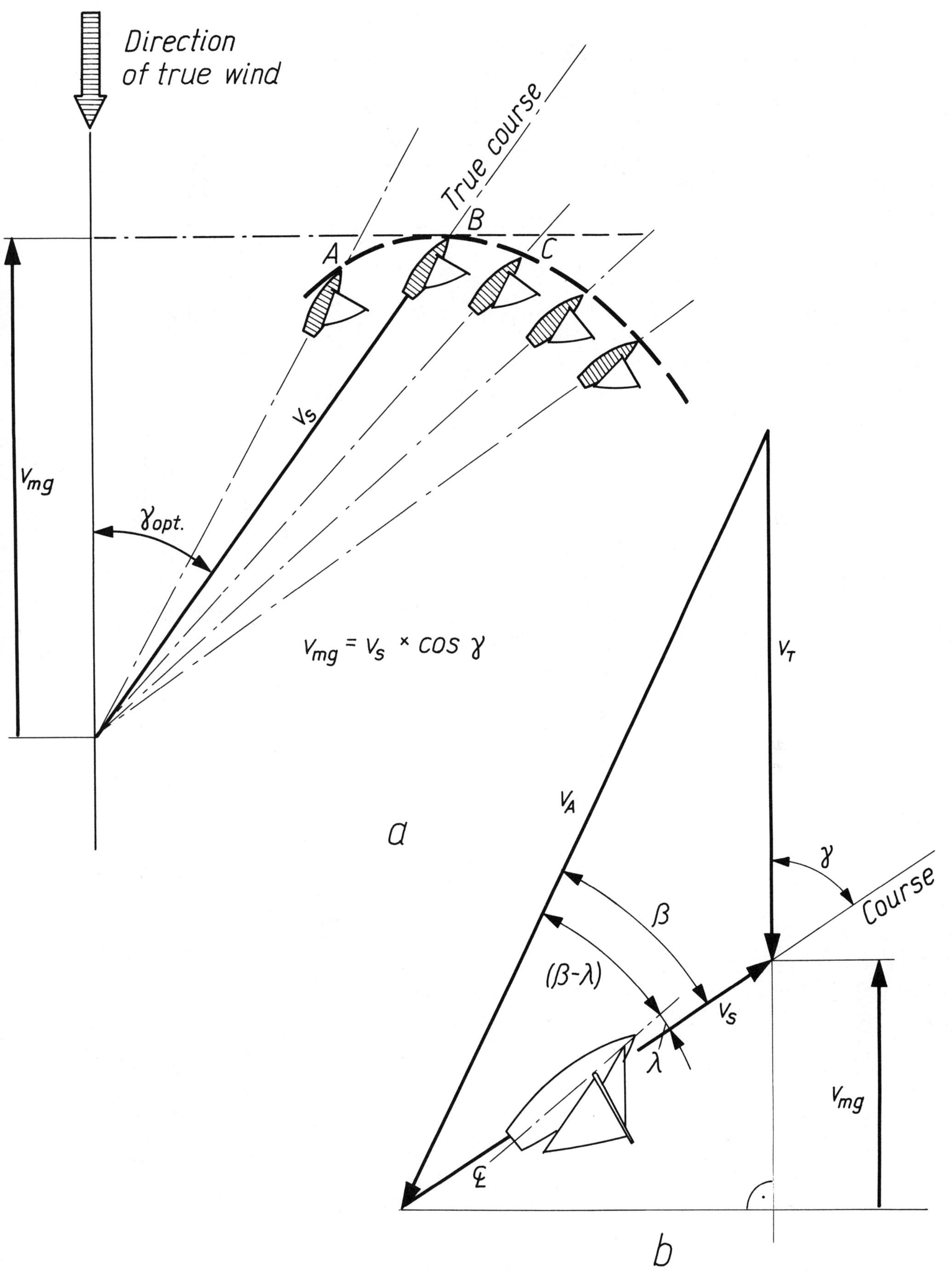

Direction of true wind
True course
A
B
C
V_S
V_{mg}
$\gamma_{opt.}$
$V_{mg} = V_S \times \cos\gamma$
a
V_T
V_A
γ
Course
β
$(\beta-\lambda)$
V_S
λ
V_{mg}
℄
b

Fig. 194

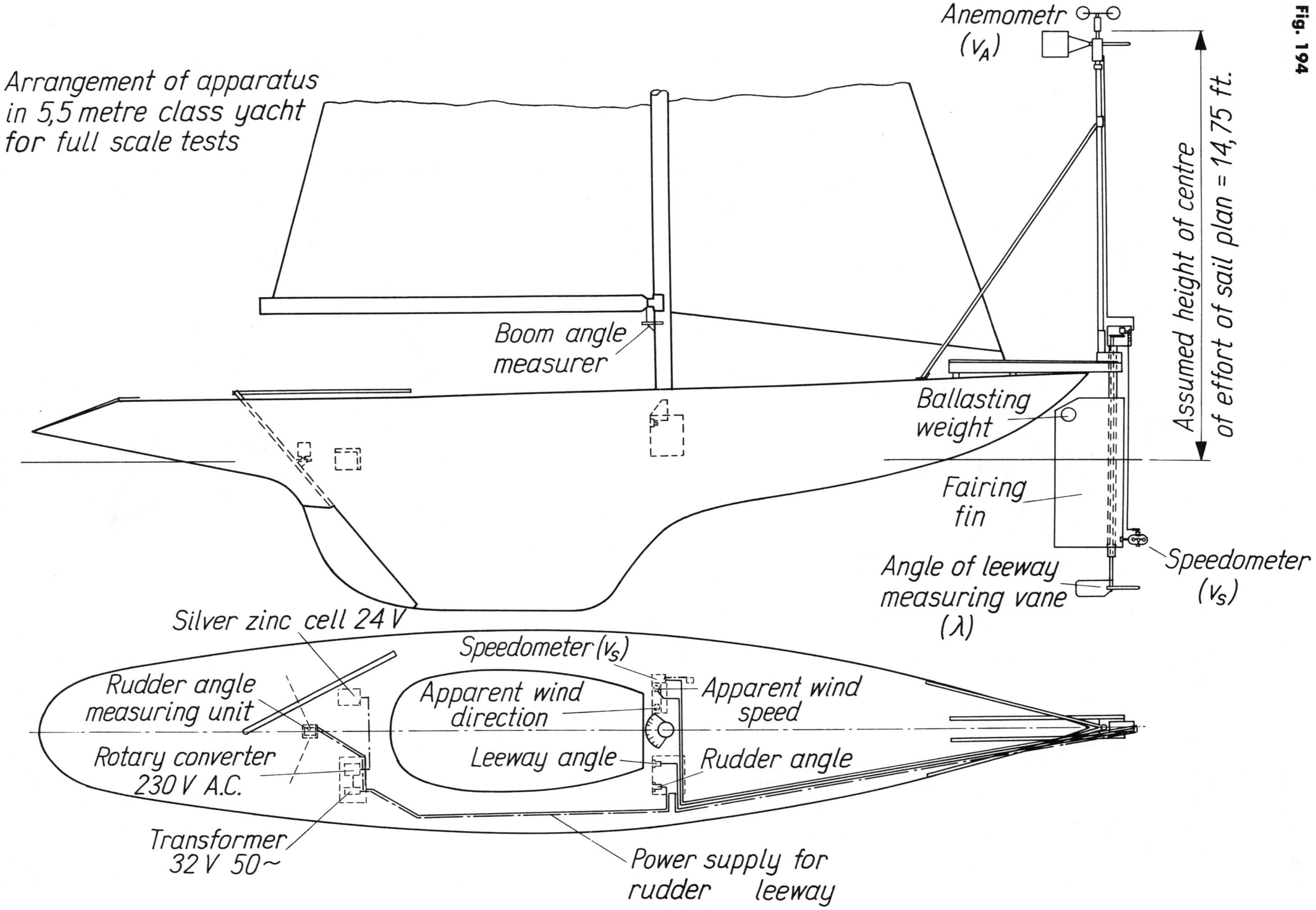

Arrangement of apparatus in 5,5 metre class yacht for full scale tests

Anemometr (v_A)

Assumed height of centre of effort of sail plan = 14,75 ft.

Boom angle measurer

Ballasting weight

Fairing fin

Speedometer (v_s)

Angle of leeway measuring vane (λ)

Silver zinc cell 24 V

Speedometer (v_s)

Rudder angle measuring unit

Apparent wind direction

Apparent wind speed

Rotary converter 230 V A.C.

Leeway angle

Rudder angle

Transformer 32 V 50~

Power supply for rudder leeway

vertical rod sufficiently far in front of the jib to avoid any interference effects and at the height of the calculated center of effort of the sail plan.

A speedometer which measured the mean speed of the yacht through the water v_S was attached to a fairing fin, which was free to rotate on a vertical rod and aligned itself in the direction of motion. An attempt was also made to measure the angle of leeway (yaw) by fitting a vane below the fin. Deviation of the vane was translated into a direct angular reading by electrical means. This unit, however, was not completely satisfactory.

On these full-scale trials, *Yeoman* was sailed by an experienced helmsman and crew who were attempting to steer the best possible course to windward. Each experiment lasted approximately 30 seconds, during which v_S, v_A, β-λ, and λ were measured, as well as angles of sail trim, heel, and also the angle of the rudder.

When the values of v_S, v_A, and β are known, solving the vector triangle shown in Fig. 193b will give the values of v_T, γ, and v_{mg}. The simplest solution will be found by using a ruler, compass, and protractor.

Figure 195 illustrates the relationship between v_{mg} and true wind speed, v_T, discovered for *Yeoman* during these different tests and includes predictions from models. All the values of v_{mg} fell within the area on the left of the envelope curve, which clearly represents the best windward performance of which crew and yacht were capable. During the test on Southampton Water (the results of which are recorded in the continuous line on Fig. 195) the yacht was skippered by Charles Currey, a well-known dinghy helmsman. It is worth noting that the performance predictions made with models in the towing tank correspond almost exactly to this curve, and this good measure of agreement continues until true wind speeds of 9 to 10 knots are reached. At higher wind velocities actual full-scale performance deteriorates in comparison with the model predictions, chiefly because of the increased resistance developed when sailing in the waves created by the stronger winds. These conditions could not be reproduced in the towing tank tests. The broken curve in Fig. 195 records the results obtained during performance trials on the King George VI fresh-water reservoir near London. Wind and water conditions for these trials were very similar to those encountered on Southampton Water, and the yacht was skippered by an equally experienced helmsman from the heavy-keel boat classes. Figure 196 shows that for the same apparent wind speed, v_A, the yacht sailed approximately 0.5 knots faster on the reservoir than on Southampton Water. In addition, the angles of apparent course, β, were greater on the reservoir tests (Fig. 197). However (as Fig. 195 shows), the results, as calculated for the reservoir, reveal that the greater speed through the water gained by sailing freer nevertheless produced a poorer performance to windward. This proves that the closer a yacht is sailed to the wind without undue "pinching" the higher will be the speed made good to windward. Another result of sailing the yacht freer on the reservoir was that the higher angle of apparent course β produced a greater angle of heel Θ (Fig. 198).

Fig. 195

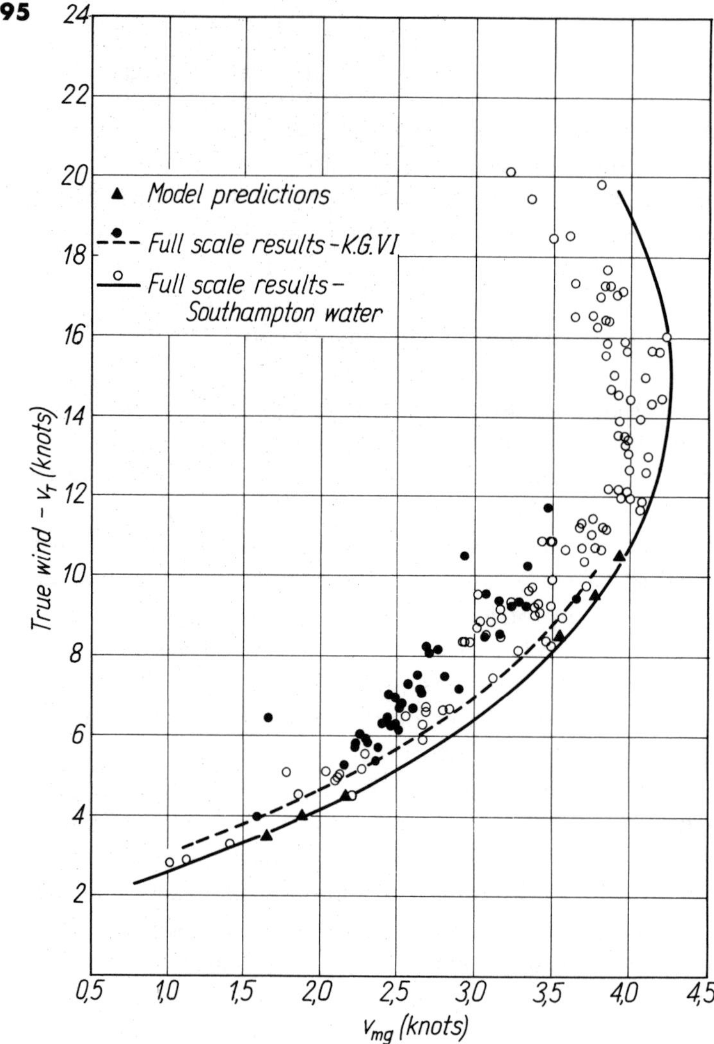

Fig. 196

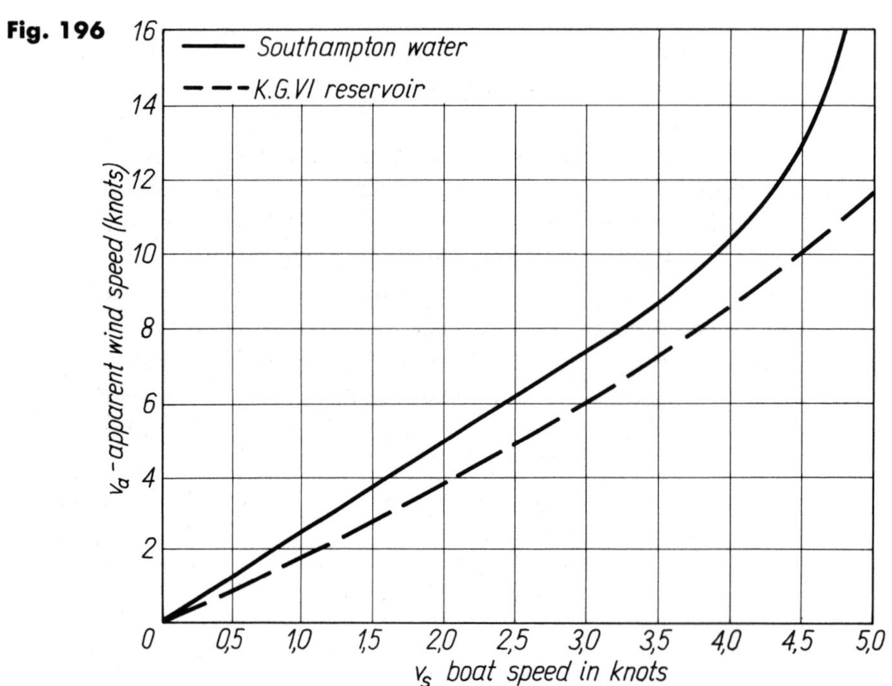

Fig. 197

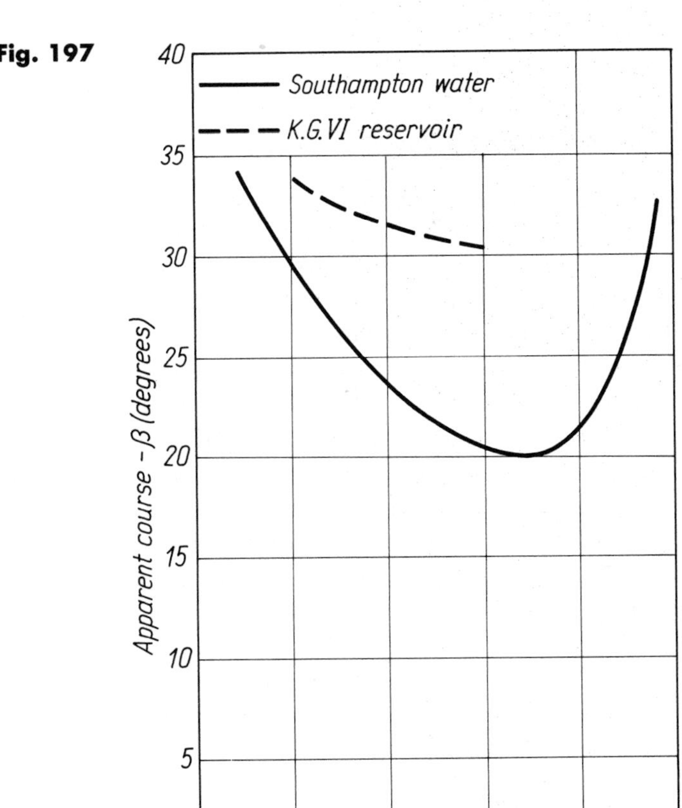

Fig. 198

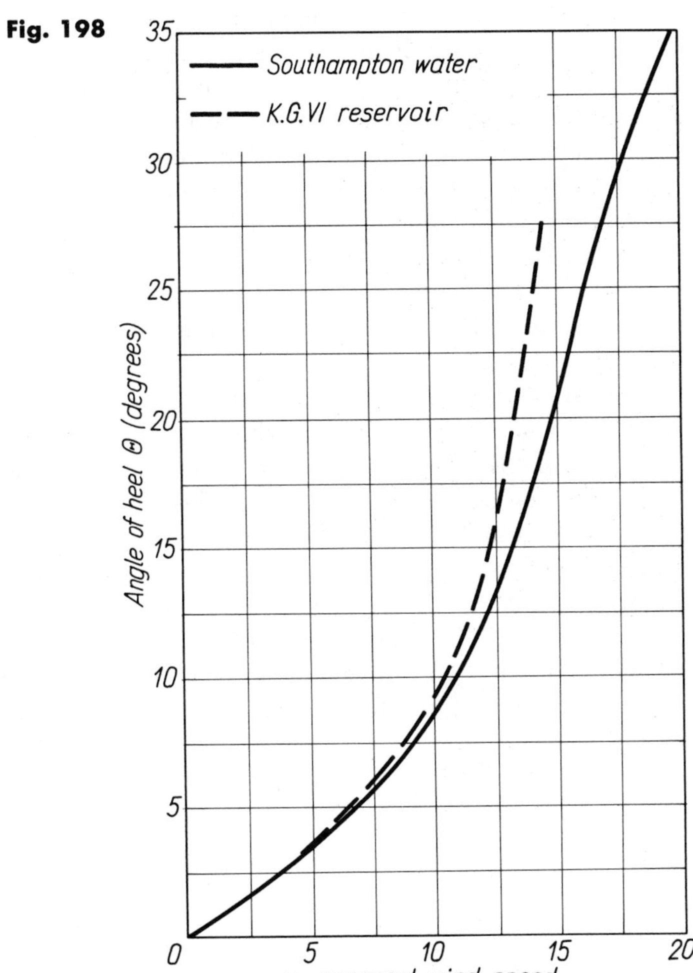

The results of the full-scale trials indicate that there is an optimum angle of heel at which the yacht should be sailed for each value of true wind speed. Figure 198 shows these optimum angles for *Yeoman* over the whole range of wind speeds, v_A. For example, the critical amount of heel appeared to be 35° in a true wind speed, v_T, of 14–15 knots, corresponding to 20 knots apparent wind speed, v_A. A further increase in heel angle produced inferior results to windward, because of the increased resistance of the heeled hull and keel and also the reduced aerodynamic efficiency of the rig. This is emphasized by the curve of optimum speed made good to windward in Fig. 195, which reaches a peak value of about 4.25 knots when the true wind is around 15 knots. The yacht was sailed in Southampton Water on several occasions when the true wind speed exceeded 15 knots, always with decreased values of v_{mg} to windward of about 4.0 knots. In these high, gusty winds, the yacht was heeled to 40° and more, considerable use of the rudder being needed to keep the yacht on her course.

The variations in yaw angle, boom angle, and rudder angle for the full-scale trials are given in Fig. 199. Boom angles increased from 4.5° to 6° as the true wind speed increased from about 5.0 to 20.0 knots. Naturally the angle of the boom does not fully reflect the changes in the angle of attack of the mainsail, since this falls automatically to a certain extent when the speed of the wind increases, because of the effects of heel and of the twist in the sail.

Two interesting conclusions can be drawn from the results of the *Yeoman* tests. Firstly, the chances of achieving optimum performance close-hauled, even with an experienced crew, are less than one in ten, racing tactics not considered. In fact, all the accumulated data of these full-scale trials show that less than 10 per cent of tests produced optimum values of v_{mg} to windward. Therefore, even with an experienced helmsman and crew, the best performance was very difficult to achieve, no doubt chiefly because wind force and direction were never absolutely constant for a sufficiently long period. There must be some time lag between the movement of the yacht off course and correcting action being taken by the helmsman, and this means a decrease in close-hauled performance. Even over such a comparatively short period as 30 seconds, the trials showed that appreciable variations in wind force and direction were occurring continually, especially at the higher wind speeds.

This suggests that the 10 per cent of "runs" in which the helmsman did achieve optimum performance were those in which, for 30 seconds, wind force and direction were reasonably steady and required the minimum use of the rudder. However, the alarming statement that a first-class helmsman will only once in ten times achieve optimum performance to windward should not be seen entirely as a reflection on his abilities, but rather as implying that in a variable gusty wind, particularly at higher wind velocities, an ideal performance to windward is virtually impossible. The considerable difference in the performance achieved by one yacht under the two different helmsmen reflects the basic difference in the techniques of sailing a light dinghy and a heavy yacht. Expert dinghy helmsmen

Fig. 199

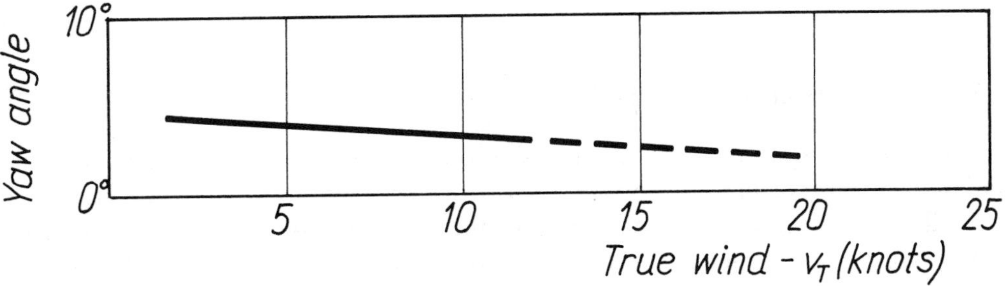

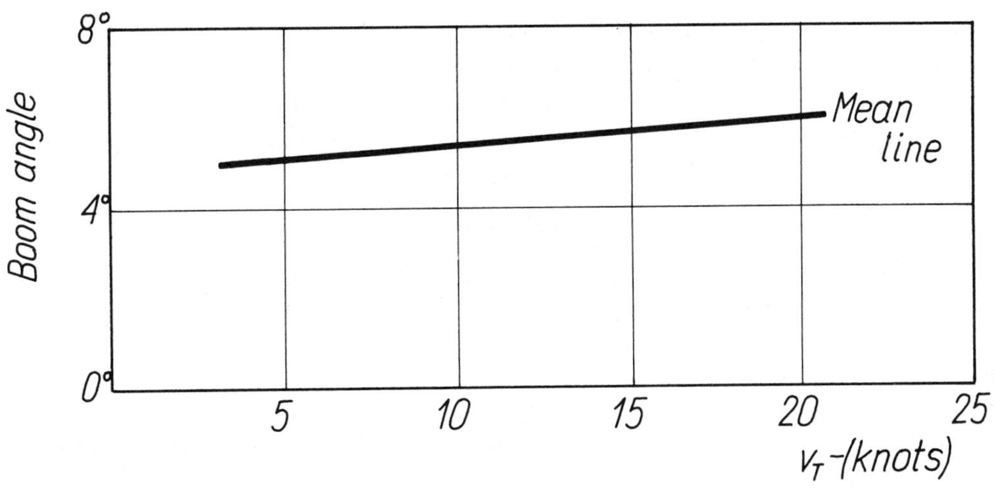

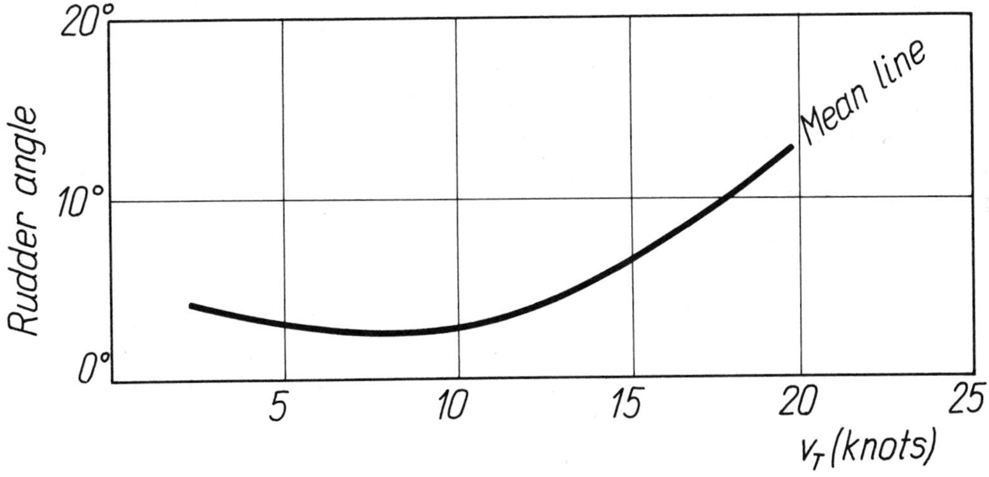

are accustomed to reacting to slight variations in wind direction or strength, and follow minor wind shifts more closely than skippers of heavy yachts do.

The second conclusion reached is that some guide as to whether a helmsman is "pinching" or sailing too free, other than pure instinct or intuition, seems to be essential in first-class competition. It is suggested that the helmsman's skill could be assisted by wind indicator vanes fitted to an extension of the crosstrees, one of these vanes being a fixed vane, which can be preset to any chosen angle, the other a free vane to indicate the apparent wind. Two sets of vanes, port and starboard, would be needed, though only that on the weather side would be in use. The fixed vane would be set at the optimum angle to the apparent wind, as suggested by experience, or as indicated in the performance curve for the 5.5-Meter class. The helmsman then has to sail so that the free vane keeps in line with the fixed. During the full-scale trials described, both helmsmen commented upon the invaluable aid given by vanes of this type.

It is also possible to construct a relatively simple electronic computer, in fact a "v_{mg} meter" which would indicate the v_{mg} values on a dial as an output. The input would be in the form of electrical signals corresponding to variations in v_A, v_S, β-λ, and λ, as recorded on the instruments described previously.

(c) Methods of Performance Prediction

There is no result in nature without a cause; understand the cause and you will have no need of the experiment.

LEONARDO DA VINCI

The last chapter discussed the problem of measuring the performance of an existing yacht. This chapter will attempt to show how to predict the performance of a yacht before she is launched.

It is, obviously, the action of forces which makes a yacht move. When the motion is steady, all the forces and moments produced by the action of the air on the sails must be balanced by the combination of hydrodynamic and gravitational forces and moments developed on the hull. Figure 200a, b, and c presents simple diagrams of the forces and moments acting on a close-hauled sailing yacht.

The total aerodynamic force F_T has a number of effects:

(a) Its first component, the driving force F_R (Fig. 200a and c), makes the yacht move and produces at the same time an aerodynamic pitching moment M_{PA}, which tries to change the trim of the hull by the head, that is, to depress the bow. F_R and M_{PA} have to be balanced by an equivalent hydrodynamic system, the resistance R and the hydrodynamic pitching moment M_P which are equal in magnitude and opposite in direction.

(b) The aerodynamic heeling force F_H (Fig. 200b) can be resolved into two components, lateral (or horizontal):

$$F_{lat} = F_H \times \cos \Theta$$

and vertical

$$F_v = F_H \times \sin \Theta$$

It is these which produce as their effects drift (leeway) (λ), heel (Θ), and the increase in the weight of the yacht by

$$F_H \times \sin \Theta$$

Fig. 200

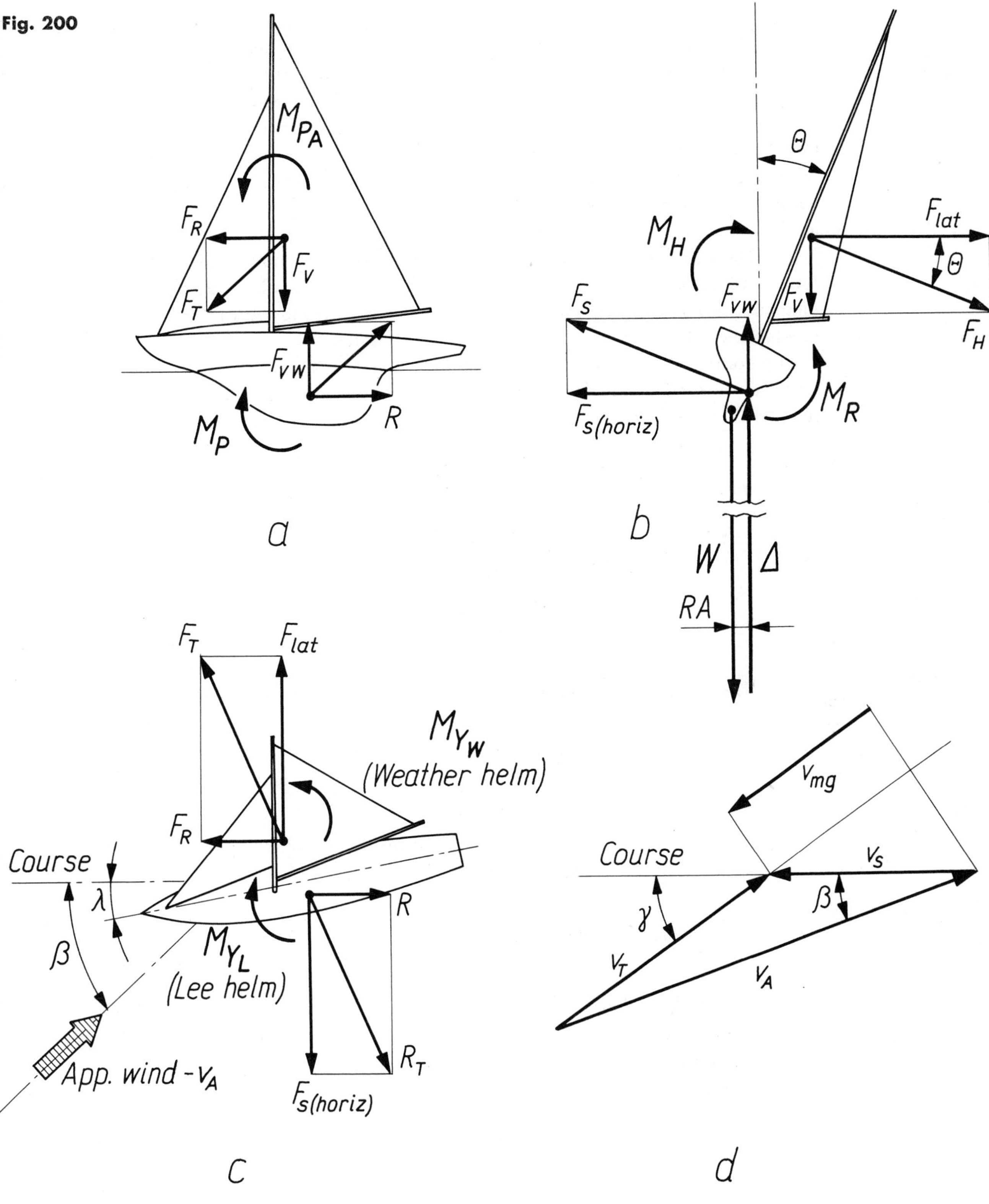

M_PA
F_R
F_V
F_T
F_VW
R
M_P
a
Θ
M_H
F_lat
Θ
F_S
F_VW
F_V
F_H
M_R
F_s(horiz)
b
W
Δ
RA
F_T
F_lat
M_YW
(Weather helm)
F_R
Course
λ
β
M_YL
(Lee helm)
R
R_T
F_s(horiz)
App. wind -v_A
c
v_mg
Course
v_s
γ
β
v_T
v_A
d

The F_{lat} and F_v components meet the resistance of the equal and opposite hydrodynamic forces F_s (horizontal) and F_{vw}, developed upon the yacht's immersed hull. The heeling moment, M_H, has to be balanced simultaneously by the righting moment, M_R, which is produced by the sideways movement of the center of buoyancy relative to the center of gravity. This introduces a righting arm, RA, whose length varies with the angle of heel. The vectors of the forces W and Δ on the diagram have been contracted compared with those of the aerodynamic forces because of the lack of space in the drawing. For heavy-keel boats, even in strong winds, the vectors (forces) W and Δ are actually 15 to 20 times greater than that for F_H.

(c) The aerodynamic and hydrodynamic forces in the horizontal plane (or sea level) are presented in Fig. 200c. For steady progress along a course β, the moments M_{YW} (weather turning) and M_{YL} (lee turning) must be balanced to prevent the boat yawing; this is done with the rudder.

The combined effects of a, b, and c mean that there are six equations which must be satisfied simultaneously for a yacht to be able to sail to windward in steady sailing conditions:

Forces

(i) $F_R = R$
(ii) $F_{lat} = F_s$ (horizontal)
(iii) $F_v = F_{vw}$

Moments

(iv) $M_{PA} = M_P$
(v) $M_H = M_R$
(vi) $M_{YW} = M_{YL}$

Since the aerodynamic forces on a sail have been shown to vary according to

A
- apparent wind speed—v_A
- course—β
- sheeting—δ (or angle of sail incidence α)
- angle of heel—Θ etc.

and that, similarly, the hydrodynamic forces produced by the action of the water on the immersed body of the yacht depend on

H
- boat speed—v_s
- leeway—λ
- heeling angle—Θ etc.

therefore any method of performance prediction can be reduced to establishing those conditions mentioned in groups A and H which will satisfy the equilibrium of forces and moments as set out in equations i to vi.

A cat-rigged dinghy, sailed upright, or nearly upright, provides a simple example of performance prediction that uses a minimum of sail and hull data. In fact, the following equations can be omitted altogether:

(iii) The downward aerodynamic component F_V is negligible when the angle of heel is small, and so there is no additional sinkage of the hull to increase its buoyancy and resistance.

(iv) The aerodynamic pitching moment M_{PA}—or tendency of the bow to be depressed—can be neutralized by the proper positioning of the crew along the centerline.

(v) The heeling moment M_H can also be balanced if the crew acts as suitable ballast—keeping boat upright. This prevents the angle of heel from impairing sail and hull efficiency.

(vi) If the boat is well balanced and tuned and is not heeling, the yawing moments M_{YW} and M_{YL}, which tend to change the course β, have no appreciable effect on the resistance and so can be ignored as well.

Therefore, with a reasonable degree of accuracy the whole problem can be reduced to a consideration of the forces acting horizontally only:

$$F_R = R$$
$$F_H = F_s \cong [F_{lat} = F_s \text{ (horiz.)}]$$

This is the exact equivalent of the situation presented in Fig. 80, and when expressed in mathematical terms, it satisfies the fundamental requirements of balance:

$$F_T = R_T$$
$$\beta = \epsilon_A + \epsilon_H$$

At this point, the data (acquired from model or full-scale tests) needed to be able to predict the performance of a dinghy sailing upright are:

1. The properties of the sails and rig (for a given camber, A.R., and sail plan), that is, the variations in total aerodynamic force F_T due to apparent wind v_A, angle of incidence α (or sheeting angle δ), and course β.
2. The properties of the particular hull, that is, the variation in the resultant hydrodynamic force R_T due to boat speed v_s and leeway λ.

Having gained this knowledge of sail and hull characteristics, the next step is to solve this problem: at what values of apparent wind speed v_A, boat speed v_s, and course β, will the aerodynamic force F_T be balanced by the water force R_T due to the boat's speed v_s and leeway λ? With these questions answered, the velocity triangle in Fig. 200d can be plotted to find values for v_T, γ, and v_{mg}, in other words the boat's optimum performance.

Here is a further illustration of this problem demonstrating a simple graphic method, for although the subject may seem complicated it is well worth study, since it makes it possible to understand fully the general behavior pattern of a sailing yacht. The method itself could be tried as a "winter game" for keen sailors wanting to increase their knowledge of the importance of such factors as sail camber, reefing in strong wind, ballasting, and the reduction of resistance on their boat's performance. In the example given below, the hull properties are taken from full-scale towing tank tests of an International Canoe. The boat has been assumed to be cat-rigged, with a sail area of 10 sq. m. (107 sq. ft.). This is not strictly correct, as the boat was sloop-rigged, but the object is rather to show how the graphic method is applied than to calculate the performance of a particular boat. The conclusions reached will probably apply generally to all yachts sailing upright, including catamarans. The method can be extended to include the study of the influence of such factors as angle of heel, changes in longitudinal trim, and the weight of the helmsman on the craft's behavior. Some of these will be considered.

The properties of the sail can be conveniently expressed by using the polar diagram (Fig. 201). This shows how the vector representing the total aerodynamic force F_T alters in length (magnitude) and direction as the sail's angle of incidence α and the apparent wind v_A are altered. As figures for the actual forces on the sail of a full-size boat are needed, these were obtained by multiplying the coefficients C_L and C_D of Fig. 45 by $0.00119 \times v_A^2 \times S_A$. For each value of apparent wind speed v_A this will produce a set of different size graphs, like those shown in Fig. 201 for $v_A = 6$ knots (10.15 ft./sec., a light breeze) and $v_A = 14$ knots (23.65 ft./sec., a moderate breeze).

The hull properties can also be expressed as a series of curves showing how the hydrodynamic force, R_T, varies with the boat speed, v_S, and the leeway angle, λ (Fig. 202). The set of curves given was plotted for boat speeds, v_S, increasing from 2.0 to 6.0 knots, in steps of 0.5 knot.

Both diagrams of forces in Figs. 201 and 202 must be drawn to the same scale, and the set of curves for the hull should be prepared on transparent paper. Figure 203a shows sail and hull forces balanced. A sheet prepared from Fig. 201 is shown and represents a single sail polar curve for a particular value of v_A. To this is pinned, through their point of origin O, a transparent overlay of Fig. 202. Note that the vector F_T, representing the total aerodynamic force, at the angle of incidence $\alpha_{,}$, and at an apparent wind speed $v_{A,}$, is equal in magnitude and opposite in direction to the vector R_T, representing the resultant hydrodynamic force, when leeway angle is $\lambda_{,}$ and the boat's speed is $v_{S,,,}$. Since both forces F_T and R_T are acting along the same straight line, the boat must be sailing steadily along a course $\beta_{,} = \epsilon_A + \epsilon_H$.

It is more convenient to find the equilibrium conditions for v_A, v_S, α, λ, and β of the aerohydrodynamic forces as in Fig. 203b, by rotating the overlay from Fig. 202 clockwise about the origin O. At the point where the particular hull curve for a selected v_S just touches the sail curve, the hull and sail forces are equal. The course angle $\beta_{,}$ is then read on the scale on the underlay between the direction of the apparent wind and the course sailed. This $\beta_{,}$ represents the smallest

Fig. 201

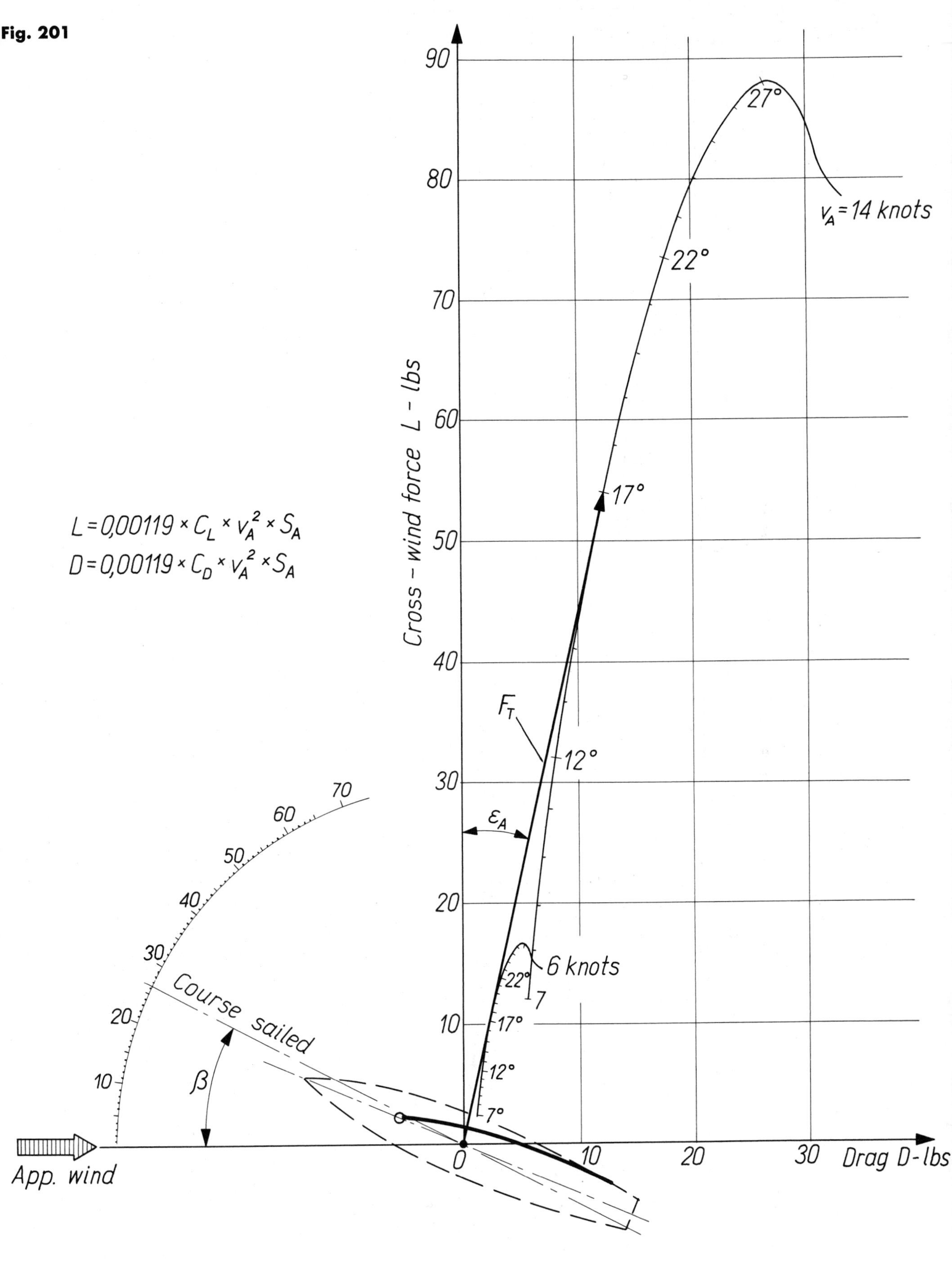

$L = 0{,}00119 \times C_L \times v_A^2 \times S_A$
$D = 0{,}00119 \times C_D \times v_A^2 \times S_A$
Cross - wind force L - lbs
Drag D-lbs
v_A = 14 knots
6 knots
27°
22°
17°
12°
7
F_T
ε_A
Course sailed
β
App. wind

Fig. 202

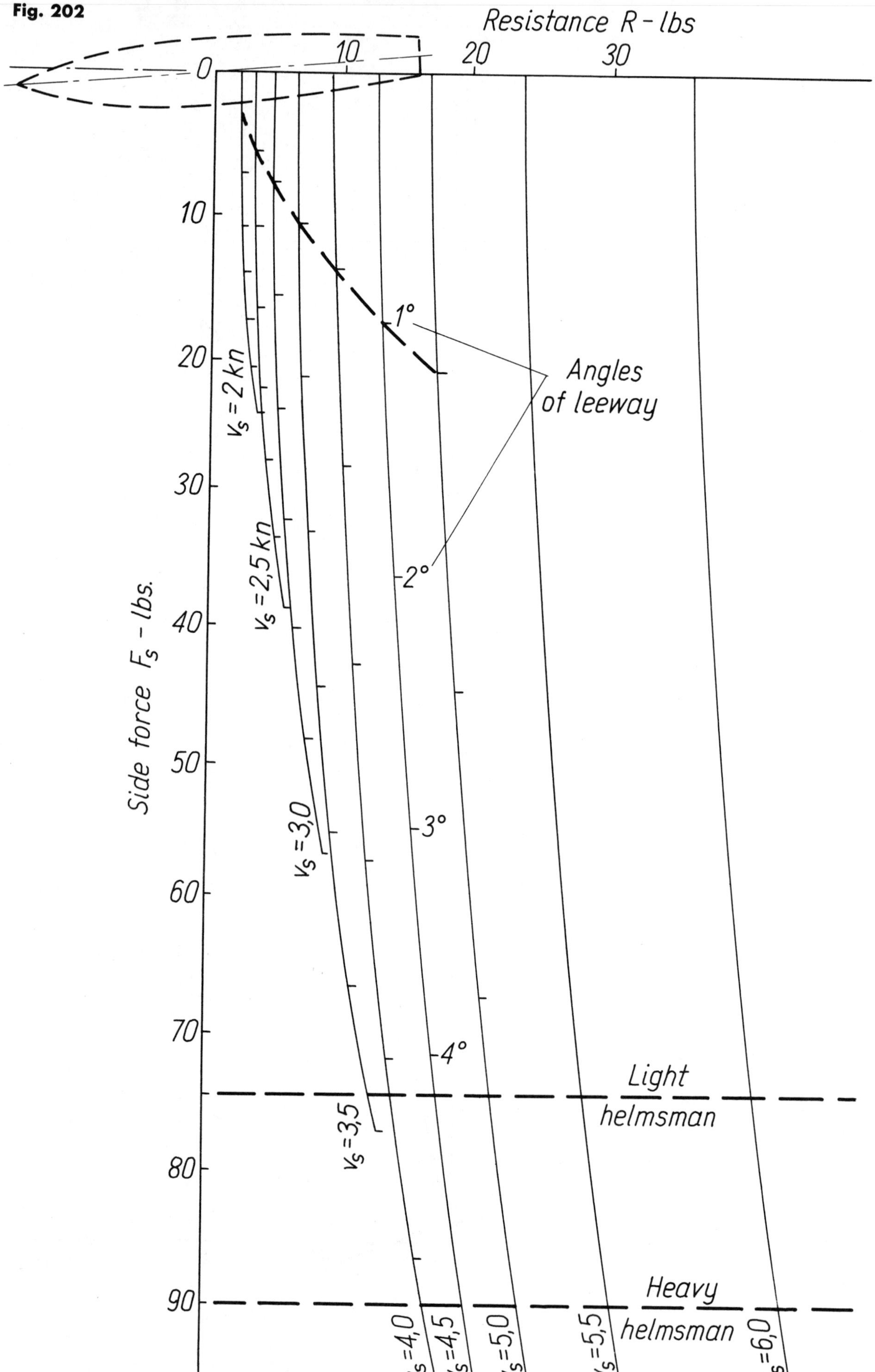

Resistance R - lbs

0 10 20 30

Side force F_s - lbs.

10 20 30 40 50 60 70 80 90

$v_s = 2\,kn$

$v_s = 2{,}5\,kn$

$v_s = 3{,}0$

$v_s = 3{,}5$

$v_s = 4{,}0$ $v_s = 4{,}5$ $v_s = 5{,}0$ $v_s = 5{,}5$ $v_s = 6{,}0$

1° 2° 3° 4°

Angles of leeway

Light helmsman

Heavy helmsman

Fig. 203

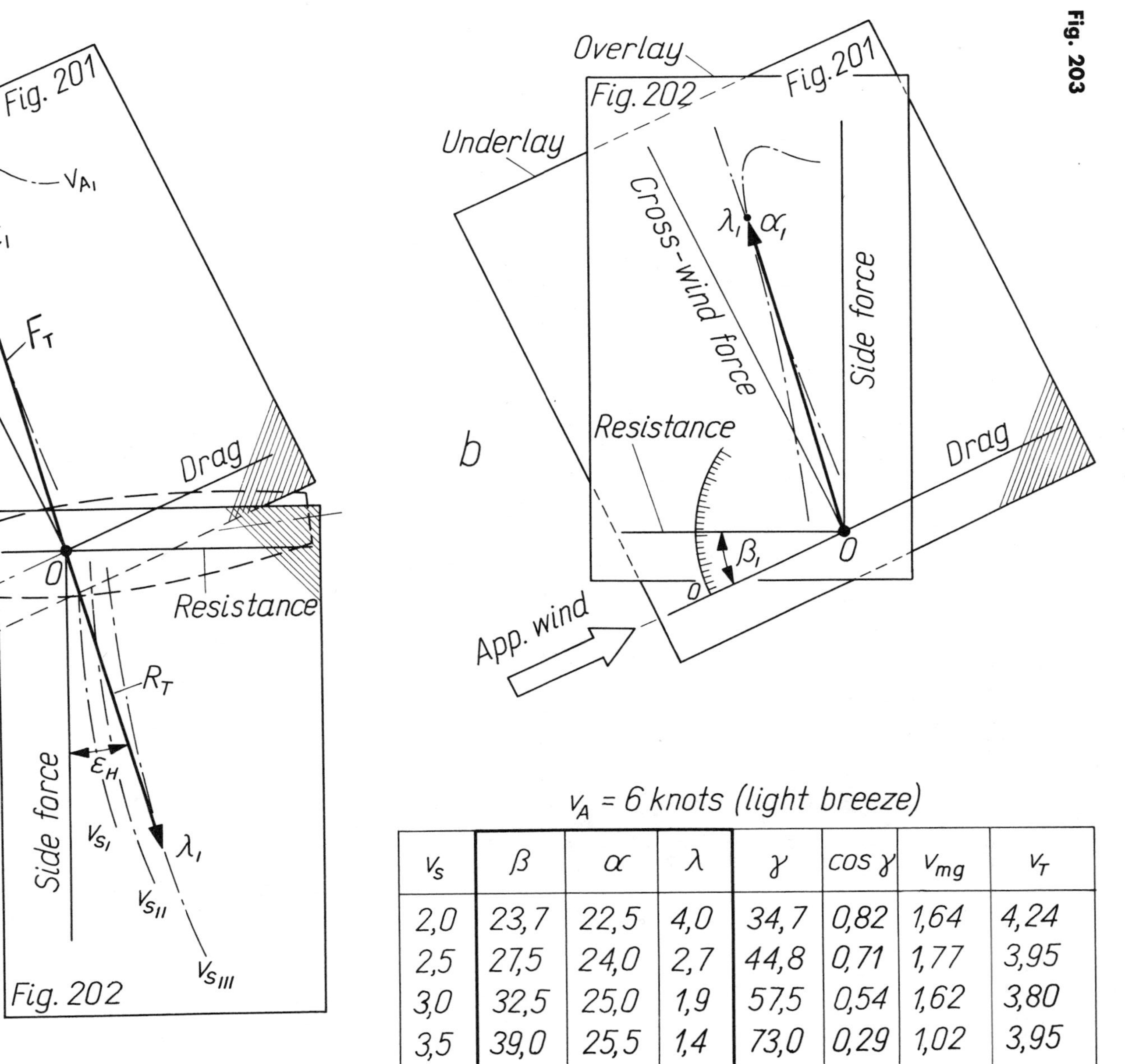

v_A = 6 knots (light breeze)

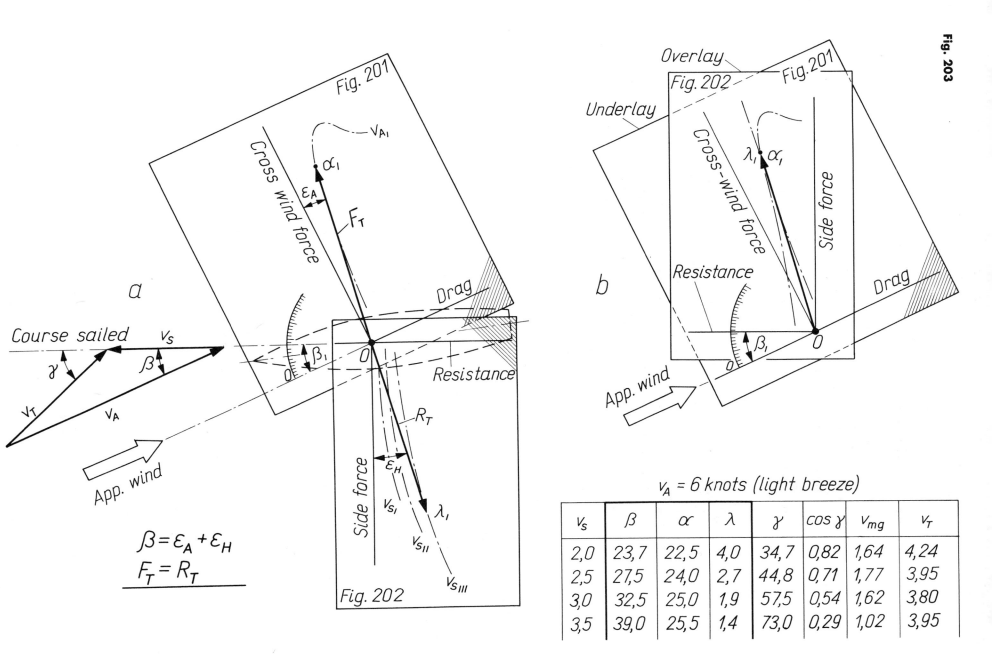

v_S	β	α	λ	γ	$\cos\gamma$	v_{mg}	v_T
2,0	23,7	22,5	4,0	34,7	0,82	1,64	4,24
2,5	27,5	24,0	2,7	44,8	0,71	1,77	3,95
3,0	32,5	25,0	1,9	57,5	0,54	1,62	3,80
3,5	39,0	25,5	1,4	73,0	0,29	1,02	3,95

angle at which sailing to windward is possible for a selected apparent wind v_A and boat speed v_s. The values of the angle of incidence α, and the leeway angle λ, are also found from the contact point of the two curves.

By taking as an example the sail curve when $v_A = 6$ knots (the light breeze) and repeating the process described for the hull curves when $v_s = 2.0, 2.5, 3.0, 3.5$ knots, and so on, the corresponding values of β, α, and λ were tabulated, as shown at the right-hand bottom corner of Fig. 203.

The table was completed by deriving the values for γ, v_{mg}, and v_T from the triangles of velocities (in Fig. 204). The geometrical construction of this figure needs only a ruler and a protractor. The velocity vectors must be drawn to a suitable scale, say 1″ = 2 knots. The speed made good, v_{mg}, could be derived geometrically (as shown in Fig. 193b) or from the formula $v_{mg} = v_s \cos \gamma$. The values of γ, v_{mg} and v_T were found in this way. Although the table in Fig. 203 relates only to $v_A = 6$ knots, the calculations were also carried out for $v_A = 10, 14, 18$, and 20 knots, so that v_{mg} could be plotted against v_T as in Fig. 205. The "hairpin" shape of these curves is quite characteristic, and gives a definite maximum value of v_{mg}, corresponding to the particular course, sail sheeting, etc.

Fig. 204

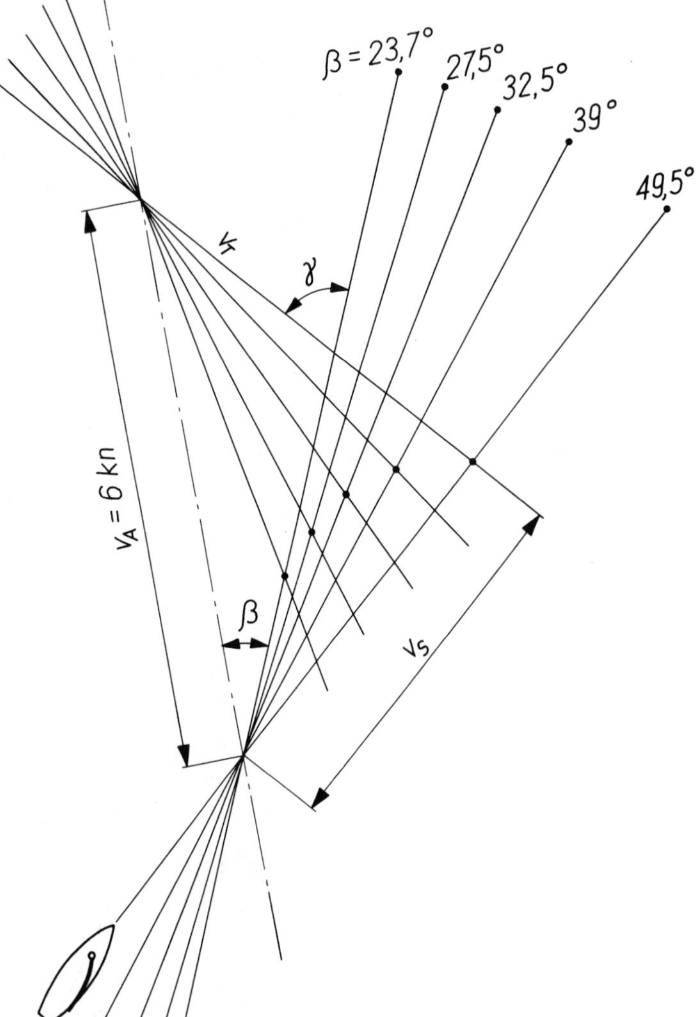

Fig. 205

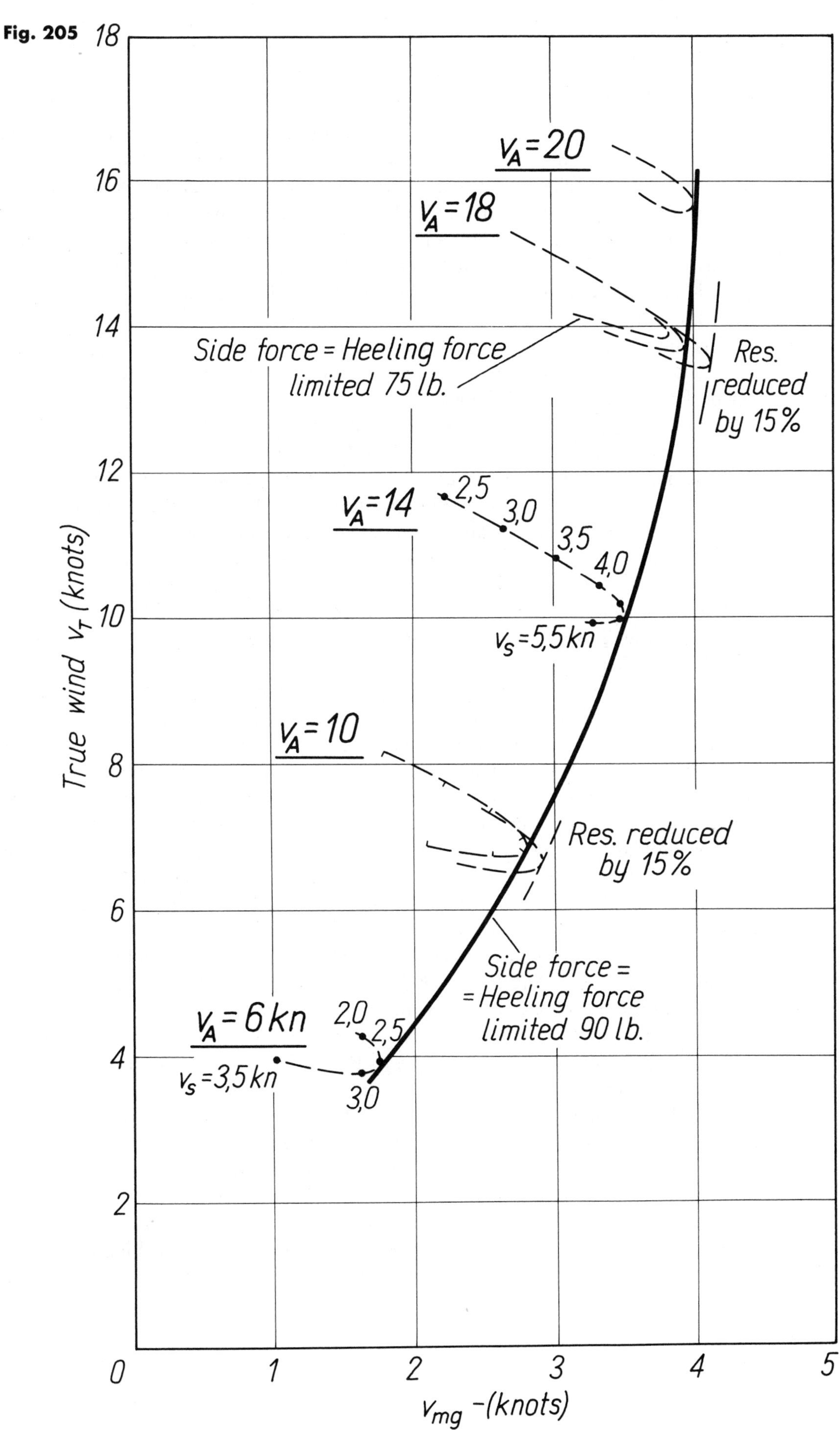

$v_A = 20$
$v_A = 18$
Side force = Heeling force limited 75 lb.
Res. reduced by 15%
$v_A = 14$
2,5
3,0
3,5
4,0
$v_S = 5,5\,kn$
$v_A = 10$
Res. reduced by 15%
Side force = = Heeling force limited 90 lb.
$v_A = 6\,kn$
2,0
2,5
3,0
$v_S = 3,5\,kn$
True wind v_T (knots)
v_{mg} -(knots)
0
1
2
3
4
5
2
4
6
8
10
12
14
16
18

If now an envelope curve is drawn round these, touching tangentially the points of maximum v_{mg}, this curve will represent the best possible v_{mg} that can be attained at a given true wind speed, v_T, for the basic sailing conditions assumed. In other words, for the particular hull, sail, and helmsman, the boat can only sail on, or to the left of, the envelope curve in Fig. 205. This envelope curve shows the best performance for the boat, assuming that the helmsman—a "heavy type"—can provide enough ballast to resist the heeling force of 90 lb. developed on the sail (see Photo. 29).

This limit, marked in Fig. 202, restricts the permissible amount of side force $F_s = 90$ lb. If the heeling force exceeds this, the boat cannot be sailed upright and her performance begins to decline.

There are certain variations possible on the basic performance curve in Fig. 205. For example, a lighter helmsman might only be able to balance 75 lb. instead of the assumed 90 lb. of heeling force, and would be forced to ease the sheets earlier to keep the boat nearly upright. The graph in Fig. 205 shows that when $v_A = 18$ knots, this reduced ability to keep the boat upright would result in a reduction in the optimum v_{mg} of 2.8 per cent. If the windward leg of a race was 2 nautical miles, the heavy helmsman would gain a lead of about 50 seconds over his lighter rival. This is why Paul Elvstrom, the Olympic Finn Champion, wears several sweaters in rough weather and takes care to see that all are soaking wet—and therefore heavy.

Figure 205 also shows how performance is affected when hull resistance is reduced. For example, a reduction of 15 per cent will mean that for lower speeds, when $v_A = 10$ knots, the increase in v_{mg} is about 6.5 per cent, while in a higher speed range, when $v_A = 18$ knots, the increase is only 5 per cent. In practice, this increase of 6.5 per cent would mean a gain of nearly 2¾ minutes on a windward leg of 2 nautical miles, a useful margin over one's competitors.

This method also makes it possible to analyze the influence of different sail properties, such as camber and reduction in sail area, on the behavior of the yacht.

The data used in obtaining the optimum performance curve can be presented in many different ways, and so made to yield much useful information. The values of β, α, and the sheeting angle δ can all be plotted against v_{mg}, as has been done in Figs. 206, 207, and 208. Figure 207, for instance, shows how the angle of incidence, α, of the sail varies for each wind speed, v_A. Once again, the curve for each specific v_A has one point where v_{mg} is at its maximum, which corresponds to the equivalent point on the best v_{mg} curve in Fig. 205. A similar curve can therefore be drawn on Fig. 207 to show how the optimum sail angle of incidence varies with the v_{mg}. It also shows how quickly a helmsman can lapse from optimum performance if the sail incidence on a particular v_A "hairpin" is a few degrees out.

It may be even more instructive to plot this optimum sail incidence curve against v_T. This can easily be done from Fig. 205 by converting the optimum v_{mg} values to the equivalent values of v_T. This curve, and similar ones for true course γ, apparent course β, leeway λ, and sail sheeting δ are shown on Fig. 209. These curves, of course, refer only to optimum sailing conditions. The curve for the angle

Fig. 206

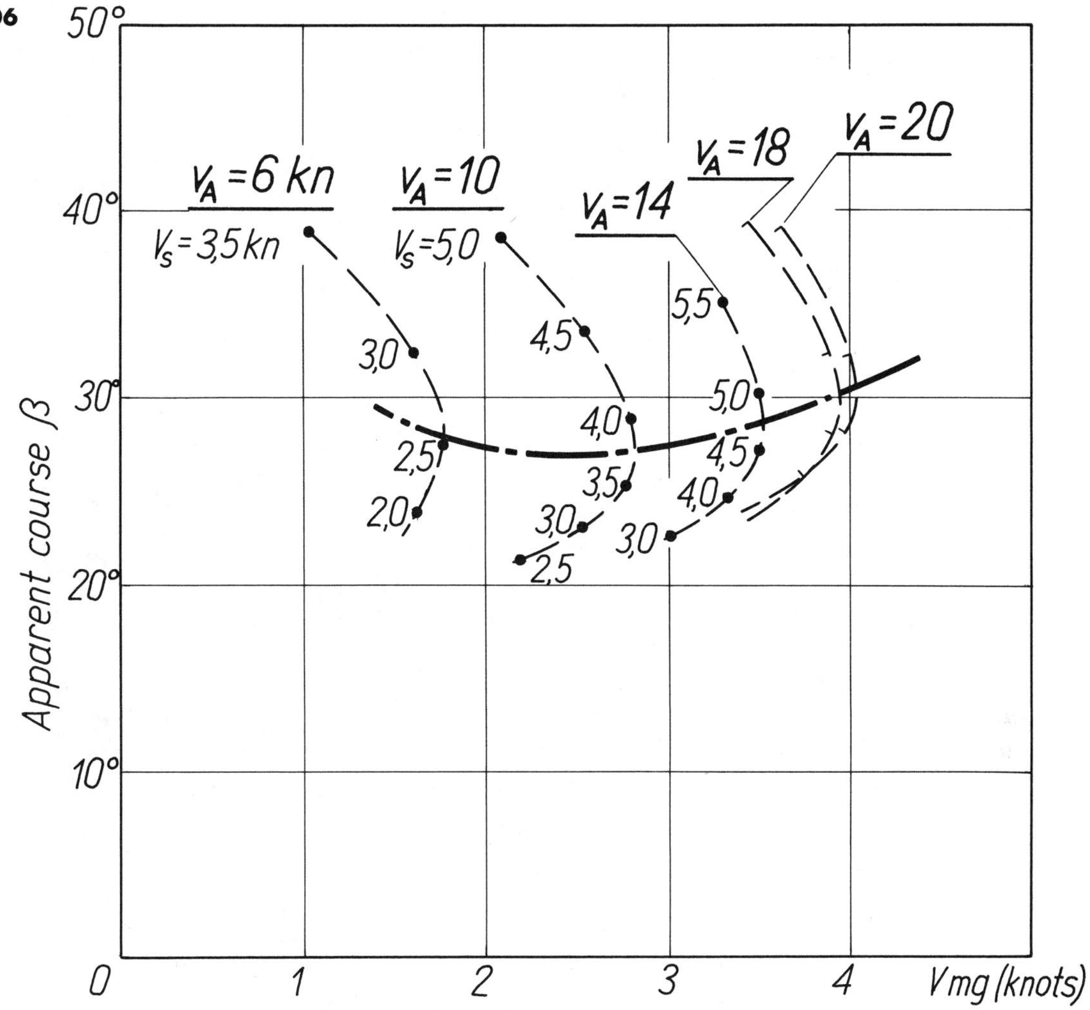

Fig. 207

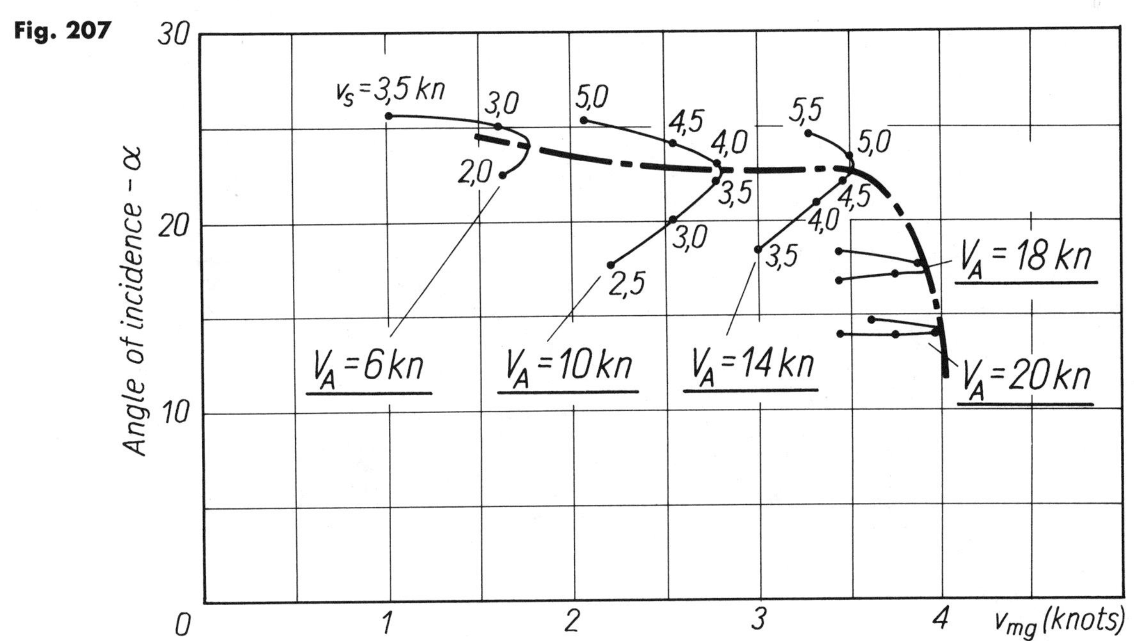

Fig. 208

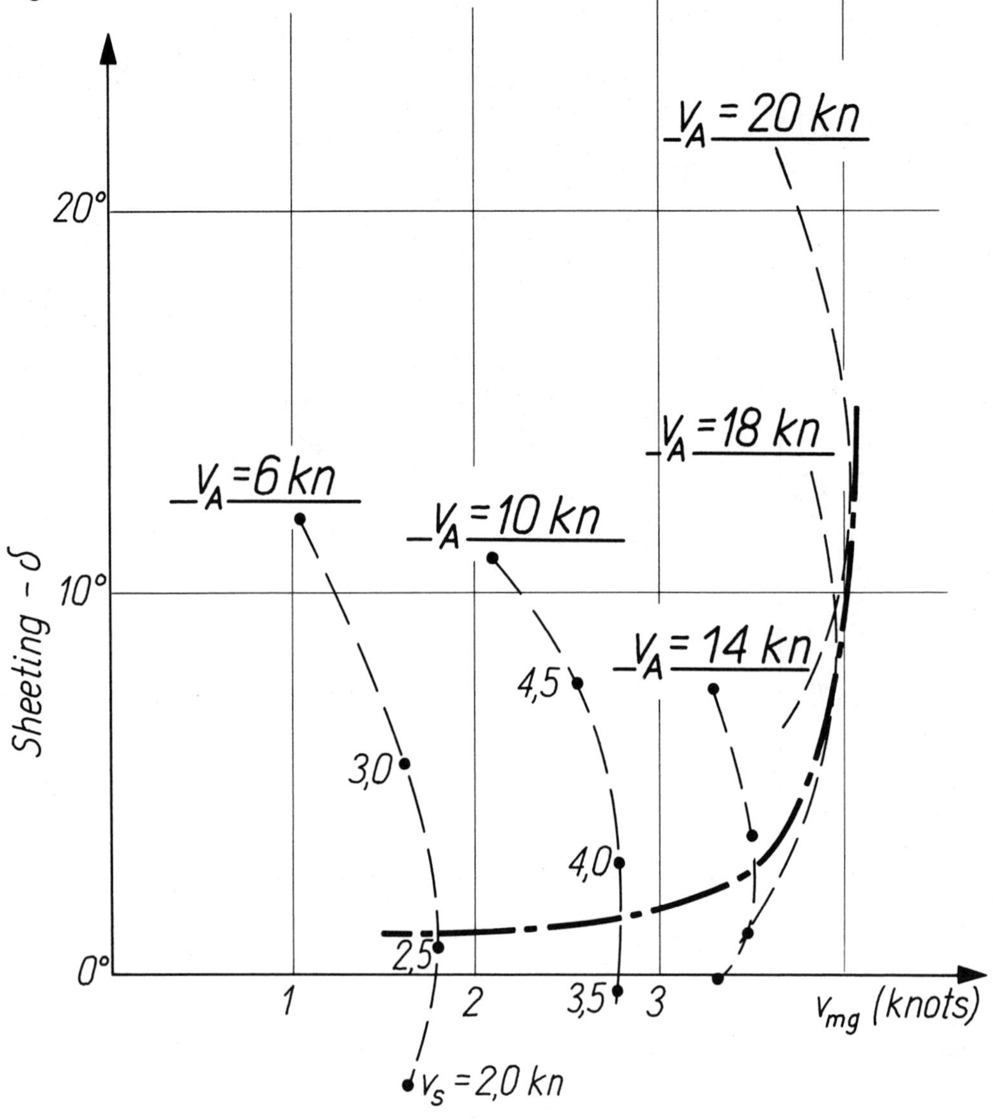

$V_A = 20\ kn$

20°

$V_A = 18\ kn$

$V_A = 6\ kn$

$V_A = 10\ kn$

Sheeting – δ

10°

$V_A = 14\ kn$

4,5

3,0

4,0

2,5

0°

1

2

3,5

3

v_{mg} (knots)

$v_s = 2{,}0\ kn$

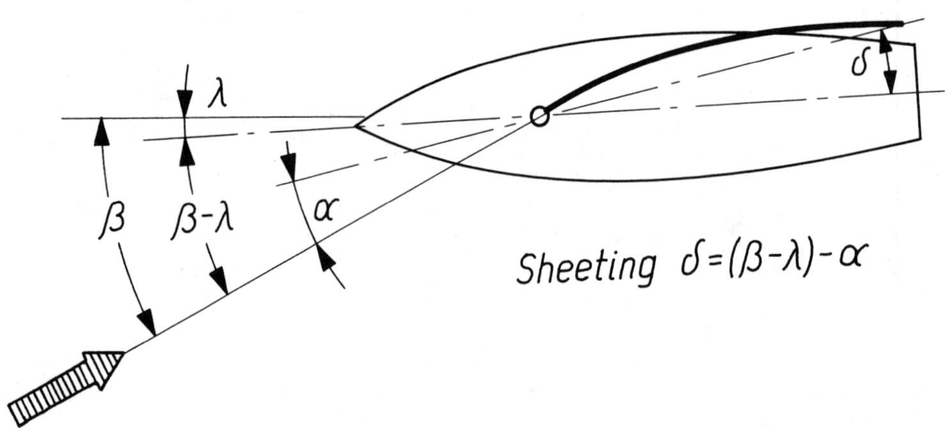

Fig. 209

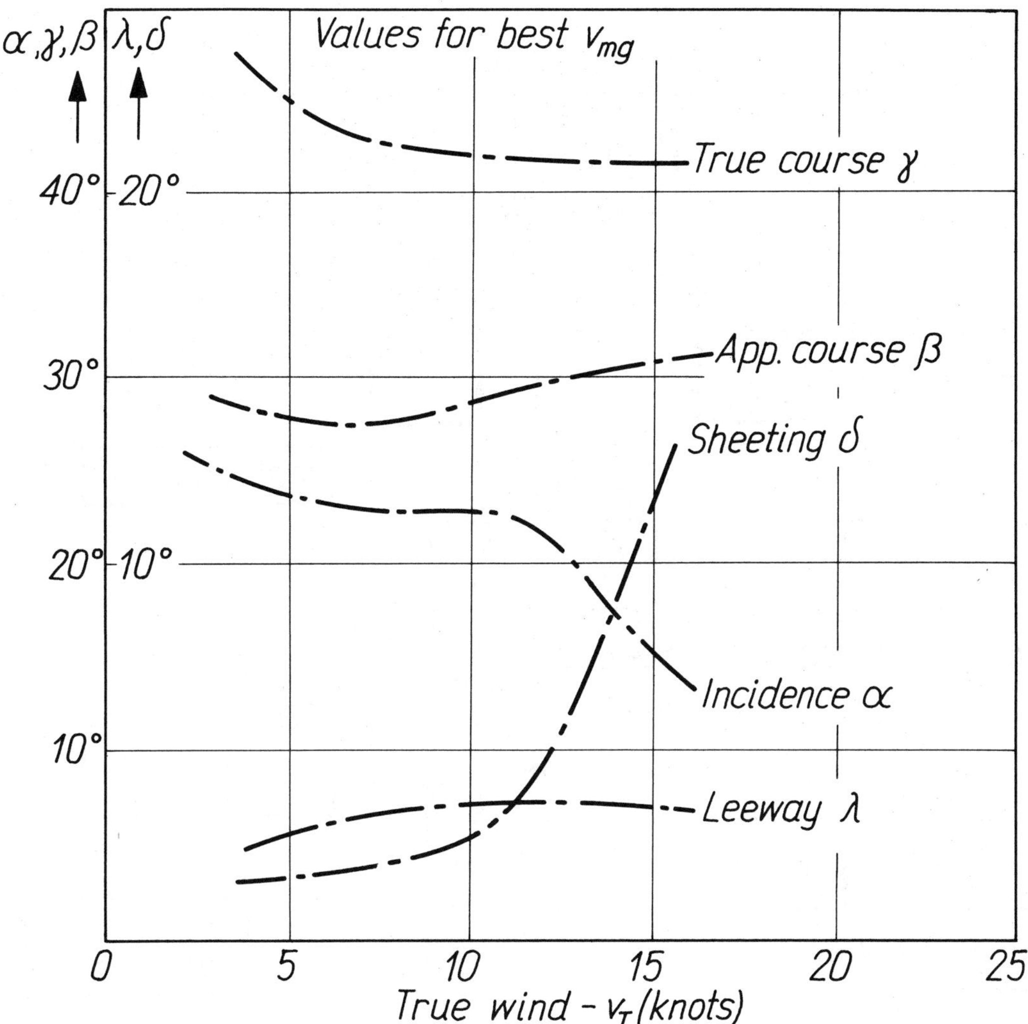

of sail incidence α is particularly interesting. As we know, sail incidence α can be changed in practice for a particular course β by altering the sail sheeting angle δ. Over the lower wind speed range, the optimum angle α seems to remain fairly constant and at a relatively high value, but as the wind speed v_T increases, incidence decreases quite sharply. A comparison of the values in this graph with those of the related sail polar diagrams in Fig. 81, which were discussed in an earlier chapter, shows that as the wind force increases, incidence α changes from that yielding the maximum driving force F_R ($C_{R\,max}$) to that giving C_H/C_R min. or even below. In other words, when sailing close-hauled in light winds, the sail must be trimmed well in, but it is possible to overdo it. If the wind is light and its strength variable, it would pay to keep the sheeting fairly constant and concentrate on sailing the best course. In strong winds, on the other hand, the sail incidences for optimum performance are considerably lower, and the sheeting angle δ is far more important than in lighter winds. If the wind's strength is variable, the sheet must be played to suit it. In fact, the old rule about "easing the sheets till the luff

Fig. 210

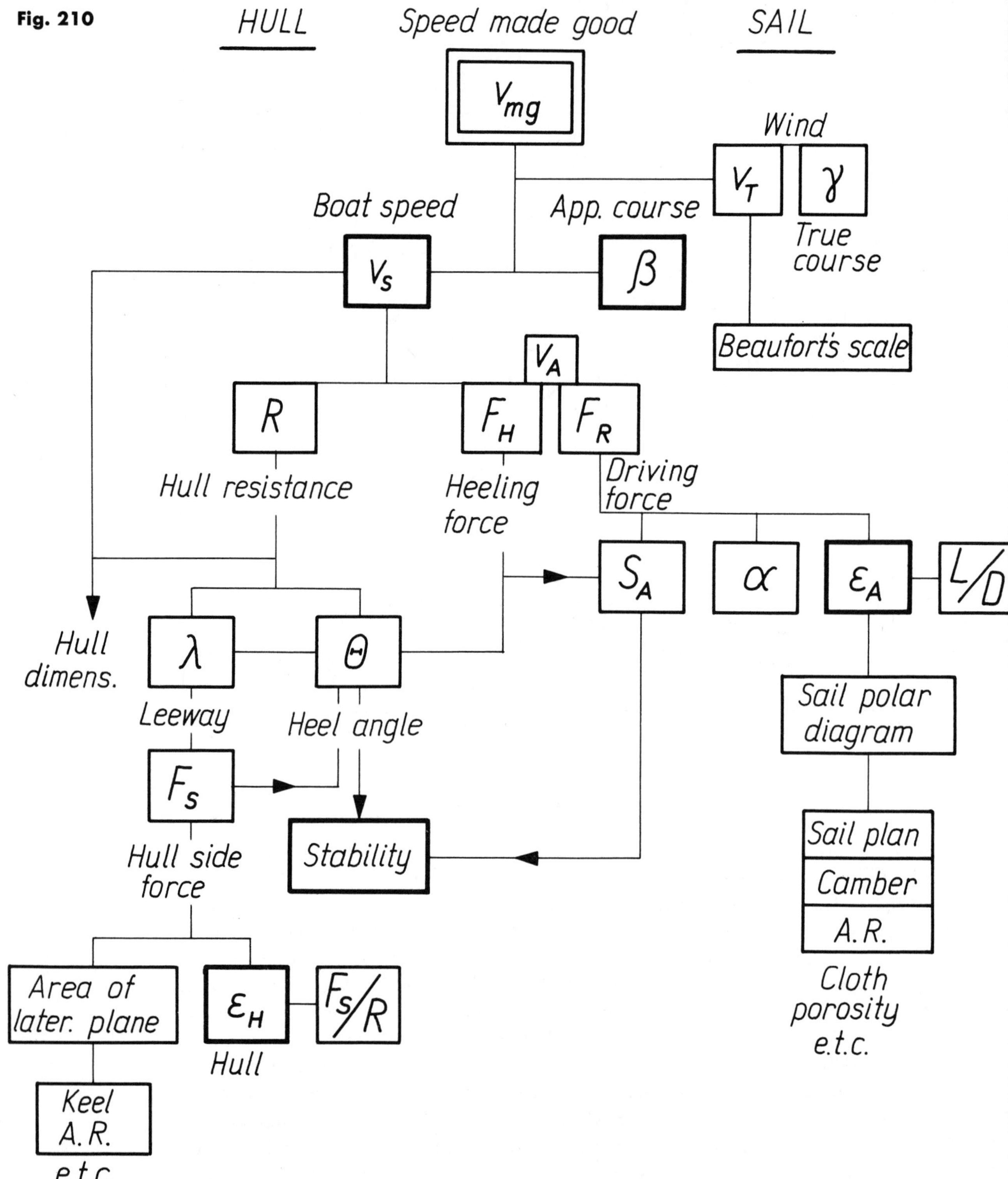

HULL
Speed made good
SAIL
V_{mg}
Wind
V_T
γ
True course
Boat speed
App. course
V_S
β
Beaufort's scale
V_A
R
F_H
F_R
Hull resistance
Heeling force
Driving force
S_A
α
ε_A
L/D
Hull dimens.
λ
Θ
Leeway
Heel angle
Sail polar diagram
F_S
Stability
Hull side force
Sail plan
Camber
A.R.
Cloth porosity e.t.c.
Area of later. plane
ε_H
F_S/R
Hull
Keel A.R.
e.t.c.

of the sail starts to lift" has been proved wrong at last. Indeed, it is a serious error in light winds, and only approaches the truth in the strongest.

These conclusions about sheeting for different winds should be borne in mind when considering the effect of the sail's camber on performance. Here again, theory is confirmed by practice. Helmsmen of racing classes such as the Finn, Star, and Flying Dutchman, where the camber of the sail can be controlled by bending the mast, are particularly conscious that, in general, flat sails are needed in strong winds and full sails in light winds. A further study of Figs. 83 and 84, which show the effect of camber on aerodynamic forces, can help to explain this. Figure 81 has already shown that in light winds, when sailing close-hauled, a large driving force F_R is required from the sails and that the heeling force F_H is of secondary importance. Figure 84 makes it clear that in these conditions, a full sail is required. As the wind increases, however, the heeling force grows in importance, and a low value of ϵ_A (or its equivalent C_H/C_R min.) is required, and so the sail must be flattened.

Some of the major factors in sail and hull which can affect the performance of a boat have been treated in this section, not exhaustively, but briefly, to try to increase our understanding of how and why a yacht sails. Knowing the answer to these two questions will probably help to improve the yacht itself. Figure 210 presents a block diagram proposed by Professor Ata-Nutku, containing the most important factors, those which determine the yacht's performance, which is reflected by her speed made good, v_{mg}. Most of them can be influenced by the designer, many depend on the crew, and not all are sufficiently well known. The number of factors known to affect the behavior of the yacht is increasing as our knowledge of sailing improves, yet for some time to come yacht designing will remain a mixture of art and science. The difficulties confronting a yacht designer may be better appreciated in the light of the words of Professor E. J. Richards, head of the Department of Aeronautics at the University of Southampton, who said, when opening the Conference on Yacht Design Research, in March 1962: "Yacht design, as carried on at the present, is rather like making love to a woman. The approach is completely empirical. At the end, the male, even though he might be successful, usually had no idea of just how and why he had succeeded."

3. STABILITY AND "BALANCE" OF A YACHT

As a result of the combined actions of aerodynamic and hydrodynamic forces, the attitude of the hull of a yacht while under way can vary in three planes (see Fig. 211):

(a) The midships plane (heeling, rolling)
(b) The symmetry plane (changes in longitudinal trim, pitching)
(c) The load waterline plane (change in the direction of motion, yawing)

In line with this division, three types of yacht stability—lateral, longitudinal, and directional—will now be considered.

In broad terms, stability can be defined as the natural tendency of a vessel to remain in or return to her original upright position despite the disturbing forces of wind and water. Stability is therefore one of the fundamental properties of any yacht, and depends on:

1. The shape of the hull
2. The distribution of the ballast in relation to full form
3. The magnitude of the aerodynamic forces
4. Her attitude when sailing under various weather conditions, and a few other factors of lesser importance

(a) Lateral Stability

From the point of view of safety, lateral stability is more important than longitudinal or directional stability, yet, like these, it affects the boat's speed and her

Fig. 211

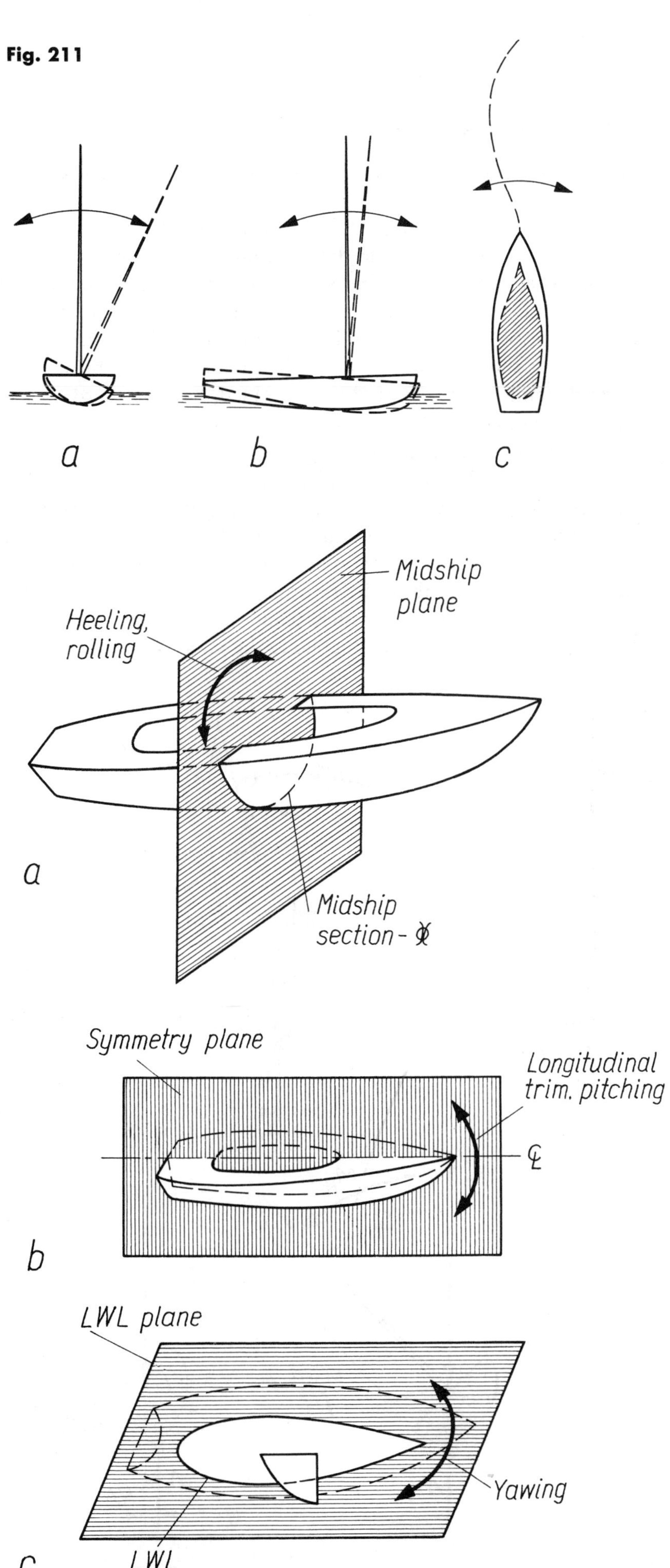

a
b
c
Midship plane
Heeling, rolling
a
Midship section - ⊗
Symmetry plane
Longitudinal trim. pitching
℄
b
LWL plane
Yawing
c
LWL

ability to go to windward and consequently her optimum performance as a racing yacht.

An Olympic class Dragon, and a typical modern fast cruiser, the *New York 32* (see Fig. 155) will be used to demonstrate the influence of lateral stability on the performance of the yacht. However, some important factors in the shape of the hull which determine its stability must be considered first. Suppose a centerboard dinghy is subject to a specific heeling moment M_H, caused by wind pressure on the sails (as shown in Fig. 212a–e). In case a the equilibrium of aerodynamic and hydrodynamic forces cannot be maintained, because there is no moment opposing the heeling moment M_H, and so the yacht will heel through the angle Θ. As a result of this heeling the center of buoyancy, CB, is shifted to leeward and a righting moment $M_R = \Delta \times RA$ appears, acting in opposition to M_H. When the two moments M_H and M_R become equal in magnitude and opposite in direction, the yacht will reach the state of equilibrium shown in b, and will then sail at a constant angle of heel Θ_1. As the wind increases, however, and the heeling moment M_H becomes greater than the righting moment M_R, the yacht will heel through positions c and d to e, at which point she capsizes. At position d the forces of buoyancy and gravity are acting along the same straight line, and because RA = 0

Fig. 212

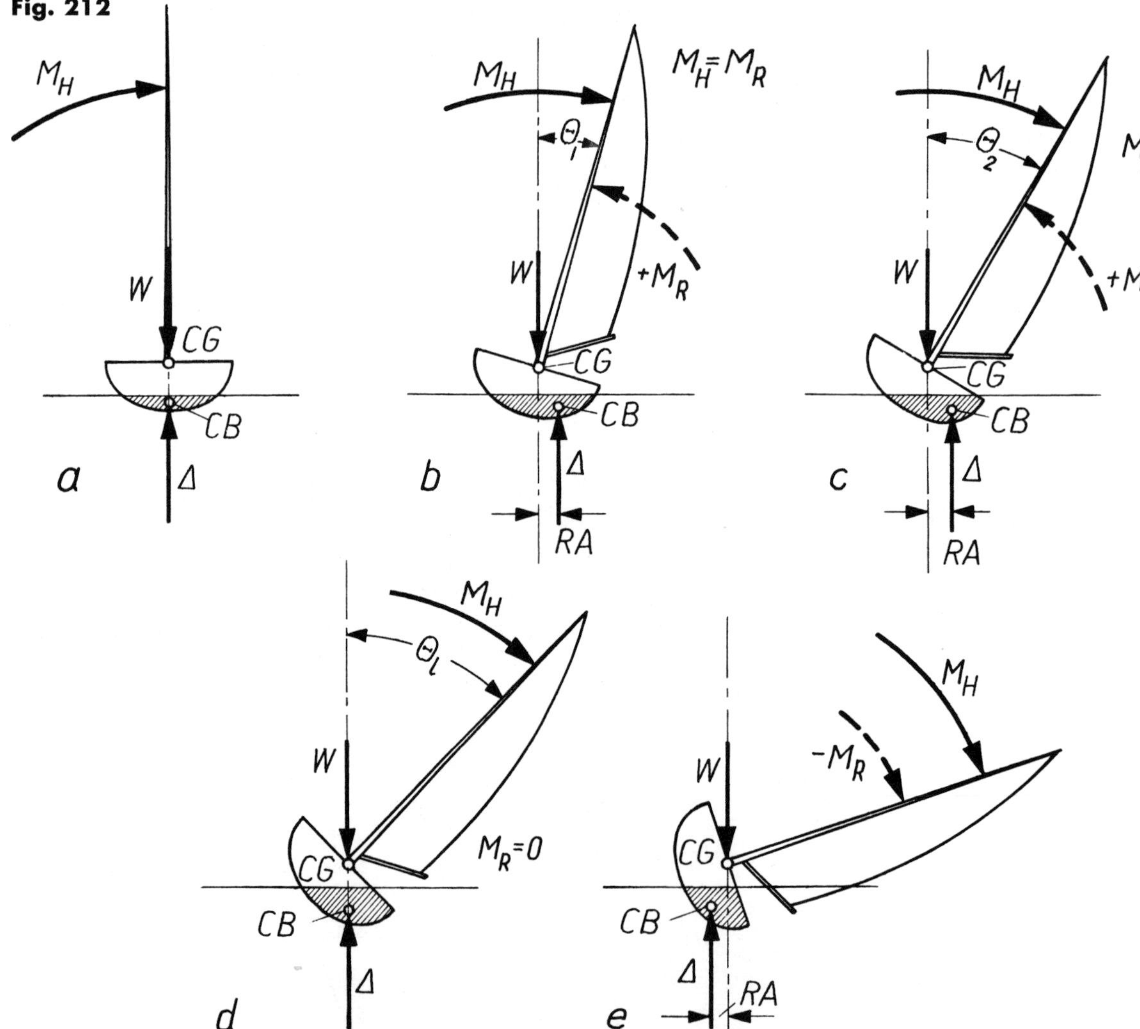

Fig. 213

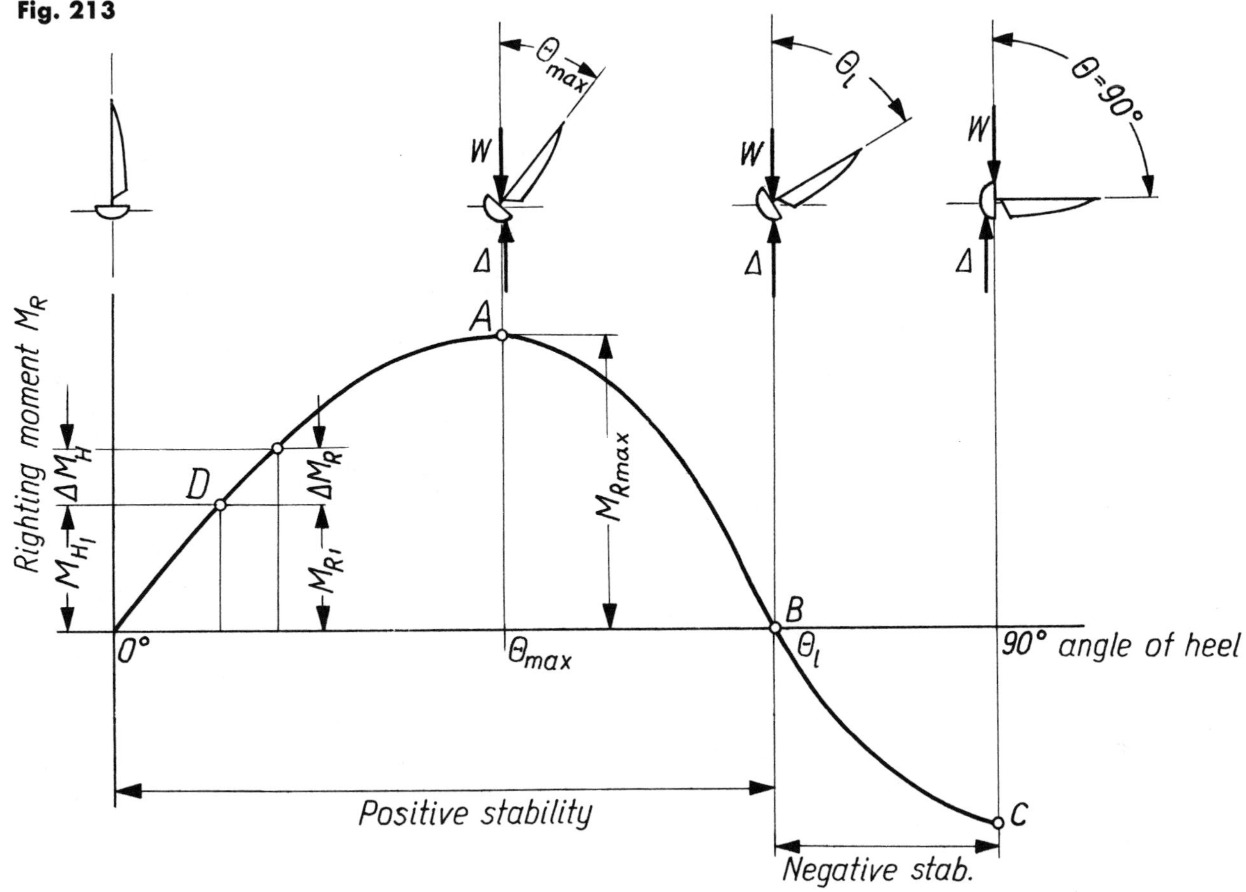

there is no righting moment, and the yacht has reached the point of unstable equilibrium. When the angle Θ increases further, the righting moment M_R, created by buoyancy, is negative, that is, it acts in the same direction as the heeling moment M_H, and will certainly help to capsize the yacht.

A stability curve for this case can be drawn (as in Fig. 213), where the righting moment, M_R, is plotted against the angle of heel, Θ. As the angle of heel, Θ, is increased, so the righting moment, M_R, rises to reach its maximum value, $M_{R\,max}$, at the angle Θ_{max}, where the shift in the center of buoyancy, CB, is furthest from the line of action of the weight of the yacht, W. The portion of the curve along OA therefore represents increasing stability of the yacht, and in this range any increase in the heeling moment, ΔM_H, will be opposed by an increased righting moment, ΔM_R. The angle Θ_{max} at the point A is the limiting angle of heel for increase of *stability*.

The portion of the curve AB shows the drop in the righting moment, M_R, from the point where any further heeling beyond Θ_{max} involves a reduction in the righting moment, M_R. At this point sailing becomes dangerous, and sheets must be eased to spill the wind.

When the heeling angle exceeds Θ_l and passes point B, the yacht is bound to capsize even if the heeling force is quickly removed. This is known as the region of negative stability.

For centerboard dinghies the critical angles normally lie within the following limits:

$$\Theta_{max} = 30°–40°$$
$$\Theta_l = 60°–80°$$

The value of the righting moment M_R and also of the angles of heel θ_{max} and θ_l depend very much on the shape of the hull, the amount of freeboard, and the beam of the boat. For example, in Fig. 214b the stability curves are shown for two hulls similar in shape and of equal displacement, but differing in the height of freeboard, F_1 and F_2. A comparison of the values of their righting moments, M_{R1} and M_{R2}, and their angles of heel, $\Theta_{1\ max}$ and $\Theta_{2\ max}$, demonstrates that the hull with the higher freeboard will be the more stable. The initial stability for small angles of heel is similar for both hulls, but at larger angles of heel the difference is very pronounced. Sailing is thus safer on a yacht with a high freeboard.

The effect of beam on stability is shown by the example of two yachts having different beam (B_1 and B_2). In Fig. 215 it can be seen that their lateral stability is different at all angles of heel. The yacht with the broader beam, B_2, will be more stable because the righting moment M_{R2} is larger due to a longer righting arm RA_2.

Modern centerboard dinghies show a clear tendency toward increased beam, and this in turn makes it possible to increase the sail area. This trend is not entirely based on the claims of greater stability. Another important reason is that a broad flat-bottomed hull is better able to generate the hydrodynamic lift needed for high-speed sailing.

The excessive initial stability found on a beamy hull can, in the case of a heavy-keel boat, produce a large, jerky rolling motion, very exhausting for the crew and wearing on the rigging. This imposes a limit on the lateral stability possible in large cruising yachts, even though it also means sacrificing some chances of reaching higher speeds.

The stability of a yacht, then, may be said to be governed by the relationship between the CG (center of gravity) and the CB (center of buoyancy). For example, Fig. 216 shows three identical hulls with their centers of gravity in different positions: CG_1, CG_2, and CG_3. A comparison of their stability curves and righting moments leads to the conclusion that the yacht with its CG in the lowest position is the most stable. This is because when the CG is lowered, the righting arm RA is increased, and this increases the value of M_R. The idea of obtaining stability through weight led to the evolution of ballast-keel yachts, where the CG was set low in the bottom section of an elongated keel, which contained external ballast of iron or lead (Fig. 217). The weight of the ballast may comprise from 30 to 80 per cent of the total weight of the hull.

The contour of the stability curve of a ballast-keel yacht which combines stability due to hull form, with stability due to weight, is quite different from that for a centerboard dinghy (cf. Fig. 217). As the angle of heel increases, the righting arm RA also increases continuously, and the righting moment always remains

Fig. 214

Fig. 215

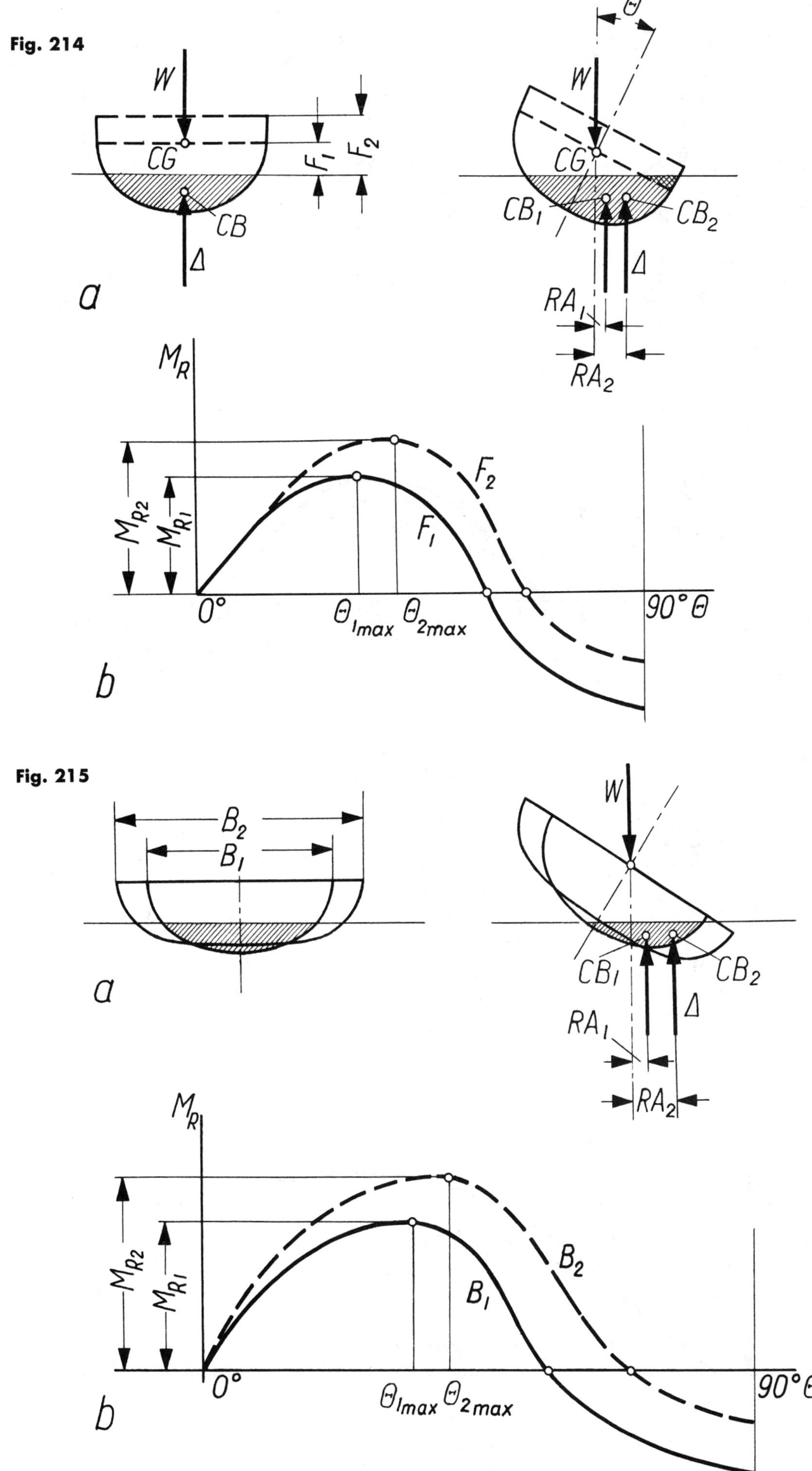

Fig. 216

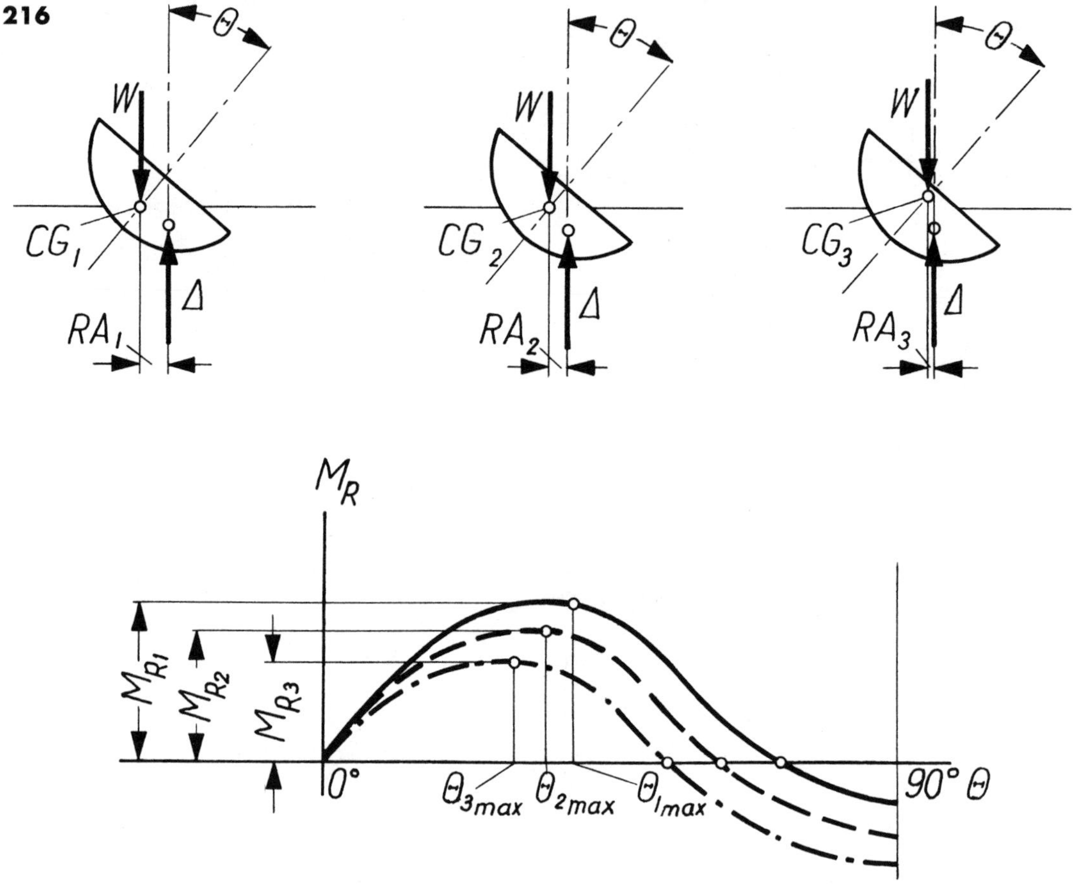

θ
W
CG1
Δ
RA1
CG2
RA2
CG3
RA3

MR
MR1
MR2
MR3
0°
θ3max
θ2max
θ1max
90° θ

Fig. 217

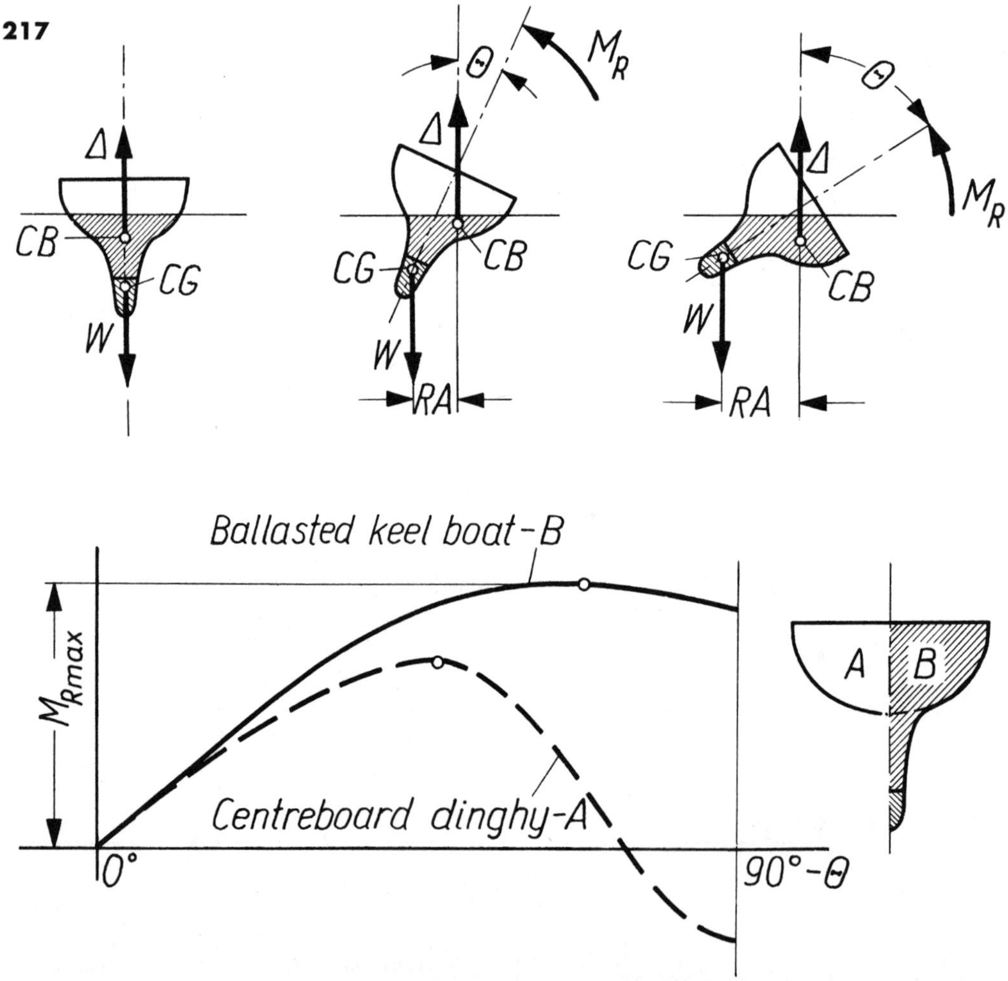

Δ
CB
CG
W
θ
MR
RA

Ballasted keel boat-B
Centreboard dinghy-A
MRmax
0°
90°-θ
A
B

positive; the yacht cannot capsize. Ballast yachts can therefore sail more safely in heavy weather, even if they do not reef, than can any yacht whose stability is due entirely to her shape.

The difference in lateral stability between a ballast-keel boat and an unballasted catamaran whose stability is derived from her load-spreading form is shown in Fig. 218. A catamaran is clearly particularly stable at small angles of heel, but

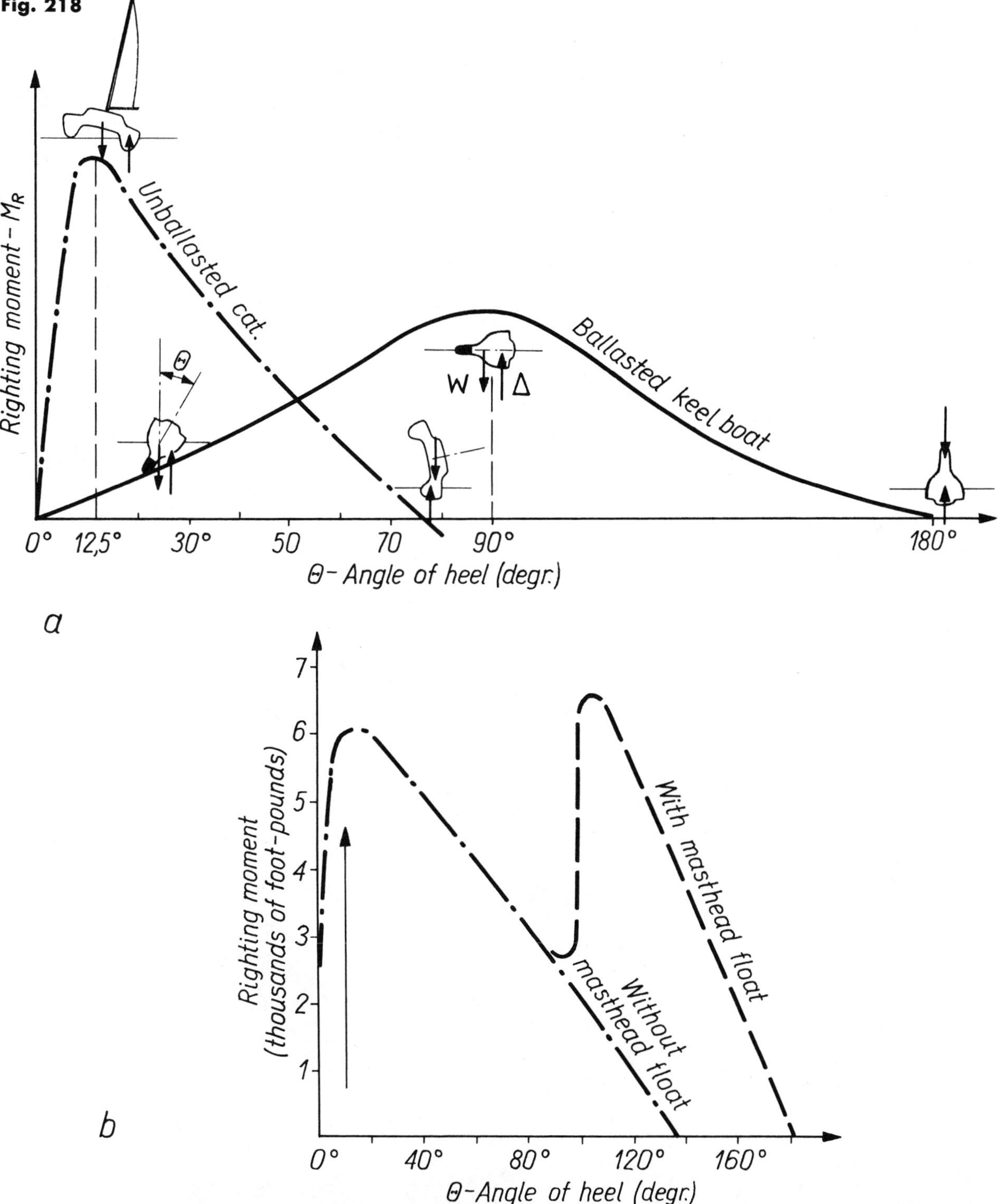

just like a centerboard dinghy she reaches negative stability at somewhere around 70°–80° of heel, a very undesirable characteristic in a cruising catamaran in particular. To ensure safety when sailing offshore, ballast stability must be combined with the catamaran's natural stability. Figure 218b shows how this problem was solved by Michael Henderson on the catamaran *Golden Miller*, where sufficient stability was obtained by suspending ballast underneath on the fins. The stability curves in Fig. 218 show that she has a reasonable range of positive stability extending to 140°. The masthead float shown in Photo. 35 is a further precaution, as its primary function is to prevent the boat being rolled beyond the angle from which the ballast still has power of recovery. The effect of the masthead float is shown in the second peak on the stability curve in Fig. 218b.

Obviously, the maximum value of the righting moment, M_R, is what limits a yacht's "power to carry sail." For a centerboarder, like that in Fig. 219a, the righting moment can be calculated from the formula:

$$M_R = W_b \times RA_1 + C \times RA_2$$

where W_b is the weight of the boat without crew and C is the weight of the crew

Thus $C \times RA_2$, the crew or "live ballast," can have a very great effect on lateral stability, on the power to carry a lot of sail, and so on the performance of the yacht. This effect is augmented when the weight of the crew is high in proportion to the weight of the boat. For modern racing dinghies C may equal 50 per cent of the boat's displacement, and sometimes exceeds this. Photograph 37 shows very well how the "live ballast" can be exploited by shifting the crew out away beyond the weather rail on trapezes to increase the value of the righting arm RA_2. 18-foot Australian skiffs with four men out on trapezes, displacing about half a ton in sailing trim, have often reached speeds of 20 knots, a speed/length ratio $(v_s/\sqrt{L}) > 4.5$.

Photo. 37

Fig. 219

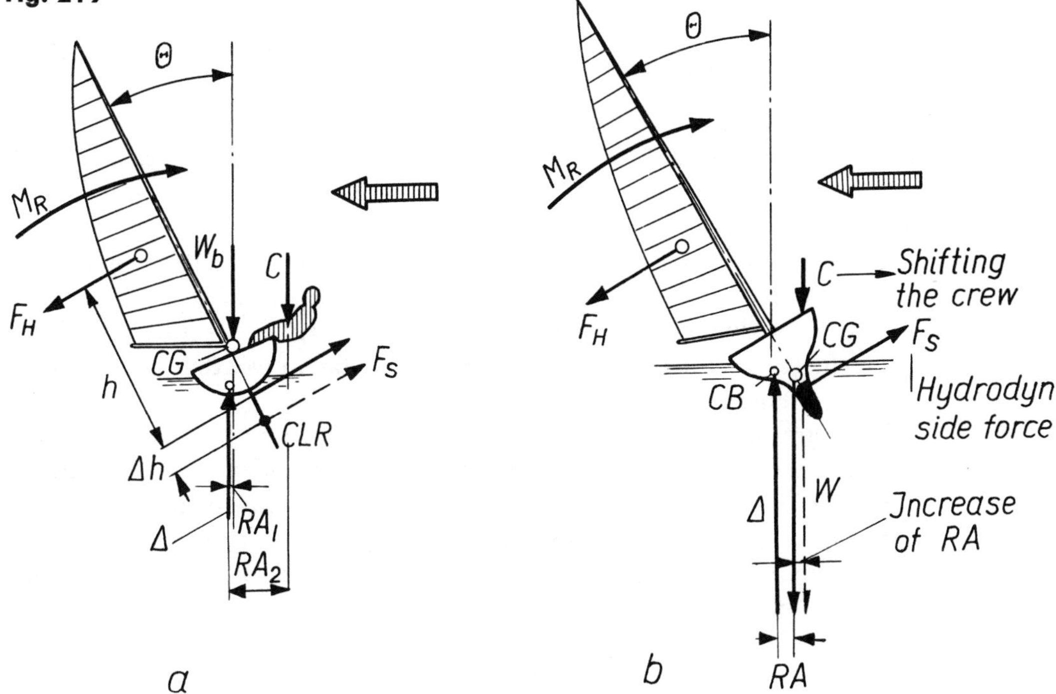

By analyzing Fig. 219a, assuming the motion to be steady, so that the angle of heel, Θ, is fairly constant and the righting moment, M_R, must balance the heeling moment M_H, we deduce

$$M_H = M_R = F_H \times (h + \Delta h)$$

where: F_H is the aerodynamic heeling force

h is the height of the CE above the CLR, when the centerboard is partly up

(h + Δh) is the height of CE above CLR when the centerboard is fully lowered

Therefore the magnitude of the heeling moment, M_H, depends on the arm (h + Δh) on which the force couple F_H and F_S acts. A practical deduction from this is that when jibing a racing dinghy in a strong breeze it is safer to keep the board up, since the capsizing couple is appreciably less than when the centerboard is fully down. Moreover, when close reaching in heavy weather it is advisable to lift the plate a half or two-thirds up, as this will help to keep the boat upright without having the sails fluttering and will also reduce eventual weather helm. This applies particularly in high-speed sailing. As a general rule, the higher the boat's speed and the broader her course, that is, reaching or running, the less the need for the board to be fully lowered. However, when the boat has a tendency to roll heavily, lowering the plate right down will tend to damp this.

A further point to bear in mind is that on a windward course the magnitude of the heeling moment, M_H, may increase suddenly if the centerboard touches the bottom. The arm h of the heeling force F_H becomes longer by Δh (that is, approximately half the length of the CB). If the helmsman is balancing the boat at the limit of his physical capacity, touching the ground with the plate may cause a capsize that is especially unexpected because the sudden increase in the heeling moment occurs without warning, whereas a gust of wind, for example, can be detected on the surface of the water.

The conclusion reached from studying Figs. 219a and 219b would be that the significance of the crew's weight, C, however important it may be on a light-displacement dinghy, has relatively little effect on the stability of a keel yacht. Nevertheless, it still pays for them to keep as far to weather as possible, particularly in moderate or heavy weather.

Photograph 38, an example of what may be attempted, shows the 12-Meter *Weatherly* with the "crew of ox-like docility" suspended on the gunwale in an attempt to shift the CG away from the centerline. This means in effect that, depending on the vessel's displacement, the weight of the crew and the angle of heel, the resultant vector W, representing the total weight of the yacht, will cross the symmetry plane lower down, while the righting arm, RA, increases (Fig. 219b). The yacht behaves as if her center of gravity had been lowered.

Figure 220 gives the results of experiments carried out in the Stevens Institute, United States, on a *New York 32* (see also Fig. 155). The data, taken from Technical Memorandum No. 85, indicate the relationship among stability (actually, position of CG), sail area, and windward performance. Figure 220 shows the changes in sail area and CE height and also in the position of the CG. With three different sail areas and three different positions for the CG, nine different combinations were used when analyzing the results. Each of these naturally gave a differ-

Photo. 38

Fig. 220

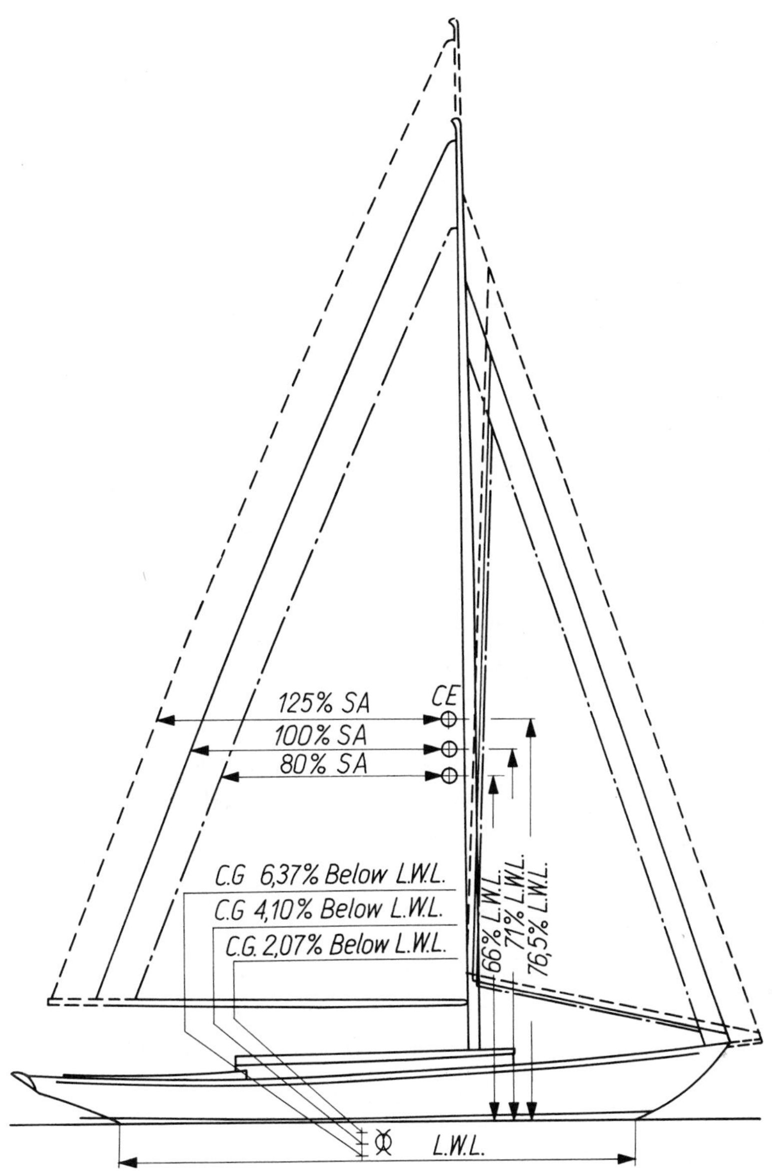
125% SA
100% SA
80% SA
CE
C.G 6,37% Below L.W.L.
C.G 4,10% Below L.W.L.
C.G. 2,07% Below L.W.L.
66% L.W.L.
71% L.W.L.
76,5% L.W.L.
L.W.L.

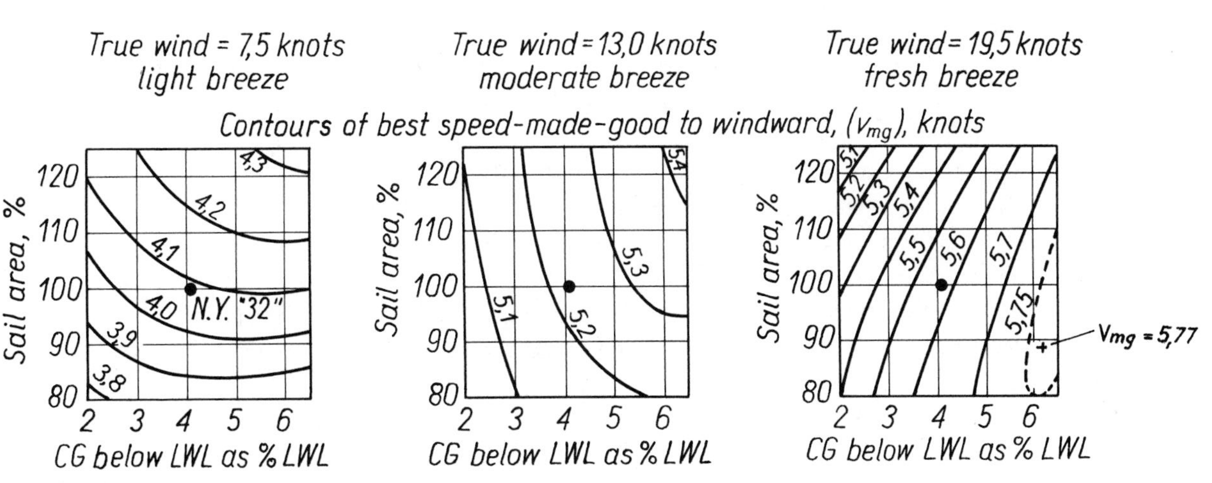
True wind = 7,5 knots
light breeze
True wind = 13,0 knots
moderate breeze
True wind = 19,5 knots
fresh breeze
Contours of best speed-made-good to windward, (v_{mg}), knots
Sail area, %
CG below LWL as % LWL
N.Y. "32"
V_{mg} = 5,77

ent speed made good to windward (v_{mg}). The results are shown in the lower part of Fig. 220, presented in the form of contour diagrams of v_{mg}, on grids of sail area and CG position at three standard true wind speeds.

A concrete example is perhaps the best way to explain this method of plotting. Near the center of each diagram is a spot which represents the *New York 32* as designed. This lies on the 100 per cent line of the sail area scale at the left-hand edge of each diagram, and at 4.1 per cent LWL on the "CG below LWL" scale along the bottom. The speed made good (v_{mg}) say in a light wind of 7.5 knots can be read from the diagram on the left-hand side. The point of best v_{mg} for the *New York 32* lies between the lines marking 4.0 and 4.1 of constant best speed made good, and can be read, interpolating by eye, as 4.09 knots. Similarly, by analyzing the middle diagram, which is for a moderate breeze of 13 knots, v_{mg} is found to be 5.23 knots and for a wind of 19.5 knots it is just below 5.6 knots.

The facts revealed by this study of the performance of a particular type of boat are in some cases of general significance as well.

In light weather conditions (v_T = 7.5 knots), sail area is the dominant speed-producing factor, especially when associated with a low center of gravity (high stability). Any increases in both sail area and stability are subject to the law of diminishing returns, as far as speed is concerned. For increase in the stability, the peak speed, v_{mg}, is reached within the range tested. For example, the boat with 90 per cent sail area can attain a v_{mg} of 3.99 knots when her CG is about 5 per cent below the waterline, but with either a lower or higher CG she would be slower, which suggests that heeling can be reduced too much.

In moderate winds (v_T = 13 knots) stability has become the dominant speed-producing factor, especially when associated with a large sail area. The range of v_{mg} resulting from tested range of SA and stability is very much smaller than in light winds, and varies from 3.6 per cent above to 3.7 per cent below the standard *New York 32*. It is therefore quite difficult to improve the moderate weather performance by making changes in sail area or stability.

In heavy weather conditions (v_T = 19.5 knots) stability is the primary factor controlling v_{mg}, whereas large sail area is a definite hindrance unless combined with very high stability. An actual maximum v_{mg} = 5.77 knots occurs at the point on the diagram corresponding to 89 per cent of normal sail area with CG about 6.2 per cent below the waterline. Reefing down to 80 per cent sail area or a little below would increase the v_{mg} speed of a *New York 32* by about 0.1 knots. The range of v_{mg} shown in the diagram is from 3.5 per cent above to 10.5 per cent below the standard *New York 32,* which shows that in a strong wind the speed falls off rapidly when too much sail area is matched with too little stability, because of the big angle of heel and the leeway involved.

In a light breeze (v_T = 7.5 knots) shifting the crew, a total weight of 1000 lb., four feet to weather of the centerline of the *New York 32* has no effect on v_{mg}. But in the moderate breeze (v_T = 13.0 knots) and in heavy weather (v_T = 19.5 knots) this increases the v_{mg} by 1.3 per cent and 1.6 per cent, respectively. It must be remembered that the weight of the crew only composes about 4 per cent of the total displacement of the yacht.

In the Olympic Dragon class the weight of the crew is about 10 per cent of the total displacement, and so the effect of crew movement is naturally greater than in the heavy-displacement *New York 32*. Interesting conclusions relating to the Dragon can be found in Report No. 2 of the Yacht Research Council (Great Britain). They are based on calculations and experiments carried out on a full-scale yacht, and their main purpose was to determine the legitimate changes a crew could make to the yacht's weight and the distribution of movable ballast to improve the performance under sail. It was found that shifting the crew, weighing 420 lb., 2 ft. 6 in. to windward gave an increase in v_{mg} of approximately 0.2 knots, i.e. more than 5 per cent. Optimum v_{mg} for each of two crew positions is shown in the graph in Fig. 221. Perhaps the most unexpected conclusion to be derived from these tests is that changes of displacement (39 cwt. to 43 cwt.) play a negligible part in the performance of a Dragon when going to windward, and also that adding 4 cwt. to the yacht's displacement did not reduce the speed. The best all-round performance is to be expected from the lightest hull, sailed by the heaviest possible crew, prepared to "sit-out" when going to windward.

Fig. 221

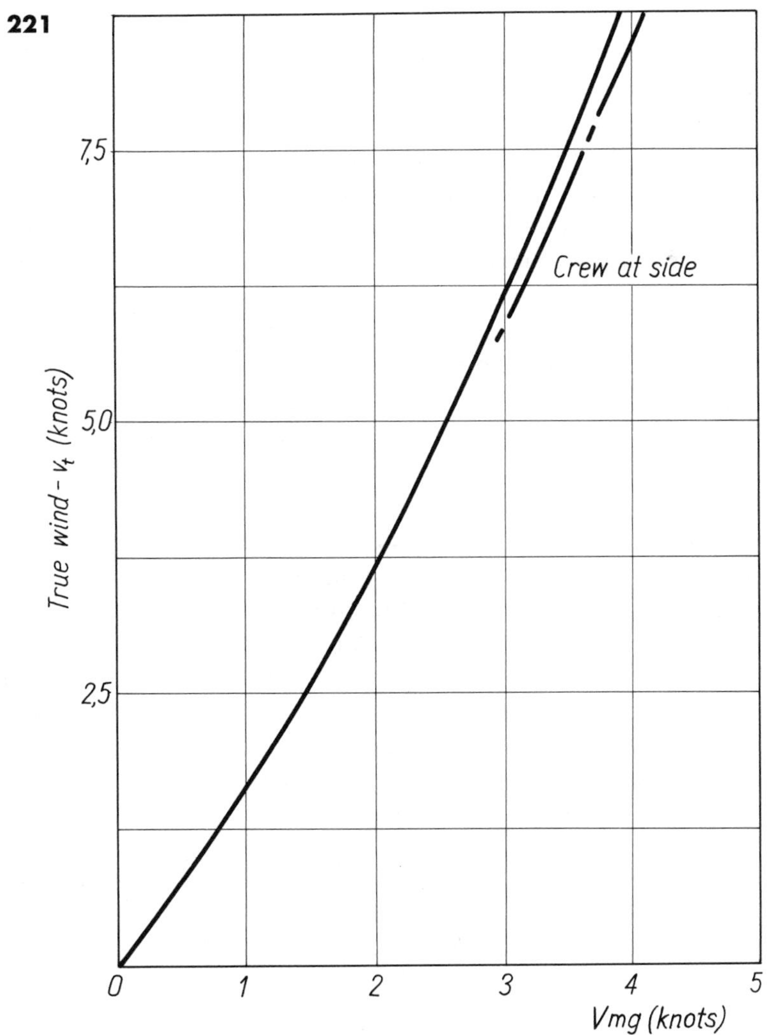

(b) Longitudinal Stability

Some ships sailed fast on an even keel, others had to be trimmed quite one foot by the stern, and I have heard of a ship that gave her best speed on a wind when so loaded as to float a couple of inches by the head.

J. CONRAD, *The Mirror of the Sea*

Compared with her lateral stability, the longitudinal stability of a yacht is relatively great, and the changes in the longitudinal trim of the hull when under way are small. For this reason the influence of the trim of the hull on the hydrodynamic resistance is small in comparison with that due to heel, particularly where heavy-keel boats are concerned. Nevertheless, even these little changes in resistance produced by the trim must be taken into consideration if the best is to be got out of a racing boat.

Changes in longitudinal trim are caused by the action of the driving force F_R on the sail, which in turn depends on the course being sailed and the strength of the wind. The force F_R acting on the arm h (see Fig. 222) induces a pitching moment, which depresses the bow and shifts the CB forward. Equilibrium will be reached when the following equation of the moments involved is fulfilled:

$$F_R \times h = \Delta \times l$$

The extent of the shift forward of the CB in relation to the CG is determined not only by F_R but also by the reserve of emergency buoyancy in the bow. The crew could be moved toward the stern to try and preserve level trim. The CG would then be displaced to CG_l by Δl, and this would allow the new CB to move to the position of the former CG (when $l = \Delta l$). In this way the hull would retain the level trim it normally has when no aerodynamic forces are acting on the yacht.

Figure 222a, b suggests that the magnitude of the pitching moment varies and demands appropriate movements from the crew along the hull. Moving the crew along the gunwale is especially desirable in strong winds, and in light-displacement racing dinghies. The crew would be well advised to keep forward when the boat is close-hauled and to shift toward the stern as the boat bears away from the wind. On a reach when the greatest aerodynamic force is developed, the crew are recommended to go as far astern as possible, while when running they would be a little further forward.

It has already been shown that at higher speeds hydrodynamic lift pushes the bow upward, an action quite the opposite of the pitching moment. To maintain proper trim, therefore, the shifting about of the crew must not be so extensive as it might be had only aerodynamic forces to be considered. The longitudinal ballasting of a yacht by a moving crew should therefore compensate for the difference between the lifting tendency of the hydrodynamic forces and the depressing action of the sails. In a light, fast dinghy, when sailing at high speeds, it is above all necessary to maintain the hull's angle of trim, a fact already mentioned (Part III, Chap. 1 [c], which dealt with Basic Stages in Yacht Motion).

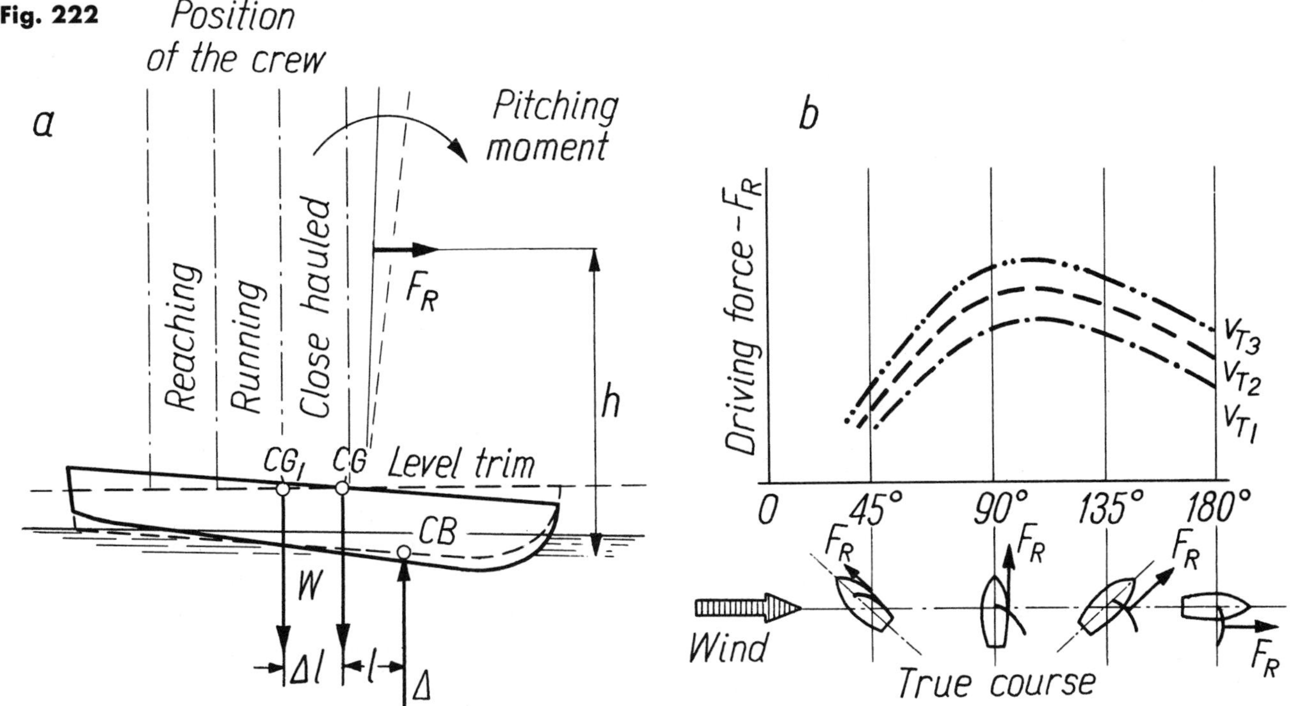

The shifting of the crew also influences the directional stability of a yacht. This can be confirmed by trying the following experiment. When sailing to windward, make the sheets fast and fix the tiller. Then it will be found that moving the crew can make the boat luff or bear away.

Some of the results of investigations into the effects of trim changes on the performance of a Dragon class yacht are illustrated in Fig. 223. When the boat's speed on a windward course was $v_s = 3$ knots there was a small increase in speed made good, v_{mg}, when the yacht was trimmed level or slightly by the stern. At $v_s = 5.5$ knots, also to windward, there was a similar small increase of v_{mg} when the yacht was trimmed by the head.

However, trimming by the head or by the stern causes additional resistance when sailing upright, and so level trim gives a Dragon its best performance when running before the wind.

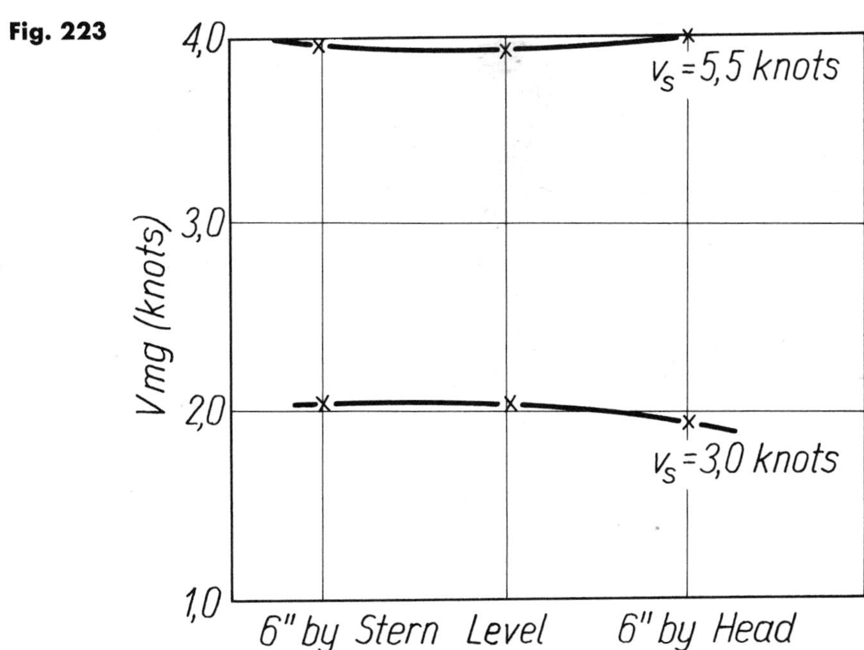

(c) Directional Stability: "Balance"*

Satisfactory directional stability, also referred to as the "balance" of a yacht, is the property of needing little helm to maintain a given straight course, whatever the boat's sailing attitude, conditions, or speed. Good "balance" is of considerable importance, for a badly balanced boat is tiring to sail, slow and even dangerous. In discussing the problem of the well-balanced yacht it is important to distinguish between the helm angle which the tiller makes with the centerline, and the "feeling" of weather or lee helm experienced by the helmsman. There are many misconceptions about it, and in many cases the terminology used is ambiguous.

A dinghy is shown in Fig. 224 as an example of this. The drawing a shows that the rudder acts in a manner similar to the centerboard, and produces a substantial proportion of the total side force, F_S, needed to resist the heeling force, F_H. This contribution by the rudder to the side force $F_{s(r)}$ reduces the leeway the boat makes from what it would be if the centerboard alone bore the full burden of the heeling force. The leeway-resisting function of a rudder is thus very useful, and for it to have its fullest effect the helmsman must maintain a certain angle of weather helm, i, that is, keep the forward end of the tiller pointing to weather in order to exert a force on it which is directed to weather. It can be seen that the magnitude of the force which the helmsman feels on the tiller will depend on the hydrodynamic force $F_{s(r)}$ and the distance of the center of pressure, $CP_{''}$, from the pivot line. When the sweep-back of the rudder blade is considerable, and $CP_{''}$ is well away from the pivot line, the feeling of weather helm torque may increase and give a false impression of the actual weather helm the boat is carrying.

One might suppose that keeping the rudder centered would be enough to produce side force, but in fact the direction of the water flow around hull, center plate, and rudder varies from place to place. Side wash under the forward part of the hull increases the angle of leeway (or angle of attack) at the center plate, which then diverts the flow back again, canceling or even reversing its sideways component. Thus the rudder, if centered, may have a zero or even negative angle of attack while sailing to windward. By maintaining a weather helm angle of a few degrees, the helmsman can let the rudder share in generating the leeway-resisting force F_S.

It may be also added that so-called perfectly balanced boats, where the helmsman does not feel any weather helm torque and the tiller may be let go when it is dead amidships, are not fully efficient, since the rudder contributes nothing to the lateral resistance.

Experiments with racing dinghies have proved that most of them go best to windward with a small amount of weather helm. In a well-balanced boat when the tiller is released, there must be a tendency to luff gently, but never to bear away, for this would mean that the action of the rudder was contrary to that of the centerboard or fin, a definitely undesirable characteristic.

* This chapter supplements Center of Effort and Its Relation to Directional Balance of a Yacht, Part II, Chap. 13(a).

Fig. 224

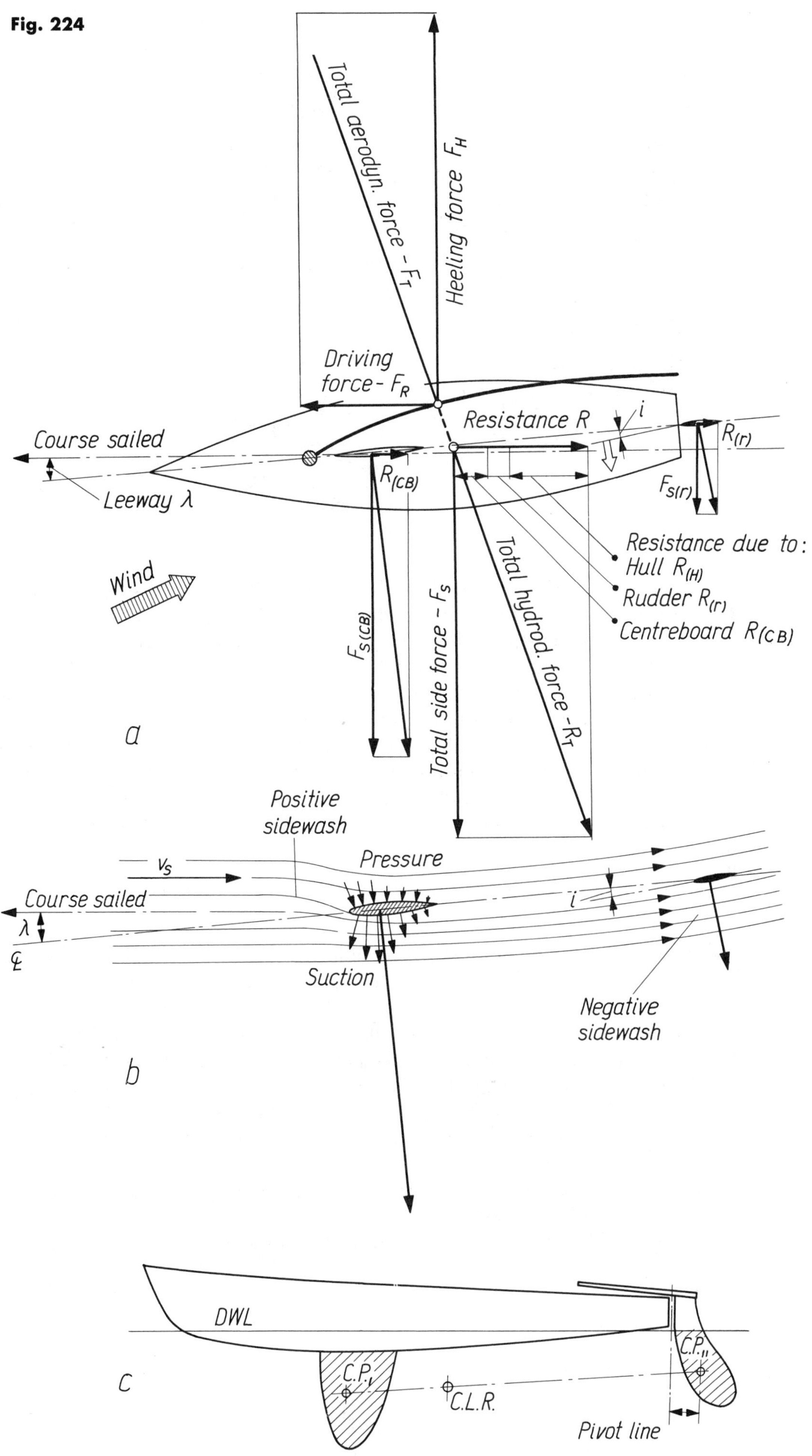

Total aerodyn. force - F_T
Heeling force F_H
Driving force - F_R
Resistance R
i
$R_{(r)}$
Course sailed
Leeway λ
$R_{(CB)}$
$F_{S(r)}$
Resistance due to:
Hull $R_{(H)}$
Rudder $R_{(r)}$
Centreboard $R_{(CB)}$
Wind
$F_{S(CB)}$
Total side force - F_S
Total hydrod. force - R_T
a
Positive sidewash
v_S
Pressure
Course sailed
λ
℄
Suction
Negative sidewash
b
DWL
C.P.I
C.L.R.
C.P.II
Pivot line
c

Fig. 225

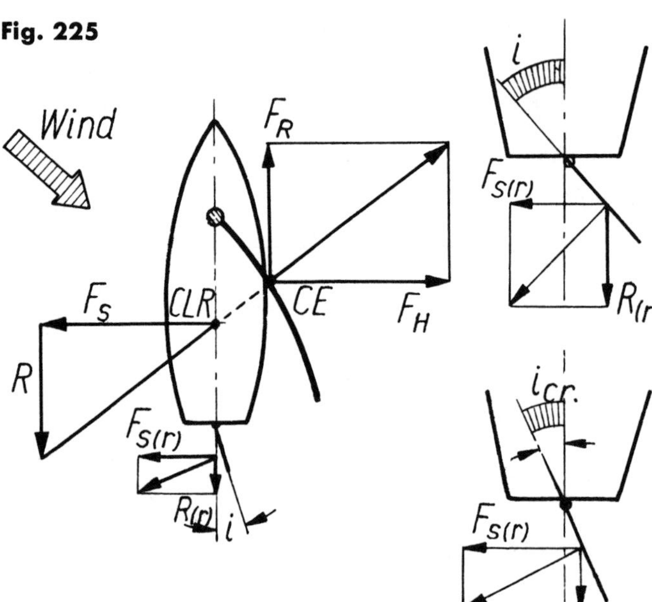

The total resistance of the boat, R, consists of R_H, $R_{(r)}$ and $R_{(CB)}$. A comparison of these reveals that the resistance due to the rudder $R_{(r)}$ is not excessive so long as the helm angle i is small (Fig. 224a). How big may it be then? This can be found by repeating the analysis of Fig. 169, in which the hydrodynamic coefficients for a flat plate and a streamlined profile are presented. There exist for different rudders, certain efficient angles of incidence, i, at which a relatively great side force, $F_{s(r)}$, can be produced for a small cost in resistance, $R_{(r)}$. There is also a definite critical angle of attack i_{CR} for the rudder (see Fig. 225), and exceeding this will reduce the side force, $F_{s(r)}$, and rapidly increase the resistance to forward motion, $R_{(r)}$.

In a sailing yacht where the lateral area is divided between fin and rudder, the latter has two fundamental functions:

(a) To produce side force, $F_{s(r)}$, to increase lateral resistance to leeway
(b) To steer the boat

In both cases the criterion of rudder efficiency is the extent to which it develops a large side force, $F_{s(r)}$, at a small helm angle or, in other words, for the smallest additional resistance $R_{(r)}$ (the range of most efficient angles of attack, i, being 10°–12°). It is important to realize, however, that the rudder that best fulfills function (a) can have a limited reserve power for such emergency use as a sudden need to control the boat's motion in heavy seas, coping with heavy rolling, heeling, a tendency to broach to in big waves, sudden turns, and the like. A rudder which is quite sufficient in light airs may prove to be too small for perfect control when reaching or running in a strong breeze. If a boat shows these symptoms, the rudder area must be increased, or the initial weather helm of the boat when upright and in light weather must be reduced.

Figures 224c and 225 also make it clear that the position of the center of lateral resistance, CLR, depends not only on the proportion of area of the centerboard, or fin, to area of the rudder, but also on the way in which the rudder is employed to produce side force. When one adds to these the possibilities of changing the position of the rig in relation to CLR, and altering the sail plan, it is clear that there are many factors to be considered when determining the proper directional balance of any boat.

It is perhaps useful to note that the center of pressure, CP, of a flat plate lies about ⅕ or ¼ of the width of the plate from its leading edge, when the angle of incidence is around 3°–5°. In practice this marks the limits of angle of leeway for a good boat sailing well close-hauled. With a streamlined plate whose thickness varies from 1/10 to 1/20 of its width, the CP remains more or less fixed at about 25–28 per cent of the width of the plate from the leading edge over an angle of incidence range of up to 25°.

Previous chapters have shown that bad directional balance is produced by the change of trim when the boat heels, and that therefore it is very difficult to tune the boat perfectly for all conditions. A compromise must be found, so that the boat will balance really well in most ordinary weather conditions, and especially within a specified range of angles of heel. This does not apply so much to racing dinghies which can be sailed upright.

Keel boats, like centerboard boats, seem to achieve their highest speed to windward with a small amount of weather helm. It is therefore important to know the effect of helm angle on hull resistance.

Experiments on a model of a 6-Meter hull in the Stevens Institute, United States, according to Davidson's interpretation (see Fig. 226), indicate that changing the helm by a few degrees from lee to weather was an effective way of moving the

Fig. 226

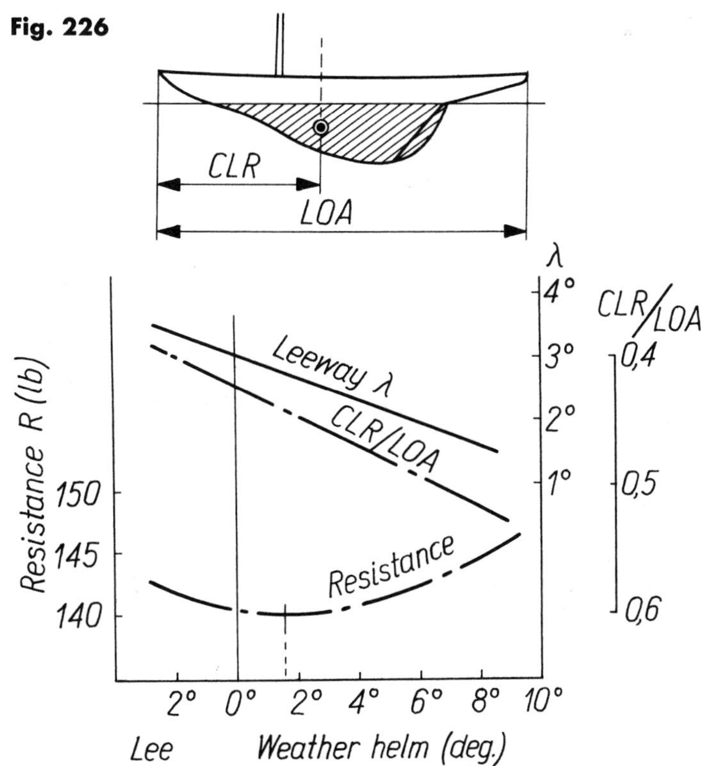

CLR aft. It also reduced the leeway, but made the resistance first drop and then rise. If the initial drop in resistance can be attributed to the reduced leeway made by the hull proper, as distinct from the keel, which seems probable, then the hull is evidently very sensitive to small changes in leeway. The subsequent rise in the resistance does not necessarily upset this reasoning, for it can be explained on the grounds that the continued increase in weather helm eventually increases the resistance of the rudder, or the rudder-keel combination, but only after the leeway has been reduced so much that further reductions have a negligible effect on the hull proper.

The 6-Meter boat itself sailed with practically no helm and was considered "well-balanced." She sailed, in fact, at nearly the best point on the resistance curve in Fig. 226, leaving no room for a significant gain from a change in the fore and aft location of the rig in relation to the hull which would alter the position of the center of effort.

The center of lateral resistance, CLR, must have been in the position given for boats carrying practically no helm (at the top of Fig. 226), which is some 45 per cent of the over-all length from the bow. It is well ahead of the geometric center of the area of the lateral plane.

(d) Maneuvering

If the rudder of a boat that has been sailing a straight course is deflected by the angle i (see Fig. 227), the boat will change direction and move along an arc of radius r. At any chosen point on this curve, the direction of the yacht's motion will be along a tangent to the curve, the tangent passing through the yacht's center of gravity, CG. Resolving the total hydrodynamic force on the rudder into those parallel and perpendicular to the motion of the yacht gives the two component forces, F_{Sr} and R_r.

The resultant motion of the yacht can be considered to be composed of progressive motion, drift, and turning about a pivot near the yacht's CG. The bow will be on the inner side of the turning circle while the stern is on the outer side, giving

Fig. 227

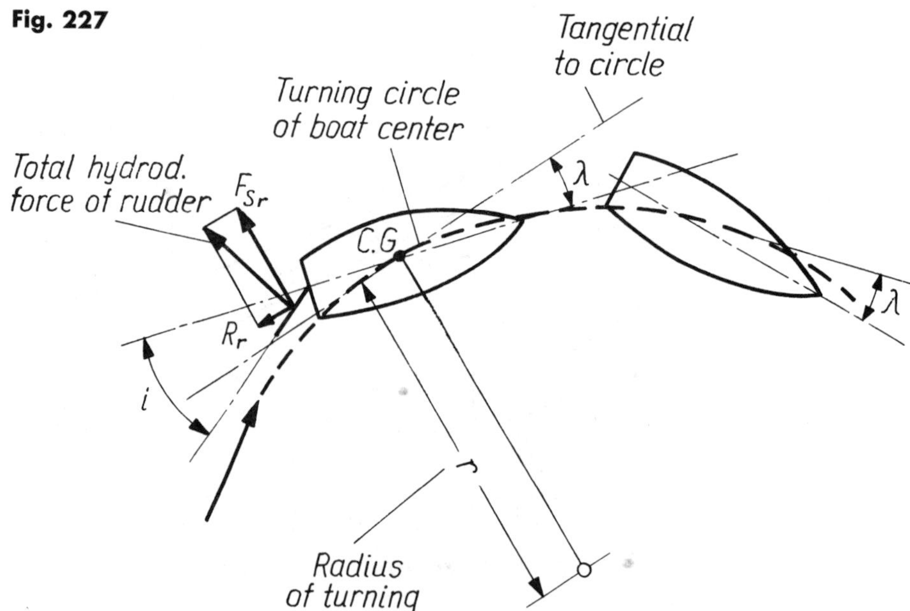

the impression the boat is "swinging sideways." This characteristic "swinging sideways" of the stern that occurs at each change of course causes many protests in races, especially when rounding buoys. It frequently causes damage when boats are turned too near the shore. In fact, only the CG of the yacht moves exactly along the turning circle, and steering is effected by the stern.

It was mentioned earlier that each deflection of the rudder is accompanied by a simultaneous increase in the hydrodynamic resistance. Maneuvering by using the rudder inevitably causes some reduction in the yacht's speed, and tacking involves a further loss because the sails are flapping for a time as the yacht changes course and crosses the line of the wind.

Racing on a course to windward may involve a great number of tacks, and the time that can be lost by faulty maneuvering should not be underestimated. The author, when training in the Star class, was able to observe that the time difference between good and bad tacking was about 4–5 seconds each time the boat went about. On a windward leg involving ten tacks, the better crew would therefore gain an advantage of 40–50 seconds, and a lead of as much as 20 lengths. For this reason the art of going about swiftly has to be practiced, so that the rudder is handled in the most skillful way with as little loss of speed as possible.

As was stated above, every rudder (a hydrofoil) has its own range of efficient angles of incidence at which the hydrodynamic force F_s is high in relation to the resistance R_r. The turn, therefore, should be begun by deflecting the rudder without exceeding this critical angle i_{cr} (cf. Figs. 227, 228). At the moment the yacht begins to turn, the deflection of the rudder should be gradually increased, as the angle of incidence i decreases while the boat turns, owing to the sideways displacement of the stern. The magnitude of the rudder angle i depends on the radius of the turn. For heavy ballast yachts, which are hard to turn, and whose turning circle has a large radius, it should not exceed $i \cong 30°$. On light centerboarders, which turn easily, the angle of the helm may be up to 60°–70°, since they almost spin round on the plate, and the radius of their turning circle is small.

Turning to windward can be improved and the time taken over it reduced if the

Fig. 228

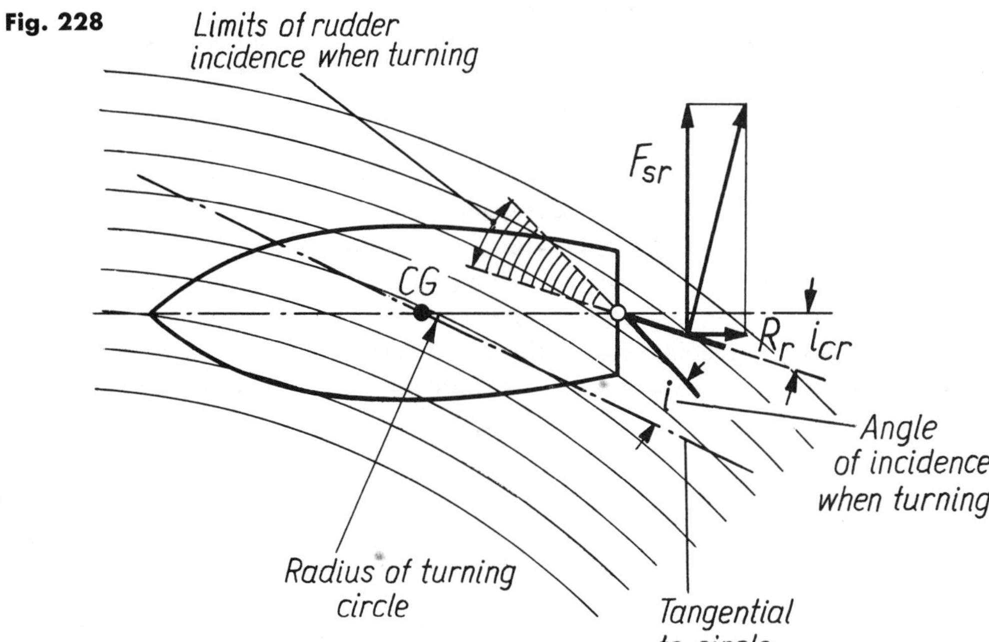

Fig. 229

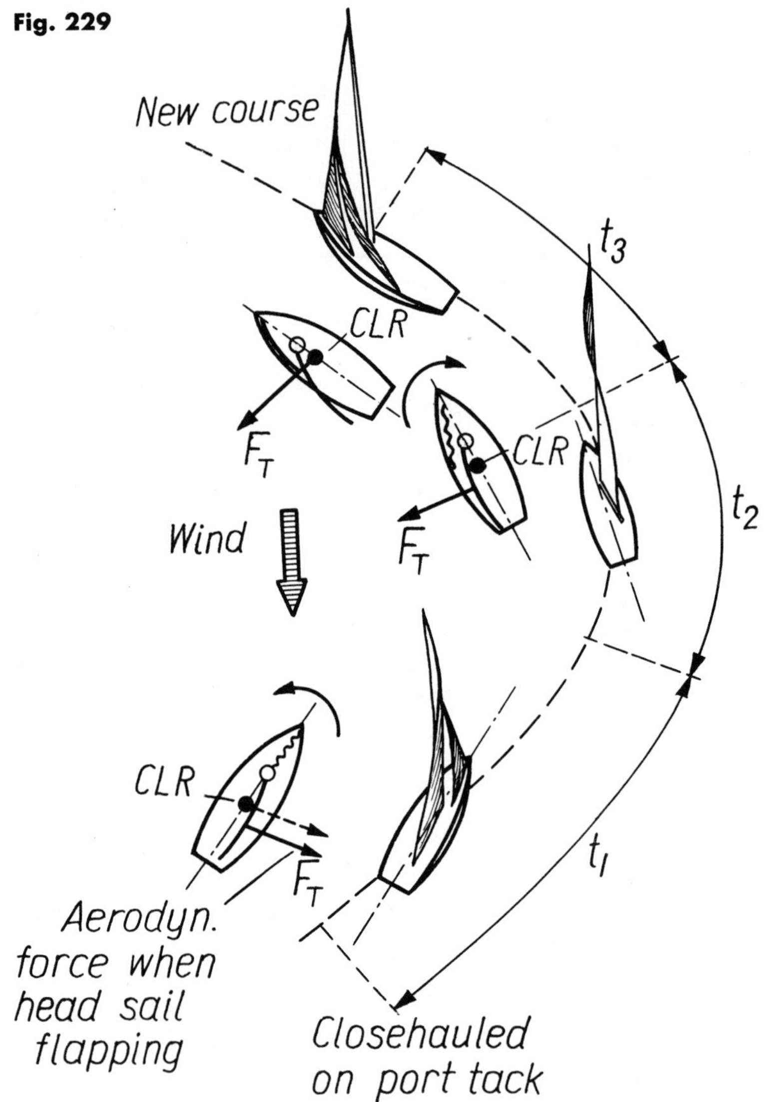

action of the rudder is supported by suitable trimming of the sails. It is sometimes desirable to induce weather helm intentionally to reduce the time the sails spend flapping as the boat turns across the wind.

Figure 229 represents schematically a change of course from close-hauled on the port tack to close-hauled on the starboard tack. The arc of the turn is divided into three sections, which the yacht covers in the periods of time t_1, t_2, and t_3. In period t_1, besides the action at the helm, the mainsail is hauled in energetically to the centerline. When the jib flaps, a yawing moment (excessive weather helm) appears as a result of the action of the aerodynamic force F_T in relation to the center of lateral resistance, CLR. This supports the action of the rudder, and together they accelerate the turn, reducing to a minimum the period t_2, during which the wasteful flapping occurs. After crossing the line of the wind, period t_3 is initiated by an immediate rise in the aerodynamic force F_T on the mainsail as its flapping stops. This causes a yawing moment in the opposite direction to the

Fig. 230

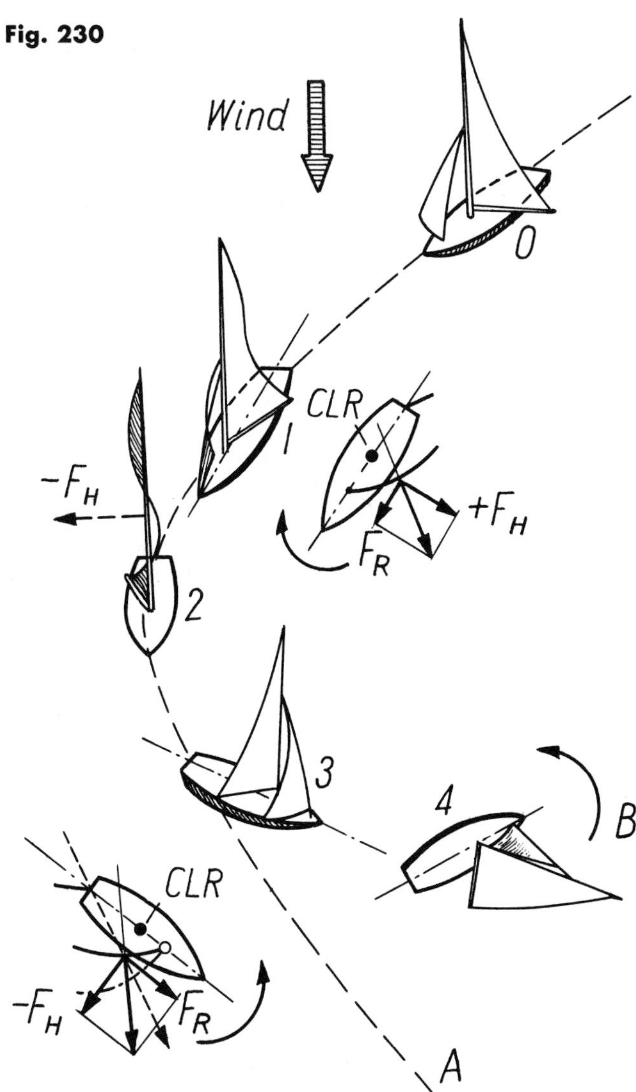

turn. Now the turn which has been carried through by the boat's inertia is arrested, and the yacht can be put on her new course by a slight checking movement of the rudder. At the end of period t_3 the mainsheet is eased so as to achieve the desired trim of the sail on the new course. At the same time the jib stops flapping, and this reduces the weather helm.

On heavy yachts of limited maneuvering ability it may be necessary to trim the jib aback to ensure that the boat will turn to windward.

Whereas tacking to windward is relatively easy, in that it can be carried out without risk even in strong winds, jibing, or tacking downwind, is often difficult, and in a strong breeze even the most experienced helmsmen avoid jibing, particularly when small centerboard boats, which are inclined to roll, are involved.

Figure 230 can help to show what happens if a boat running on the starboard tack decides to jibe. Beginning at point O, the mainsail is hauled in to the centerline and the course is slowly changed. As the wind comes almost dead astern, the speed of the boat will drop, and a strong weather helm will appear, which produces a yawing moment acting in the opposite direction to the jibe (cf. Fig. 230[1]).

The helmsman is forced to use more rudder, and the crew put their weight on the weather rail. In position 2 the mainsail swings across from left to right. In spite of a quick easing of the mainsheet a considerable force is generated on the mainsail, which causes (a) a rapid change in the direction of the yawing moment, which is now the same as that of the rudder, and (b) a considerable roll of the yacht, for force $+F_H$ is now $-F_H$. The boat has lost speed and the apparent wind is therefore stronger, and the drop in speed has reduced the efficiency of the rudder. If in position 3 strong yawing tendency is not properly countered by the rudder, and if the crew does not simultaneously shift from starboard to port, then instead of moving off along course A, the yacht will heel further and further, due to the increasing force on the sails and the increased weather helm, and will luff suddenly onto course B. Centrifugal force due to the turn augments the heeling angle. If in such a situation the crew delays the change of position from starboard to port, they may find it very difficult to reach the new weather gunwale, and will slide down onto the lee rail. In these circumstances a capsize often follows (as in Photo. 39).

The most difficult part to control is the situation in position 2 and the transition between 2 and 3, as then the helmsman and crew have to carry out a number of tasks requiring great skill and care, at a time when sudden and quickly changing forces are acting on the yacht.

Jibing can be greatly assisted by using a kicking strap or by wedging the boom in the mast as in the Finn. Then it is not necessary to haul in the mainsail to the centerline, but only to about 50°, and the boom can then be thrown over to the other side by hand when the wind is along the centerline. The forces on the sail

Photo. 39

Fig. 231

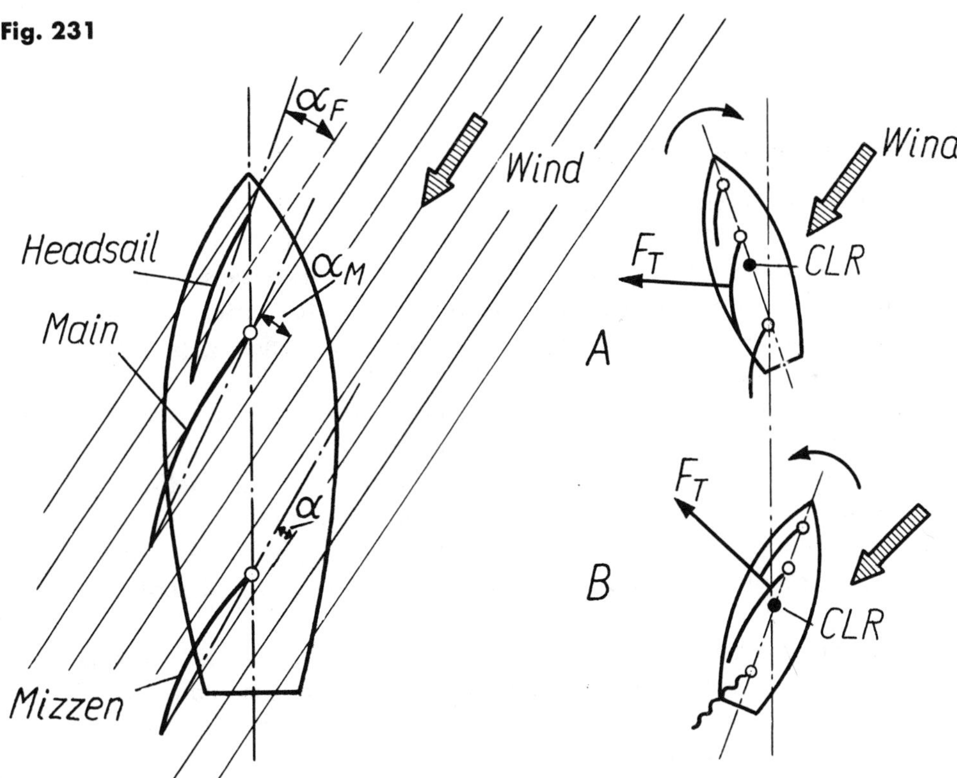

at the moment the boom is thrown across will not produce such great heeling and yawing moments as in the other method. The full maneuver of jibing is cut down, the speed loss is therefore smaller, as of course is the apparent wind, and the control by the rudder is more efficient. It is, however, still necessary to bear in mind the dynamic action of the forces on the sail, which must be counteracted at the right moment by means of the rudder and ballasting. This is what often makes the whole maneuver dangerous.

A special steering characteristic of some yachts is self-steering or, in other words, the ability of the boat to maintain a steady course relative to the direction of the wind, without helmsman. Self-steering is possible on cruising yachts, especially yawls and ketches, where suitable trimming of the sails allows one to exploit the effects of weather and lee helm. The way to trim the sails of a ketch or yawl is shown in Fig. 231. The mainsail is trimmed (α_M) so as to achieve the best results for the chosen course. The headsail is trimmed rather closer (α_F) but the mizzen is set just at the point of flutter (α). If the yacht has a tendency to carry weather helm, she will turn to windward and the mizzen will then flutter (sketch B). As a result the total aerodynamic force, F_T, will shift forward of the center of lateral resistance, CLR, and the yacht will have lee helm. Now she will bear away from the wind, the mizzen will stop fluttering, and the aerodynamic force F_T will shift behind the CLR, and the yacht develops weather helm again.

Sheeted like this, the yacht will oscillate between positions A and B. If the sails are well tuned, the differences between the two courses will be very small. The helm is left free. The author, when sailing in a 13-ton ketch, was able to confirm that the difference in the courses of a well-tuned self-steering yacht in moderate winds did not exceed $\pm 2°$.

Trimming for self-steering in a sloop- or cat-rigged boat, though more difficult, is nevertheless possible. As in the case just described, use is made of the variations in the aerodynamic forces which depend on the angles to which the sails are trimmed in relation to the wind direction and the centerline. Of course, since in a self-steering setup not all the sails are working with equal efficiency, performance is not as good as it would be if the yacht were steered by a skillful helmsman. Self-steering depends to some extent on the yacht's natural ability to keep on her course, and on the condition of the sea. Yachts with long overhangs, being easily turned, are not good at steering themselves. Big waves also affect self-steering. By using a spinnaker which is screened when the yacht bears away from the wind it is possible to achieve self-steering on a reach. Self-steering before the wind is relatively easy, especially if a twin spinnaker is used; this was described earlier (Fig. 119).

Setting a yacht to drift to ride out a storm is another form of self-steering. The technique for this relies on maintaining the yacht in a safe position relative to the waves, while making gradual progress against them. The yacht can be set to drift with the wind, and will make 1.5 to 2.5 knots and will not suffer damage from the waves, as her speed, in relation to them, is negligible.

The principle is to let forward and after sails work against each other. As in Fig. 232, the storm headsail trimmed to windward makes the boat move astern, and at the same time turns her off-wind. In position 1 the mizzen starts to work, driving the boat forward and turning her to windward. When position 2 has been reached the process is repeated. The rudder is fixed on the weather side, at the weather-helm angle. By varying the area of the headsail in relation to the mizzen it is possible either to achieve a resultant motion over the waves or to drift with them. To move over the waves is only possible when the sail that causes the forward motion has the larger area. The angle between the centerline of the yacht and the wind will be 50°–60°, depending on the way the sails are set and their areas.

Finally, it is worth mentioning how a dinghy behaves when, after an unsuccessful attempt to go about, speed is lost and the boat may begin to drift. Many helmsmen become nervous and fear that the yacht does not want to bear away from the wind onto the course desired in spite of trimming the mainsail against the wind. This is especially common with small sailing dinghies (Fig. 233). Often a helmsman, wanting to bear away from the wind quickly, will begin to row with the rudder and push the boom against the wind. These actions are not usually beneficial, because the tendency to excessive weather helm which the action of the aerodynamic forces on the sails produces cancels the effect of the rudder. The most useful advice one can offer is to lift up the plate, thus shifting the center of lateral resistance astern. Then by trimming the mainsail against the wind, lee helm will be produced, and thus the chosen direction can easily be gained. On yachts with several sails the desired bearing away is achieved by trimming the headsails to windward and leaving the mainsail free.

Fig. 232

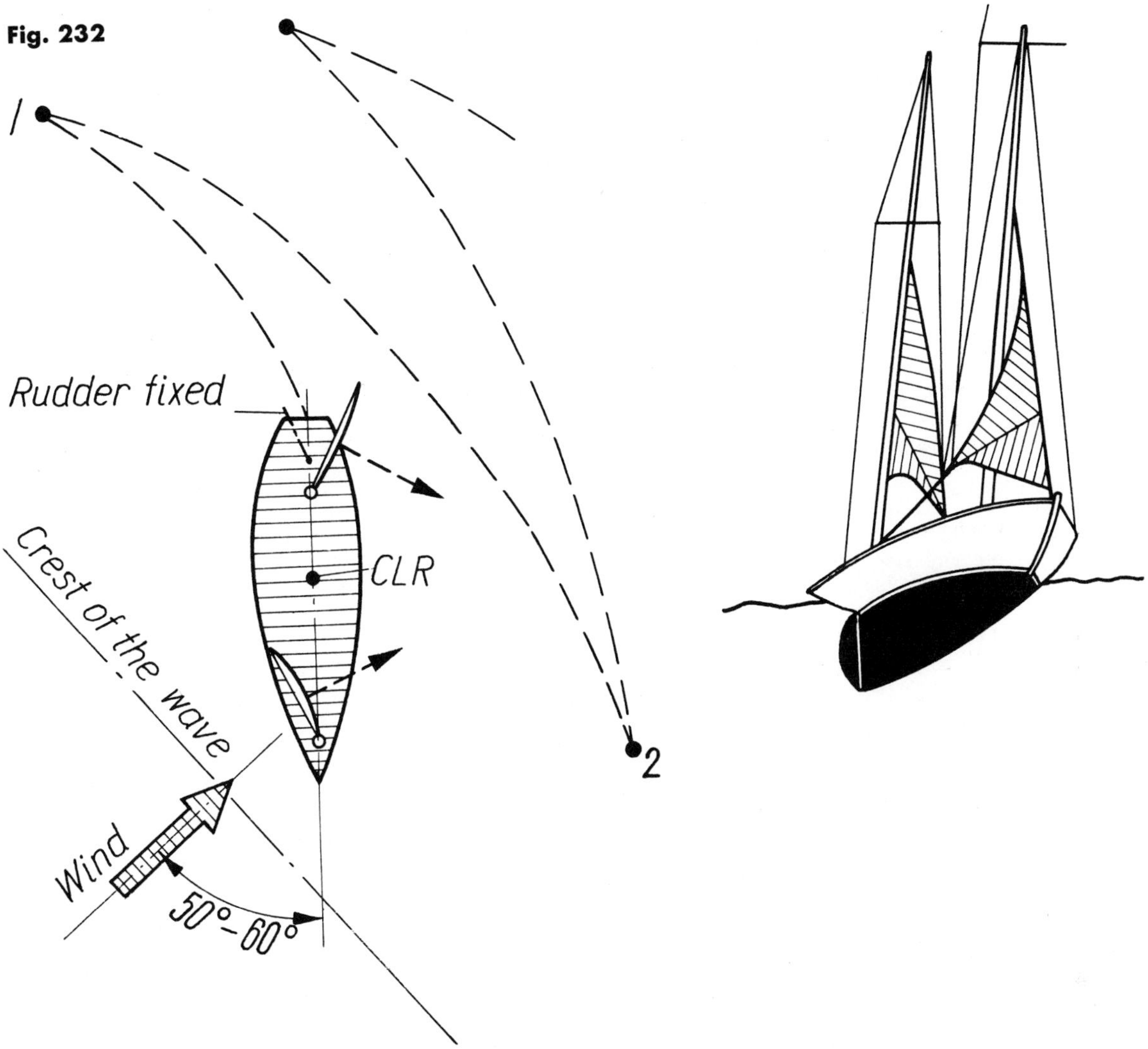

1

2

Rudder fixed

CLR

Crest of the wave

Wind

50°–60°

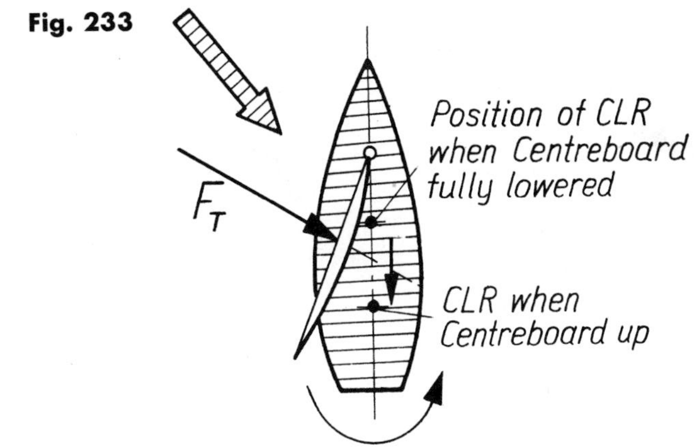

Fig. 233

PART IV

WIND AND WATER

Fig. 234

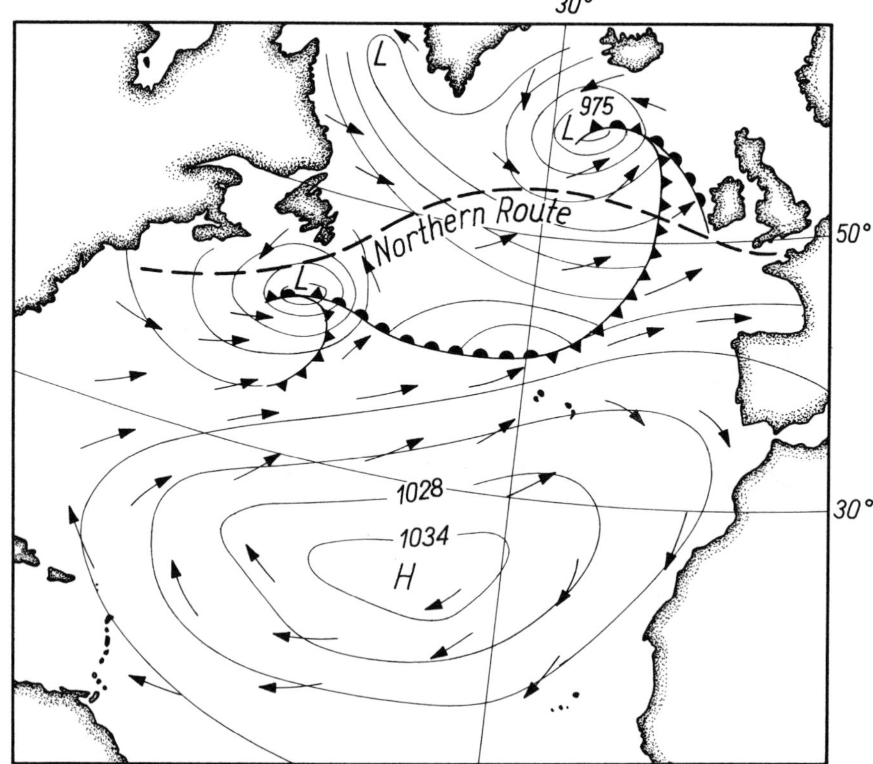

A. Typical pressure and wind distribution in the North Atlantic (Summer)

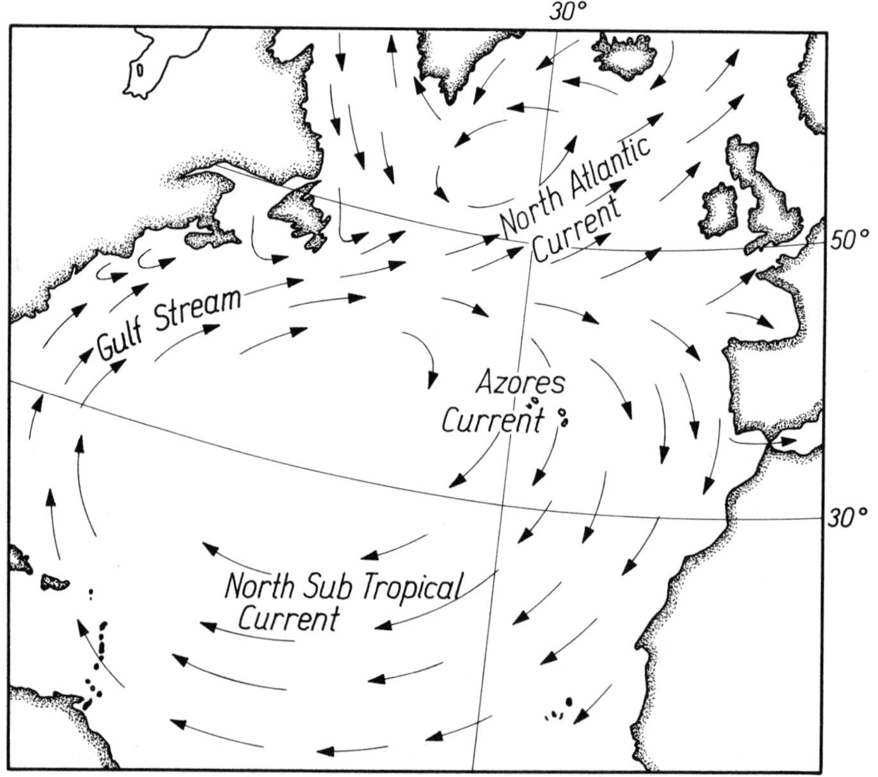

B. Ocean currents linked to the wind patterns

1. WIND

> There is no part of the world of coast, continents, oceans, seas, straits, capes and inlands which is not under the sway of a reigning wind, the sovereign of its typical weather. The wind rules the aspects of the sky and the action of the sea. But no wind rules unchallenged his realm of land and water.
>
> J. CONRAD, *The Mirror of the Sea*

Every yachtsman, no matter whether he be racing or cruising, tries to get a forecast of the wind's direction and strength, before setting sails. A correct "weather oracle" can often influence the crew's efforts to complete their self-chosen task.

Before a long offshore race most attention will be given to getting a synoptic picture of the weather over a broad area, while for racing in sheltered waters an intimate knowledge of local wind conditions will be more useful.

(a) The Significance of Barometric Depressions (Lows)

Weather conditions, and therefore winds, over large areas come under the influence of "lows" moving constantly from west to east (cf. Fig. 234). Lows or cyclones, where the air (wind) moves inward in a spiral, usually travel at an average speed of 20 knots or even more. The winds within them may reach speeds of 120 knots; however, although this occurs very seldom, strong winds are a characteristic of these rapidly moving violent atmospheric disturbances. This was fully exploited by the masters of sailing ships in the past, who, by sailing on the edge of a moving low, were able to reach high speeds. For example, at the beginning of the nineteenth century a voyage from Europe to Australia lasted about 200 days. Half a century later, after the quickest route had been plotted by Maury, who took into consideration the most advantageous wind systems, this voyage had been shortened to 80 days.

In the northern hemisphere winds rotate anticlockwise round the "lows." As Fig. 235 shows, the winds in a cyclone may aid or hinder the progress of a sailing craft, depending on the position of the yacht in a particular quadrant. For example, if a yacht follows the course AB, which cuts through the depression system, then in position 1 she will be reaching on the port tack. In position 2 she is forced to sail close-hauled, still on port tack. When the yacht passes to quadrant II, however, she is forced to go onto a starboard tack. Clearly, therefore, the art of offshore sailing involves not only a skillful use of the possibilities offered by the yacht's aerodynamic and hydrodynamic efficiency, but also a knowledge of how to take

Fig. 235

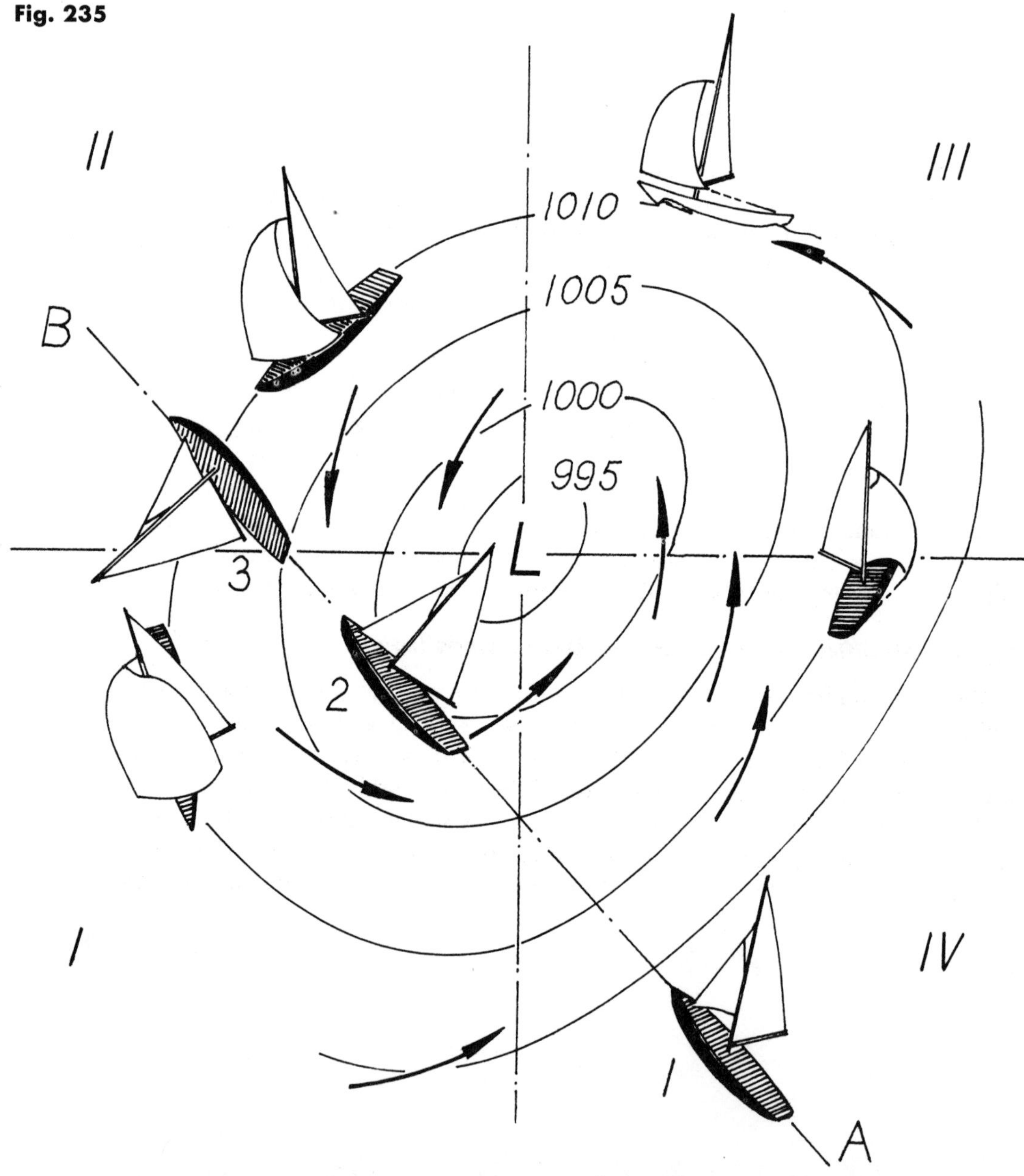

advantage of the meteorological conditions met with. This is most striking in the somewhat longer offshore races.

As an example of this, let us consider the transatlantic race, which is run along the northern route in the region of the track followed by lows. The results of these races, as a rule, are decided by eastward-moving depressions, which the racing fraternity have nicknamed "expresses." A boat which catches a cyclone and keeps inside its sphere of influence may pass the finishing post at Marstrand (Sweden) as much as 5 days earlier than her rivals who "missed the express."

It was shown earlier that heavy-keel yachts, in the most favorable weather conditions, can attain a maximum relative speed $v_{max} = 1.4\sqrt{LWL}$. Clearly, then, a yacht with a longer waterline length, and so with a higher relative speed, will have a better chance of keeping in contact with a low for a longer time. Thus in the same weather conditions a 40-ft. yacht could sail 8.8 knots, while a 30-ft. yacht could only reach 7.7 knots, because—

$$v_{s\ max} = 1.4\sqrt{40} = 8.8 \text{ knots}$$
$$v_{s\ max} = 1.4\sqrt{30} = 7.7 \text{ knots}$$

The handicap calculated from the rating formula will not compensate for this, as weather is not a factor considered in working out a yacht's rating. Naturally, a more efficient crew, better navigation, sailing the yacht to her best advantage, especially at night, and so on, may give the victory to a yacht of shorter waterline length, but even the best crew cannot fully exploit the possibilities of the weather on a yacht with too low a relative speed. Experience suggests that yachts which race across the Atlantic should have a waterline length of about 36–40 ft.

In the example described, the depressions were moving in approximately the same direction as the race. Figure 236, however, shows what happens when the center of a depression moves at an angle across the course. The track of the low is shown by the broad arrow, and the course of the race is across the Baltic from Hel (A) to Hoborg (B). Now, if the actual wind blowing near Hel at the start were all that could be known, the shortest course, AB, would be assumed to be the most advantageous. But as the depression will be moving eastwards, somewhere near point O, a boat would find herself compelled to tack close-hauled against a rising wind and rougher sea.

In fact, during the race, what started as a south wind will change to a westerly, then to a northwesterly, and finally to a northerly wind. A more advantageous plan, therefore, would be to anticipate these changes and follow the course ACB. This will ensure a favorable wind for the whole race, and higher speeds will be reached.

Anticyclonic areas of high pressure generally move slowly, and the winds rotate around them in a clockwise direction, the opposite way to the cyclonic winds. Because the air mobility of anticyclones is much slighter, the possibilities of utilizing the associated winds are much less than with cyclones.

To take full advantage of variable weather, the full synoptic weather chart of the area must be studied before any of the longer races begin. The meteorologi-

Fig. 236

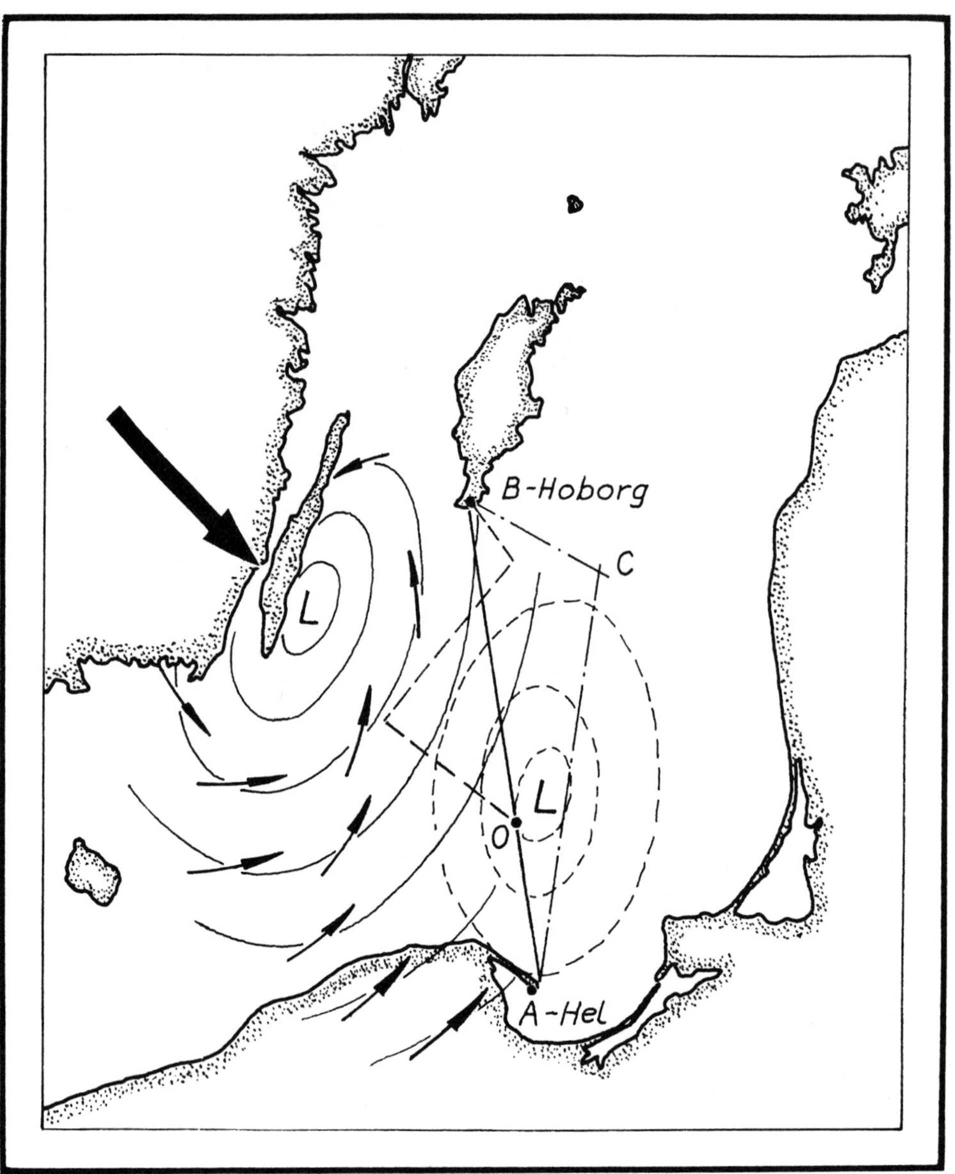

cal service may supply weather maps, and similar forecast charts can be prepared from broadcast weather forecasts. The main need is to plot the isobars on a map of the region involved, and then during the race, by noting variations in pressure and wind direction, it is possible to deduce in which quadrant of the depression (or anticyclone) the boat is sailing. This makes it possible to determine the direction in which the weather formation is moving, its speed, and forthcoming variations in the wind. A quick change in wind direction indicates that the isobars are concentrated in a small area, and one may assume that the focus of low or high pressure is small and that the boat is at its center.

The forecasting process is simplified because cyclones do not travel along irregular paths but follow definite tracks. For example, the cyclonic tracks for the North

Sea and the Baltic are shown in Fig. 237. It must be emphasized that the character of the winds in a cyclone depends to a large extent on the track it is following. Details of these for the oceans and lesser seas are published in various "Aids to Navigation."

The conclusions reached by observing changes in wind direction and barometric pressure can be tested by watching for such other signs of approaching changes in the weather as nature offers. The color of the sky at sunrise and sunset; the concentration, shape and movement of the clouds; different light phenomena in the atmosphere; the behavior of birds, and so on, can greatly assist in the correct assessment of the weather situation and in forecasting changes.

The language of many maritime nations contains pithy, rhyming proverbs for predicting weather changes, which embody the experience of generations of sailors, such as:

Fig. 237

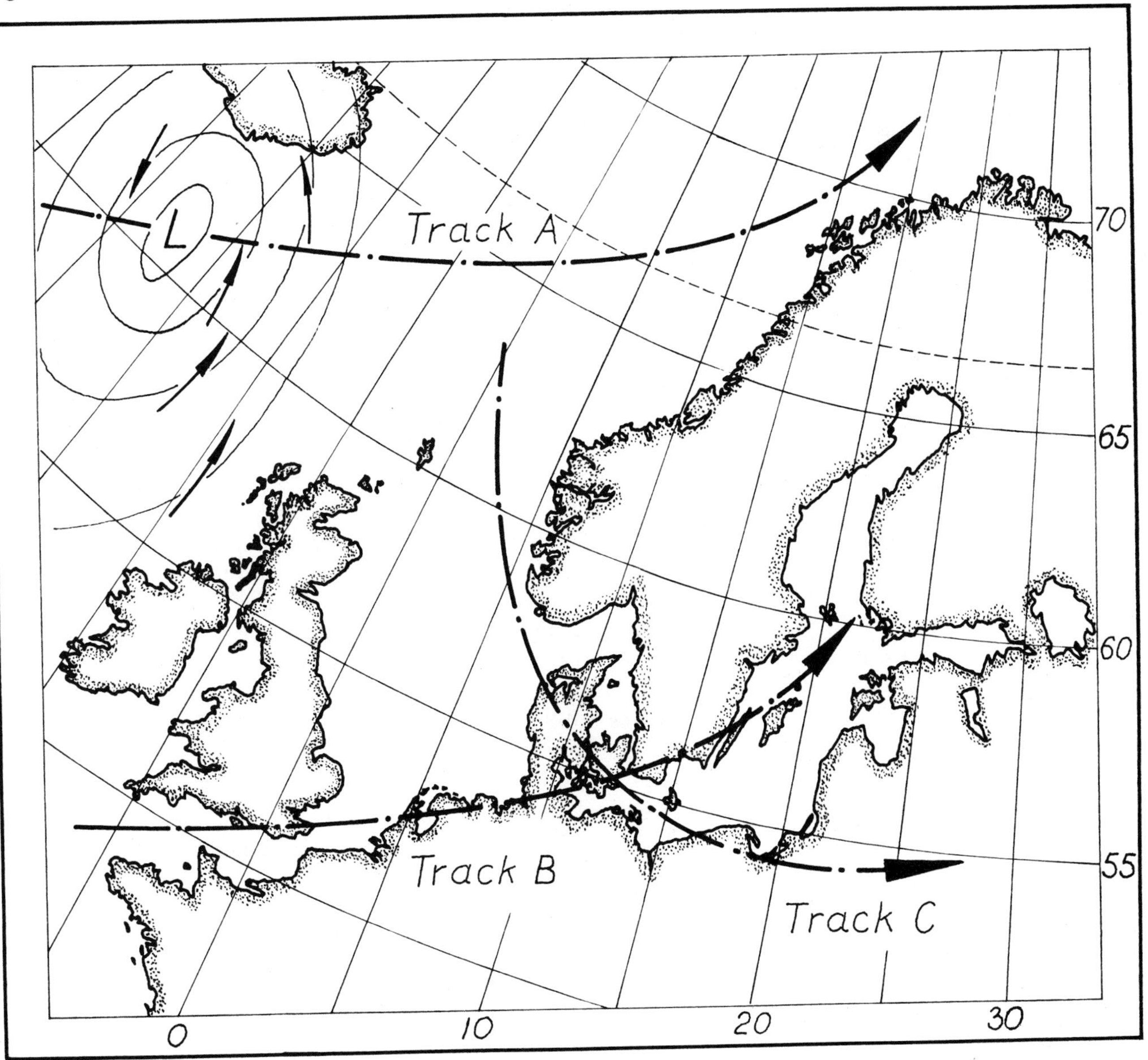

When the wind shifts against the sun,
Trust it not, for back it will run.

The clouds look black, and the glass is low;
Last night the sun went pale to bed;
The halved moon now hides her head.

Look out, my lads! A wicked gale
With heavy rain will soon prevail.

First rise after low
Foretells stronger blow.

The purpose of all these proverbs is to help sailors forecast the wind changes in the immediate future, for to them "the weather" means, above all, the wind.

(b) True Wind Structure

The surface wind (the actual wind from 0 to 100 ft.) differs considerably from the wind aloft, whose direction and speed can be observed from the movements of the clouds. The factors which determine the quality of the surface wind are:

(i) The pressure gradient
(ii) The sun's heat input
(iii) The height above water level
(iv) The thermal differentiation of the area
(v) Wind barriers, such as local obstructions, etc.

Factors ii–v deform the basic wind structure and are the principal cause of local winds. Because of them, the wind which actually interests the sailor is never constant in direction or strength.

In the discussion earlier of Figs. 71 and 72 it was mentioned that there is a definite wind velocity gradient produced by its friction against the water surface. The gradient is definable as the rate at which the true wind increases according to its height above the water level. This affects the direction of the apparent wind, and therefore the efficiency of the sail. Meteorological investigations have revealed that this velocity gradient varies according to the extent the sky is covered by cloud, the wind speed, and wind turbulence. From Fig. 238 it can be seen that in a light wind, a smooth sea, and an overcast sky, the wind velocity changes are relatively great. In such conditions, therefore, the permissible twist in the sail from the boom to the top of the mast can be greater because of the twist in the apparent wind. In gusty, turbulent winds the velocity gradient is much smaller, and so it is desirable to reduce the twist in the sail as much as possible.

The presence of the yacht's hull between the water surface and the sail reduces the velocity gradient comparatively to that shown in Fig. 238. The presence of the hull induces a contraction of the air flow above the deck, and this accelerates the wind speed here, reducing the effect of the true wind vertical gradient on the apparent wind speed. An interesting analysis of this phenomenon is given in

Fig. 238

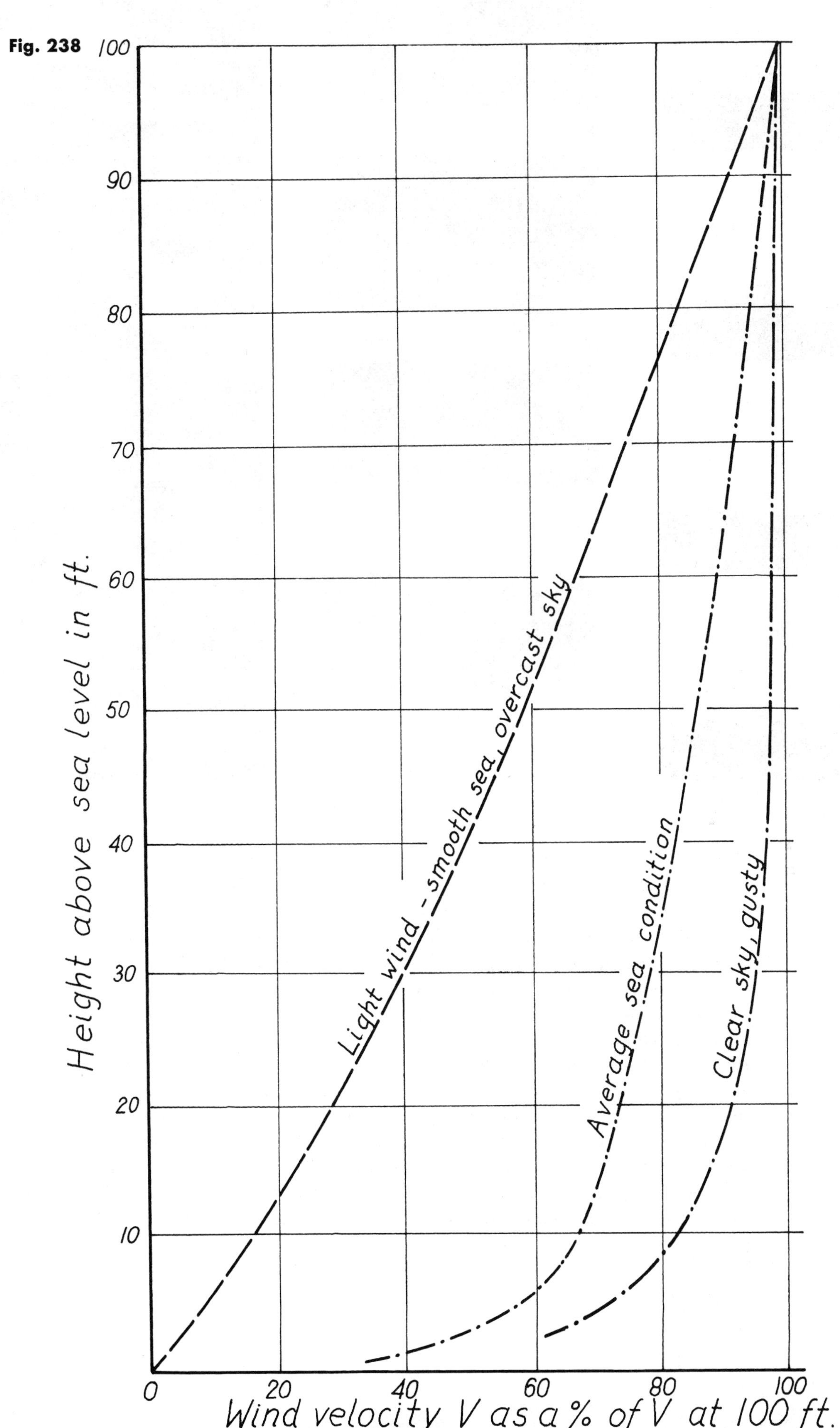

100
90
80
70
60
50
40
30
20
10
0
20
40
60
80
100
Height above sea level in ft.
Wind velocity V as a % of V at 100 ft.
Light wind - smooth sea, overcast sky
Average sea condition
Clear sky, gusty

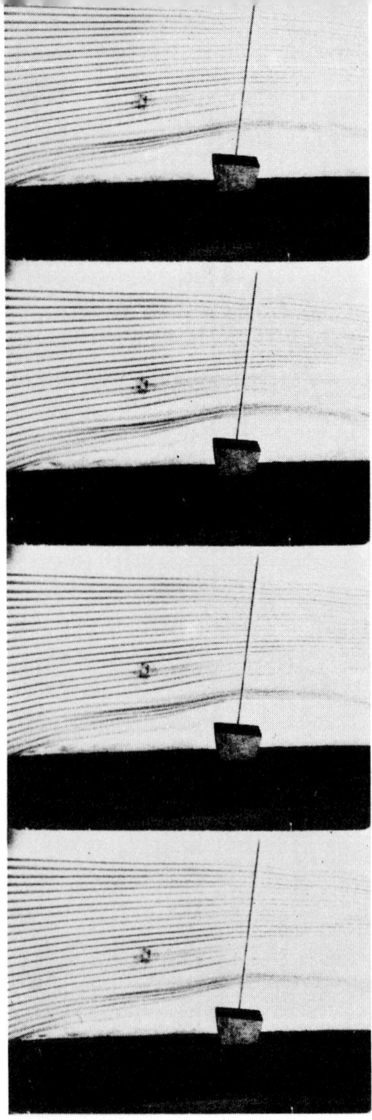
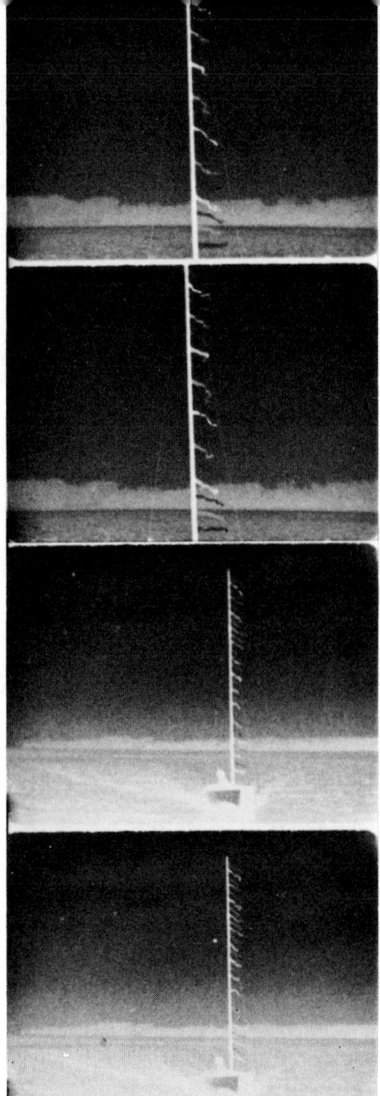
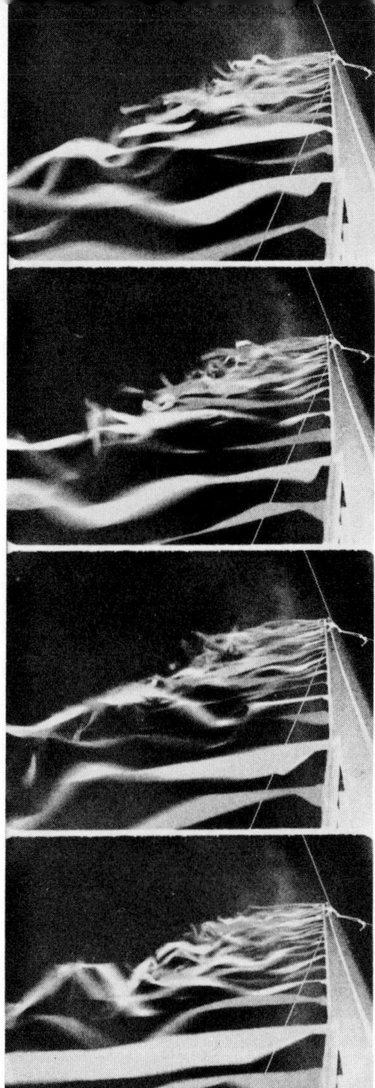

Photo. 40 **A** **B** **C**

Photo. 40 (a, b, and c), reproduced here from the film *Airflow* by Austin Farrar and General J. Parham. Pieces of tape were tied to the dinghy's mast, and then the dinghy was towed at a fixed angle to the true wind. Photograph 40c does not reveal any twist in the apparent wind v_A, as all the tapes, whatever their height, have remained in the same plane. This is yet another proof to shatter the theories of those who hold that a twist in the sail is always desirable.

It is well known from practice that the type of surface over which the wind is blowing can cause a horizontal shift in the wind. Fluctuations in wind direction are clearly noticeable near the shore. No matter whether the wind is onshore or offshore its direction changes so that it crosses the line of the coast at an angle of approximately 90° (see Fig. 239a). This shift in the wind can be used to advantage during a race if the course lies near the shore. Figure 239b shows how one can profit from this change in the wind. Assuming that yachts A and B crossed the starting line at the same time, one would expect that the helmsman of A, having chosen the better course, would round buoy No. 1 before yacht B. The influence of

Fig. 239

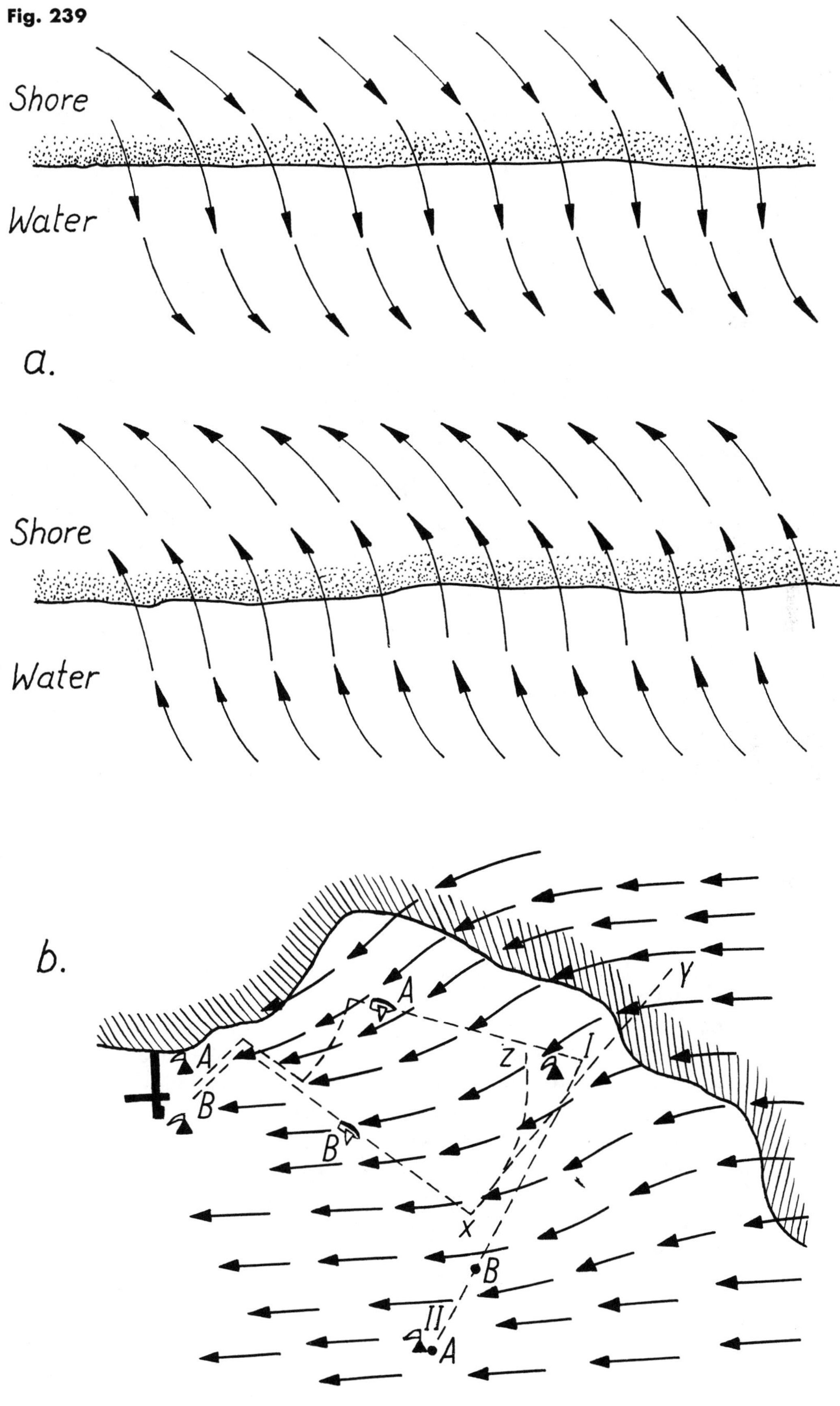

Shore
Water
a.
Shore
Water
b.
A
A
B
B
Z
I
Y
X
B
II
A

Fig. 240

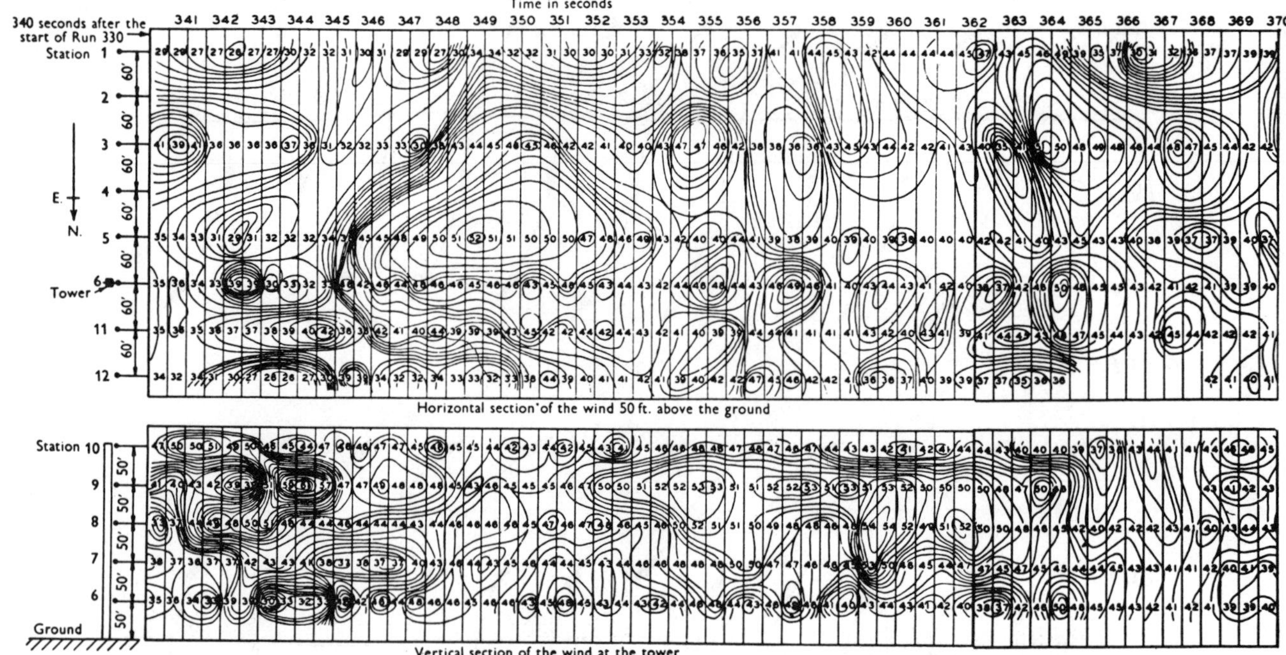

the coastline on the wind is especially noticeable when one is approaching the shore sailing close-hauled. Now when yacht B reaches point X and tacks toward buoy No. 1, one might conclude, from the direction of the wind at X, that by sailing along a course X-Y the buoy will be reached on the starboard tack. Nevertheless, as she approaches the coast, the wind may shift enough to force her to bear away along the course X-Z, and consequently to incur a loss of time.

The influence of the surface over which the air is moving is also responsible for the wind's turbulent character. Air, like water, only maintains a steady laminar flow at low speeds and over a smooth surface. Unevenness in the ground, and the vertical air movements caused by thermal differences, create wind turbulence, which manifests itself in fluctuations in speed and direction.

Interesting conclusions can be derived from the measurements made by Sherlock and Stout, which were presented in the form shown in Fig. 240. These measurements were made with quick response anemometers which recorded electrically. Some of these were mounted 50 ft. above the surface, 60 ft. apart, in a line at right angles to the wind direction, while others were placed at 50-ft. intervals on a 250-ft. tower. Lines of constant wind speed were plotted for both the horizontal and vertical sections, and these show the character of the wind turbulence. The numbers marking the lines give the average wind velocity in miles per hour for the half-second interval in which it is shown. The prevailing wind was westerly. An interesting but unexplained phenomenon is that the wind tends to rise rapidly to its maximum in a gust, but falls away more slowly.

The temperature of the surface has a marked effect on wind turbulence and gusts.

If the surface is cooler than the moving air masses, it tends to stabilize the wind and slow it down. A warm surface, on the other hand, causes a rapid increase in speed in cool, fresh air masses. It is the cooling of the land in the evening which is the main reason why winds tend to drop later in the day. Sailors are also aware that in the spring, while the sea's temperature is still low, the wind is usually steady and not gusty. In spite of strong winds the sea's surface will remain relatively smooth, for the character of the wave formation depends on the character of the wind. A squally wind will induce very much greater waves than a steady wind. Far off-shore, a wind force of 6° B produces waves similar to those which may develop close to land in winds of 4° B. As a rule, the further from shore the steadier the wind.

Periodic variations in true wind, in gusts and puffs, also cause, as one would expect, variations in the direction of the apparent wind. This can be exploited by a skillful helmsman.

If a boat is sailing close-hauled (as in Fig. 241), then in position 1 the mainsail is trimmed to suit the apparent wind OB at an angle α. The vector AB gives the speed of the yacht, and OA the speed of the true wind. If at position II the speed of the true wind increases to a value of O_1A, the yacht, due to her inertia, will not change her speed immediately. However, the direction and magnitude of the apparent wind will change from OB to O_1B, thus increasing the angle of the sail α by $\Delta\alpha$. If the sails had previously been trimmed to the optimum angle α, the angle at which the most advantageous aerodynamic force was developed, then to maintain the same angle (or even to reduce it to retain stability) either:

1. The sheets must be eased, as in position II, or
2. The boat must luff, as in IIa

During the gust the yacht will accelerate as in position III, and this will cause another shift in the direction of the apparent wind from O_1B to O_1B_1. To prevent the sails fluttering, the sheets must now be hauled in to preserve the desirable trim angle α. Those who luffed to position IIa will not get much benefit from tightening the sheets and will have to bear away onto their original course.

A squall lasting one or two minutes, then, can help a yacht in two ways. She can either continue on her original course and increase her speed or, by luffing, work up a little to windward, nearer the next marker buoy by distance l. The actual situation in the race will determine which is the more profitable move, and the strength of the gust and the type of yacht have to be borne in mind as well. In a strong squall luffing may be more appropriate, since it will help preserve stability.

Besides these fluctuations in speed, there are also variations in the direction of the true wind. Broadly speaking, one can assume that if the prevailing direction of the true wind on any day has a tendency to change, this change will in general be made in the same way, that is, always backing or always veering, following an increase in speed.

Skillful exploitation of changes in the wind's direction is very important, espe-

Fig. 241

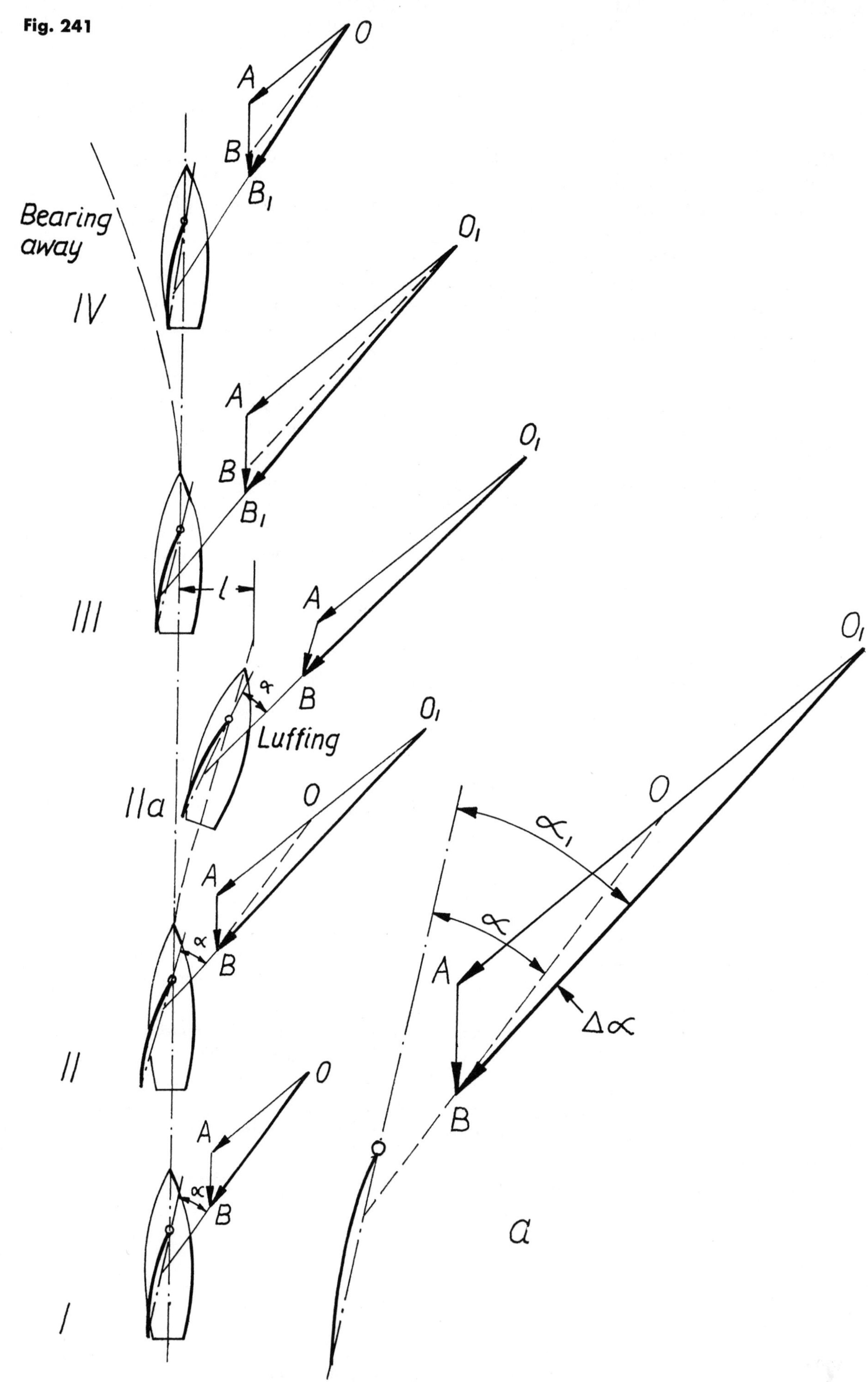

O
A
B
B_1
Bearing away
IV
O_1
A
B
B_1
III
l
O_1
A
B
α
Luffing
IIa
O_1
O
A
B
α
II
O
A
α
B
I
O_1
O
$α_1$
α
A
Δα
B
a

cially when sailing to windward. Figure 242 shows two yachts which have turned at the marker buoy I and are now beating toward buoy II. The watchful helmsman of yacht B, sailing on the port tack, notices the wind shift when it occurs, and quickly tacks onto starboard. These tactics allow him to lay buoy II without further tacking. The less observant helmsman of yacht A, choosing his tack without any proper consideration of possible wind shifts, finds himself behind his opponent.

When beating to windward, at an angle of 45° to the true wind, the distance covered will be 141 per cent of the distance in a straight line, as between buoys I and II in Fig. 243. The geometrical constructions of this figure show that by making skillful use of wind shifts of no more than 5° the distance to be covered by tacking will be reduced to 130 per cent of shortest distance. If the wind shifts are as much as 10°–15°, the distance gained by exploiting them will give a skillful helmsman a big margin over one too careless to pay attention to variations in the wind.

Yet it is difficult for a helmsman to react correctly to changes in wind direction, since his attention is usually distracted by so many other factors. For getting proper benefit from wind shifts nothing is more helpful than keeping a constant check on the course by observing objects in the distance, including marker buoys

Fig. 242

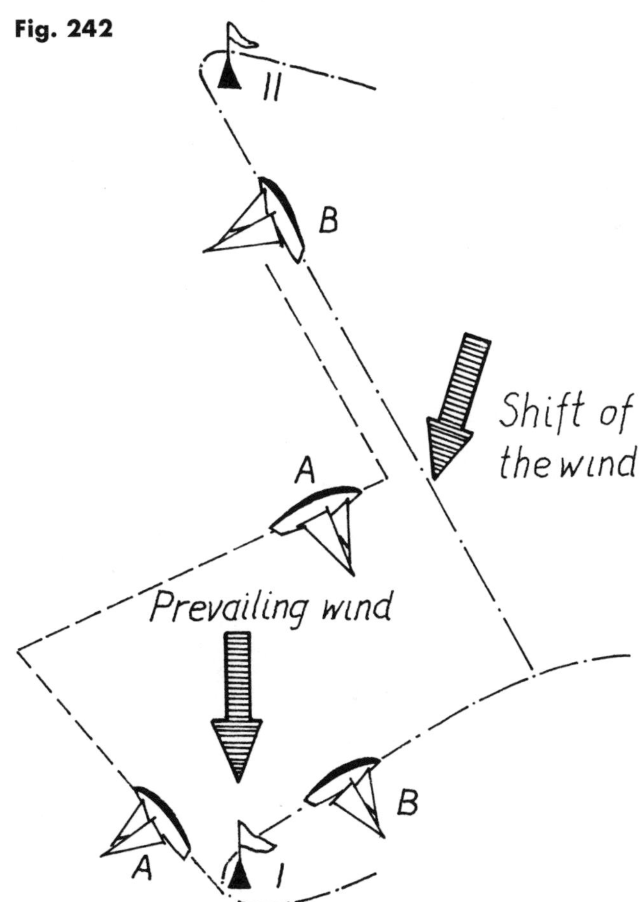

Fig. 243

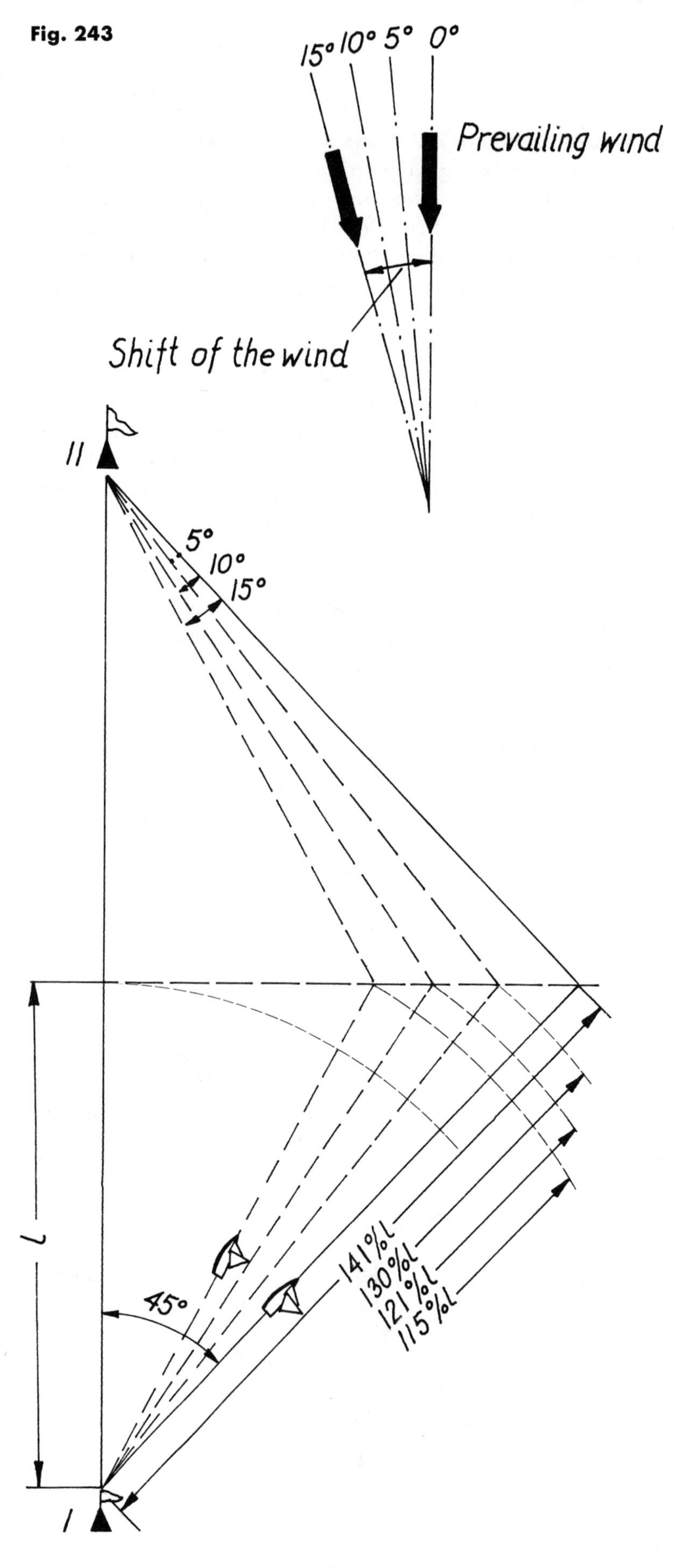

15° 10° 5° 0°
Prevailing wind
Shift of the wind
II
5°
10°
15°
45°
l
141%l
130%l
121%l
115%l
I

and rival yachts, or by watching the compass. However, since an increase of true wind speed gives an impression of a wind shift, as the burgee shows the apparent wind as coming more from the beam (cf. Fig. 241, I, II), it is vital to distinguish between this and a change in direction of true wind. One should only tack for a change in direction. How often one should go about depends mainly on the type of yacht being sailed. Modern centerboard boats will turn in a few seconds, and the loss on each turn is so small that it pays to tack at almost every shift in the wind. Heavy-keel yachts, with their greater inertia, normally lose speed while tacking across the line of the wind, and only gain speed slowly on a new course. For such boats, only a really big shift in the wind justifies a change of tack. Nevertheless variations in wind direction are so important that they must not be ignored. In long-distance races the correct trim of the sails in a variable apparent wind is especially important at night. The helmsman's chance of keeping the sails at their correct trim is limited, and special electrical wind indicators can be very helpful.

(c) Local Winds

The fact that different parts of the globe warm up at different rates is the principal cause of the various circulatory movements of the earth's atmosphere; winds are the horizontal movements of these displaced air masses. A sea breeze is undoubtedly the best-known example of this phenomenon of atmospheric circulation.

To keep the circulation going, a constant supply of thermal energy is needed. As in fact the supply of this energy increases in the afternoon, the rate of circulation then rises; the intensity of the thermal wind derives directly from the amount of thermal energy absorbed by the air and converted into air's kinetic energy—wind.

Numerous measurements have proved that the thermal wind increases with the rise of the temperature gradient. The strongest wind of this type can therefore be expected in the vicinity of the coastline, since it is there that the greatest differences in the gradient of temperature of neighboring air masses are found.

The range of a sea breeze, like its speed, will be greater for a greater thermal variation in the surface below. Surfaces, therefore, which can be warmed quickly when the sun shines on them, like sand near a cold sea, favor the development of a strong steady sea breeze, while, on the other hand, if adjacent surface areas are of high thermal capacity, like woodland, this will not favor the formation of a strong onshore breeze.

The sea, or onshore, breeze begins about 9:00 or 10:00 A.M. and ends at sunset. The strength of the wind increases gradually, reaching a maximum, possibly about force 4, during early afternoon.

Sea breezes do not cause high waves, because their range is limited. Their effect seldom extends more than a few miles out to sea, and so, in certain circumstances, since the waves are negligible, the stronger sea breezes allow yachts to achieve higher sailing speeds.

Vertical thermal currents in the atmosphere are revealed by clouds of the cumulus type (Cu). They can be observed during sunny weather over the land, even

Fig. 244

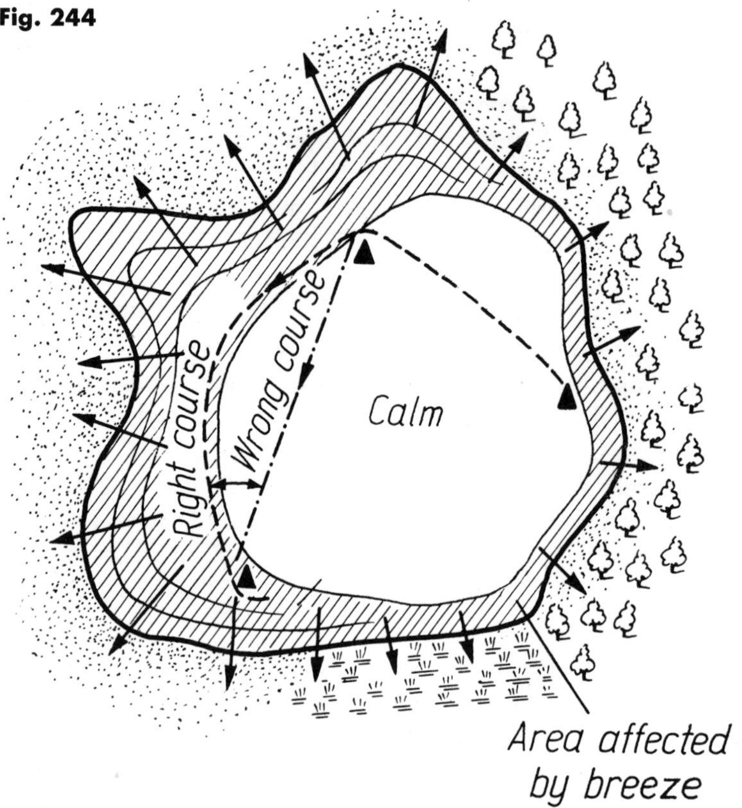

though the skies over the sea may remain clear, and usually foretell that a sea breeze is developing.

Naturally, sea breezes can be observed most clearly when there are no strong winds caused by the barometric weather system, which can deform the strength and direction of the sea breeze. In certain latitudes, to which cyclones or depressions do not, or only very rarely, penetrate and the weather system depends on anti-cyclones, as in Italy for instance, the sea breezes are very fierce and appear with the regularity of clockwork.

A similar cycle of local winds of daily occurrence can be encountered over the larger lakes, and is called a lake breeze. These are weaker than sea breezes, but can still be of great assistance, especially on days when the gradient wind is very light or nonexistent. As with the sea breeze, a lake breeze blows at right angles to the coastline, and its range and strength depend on the land's thermal topography.

An example of a lake breeze is given in Fig. 244. If the day is sunny and windless, the range of the breeze may be revealed by small ripples (capillary waves) which cover the surface adjacent to the beach, while frequently the center of the lake lies glittering in the sun as motionless as a mirror.

In very light winds the race may become a "drifting match," when the wind varies from flat calm to delicate puffs, shifting direction continually. Under these conditions one must watch for local coastal winds like those described above.

It can be seen from Fig. 244 that it would pay to sail the long way round, and keep closer to the coast, rather than to take the shorter, straight course between buoys. By keeping within the range of the breeze it will be possible to cover the longer distance faster, perhaps without even touching the sheets or tacking or jibing, and thus to sail round the lake while calm reigns in the middle. In a case like this, as racing yachtsmen well know, there is no reason to be afraid of bearing well away from the shortest course in search of a better wind. The risks involved in finding one's own path do not always lead to loss of ground.

Similarly, on a big river there is frequently some breeze near the bank during hot weather. In the evening after sunset the best chance of picking up a land breeze is found near a dry coast free from afforestation. Local thermal winds are most apparent during the summer. In spring and autumn, when the difference in temperature between sea and land is small, the thermal winds die out.

Gusts and puffs of wind are frequently caused by rising and falling thermal currents disturbing the air currents moving parallel to the surface of the earth, and this type of thermal circulation can affect the technique of yacht racing.

The so-called fine weather cumulus not only indicates the type of weather but also demonstrates the existence of the vertical currents responsible for this kind of cloud formation. The effect of air circulation on the speed of the surface wind is shown in Fig. 245. Near the surface the thermal current changes direction through 180°. If we assume that the speed of the thermal circulation is 6 ft./sec. and the speed of the prevailing surface wind is 15 ft./sec., then clearly the resultant wind affecting sailing boats will vary between 9 and 21 ft./sec. In "drifting match" conditions, when there is little or no wind, a thermal circulation which reveals itself through unexpected gusts and puffs may upset the calculations of the competing yachts. Even if the boats are close together the puffs may affect them

Fig. 245

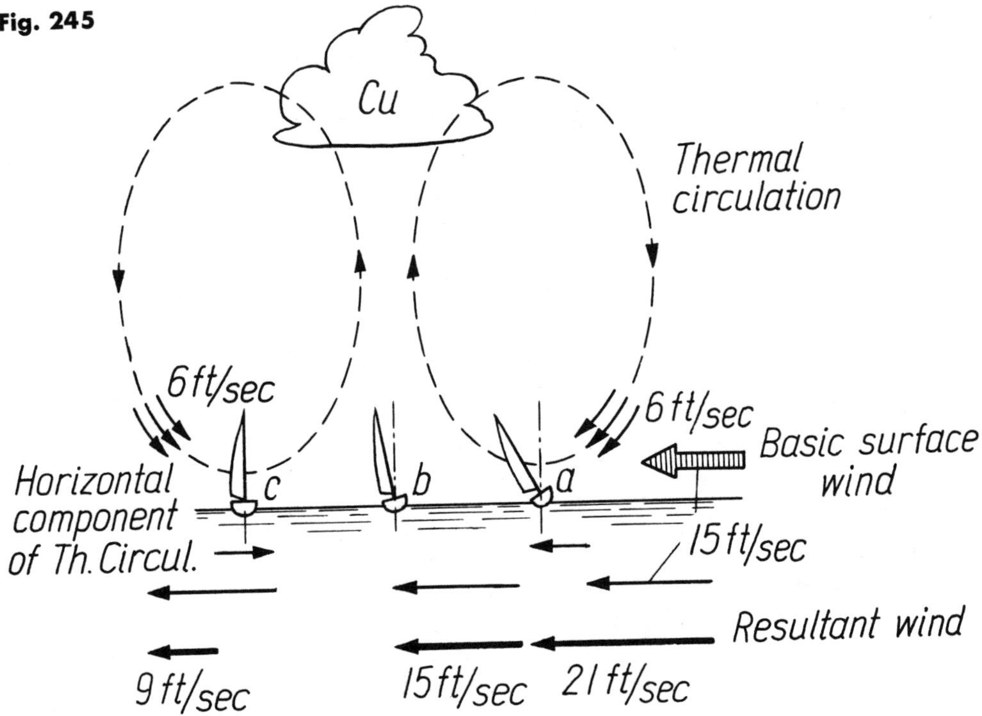

quite differently. In Fig. 245 yacht a is benefiting from a wind blowing at 21 ft./sec., whereas yacht c will lose ground through feeling only a breeze at 9 ft./sec.

Figure 246 illustrates the effect of rising and falling thermal currents near the water surface. When the descending currents (downstreams) 1 and 3 strike the water surface they will tend to spread sideways, and the resultant wind will be variable in both direction and speed.

From Figure 247a it can be seen that the combined effect of a light surface wind and thermal currents can leave two yachts sailing before the wind in opposite directions. Gusts of this kind are met with as a rule in areas covered by a high-pressure system, where conditions are suitable for the development of strong thermal circulations, whose presence will be indicated by "fine weather cumulus." Puffs of wind are revealed when they mark the surface with a faint ripple. They can appear suddenly amongst a group of sailing boats, selecting one, or perhaps a few, lucky ones and pushing them forward, sometimes for several minutes, to the envy of those left becalmed. A yacht sailing straight toward a gust that is visible on the water (Fig. 247b) must expect a change in the direction of the wind. At first (position 1) the wind will suddenly increase in force and will be ahead. Sails previously trimmed correctly will stop pulling and flutter. It will be necessary to haul in the sheets, and even to bear away from the proper course K-K. At position 2 the wind appears to come from abeam, so that sheets can be eased and speed in-

Fig. 246

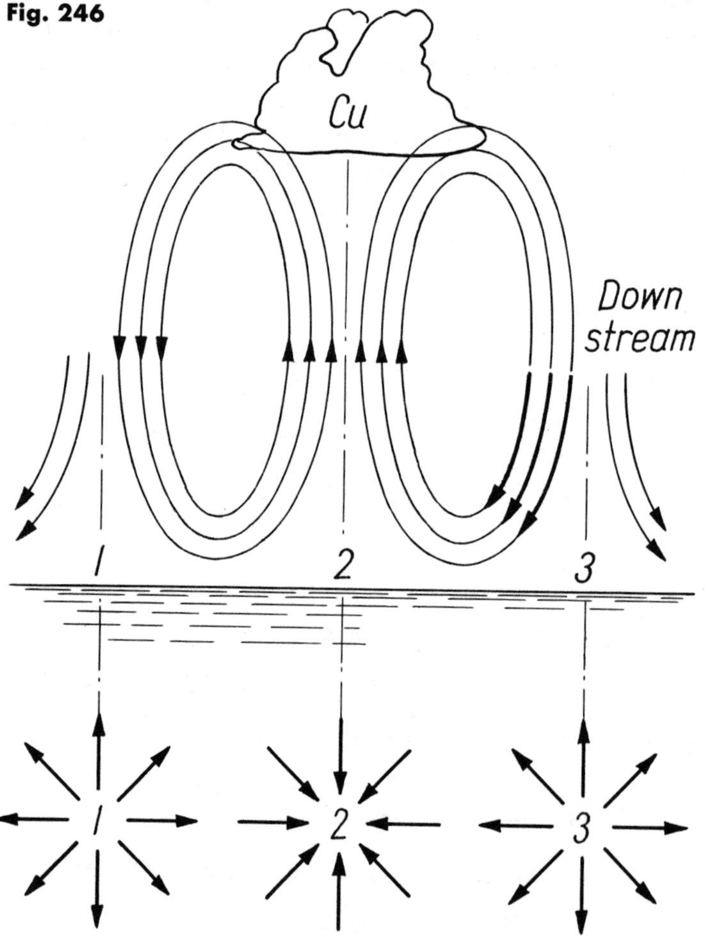

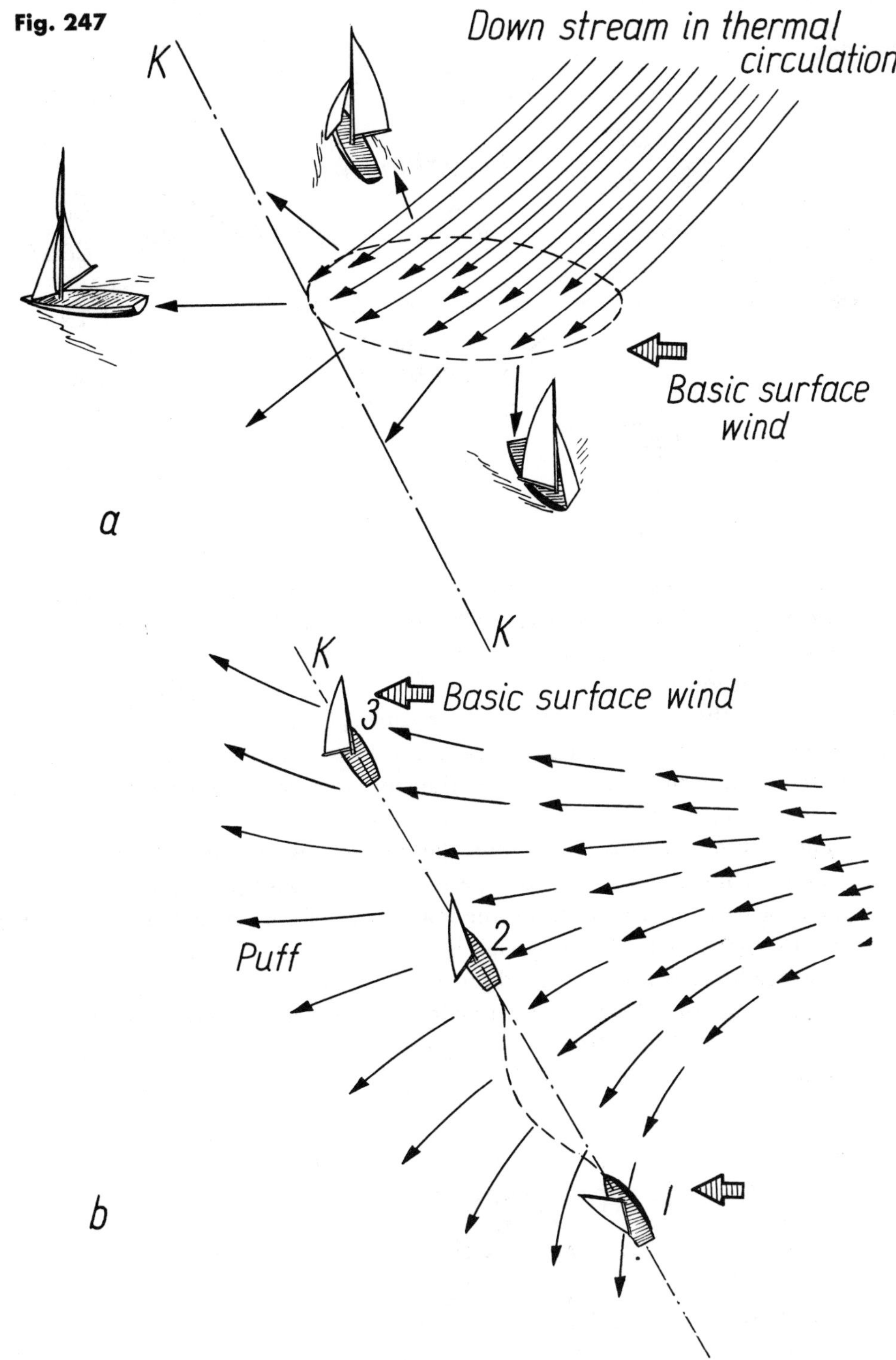

Fig. 247

creased. Around position 3 a following wind may be felt, until the light, prevailing wind takes over again and the sheets are trimmed as before.

Racing in light winds with occasional puffs demands special tactics. There is no point in sticking stubbornly to the shortest route to the next mark buoy. It is far better, if there is any chance of doing so, to sail toward a puff, and, when

Fig. 248

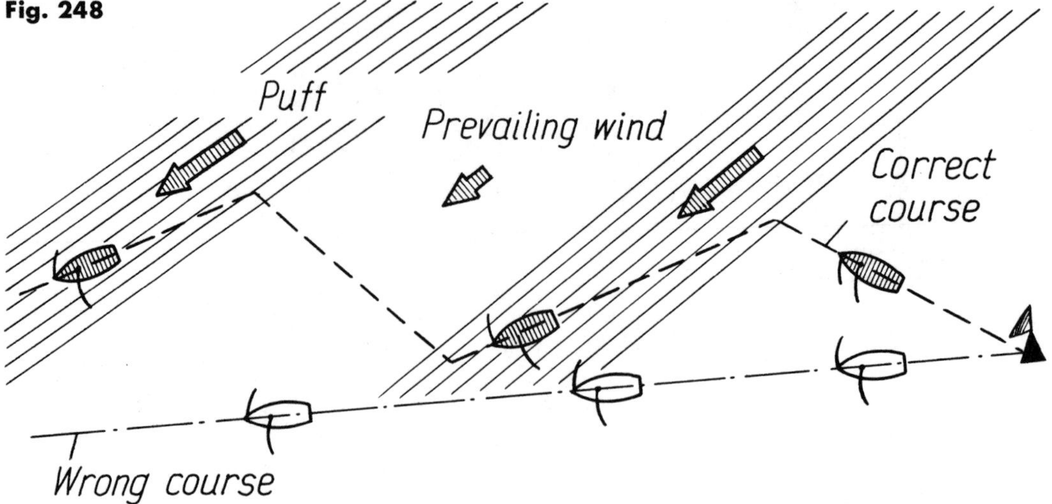

it has been reached, to keep its capricious company as long as possible on the approximately correct course. An example of right and wrong tactics for two yachts in this kind of situation is given in Fig. 248.

Winds, it must be remembered, tend to increase in strength at midday. As solar radiation is the main cause of wind, on sunny, cloudless days one would expect the greatest exchange of thermal energy into the kinetic energy of a wind at noon. It has been found that for the speed of the wind to increase during the day there must be a suitable vertical distribution of temperature in the atmosphere—vertical gradient. Observations show that the greater the gradient of temperature the greater the increase in the wind speed. The relationship is shown in Fig. 249. The figures near each curve indicate the magnitude of the vertical gradient, the change (in this case a fall) being given in degrees centigrade for each 100 m. (328 ft.) of height above the specified level. The gradient curve of 0.7°–1.0°/100 m. is characteristic for cold, polar air moving over a warmed terrain. The lowest of the gradient curves, 0.2°/100 m., is typical for the dry, warmed air masses found in stationary high-pressure systems.

Fig. 249

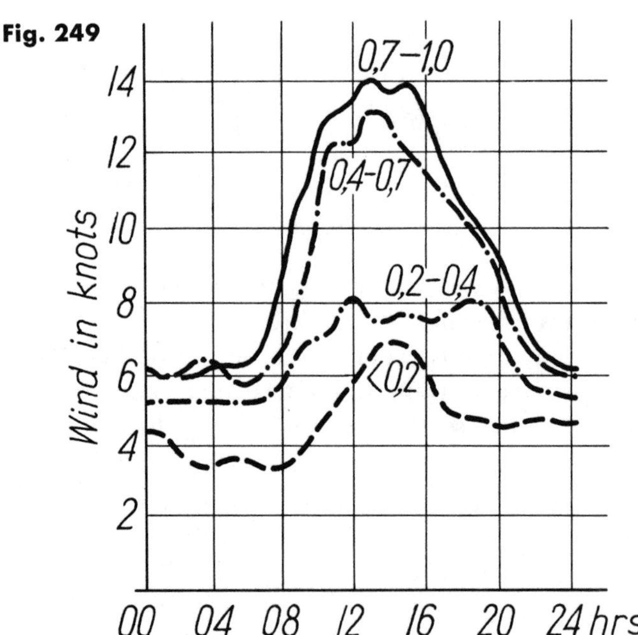

A practical problem arises when competitors due to start a race in the morning are wondering whether to use a flat sail or a full one, and whether the wind will increase and by how much. It is fairly certain that there will be some increase in wind strength in the afternoon if the area is one where the incoming air masses are fresh and cool. However, if the area has been affected by an anticyclone for some time, even if the day is sunny and cloudless, the chances of the wind strengthening are small.

Figure 249 shows that the strongest winds blow between 10:00 A.M. and 4:00 P.M. Therefore, if a race is started before noon, the possibility of a rise in the strength of the wind must be considered and flat sails chosen, to be reefed perhaps. Races that start in the afternoon are not likely to meet with stronger winds, and competitors can more easily decide to set a more cambered sail, anticipating a drop in the wind later. This rule applies, of course, only in settled weather, and not when, say, a cold front is expected.

Together with the increase in wind strength in the afternoon there will usually be a change in direction, even as much perhaps as 60°, clockwise, following the sun. Later in the afternoon a failing wind will tend to back, changing again in the opposite direction.

(d) The Wind over a Regatta Course

The wind blowing over an area where racing is taking place has already been shown to be unsettled, either in direction or speed. It is affected in addition by two other factors:

1. Obstructions, or wind barriers
2. The presence of the competing yachts

Although the prevailing surface wind is affected by the thermal conditions of the atmosphere in the unpredictable manner described, obstructions and wind barriers act on the wind according to fixed rules, so that it is possible to forecast the way in which they will disturb it. For example, in a lake or bay surrounded by hills (as in Fig. 250), even though the prevailing wind is blowing from the west, wind A

Fig. 250

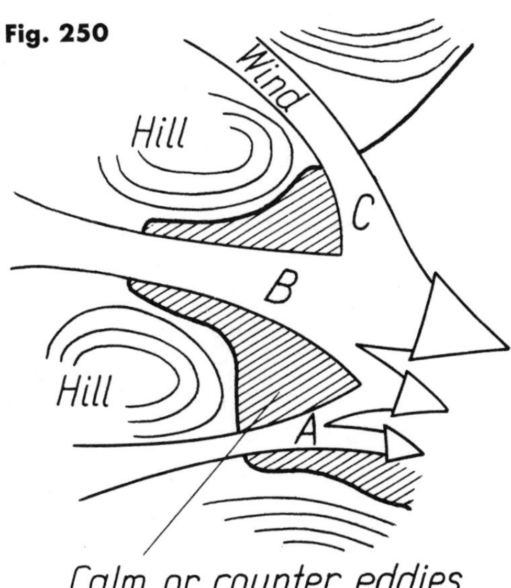

is actually blowing almost at right angles to wind C, and while the wind blows steadily enough in some places there will also be areas of turbulence and of calm. In this example the air masses are being guided over passes which control their direction.

Yachtsmen who know their local waters are usually well aware of certain wind effects, varying according to the direction of the prevailing wind. For this reason they usually prove superior to visiting yachtsmen who are racing over a course they do not know, so that they have to resolve the mysteries of the local topography by trial and error. A good plan at such a time is to study the ways of the wind by observing the ripples on the water from well above it, say, from a nearby hill, or even better to get experience on reconnaissance trips on the water. Anyway, in the earlier races it would be advisable to keep near a helmsman familiar with local conditions, rather than to strike off on a lone course, even if it looks advantageous.

A very irregular coastline affects the winds in the same way as the passes just described.

Although obstructions can cause complicated deformations of the wind, their effects can be reduced to two basic types:

1. Contraction of the air flow: this will increase, sometimes considerably, the speed of the wind for a relatively small change in direction.
2. Turbulence: this will change the direction of the prevailing surface wind, perhaps considerably, and will reduce its speed.

The first type is illustrated in Fig. 251. While a yacht is sailing on the sheltered water below a high cliff (position a), she feels only a light wind, mainly on the upper part of her sails, but as soon as she approaches an open gap (position b), she is struck by a strong wind, whose force is the greater the narrower the passage for the air stream between sections f and f_1. The formation of the coast in certain cases may produce a contraction of the flow that will double its speed; and, be it remembered, if the speed of the wind is increased twofold, the effect of the wind on the sails increases fourfold. Since a sudden gust is more dangerous than the pressure of a steady wind, it is hardly surprising that many helmsmen at such times fail

Fig. 251

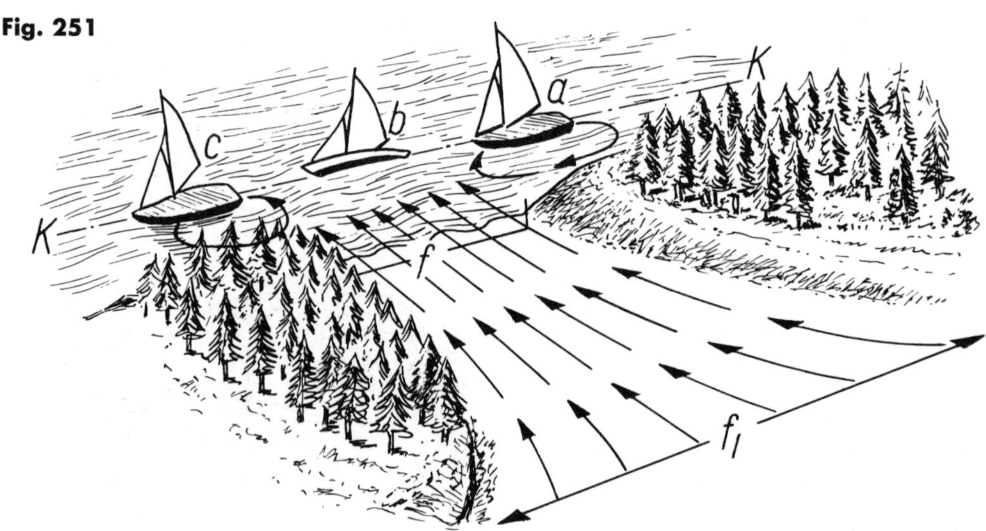

to free the sheets in time and their boats unexpectedly capsize. For this reason, anyone sailing near a coast full of sharp bends, valleys, and open spaces should be ready to take immediate action to prevent sudden changes in the lateral stability of their yacht.

Figure 252a, b, and c demonstrates the second type of wind change caused by obstructions. In a the disturbance is due to trees growing on the coast. The influence of this barrier can be felt up to a distance of 4 to 20 times its height, depend-

Fig. 252

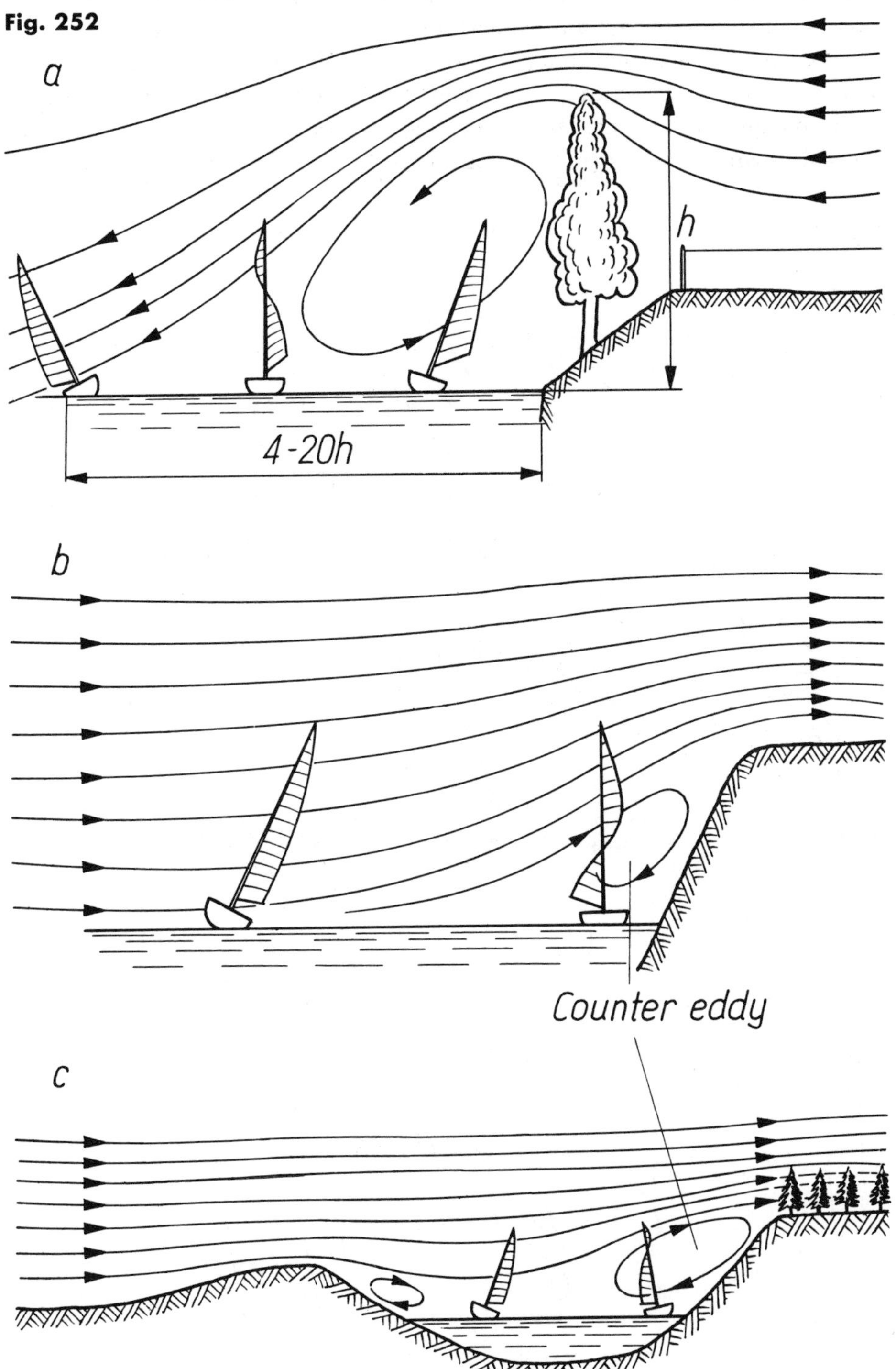

ing on its density, since a single tree will have less effect than a dense clump. The reaction of the wind to the barrier varies remarkably at different distances from it, causing apparently incomprehensible behavior on the part of the sails. Wind eddies are to be expected not only to leeward of a barrier, but also on its windward side if the distance from the barrier is small, for example, below a steep tall cliff (as in Fig. 252b, c). Again, the range of turbulence depends on the height of the barrier.

When racing, another factor that has to be kept in mind because it can cause changes in the speed and direction of the wind is the presence of rival yachts. Both experience and aerodynamic measurements have shown that the interaction between two sails is such that they will be working in rather different conditions. The sails of yachts sailing close together create a specific wind distribution, even though they appear to be affected by the same true wind. In Fig. 253, the sail of windward yacht W is causing a slight deflection of the wind to the left

Fig. 253

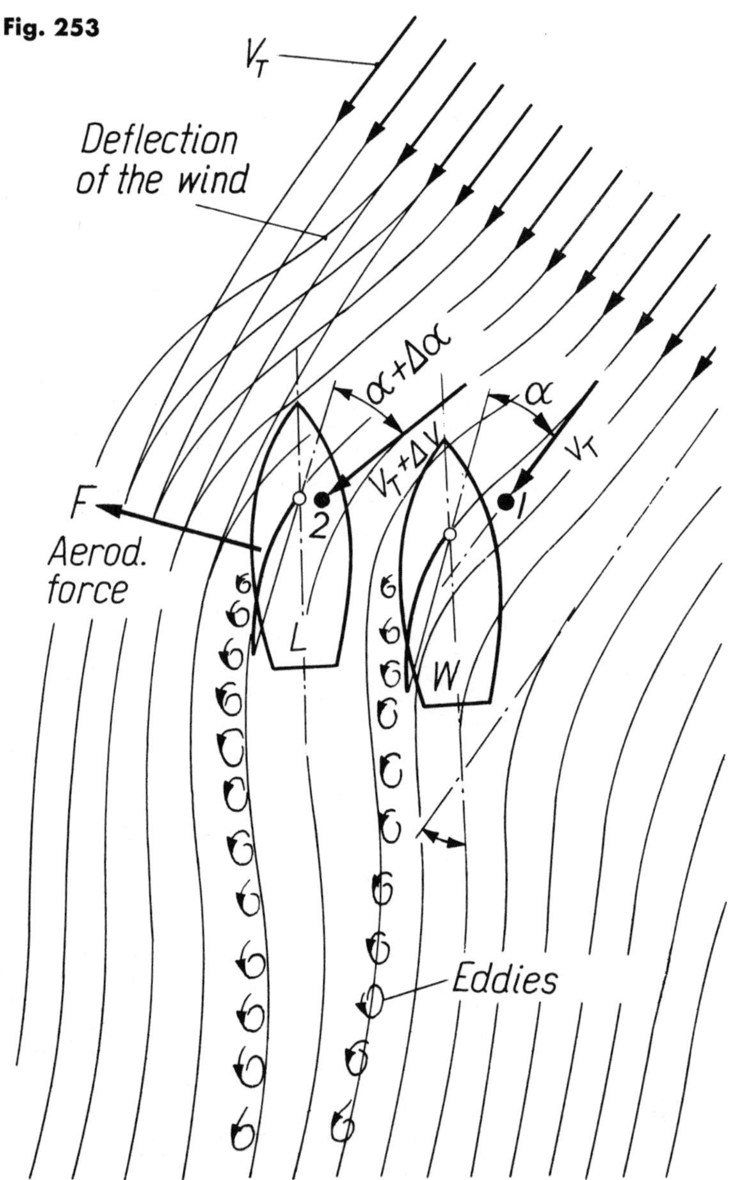

in front of her bow. If the wind velocities were measured at points 1 and 2 in the vicinity of windward yacht W, it would be noticed that the speed would be greater by Δv on the leeward side of yacht W. The direction of the wind to the leeward of yacht W, being deflected to some degree, benefits yacht L by angle $\Delta\alpha$, in as much as the wind striking yacht L will be stronger and more on the beam, giving the helmsman the chance of developing a greater driving force.

In fact, it could be said that yacht W is helping the helmsman of yacht L to sail faster. Experienced yachtsmen know this quite well, and it is not difficult for anyone who has already studied sail aerodynamics to follow. Yacht L is in what is called the "safe leeward position" (cf. also Photo. 41) and can overtake yacht W, and then luff. This is one of the classic yacht racing maneuvers.

The safe leeward position can undoubtedly be very advantageous, especially when sailing to windward in winds that are not too strong, so that it is possible to maintain the desirable lateral stability, that is, to keep the boat upright. If the wind

SAFE LEEWARD POSITION

Photo. 41

is so strong that the crew has difficulty in ballasting the boat, the safe leeward position will magnify these difficulties by increasing the tendency to heel. The helmsman would then have to either ease the mainsheet and spill some of the wind or sail at a greater angle of heel than the windward yacht. In such circumstances the safe leeward position may bring little benefit, for the aerodynamic and hydrodynamic losses suffered by a yacht which heels at an excessive angle limit any advantage that might be derived from the position.

Assuming, then, that the helmsman of the yacht in the safe leeward position does not make mistakes in sailing her, and that both yachts are of one design and similar in performance, she should overtake the windward yacht, which is said to be then in the "hopeless position" (cf. Photo. 42).

Figure 254 may explain the difficulties of a helmsman who has found himself in the "hopeless position." One may fairly accurately reckon that the aerodynamic effect F received on a sail for each unit of time is equivalent to the increase in the momentum of the air thrown by this sail in the opposite direction to F. If the mass of air thrown off by the sail is denoted by m, and the speed with which the mass m is thrown aside by v, then $F = mv$. From this formula it follows that the deflection of the wind streams to the side of the centerline will be intensified as force F is increased. Adding the speed v to the speed of the wind in front of the sail v_1 confirms that the wind streams behind the sail are deflected in such a way as to give any yacht sailing in them a closer wind, v_2, which will force her to bear away or change her tack. Now, if the yacht in the hopeless position bears away she has to

Photo. 42 HOPELESS POSITION

Fig. 254

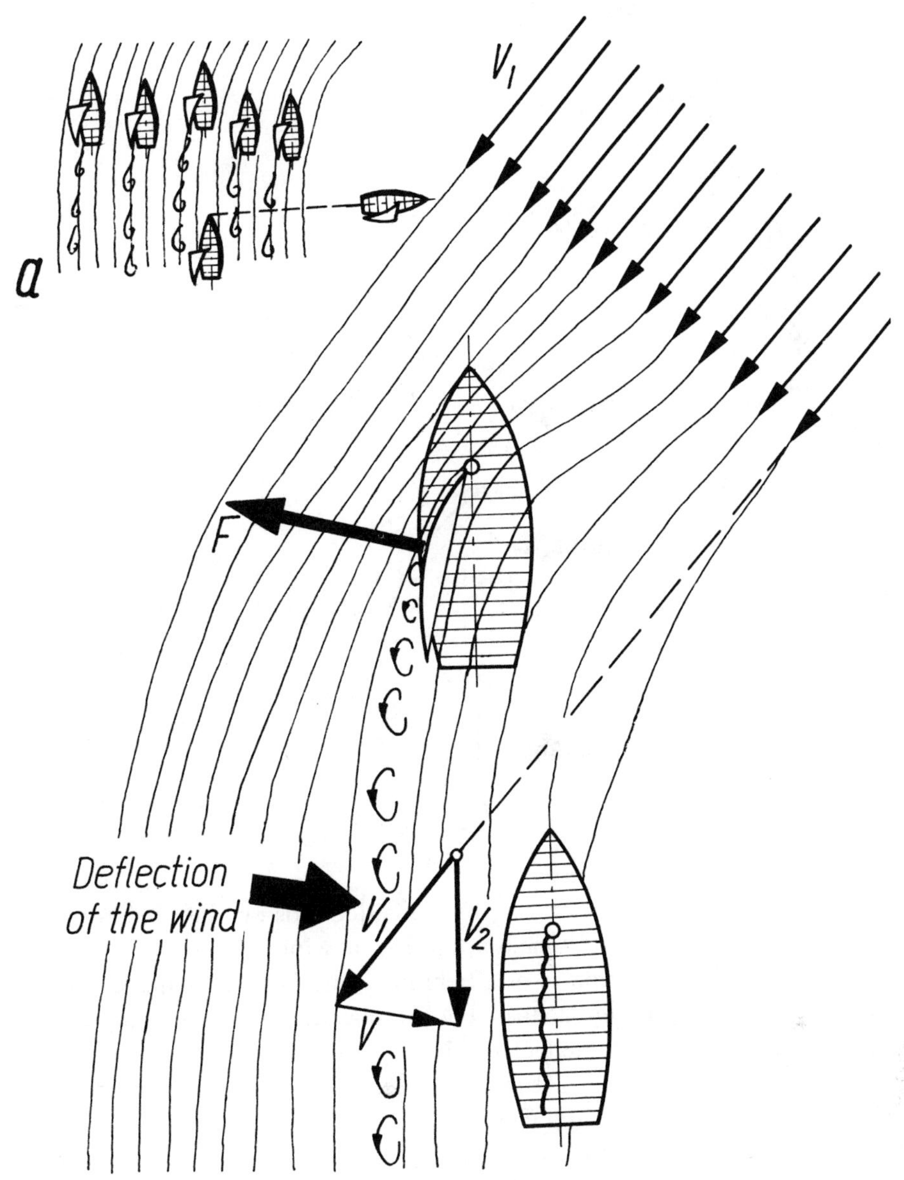

cross the turbulent wake of air and water which follow the leading yacht, and this will increase her losses.

The direction of the turbulent wake behind the sail when sailing close-hauled is deflected away from the line of the apparent wind toward the stern (Fig. 255). The span of this disturbance, or "dead wind cone," depends on the angle of sail incidence. It is not excessive for courses ranging from close-hauled to close reaching, but increases when sailing before the wind.

The influence of the wind deflection and turbulence behind a yacht can be felt

Fig. 255

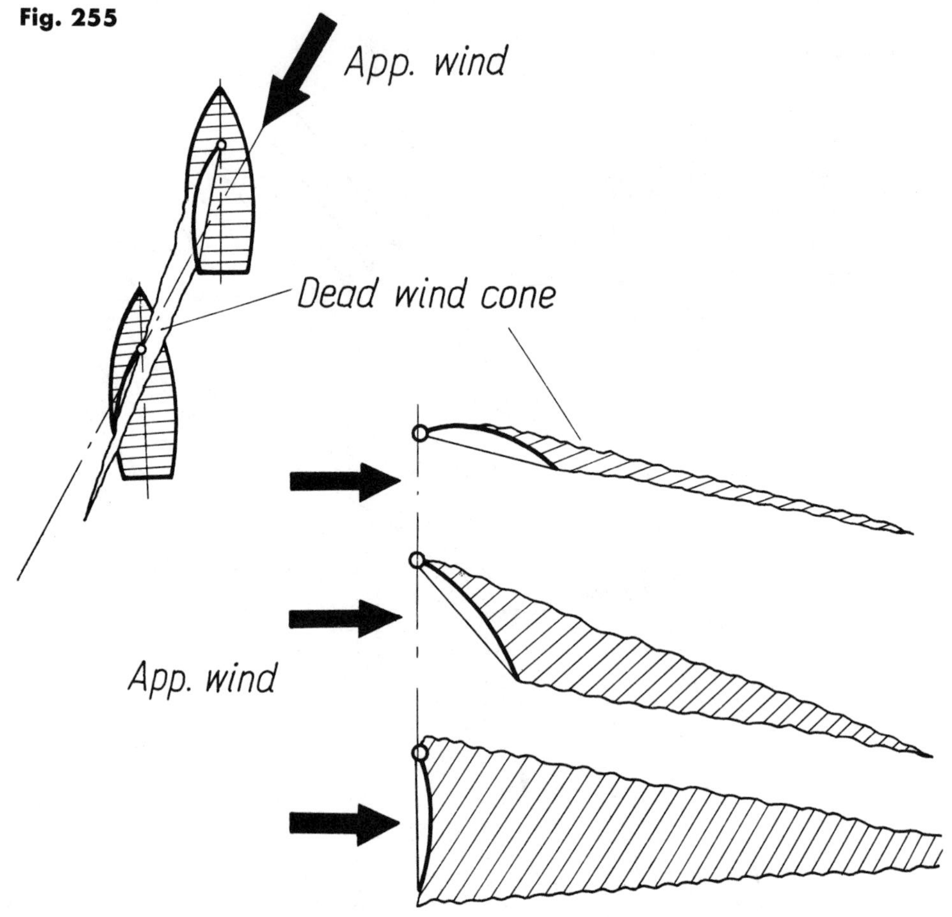

for a distance up to ten boat lengths. This depends on the speed of the wind, the course, and the number of yachts causing a wind disturbance over the course. A particularly bad position is one behind a number of yachts sailing on a close-hauled course (as in Fig. 254a). The helmsman of a following yacht will find himself facing a strongly deflected wind and eddies which absorb a considerable portion of the wind's energy. As one would expect, these disadvantages are increased if the yachts ahead are sailing close together.

Some interesting quantitative information on the interaction between two similar yachts can be seen in Fig. 256. This experiment on the effect of interference by one yacht on another was carried out by M. S. Hooper on models of J-class yachts in Fairey's wind tunnel (Photo. 1). The position of the "interfering" yacht was fixed, while the "interfered with" yacht was moved about in relation to the fixed yacht. The origin of the coordinates was chosen similarly for each yacht, and the apparent course for both yachts was 40° and the angle of heel 15°. The graph (Fig. 256) shows the contours of available driving force around the "interfering" yacht, which were measured on the "interfered with" yacht as percentages of the driving force which would be available in an undisturbed wind. The horizontal and vertical units of the graph correspond to the deck length of the yacht. The silhouette of the "interfering" yacht only is drawn, and the broken line

256

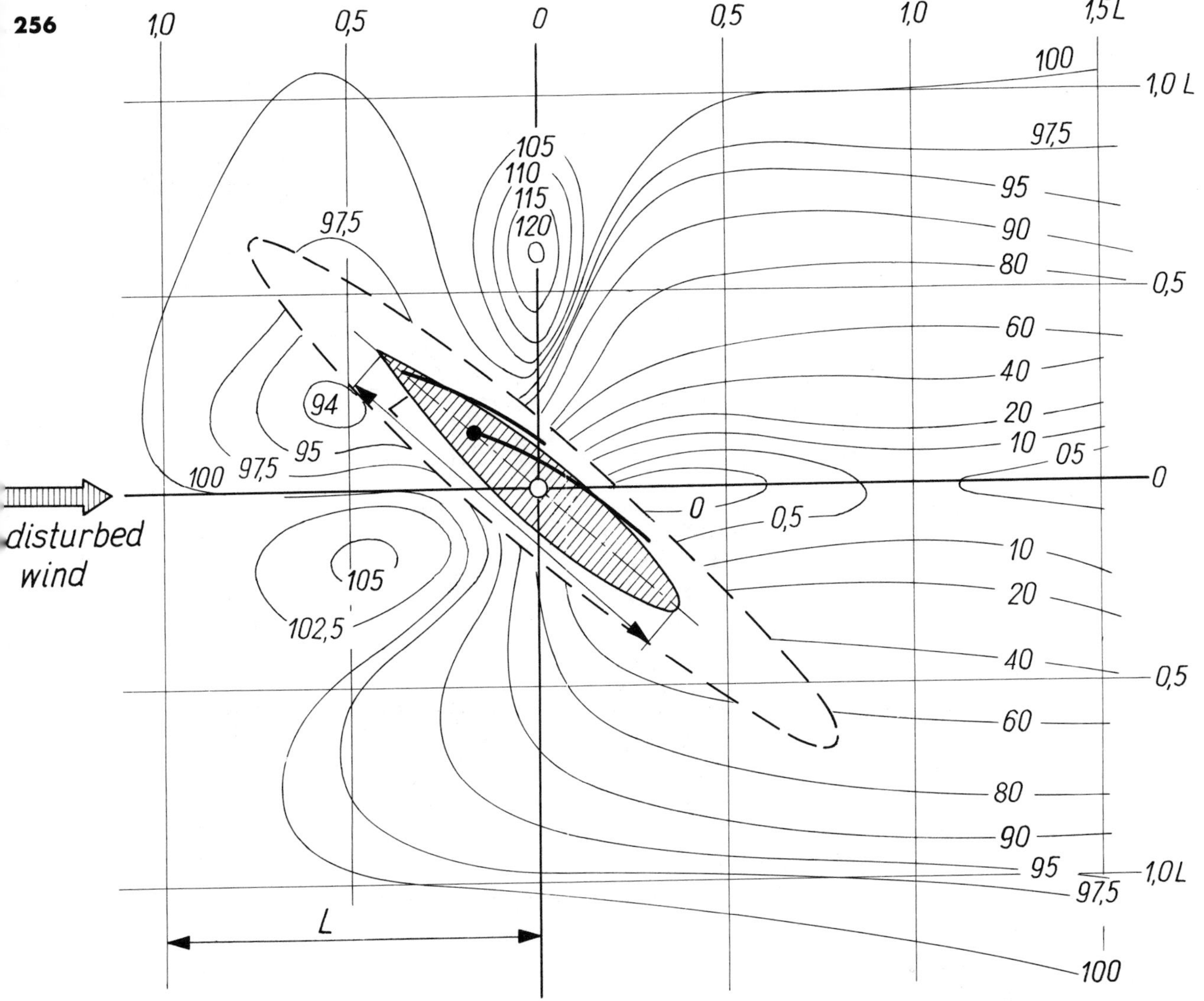

outside shows the limit of approach for the "interfered with" yacht, on the same tack and pointing the same course. Easily spotted is the area of extra driving force stretching to leeward of the "interfering" yacht, where the "interfered with" yacht can gain up to 20 per cent extra. This is the "safe leeward position." Losses in driving force, on the other hand, can amount to about 95 per cent in certain areas downwind from the "interfering" yacht.

The "hopeless" and "safe leeward" positions are well known in yacht racing tactics and are commonly used in sailing to windward. On other courses the comparable tactics involve blanketing an opponent's sails. While a detailed discussion of these tactical procedures can be left to books devoted to the technique of yacht racing, the question of blanketing when running is worth some consideration.

Some interesting experiments were carried out by Eiffel to measure the aerodynamic forces which appeared on similarly shaped plates blanketing each other

Fig. 257

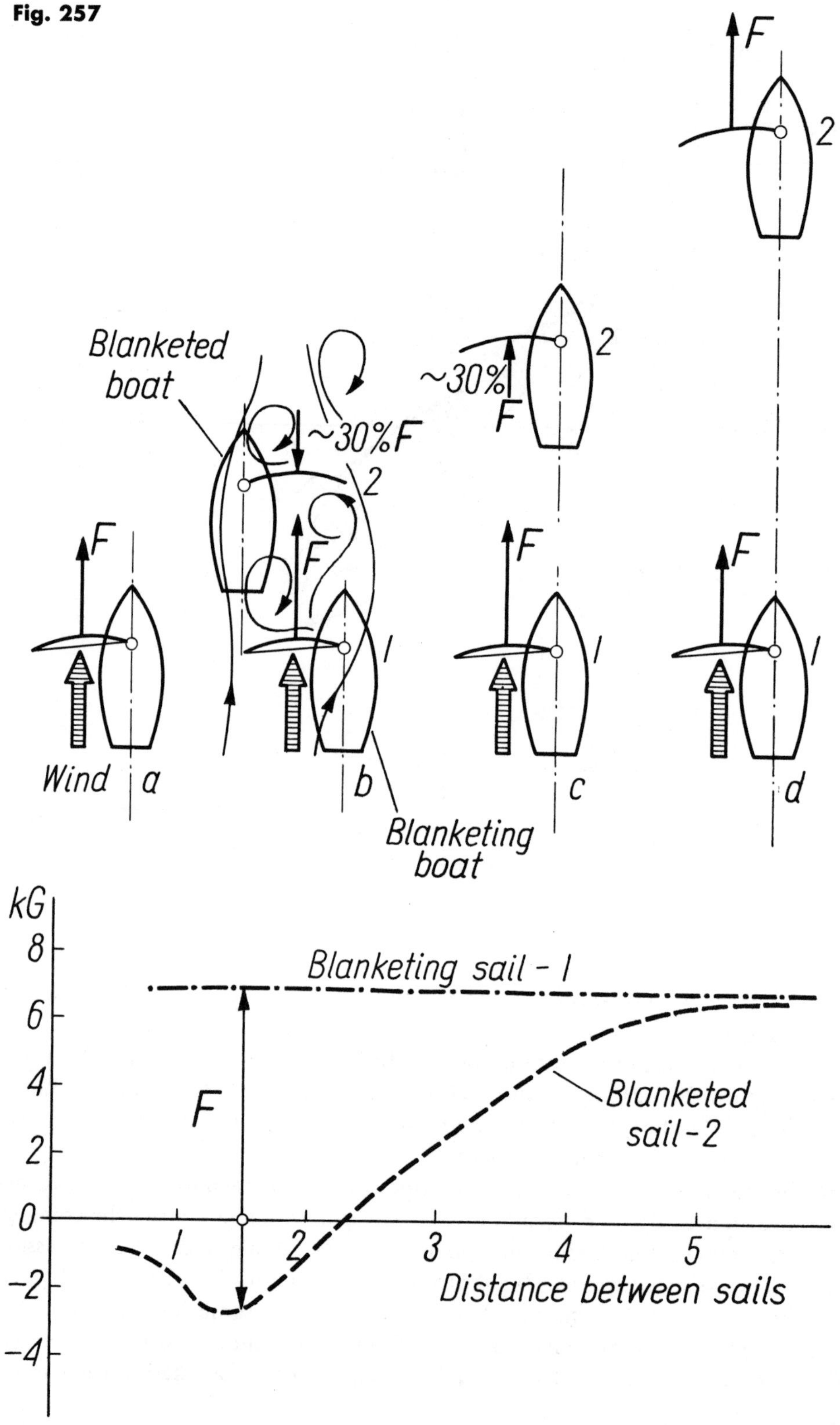

F
2
Blanketed boat
~30%F
2
~30%
F
F
F
F
F
1
1
1
Wind
a
b
c
d
Blanketing boat

kG
8
6
4
2
0
−2
−4
Blanketing sail - 1
F
Blanketed sail-2
1
2
3
4
5
Distance between sails

axially, at different distances apart. The results are presented in Fig. 257. On the vertical axis the force is given in kg., and on the horizontal the distance between the plates as a multiple of the plate's width. These results can be adapted to the situations met with when sailing before the wind.

The magnitude of the force F (Fig. 257a) on a sail without interference amounted to 6.8 kG. If sail 1 is 1.5 sail width from sail 2, then the force that acts on sail 2 is equal to 30 per cent of F and opposite to the yacht's motion. Case b therefore shows the greatest negative blanketing effect for yacht 2 in the aerodynamic shadow of yacht 1. As the distance between them increases, the blanketing effect on yacht 2 decreases in importance and practically disappears when the distance is increased to seven times the sail chord.

2. WATER

I must go down to the seas again, for the call of the running tide
Is a wild call and a clear call, that may not be denied;
And all I ask is a windy day, with the white clouds flying,
And the flung spray and the blown spume, and the seagulls crying.

JOHN MASEFIELD

The continual unstable movement of the water surface on which the yacht moves is just as significant to the yachtsman as the constant variations of the wind. So during a race particular attention must be paid to waves and currents, for each race, whether on the open sea or close inshore, presents its own problems of sea conditions and tidal currents which cannot be ignored.

A wave is not always an enemy to the yachtsman because it makes the boat pitch, roll, yaw, or even broach to; much depends on the helmsman's ability to recognize and take the best route through the waves, whatever the state of the sea. Waves contain energy and this energy can be harnessed, particularly by light-displacement craft, so as to reach high speeds.

Waves that are met with in nature are very complex, but basically they closely resemble what are known as trochoidal waves, and these may be represented graphically and analyzed mathematically so as to study the essentials of the behavior of natural waves.

(a) Behavior of Waves

Although the mechanics of wave formation and motion are by no means fully understood, it is known that it is the pressures developed by the wind that are responsible for the displacement of water particles from their normal position at rest. This movement relative to the calm-water level is opposed by the force of gravity which tends to restore the water particles to their normal level.

When the wind blows over a field of corn, each ear waves to and fro, its neighbor closely follows suit and so they seem to follow the wind across the field, though in fact each remains fixed by its roots. Similarly, the water particles in a sea wave do not follow it across the water surface, but each one describes a vertical orbit (more or less circular) as the pressure disturbance passes.

The principles of wave motion for a deep water surface wave are shown in Fig. 258. The wave profile is marked by a broken curve, while the points marked on the small circles represent the positions of free surface water particles at a specific time. If after a certain lapse of time the water particles moving in their orbits change their relative position, as in this example, by 1/12 of the circumference of the circle, then the crest of the wave will shift by the equivalent distance. The new position of the wave is marked by a continuous curve. It must be emphasized that a traveling wave is a passage of motion only, not of water. The actual movement of the water particles that compose the wave is relatively very small.

While the water particles are executing one orbit about their position at rest, the crest of the wave will shift from position 1 to position 2, by a full wave length L_w.

The period during which the wave traverses one wave length, in other words, the period of the passing of two successive wave crests through one fixed point, is called wave period T. If the height of a wave, H_w (which is equal to the diameter of an orbit 2r), and the wave period, T, are known, the orbital velocity at the surface $u_{orb.}$ is found from

$$u_{orb.} = \frac{2\pi r}{T} = \frac{\pi H_w}{T}$$

Therefore, the higher the wave, the faster is the orbital rotation of its water particles. The special importance of this is that it leads to the formation of orbital flow, of varying velocity and direction, depending on which part of the wave surface is involved. On the wave crests the direction of the orbital flow, or surface current, is the same as the direction of the wave, but in the trough it is moving in the opposite direction. The intensity of the surface currents moving with the waves is represented in Fig. 258 by arrows of varying thickness, the thickest portion of the arrow corresponding with the point at which the speed of the surface flow is highest.

From Fig. 258 it can easily be seen that the influence of the surface current on sailing craft will depend on:

1. The ratio of wave length L_w to length of hull LWL, L_w/LWL
2. The position of the boat in relation to the wave

For example, boat a in Fig. 258, sailing close-hauled and cutting across the waves at an oblique angle, will be affected by the orbital velocities, which will tend to push

Fig. 258

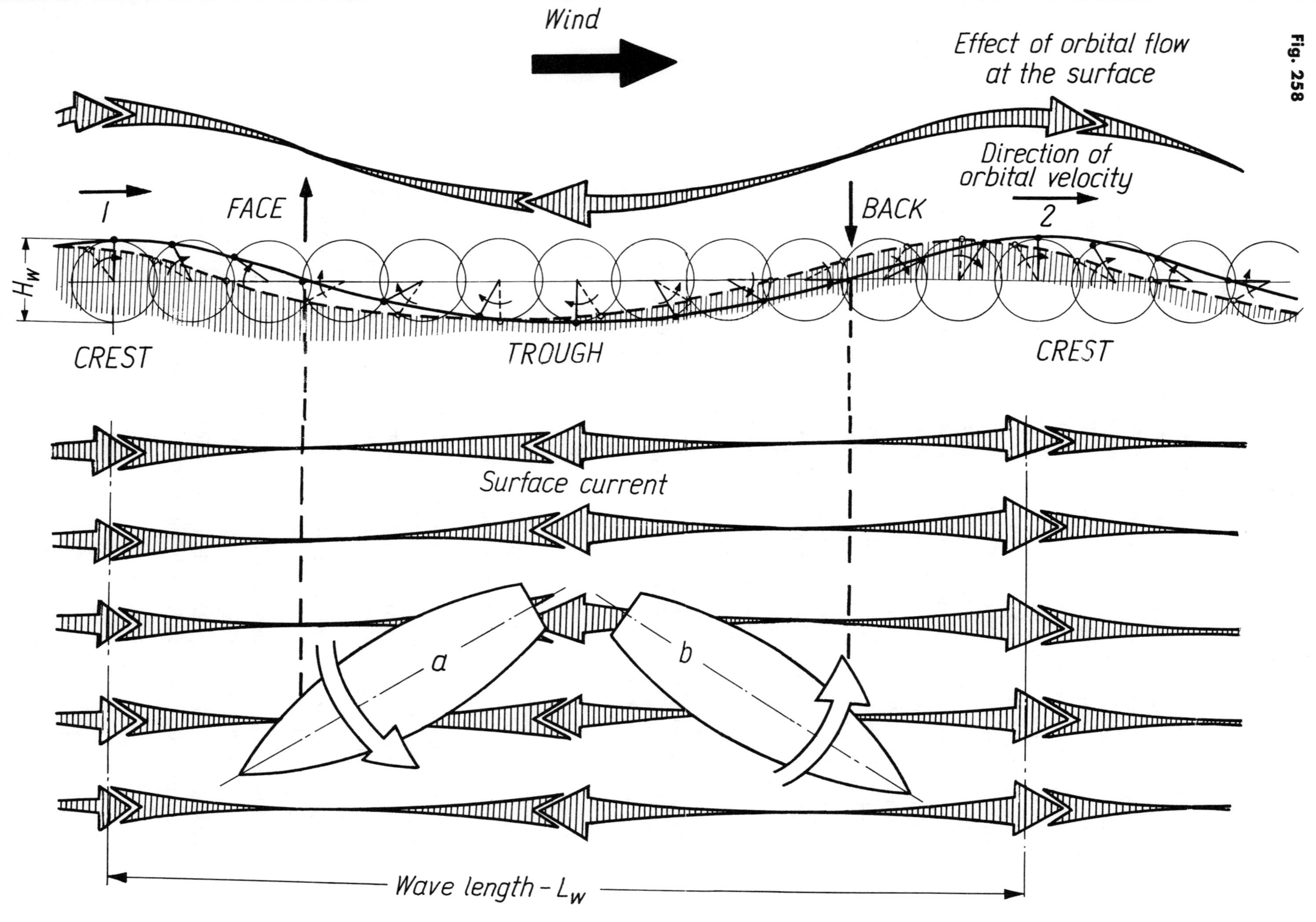

Wind
Effect of orbital flow at the surface
Direction of orbital velocity
1
FACE
BACK
2
H_w
CREST
TROUGH
CREST
Surface current
a
b
Wave length - L_w

the boat off course, while boat b, on a reaching course, will find herself turning to run before the wind. The constantly varying yawing moment requires a rhythmical correction on the rudder from the helmsman. The action of the orbital flow is greatest at the surface, and will naturally affect light-displacement craft more than a ballast-keel yacht.

When a yacht is running before a heavy sea on a course that cuts obliquely across the wave system, a marked tendency to broach to may develop due to the orbital flow in the crests and troughs of the waves. By analyzing Fig. 258 it can be deduced that this effect would be at its worst when the wave length, L_W, is approximately twice the hull length, LWL, so that when the forepart has reached the trough, the afterpart of the hull will be on the crest. In this position, quite apart from the unstable yawing effects caused by the surface flow, rudder control is reduced, because the orbital velocities can exert considerable influence on the magnitude of those local flow velocities on which rudder control depends. The side forces needed by the rudder are generated according to the square of the velocity of the flow, and the rudder can therefore lose up to 30 per cent of its efficiency if this is affected. As K. S. M. Davidson wrote:

> The deep forefoot of the earlier ships had a tendency to dig into the back of the wave ahead when the vessel was running before a heavy sea. This could [also] be dangerous, as the CLR [center of lateral resistance] could temporarily be moved a long way forward, which might lead to a loss of directional control by the rudder. In this event the vessel might broach to, slewing around broadside on and going over on her beam ends, jeopardising the rig if not having more serious consequences. It may be that the real, if only partly understood, reason why the very blunt bows persisted for so long in the square-rigged ships is that they had less tendency to dig in, and would therefore provide some safeguard against broaching to. Anyway, it is a fact that the blunt bows gave way to sharp bows only as sailing closer to the wind became possible and there was less need to run before the wind. The obvious disadvantages of the blunt bows in head seas must then have become apparent. The yacht's hull with its cut-away forefoot is much less susceptible to broaching to.

Running before a high wind and sea demands full attention from the helmsman and an awareness of possible consequences. Many large ships have been dismasted and left to God's mercy through a helmsman's carelessness.

An extraordinary case demonstrating the power of waves and orbital flow was described in the *Transactions of the R.I.N.A.* (Vol. 102, No. 2) by Peter DuCane and G. J. Goodrich. Their account is of an accident to the small sailing yacht *Tzu-Hang,* when attempting to round Cape Horn.

> The yacht was running before a tremendous gale with practically no sail and a mooring line streamed over the counter. The owner's wife, who was at the helm, noticed a sheer cliff face of water and could do nothing to avoid being overwhelmed. The next she knew she was in the water and the yacht was lying in a water-logged state with the masts and coachroof carried away. . . . From evidence found in the overhead beams, it became clear the ship had turned a complete somersault.

Fig. 259 *Crest breaking*

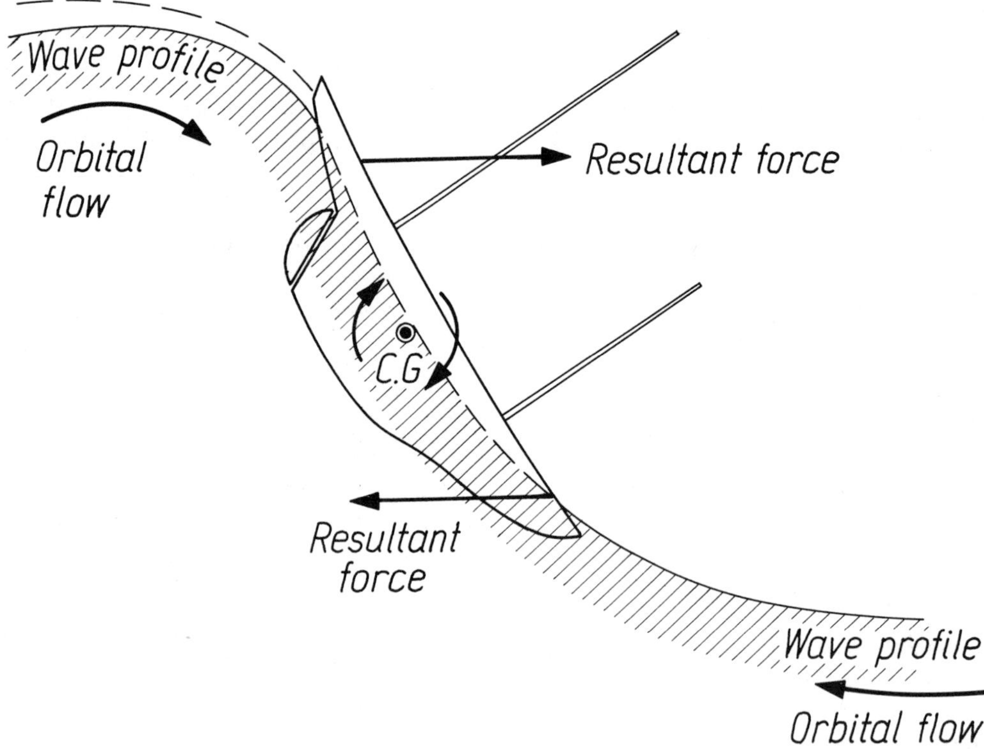

Figure 259 will show diagrammatically what in all probability occurred. This is an extreme case and bears no relation to directional stability or broaching; in fact it must have occurred with the waves from right aft. The accident to *Tzu-Hang* occurred nearly 1000 miles from the west coast of Chile. They saved themselves by a miracle of fortitude and skill to sail into Aranco Bay near Concepcion.

The length, L_w, and height, H_w, of waves rise in relation to the speed of the wind that produces them. In the initial stage of development, the wave height, H_w, increases faster than the length, L_w. The ratio of wave steepness, H_w/L_w, which at first may be around 1/10, falls off to 1/25 to 1/35 after the wind has been blowing for some time. The size and shape of the waves also depend on the "fetch"—that is, the extent of open water to windward of the observer. The curves drawn in Fig. 260, based on calculations by the Norwegian oceanographer Sverdrup, illustrate approximately the way in which wave length, L_w, and wave height, H_w (both in feet), vary in relation to wind speed, v_T (in knots), its duration in hours, and the "fetch" in nautical miles. For instance, for a wind blowing at $v_T =$ 40 knots, the wave length after 5 hours will be 150 ft., and may reach 600 ft. after 35 hours, if the necessary "fetch" of 500 miles is available. For the same 40-knot wind the wave height will rise rapidly, in the first 10–15 hours to about 30 ft., after which the rate of increase is relatively small.

The size of waves cannot be estimated solely on the basis of the wind speed, and the description of waves in the Beaufort scale is rather misleading. It is, for instance,

Fig. 260

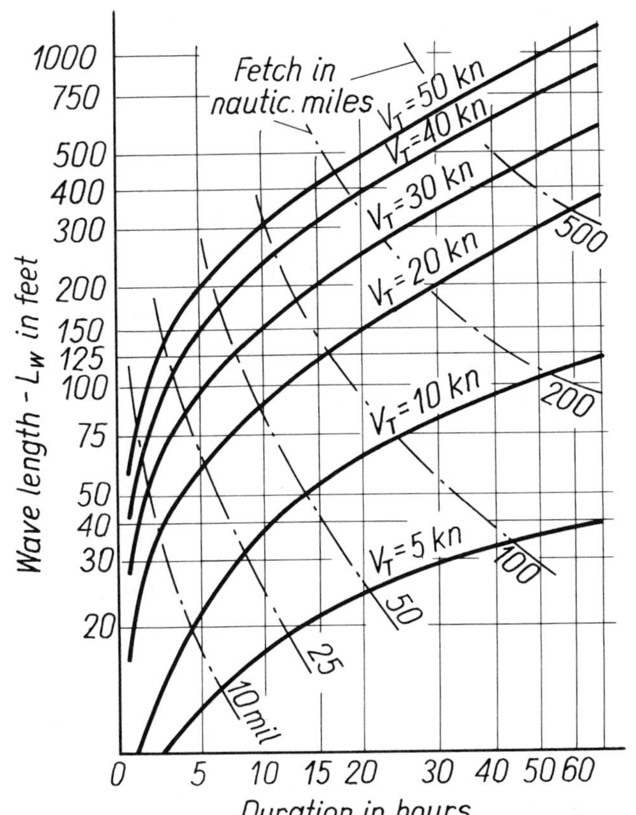

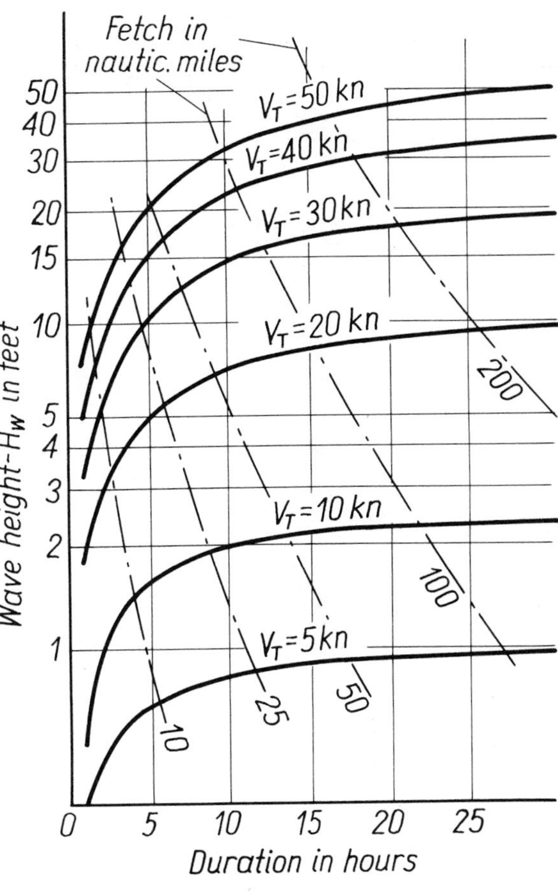

well known that storm waves in the North Atlantic can reach a height of 35 feet, with a length of 1000 ft., while those in the Baltic seldom exceed 8 ft. in height and 100 ft. in length.

The longest wave ever observed was about 2800 ft. long and traveled at a speed of 125 ft./sec. Similar waves are encountered on the wide ocean expanses, such as those between 40°–50° south where the westerly trade winds blow.

The longer the wave the greater its velocity.

If c = velocity (celerity) of a wave in ft./sec.
L_W = wave length in ft.
T = wave period in sec.

then $c = \frac{L_W}{T}$

Other relationships between L_W, T, and c are:

$T = 0.442\sqrt{L_W}$ . . . in seconds
$L_W = 5.12\ T^2$ in feet
$c = 2.26\sqrt{L_W}$ ft./sec., or $1.34\sqrt{L_W}$ knots
$c = 5.12\ T$ ft./sec., or $3.03\ T$ knots.

Fig. 261

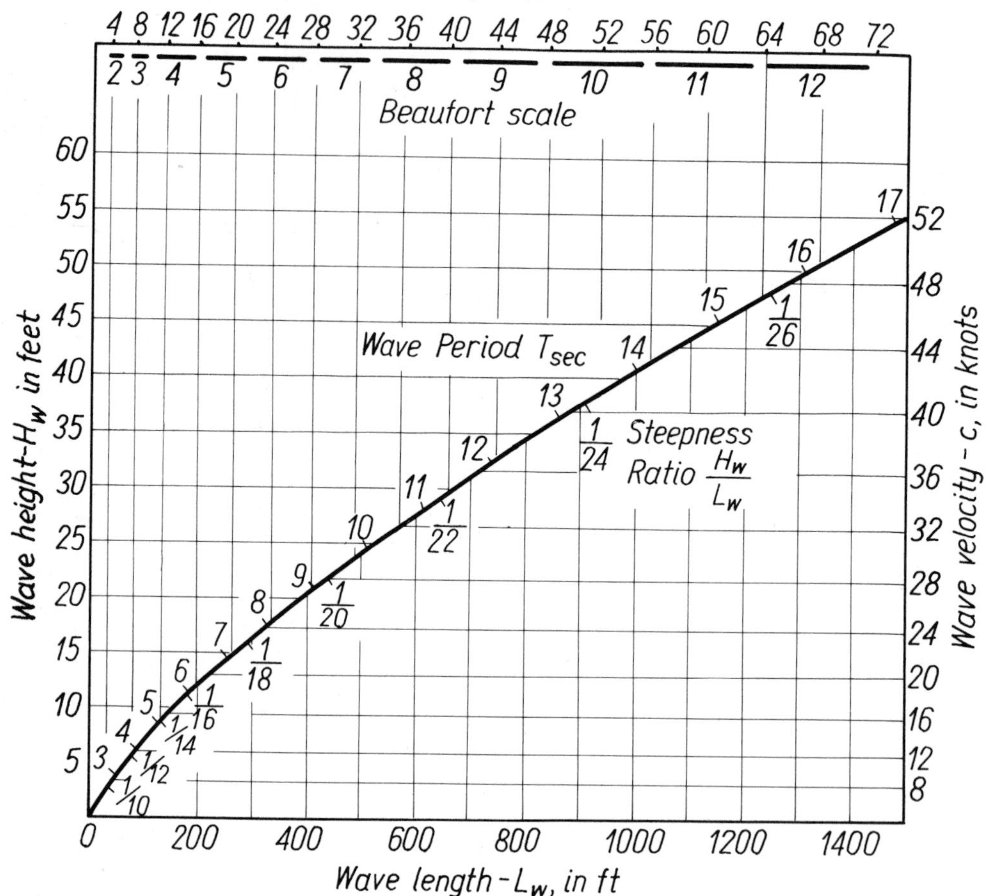

The most convenient way of measuring the speed or length of the waves is to measure the wave period T, the time needed for two successive waves to pass a given point, say a cork thrown into the water.

Figure 261 represents graphically the results of an extensive analysis by Zimmerman of the natural waves reported earlier by many observers. The curve gives the best possible empirical relationship for natural sea waves, between the variable L_w, c, T, v_T, etc., that may be expected at any chosen point in its range. The following example will explain how the graph is used. Assume that the wave length is estimated by eye as equal to 5 times the length of the vessel, which is 40 ft. long:

$$L_w = 5 \times 40 = 200 \text{ ft.}$$

Now, reading off from the 200 ft. mark near the bottom of the curve, we find that the ratio of wave steepness $H_w/L_w \cong 1/16$, and the wave period is 6.3 sec. From the scale on the right the wave velocity, c, is found to be about 20 knots, while from that on the left the wave height, H_w, is found to be 12 ft. Finally, from the scale at the top the wind velocity, v_T, is given as 16 knots, corresponding to force 4–5 in the Beaufort scale.

Exaggerated figures are often given by people who estimate the height of waves

Fig. 262

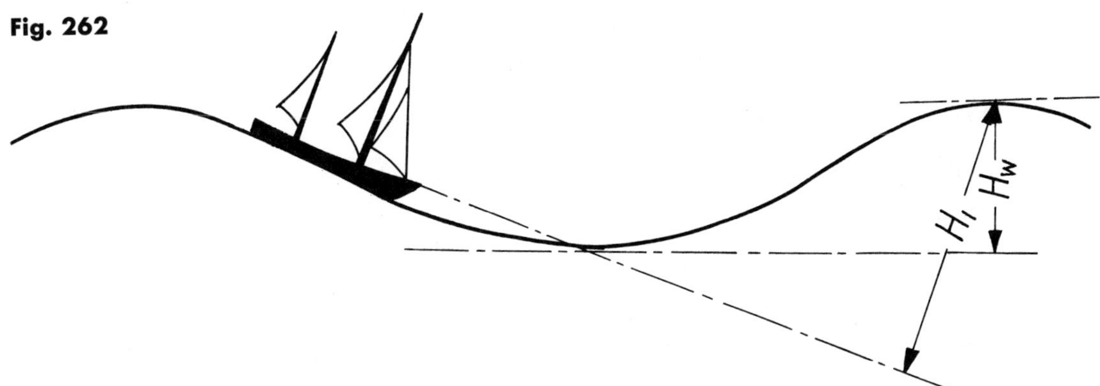

from the deck of a yacht. From Fig. 262 one can see that a completely false impression of the height may be got if the estimate is made from the angle between the crest of the next wave and a line continuing the line of the deck when the yacht is descending the slope after the crest. This height, H_1, is obviously wrong, and the true height, H_w, can only be found by measuring the height between the level of the crest and the trough—that is, it must be done when the yacht itself is in the trough.

Although there is a mathematical relation between the wave length, L_w, its period, T, and its velocity, c, the wave height H_w is only loosely coupled with these parameters. As was noted above, wave height depends on the depth of the water, the "fetch," and also on how long the wind has been blowing. Out in the deep, open sea it is not only the surface layers that participate in the oscillating movement, but the deeper levels as well. The wave energy involved in these large masses of water is not so violent at the surface. The steepness of the waves, which can also be expressed as an angle (cf. Fig. 263), does not exceed 20° in deep waters. The profile "a" of the ratio $H_w/L_w = 1/10$ relates to the initial stage of wave formation. Profile c represents the wave after a longer period of wind action, where unrestricted distance allows the wave to develop fully, and it is not so steep.

The profiles of the waves in Fig. 263 are shown to the same scale of length L_w, to illustrate the steepness ratio H_w/L_w only; in fact the "older" wave c will be longer than wave a.

Fig. 263

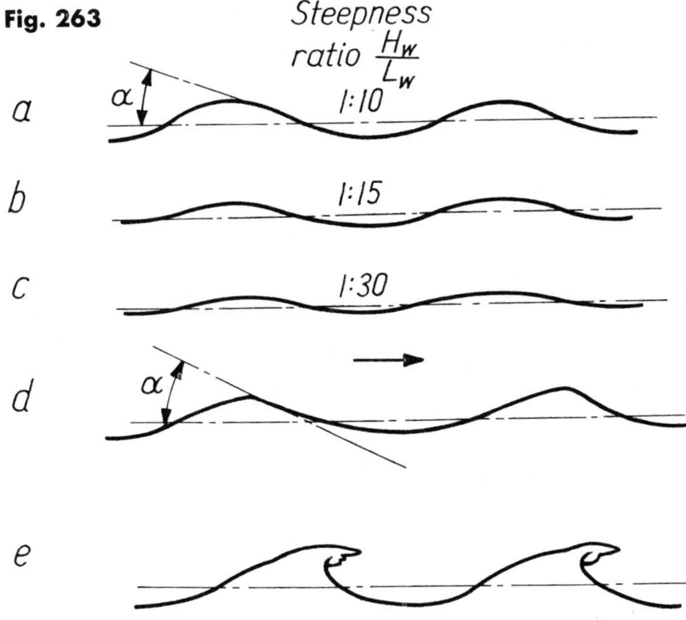

When a deep-water wave reaches a sloping beach, or shoal, and the depth of the water is less than $L_W/2$, the water particles near the bottom are constrained to move in flattened orbits of roughly elliptical shape. The profile of the wave is changed, the bottom of each trough is wider and flatter, while the slope of the crests is steeper than in the deep-water wave (Fig. 263d). At the same time the wave height increases. When the wave reaches the shallows its energy is contained in a smaller mass of water and naturally tends to dissipate violently. The wave rises steeply, with breaking crests or heavy surf (Fig. 263e). Breakers so created have great capacity for causing damage, and can make beaching through the surf impossible for small boats.

Wave refraction is also characteristic of shallow waters. Anyone can observe wave crests approaching parallel to the shore and breaking on it one after another. This happens whether the wind is blowing parallel or at right angles to the shore (Fig. 264). The term "wave refraction" is used because the process reminds one of the bending of light rays as they pass through media of different densities, caused by the different speeds of light in various media. The speed of waves changes similarly with the depth of the water. The waves that reach the shelving shore first (on the left of the drawing in Fig. 264) become shorter, slow down, and are passed by the waves which have not yet reached the shallows (like those on the right of the drawing). Thus the direction of the waves is bent, the deep-water waves catch up with those in the shallows, so that they reach the shore in almost parallel rows. Wave refraction may prove important for choosing the best course in a race in a strong wind and a breaking sea. Figure 264 illustrates a case in point. After rounding buoy I two courses are possible, I-A or I-B. I-A is clearly more profitable, since the waves away from the shore will be less steep. The extra hull resistance caused by waves and by pitching will be smaller and greatly reduced when at A the yacht tacks and sails parallel to the waves.

A yacht that chooses course I-B will sail through the stretch where the surf is formed, and hull resistance will be increased as the boat meets the steep waves. In addition, when sailing near the shore a boat meets an opposing wave current, as a result of wave refraction. This current carries the excess water, caused by the concentration of the waves, away toward an area of lower waves, and is at its strongest near the shore.

(b) Sailing Close-hauled in a Head Sea

A yacht sailing on calm water is overcoming hydrodynamic resistance which, given a steady wind, remains more or less constant. The motion of a yacht in conditions like these is said to be constant. The situation of a yacht sailing close-hauled into a head sea is quite different. The hydrodynamic resistance is increased periodically, and as a result the motion of the yacht is irregular and its average speed is lower. The extra resistance due to sea waves encountered when going to windward in a heavy sea is sometimes the cause of a considerable loss in the yacht's performance.

Fig. 264

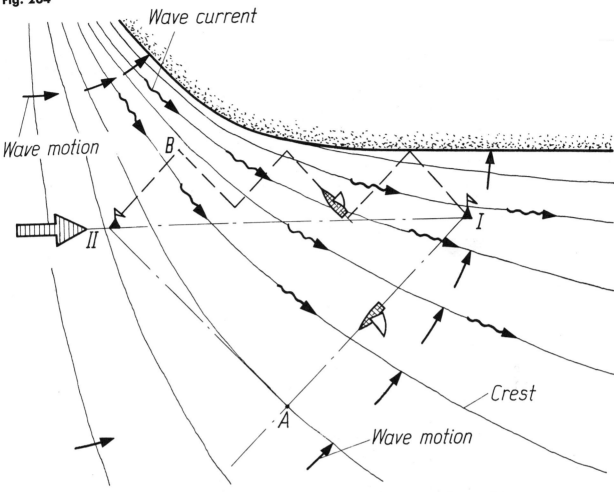

There are numerous reasons for this. Practical experience has shown that yachts sailing into a head sea may develop a continuous oscillatory pitching, which in extreme cases may be so violent as to stop effectively the vessel making headway. This compels the helmsman to "bear away off the wind to keep the sails full and the boat moving." The extent to which this reduces the speed made good to windward can easily be calculated by these trigonometrical relationships:

$$v_{mg} = v_s \cos \gamma \qquad \text{in calm water}$$
$$v_{mg} = v_s \cos (\gamma + \Delta\gamma) \qquad \text{in a head sea.}$$

which are also shown in upper part of Fig. 265.

Assuming that the waves are moving exactly downwind, then the wave velocity relative to the yacht is

$$c + v_{mg} = 2.26\sqrt{L_w} + v_s \cos \gamma$$

And therefore the period of the oscillations caused by a succession of waves will be equal to the length of the waves encountered, L_w, divided by the velocity of the waves relative to the yacht:

Fig. 265

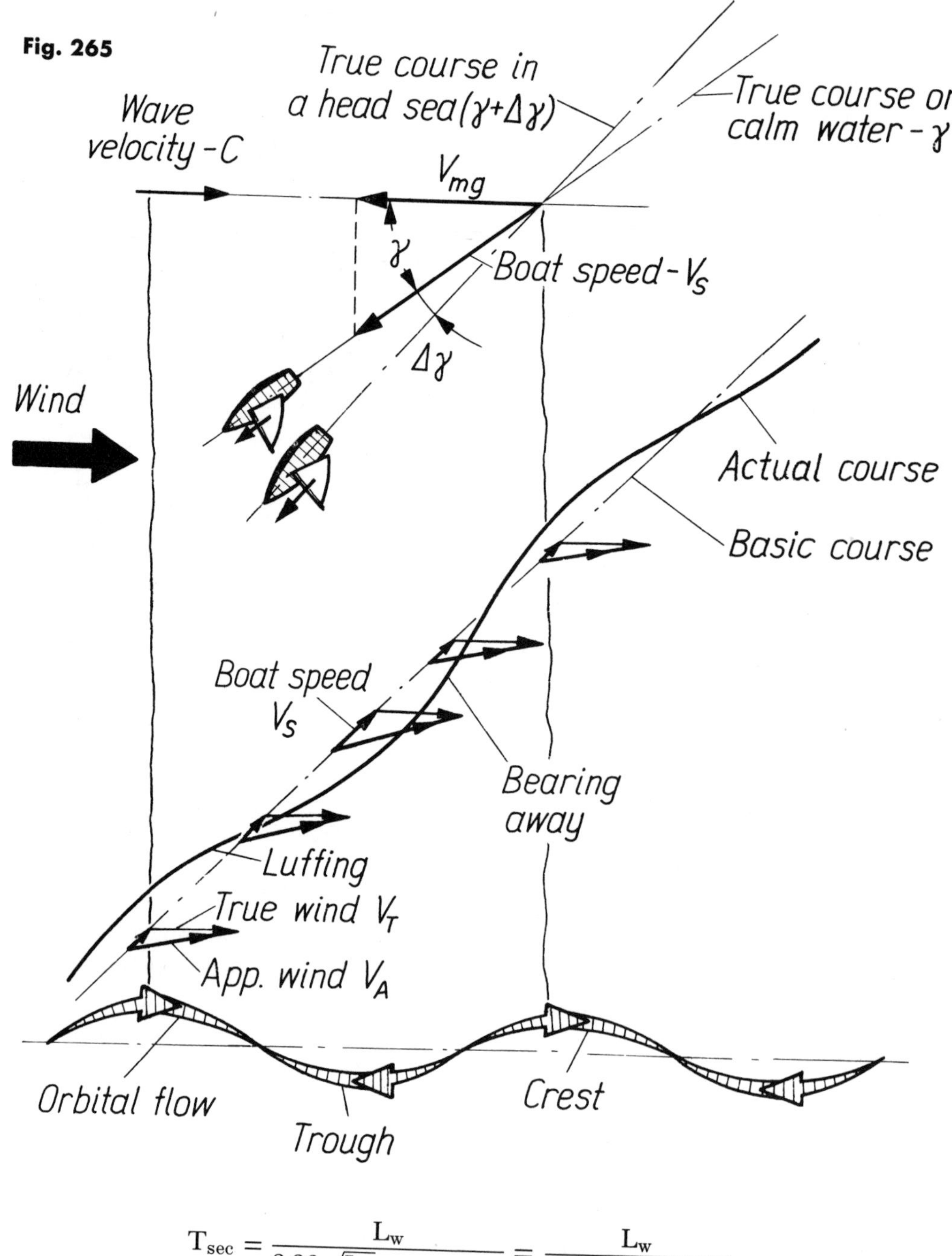

$$T_{sec} = \frac{L_w}{2.26\sqrt{L_w} + v_s \cos \gamma} = \frac{L_w}{2.26\sqrt{L_w} + v_{mg}}$$

A yacht sailing into a head sea will change her longitudinal trim rhythmically, in accordance with this "period of encounter." When it meets the crest of a wave, the bow will be partially lifted but partly immersed in the wave above her DWL due to the yacht's own inertia. The pounding or slamming that occurs invariably involves the loss of some of the vessel's motive energy. Some yachts are particularly prone to these oscillations in pitch, which can be very violent. This is caused by the phenomenon called "resonance," which occurs when the wave length and sailing course are such that the "period of encounter," T_1, experienced by the yacht is approaching that of the "natural" pitching period, T_2, of the yacht.

At this point the amount of oscillation increases considerably, even if the waves are not very high. It is the particular frequency of encounter that is all that is needed to induce violent pitching.

When a helmsman meets this synchronous pitching he may try to stop it in either of two ways:

(a) By changing the period of encounter, T_1
(b) By changing the natural period of the yacht, T_2

In the first case it is sometimes sufficient to change the course γ by $\Delta\gamma$ and to bear away from the wind. This, naturally, will affect the optimum v_{mg} when sailing close-hauled. The alternative, a change in the "natural period," can be achieved by increasing or decreasing the yacht's "moment of inertia," which is the product of mass and distance from the axis of the oscillations. A larger amount of inertia can be provided if the crew move into the ends of the boat, thus increasing the natural period, T_2. Alternatively, T_2 can be reduced below the period of encounter by keeping the crew away from the ends. Both these may reduce the heavy pitching, but obviously the effects produced by the weight of the crew will be more noticeable in a light-displacement craft than in a heavy-keel boat.

The pitching that a yacht is forced to suffer from the waves at sea can be effectively damped by an appropriate fore and aft distribution of the buoyancy of the hull. There is evidence from practical experience to show that the "symmetrical" hulls favored in Great Britain, with their full bows matching closely the stern (for buoyancy equality as the hull progressively heels), are very prone to excessive pitching. In the opinion of an American expert "it does seem foolish to try such a symmetrical hull when in open water the asymmetrical hull has been winning in various classes for years." By asymmetrical form is here meant a hull with a rather long lean entry, a slightly flared bow, and the maximum beam well abaft of amidships, with a wider section in the stern overhang.

Since violent pitching is most likely to come from the bows, there are sound reasons behind the idea of a hull with a slim bow, for such a shape will cut through the waves instead of being lifted up by them. This is shown in the top sketch of Fig. 266. Sailing in such a boat is rather a wet pursuit, but as someone said, "Sailing fast and yet dry is as impossible as making an omelette without breaking eggs." Pitching tests made by Col. C. E. Bowden on radio-controlled models about 7′6″ long have demonstrated that various asymmetrical hulls, sailed free in "scale-model" waves of various heights, were far less prone to pitching than the symmetrical hulls.

There are two other factors which periodically cause an increase in the hydrodynamic resistance, and therefore a reduction in the speed, of a yacht sailing close-hauled in a head sea.

Fig. 266

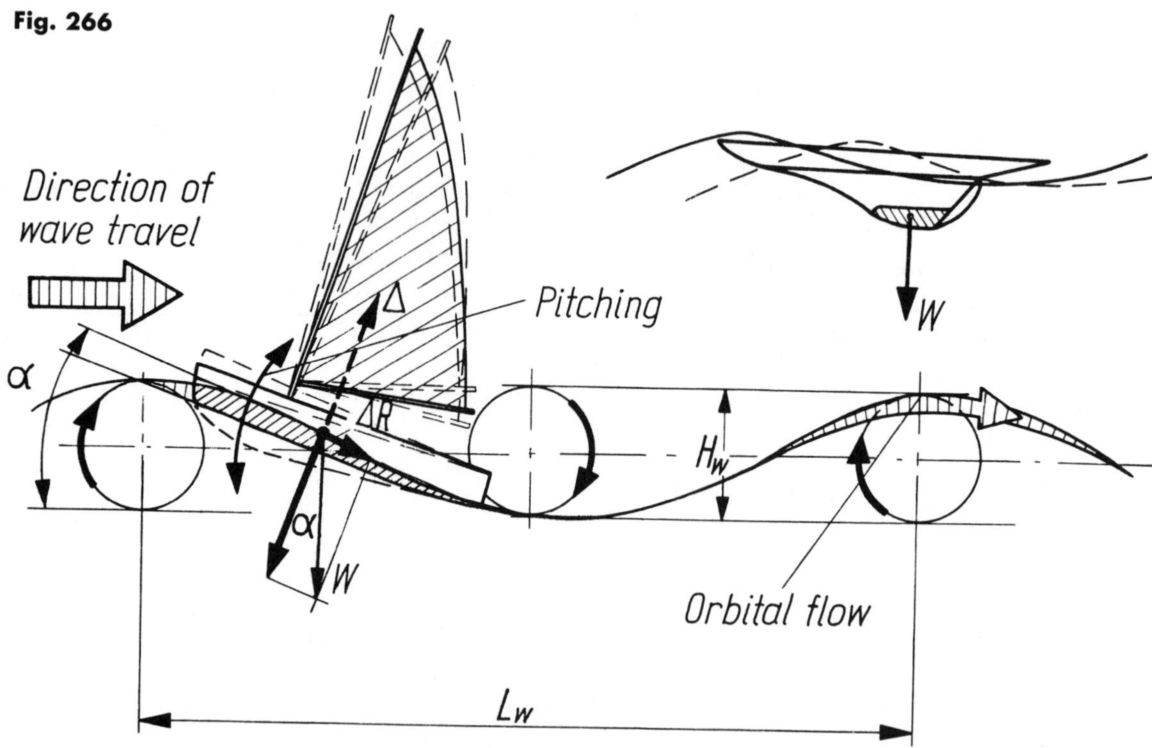

When a yacht is climbing up the wave (cf. Fig. 266), the surface current is affecting her progress, and its effect depends on the height of the wave, H_W, and the steepness ratio, H_W/L_W. As a yacht climbs up the slope of the wave, she has also to overcome the additional resistance

$$\Delta R = W \sin \alpha$$

These negative effects are only partly compensated for by the positive effect of the orbital current in the trough of the wave, where its flow is in the same direction as the yacht's motion.

The periodical reductions in the yacht's speed when passing over the crests of waves, with the resultant variation in the velocity and direction of the apparent wind, demand a special sailing technique. A comparison of the directions and velocities of the apparent wind for the different positions of the yacht in waves given in Fig. 265 shows that on the wave crests the apparent wind is weaker and slightly freer, while in the trough the wind is stronger and comes ahead. To keep the sail at its best angle of trim to the apparent wind, it is necessary to vary the course of the yacht in a rhythmical manner. As she mounts the crest of the wave, the helmsman must luff; as he passes the crest he should bear away, so that the actual course sailed will be rather sinuous.

There is still one more reason for continuous readjustment of the course to suit "the shape of the sea surface." Truly simple waves, the kind that look like corrugated iron, are seldom seen in nature. The true picture of the sea's surface is far removed from what might be called a "two-dimensional" case, in which the waves are long-crested and wave follows wave like a sort of wave train. In reality they are complex, nonsymmetrical, short-crested hillocks, and the crests do not form

Fig. 267

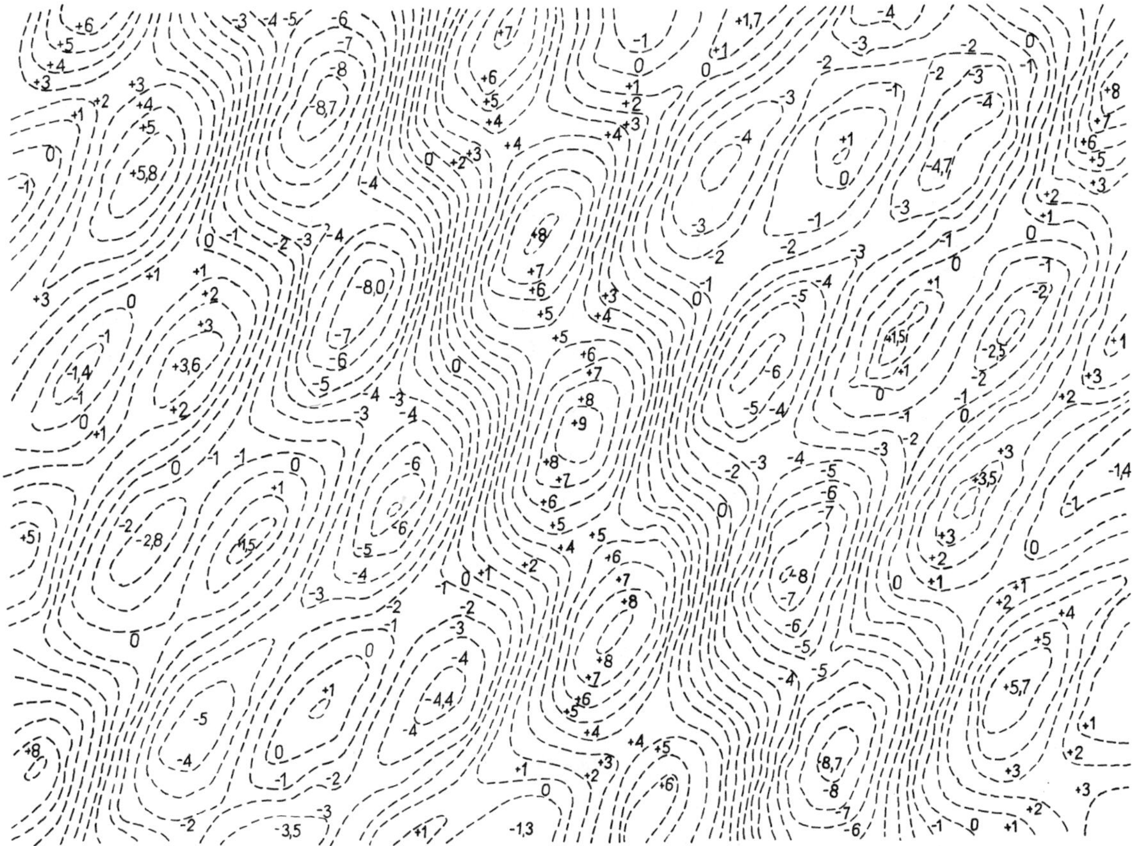

a continuous line. The natural pattern of sea waves contains steep slopes, breaking crests, and pyramidal piles of water. A typical "three-dimensional" pattern, with the contours of the waves sketched at 1-ft. intervals, is shown in Fig. 267.

The reason for this irregularity in the wave pattern is interference. Apart from the actual wind, whose reaction upon the surface generates waves of a specific length and height, the sea is influenced by the swell, a wave motion produced by distant winds, and also by the typical wind shifts that develop around barometric depressions. All these affect the sea on which the actual wind is working, and the combined effect of these different interfering waves is responsible for the irregular appearance of the waves as a series of hillocks. As an example, the interfering effect of waves can be well observed around the starting line during a regatta, when the yachts, sailing to and fro on irregular courses, create waves and cause extra roughness of the sea.

Nevertheless even in this mixture of waves of different heights and lengths, there is a certain repeating pattern, already referred to in Fig. 267.

Practical experience has shown that the higher waves appear at quite regular intervals in a group, followed by a similar group of lower waves. Old sea tales tell of the dangerous ninth wave, supposed to be larger than the other eight. Obviously it is not necessarily the ninth wave, it may equally be the seventh, fifteenth, etc., but in general the number is constant.

The technique of sailing close-hauled in rough conditions, therefore, depends on selecting among the maze of waves a course meeting the least disturbance. A yacht should never be sailed exactly along a straight line, but should follow the pattern of the waves. In particular, it is advisable to wait for a group of smaller waves before going about, for otherwise the yacht's motion can be completely stalled at the point where the sails are in irons.

It may be interesting to give some qualitative information on how large the additional resistance caused by the combination of wave form and hull length can be. The table below relates to experiments carried out in the Stevens Institute, United States, on the racer-cruiser *New York* (see Fig. 155).

Additional wave resistance encountered (in per cent):

H_w/L_w \ L_w/L	0	.2	.4	.6	.8
1/10	0	3	23	48	—
1/20	0	1	6	17	27

L_w: wave length
L: boat's waterline length
H_w: wave height

These figures show that the extra resistance met can be considerable, even in quite short waves, especially if they are steep.

(c) Sailing in a Following Sea

When running before the wind in a following sea, although the wind is steady, yachts progress in a series of leaps, periodically increasing and then reducing their speed. If several yachts are sailing side by side, the distance between them may vary as much as several lengths, and yet at the same time it is difficult for one to break away from the rest and leave them behind even when helped by a sudden burst of speed.

What, then, is the cause of these periodic spurts, and in what conditions can they be prolonged? A yacht in position "a" in Fig. 268 is moving not only because of the aerodynamic driving force F_R, but also because of other forces. When a yacht is riding down the face of a wave she receives additional impetus from the surface flow, which is acting in the direction of the course sailed. Further acceleration is provided by a gravity force component F_d due to the boat's weight, W, so that $F_d = W \sin \alpha$, where $\alpha =$ the steepness of the wave in degrees.

The resultant speed v_R of a surfing boat is therefore composed of a speed v_s which is what would be normal for the course sailed and wind strength, plus the effect of the orbital velocity $u_{orb.}$, and the effect of gravity F_d. Under the combined action of these three factors the boat may gather considerable speed, the extra

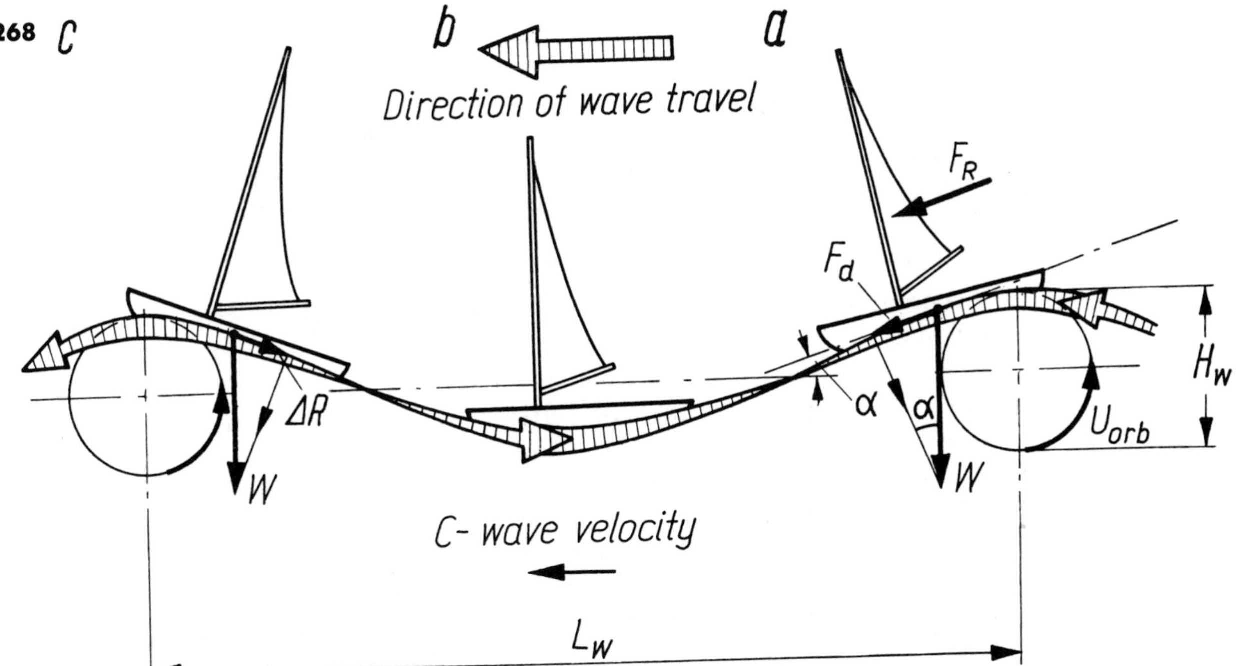

speed depending on the steepness ratio H_w/L_w of the wave, its height H_w and position of the boat on the wave.

The curves drawn in Fig. 269 give the values of the orbital velocities U-orb. for a range of wave lengths, velocities, and steepness ratios that are likely to be encountered during rather heavy weather conditions at sea. For example, if the length of the wave is 200 ft. and its steepness ratio 1/10, then the maximum surface current on the wave crest may reach 10 ft./sec. or 5.9 knots.

Fig. 269

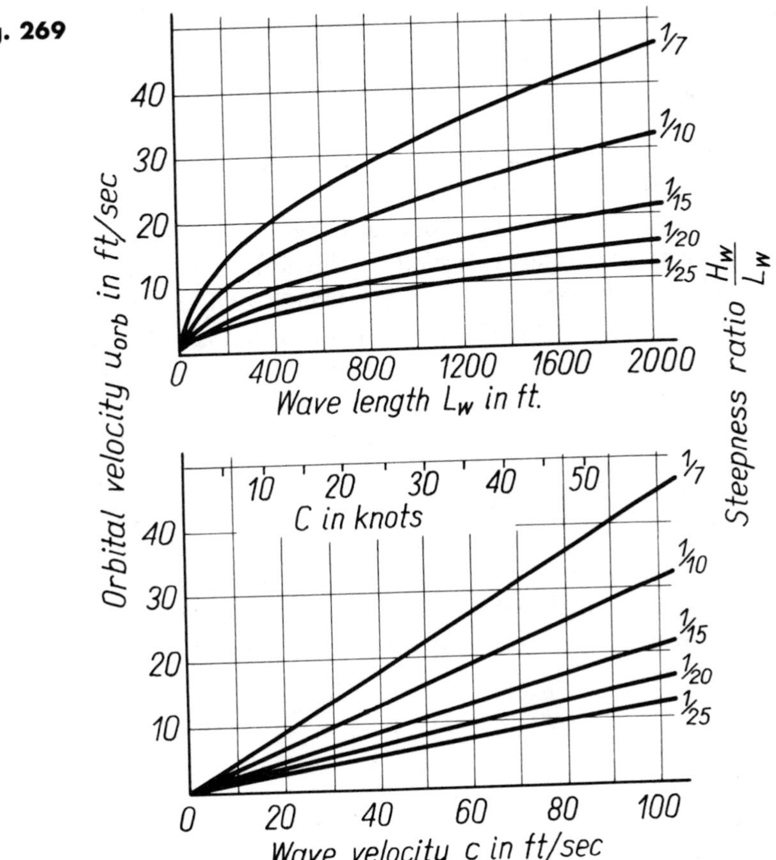

If, in such circumstances, the increase in the boat's speed due to orbital velocity ($u_{orb.}$) alone is added to the boat's basic speed (v_s), a resultant speed of

$$v_R = v_s + u_{orb.}$$

will be produced, which, besides being great fun, can also be an important race-winning factor.

As the graphs show, the orbital velocity for long waves with a high steepness ratio can exceed 40 ft./sec. Due to these properties of sea waves, the extraordinary sport of surf-riding developed on certain islands in the Pacific, as at Waikiki. The surf-riders use a flat board six to nine feet long, on which they stand and are carried to the shore by the surging crest of a wave.

For a boat to maintain her position on the crest, exploit the wave's energy, and reach high-speed sailing, she must travel at a resultant velocity (v_R) which equals the wave's velocity (c). If we take as an example a wave whose length (L_w) is 200 ft., the wave velocity (c) is 19 knots (32 ft./sec.). Racing boats such as the Flying Dutchman class, which plane at about 15 knots, are able to exploit waves of this length if the steepness ratio H_w/L_w is near 1/10. The Flying Dutchman's speed (v_s) plus effect of the orbital velocity ($u_{orb.}$) can be sufficient for the wave to lift the craft bodily and carry her along on the face of the wave.

If the steepness ratio of the 200-ft. wave is about 1/20, then the orbital velocity will be only about 2.9 knots, and so the Flying Dutchman cannot ride the crest of the wave continuously and will be left behind. At times she will be sailing in the trough of the wave and encountering a surface current running in the opposite direction, which will reduce her speed.

An unskillful helmsman can lose the favorable position "a" of Fig. 268 on the wave crest, even when the orbital velocity $u_{orb.}$ is sufficient to keep the resultant speed v_R equal to the wave speed c (i.e., $v_R = c$). By faulty trim of sails or hull (such as depressing the bow) the attainable velocity, v_R, can be decreased, the wave will overtake the boat, and shift her from position a to c and then to b. By repeating these mistakes the distance between boats sailing in a following sea will increase by leaps and bounds. In position c the advantageous effect of the surface current is largely canceled by the additional resistance ΔR due to climbing a wave slope. In position b, in the trough of the wave, the resultant boat speed $v_R = v_s - u_{orb.}$, which means that the speed is reduced by approximately 2 $u_{orb.}$ compared with that of other yachts riding on the face of the wave.

The possibility of exploiting the energy of the waves to increase the speed of the boat, therefore, is closely related to wave length L_w, steepness ratio H_w/L_w, and the yacht's attainable speed v_s. As the length of the waves increases, so their velocity c increases, and it becomes more and more difficult for a yacht to remain on the crest. Light-displacement boats with a high speed/length ratio $v_s/\sqrt{L}$, which plane easily, have a better chance of increasing their speed when sailing in a following sea than heavy boats. In average wind conditions light dinghies will do best in waves whose length is between 80 and 120 feet.

Fig. 270

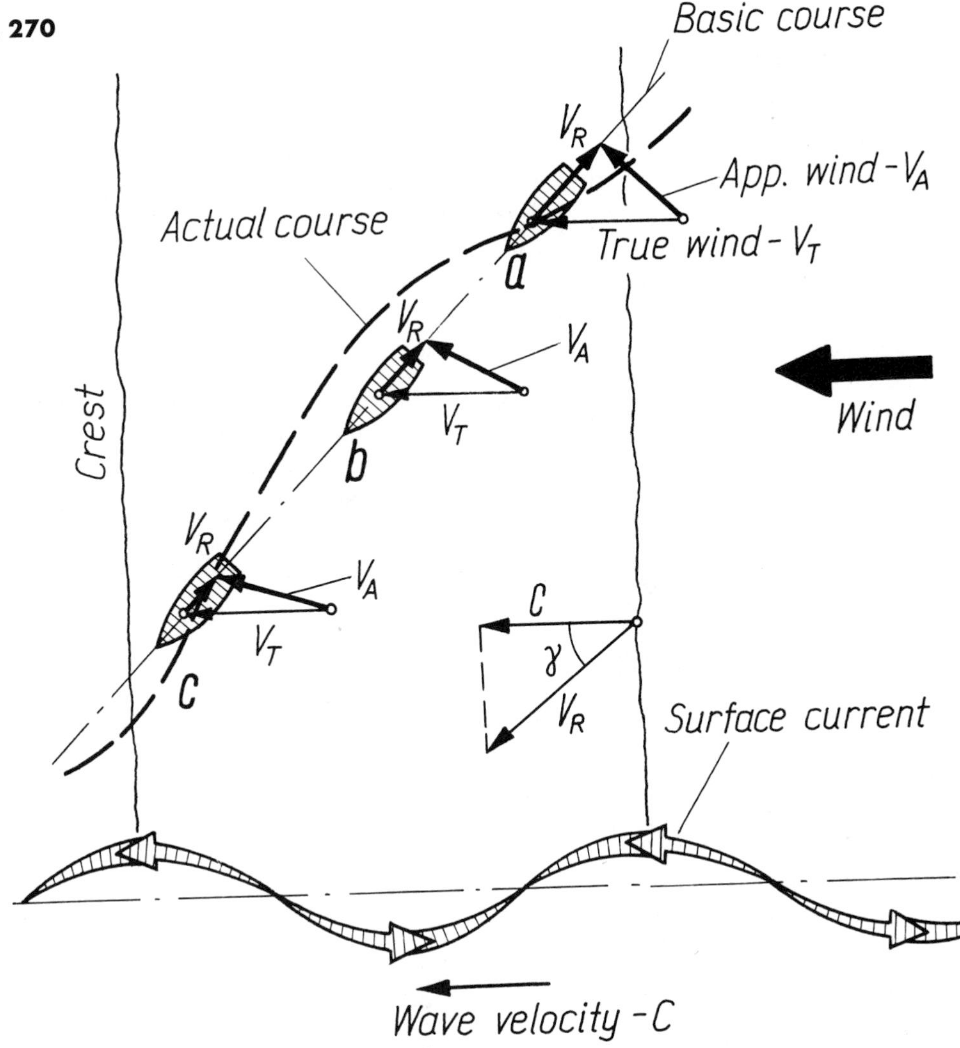

When a yacht sailing on a broad reach is cutting obliquely across the waves (as in Fig. 270), her resultant speed v_R should be greater than the wave speed c, so that the component of v_R in the direction of the wave movement is equal to that of the wave speed c, i.e.

$$v_R = \frac{c}{\cos \gamma}$$

where γ is the angle between the course sailed and the direction in which the waves are moving. If, then, the boat is crossing the waves at 45°, the resultant speed would have to be high enough for

$$v_R = \frac{c}{0.707} = 1.4c$$

for her to remain in the advantageous position "a" on the crest of a wave.

One should realize that if the boat overtakes waves or is overtaken by them, her resultant speed v_R will vary within large limits, and consequently the direction and velocity of apparent wind v_A will vary as well, demanding the proper sailing technique. To keep the sails working with maximum efficiency without changing their angles of trim the course must be altered regularly, depending upon actual position of the boat on the wave. An analysis of the directions of the apparent wind shown in Fig. 270 suggests one should bear away when in position "a" and luff when approaching position "c" (compare also Fig. 268). If the wind is strong enough for the boat to plane at "a," then, besides bearing away, it is sometimes advisable, and even necessary, to haul in the mainsheet in order to keep the sail trimmed properly to direction of the apparent wind. The hull must also be ballasted correctly longitudinally relative to the wave patterns (as shown in Fig. 271). At the same time as a rather vigorous movement is made with the rudder to bear away (when

Fig. 271

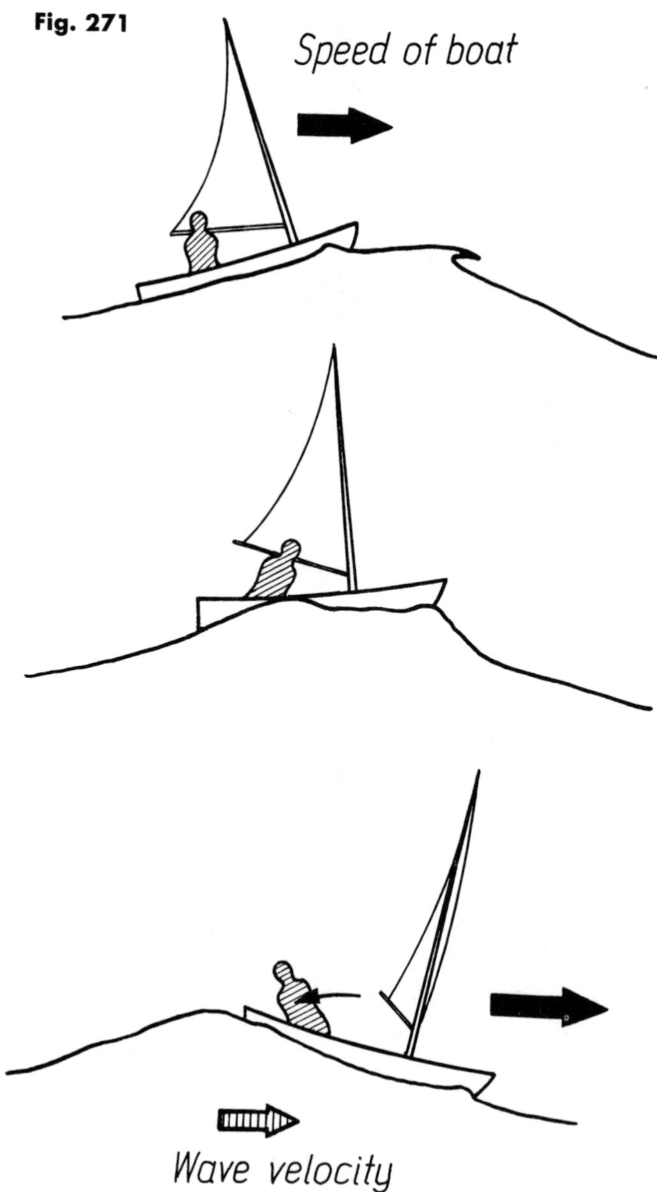

in position "a," Fig. 268), the weight of the helmsman should be flung further aft, and the boat gets an additional impetus enabling her to reach easier the planing or semi-planing. After running down the face of a steep, short, following wave, a fast boat might very well bury her bow in the back of the next one, and an inattentive helmsman may quickly find his boat flooded.

(d) Currents and Tides

The currents and streams which can be encountered on the surface waters of the seas are chiefly due to the tides, caused by the influence of the moon and the sun, and also to the winds which blow in one direction for long periods.

Wind-driven currents develop into systems such as may be found in most oceans and seas. Some of them reach considerable speeds: the Florida stream can reach 5 knots and the Mozambique stream that flows along the East African coast reaches about 3.7 knots. These currents are particularly important for yachts sailing offshore, as it is possible, for example, to cover about 100 miles in 24 hours in the Florida stream even in a flat calm. Detailed descriptions of these currents are usually to be found in "nautical almanacs."

The other type of sea current, the tidal stream, is encountered near the coast, in channels, and in bays. The cycles of these local streams are closely related to the motion of the moon and the sun. For coastal sailing, tide tables are published for all major ports and harbors, which show when the water will rise highest (high water, H.W.) and often the time of the lowest tide (low water, L.W.).

Remote islands far out in the open sea have only very slight differences between H.W. and L.W., but the differences in channels and bays can be very considerable. For example, the difference in tidal level in the Bristol Channel (Great Britain) may be more than 36 ft.

The ebb and flow of the tides along a variegated coastline often cause complex currents whose speed may reach 10 knots. Since the tide runs in twice in 24 hours, it follows that the direction of the currents can change radically in a short space of time. The maps in Fig. 272 illustrate the tidal streams of the waters around the Isle of Wight, in the south of England, and it can be seen that within an hour the tidal streams can reverse their direction completely. It is not difficult to realize the way in which these variations can affect a race, if some competitors are aware of them, while others do not anticipate, or ignore, the tidal changes.

In Fig. 273 it is assumed that before the race begins the following conditions obtain: a true wind of 11 knots from NNW, a tidal stream flowing at 3 knots from W. Had there been no current, the yachts would have been sailing in a true NNW wind, but the 3-knot westerly current means they will be sailing in a "modified true wind" from the north, as is shown by the vectors drawn in the figure at the starting line. Let us now make the simple assumption that at a certain time after the start the tidal stream will reverse its flow and run from the E at 3 knots. These tidal changes are very important when deciding which tack to choose at the start, for Fig.

Fig. 272

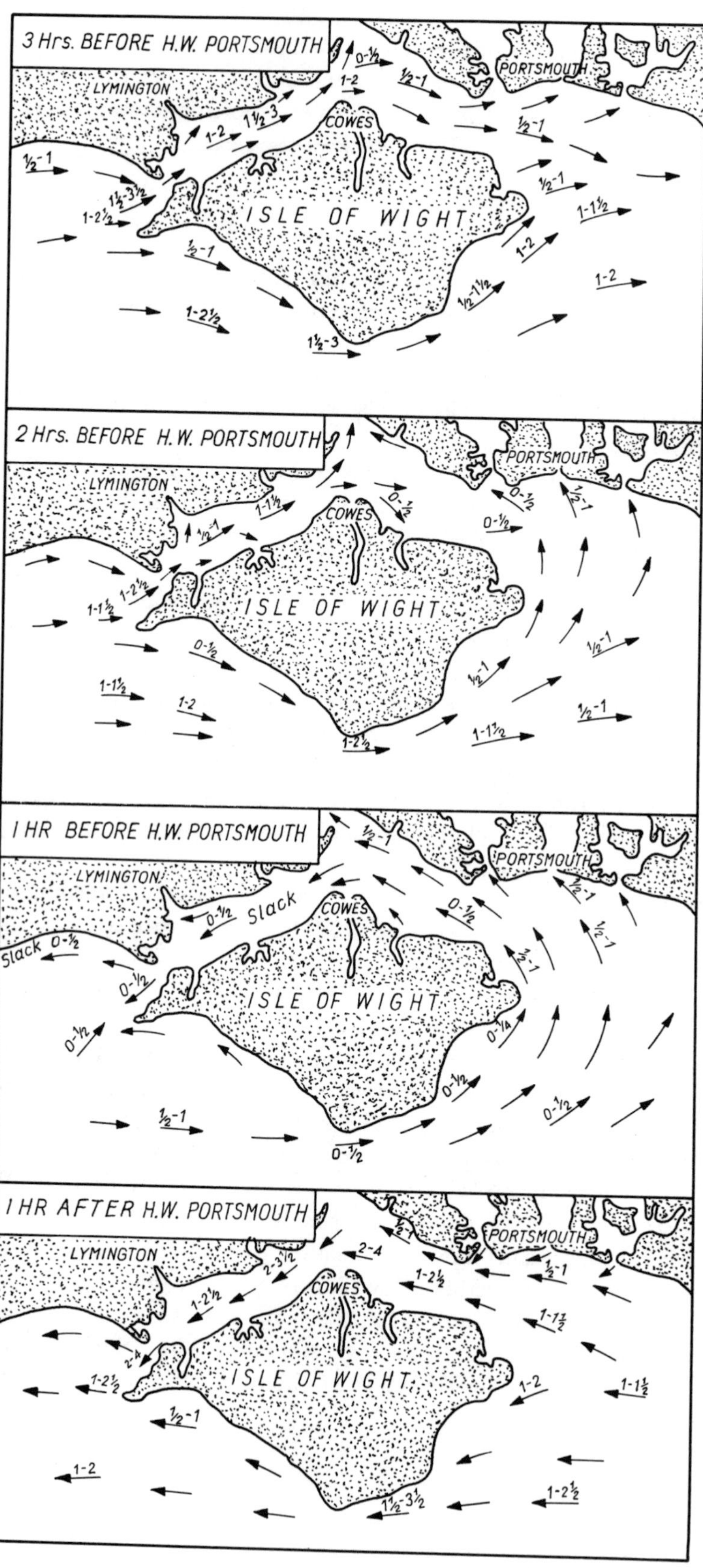
3 Hrs. BEFORE H.W. PORTSMOUTH
LYMINGTON
COWES
PORTSMOUTH
ISLE OF WIGHT
2 Hrs. BEFORE H.W. PORTSMOUTH
LYMINGTON
COWES
PORTSMOUTH
ISLE OF WIGHT
1 HR BEFORE H.W. PORTSMOUTH
LYMINGTON
COWES
PORTSMOUTH
ISLE OF WIGHT
Slack
1 HR AFTER H.W. PORTSMOUTH
LYMINGTON
COWES
PORTSMOUTH
ISLE OF WIGHT

Fig. 273

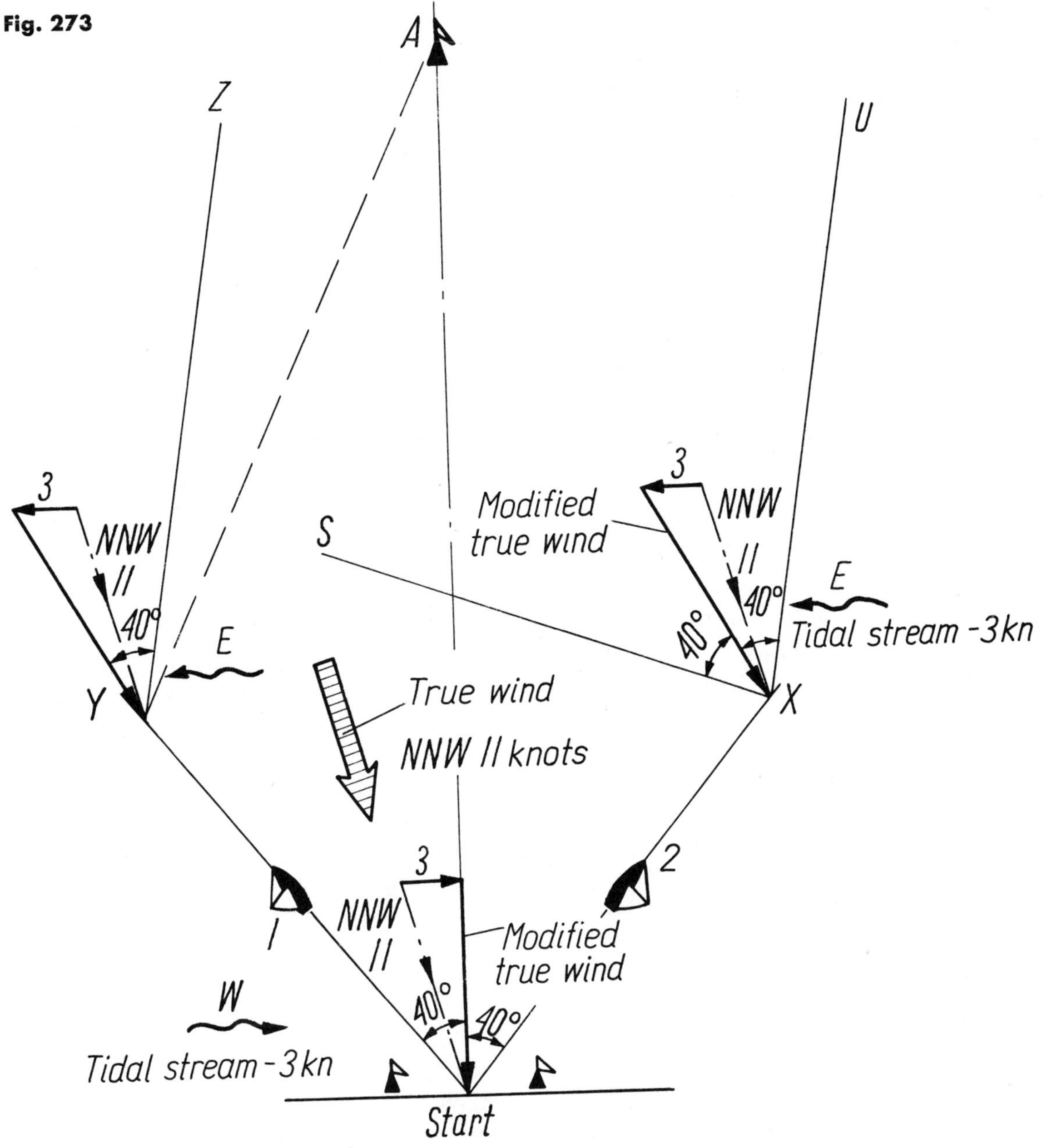

273 shows that this choice is vital. The starboard tack is in fact to be preferred, for when the tidal stream turns, yacht 1, having reached point Y, can easily sail on to the mark buoy in one tack, while yacht 2, at point X, has the choice of sailing along either X-S or X-U, neither of which is as good as Y-A. The helmsman of yacht 1, having foreseen the effect of the tidal streams, gains a big lead over his rival in yacht 2.

The speed of the currents on the surface of a river is not uniform over all the river bed, but varies according to the depth of the water. The retarding effect of friction against the river bottom is most marked in shallow water, and is much less where

Fig. 274

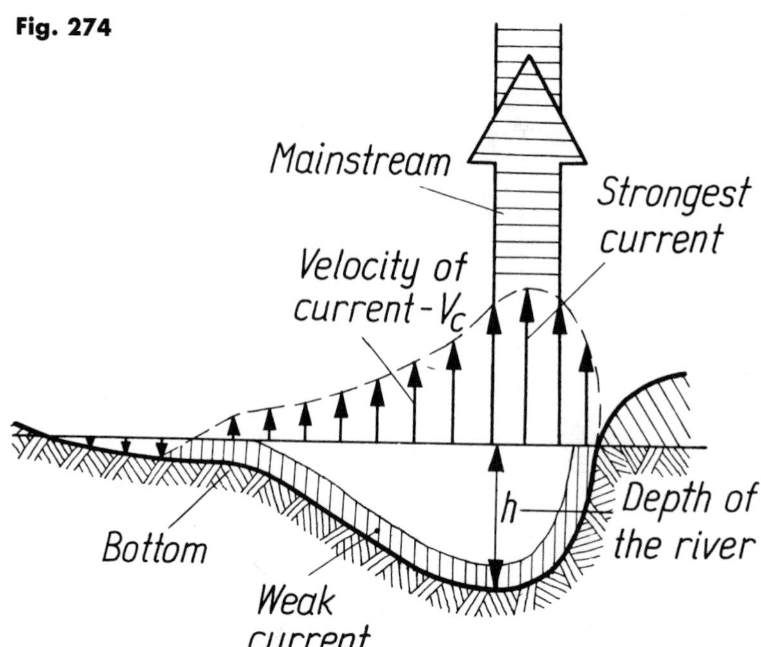

the water is deeper. Figure 274 illustrates the way different current velocities, v_c, are distributed at the surface in a vertical section taken at the straight line AB across the river shown in Fig. 275. By isolating the region of maximum speed of flow, it is possible to chart the main stream's course. Even on an apparently straight stretch there may be bends and variations in depth which make the main channel writhe like a snake from bank to bank.

The problem of racing on a river is to discover this main stream and to plan the course which allows for the velocity of the river current v_c, the wind, the boat's speed v_s, and the course set, and combines them best. The effect of current velocity, v_c, on the boat's resultant speed, v_R, when going up or down the river, is greater the greater the ratio of v_c to the boat's attainable speed v_s, when she is not influenced by a current.

The resultant speed when sailing downriver is $v_R = v_s + v_c$ and when sailing upriver $v_R = v_s - v_c$.

How much can be gained, then, by skillful exploitation of the main stream?

The evaluation of the speed of a river's flow can be based on the table below, which sets the velocity of the current, v_c, in ft./sec., on the river surface in its relationship with the depth of the river bed and the average hydraulic slope of the river expressed as parts per thousand.

Slope of the river in 0/00 \ *Depth of river bed in ft.*	0.6	1.5	3.0	4.5	6.0	9.0	12.0
0.15	0.45	0.84	1.38	1.83	2.22	2.97	3.63
0.20	0.51	0.96	1.56	2.07	2.46	3.36	4.11
0.25	0.57	1.08	1.74	2.31	2.70	3.78	4.71

Fig. 275

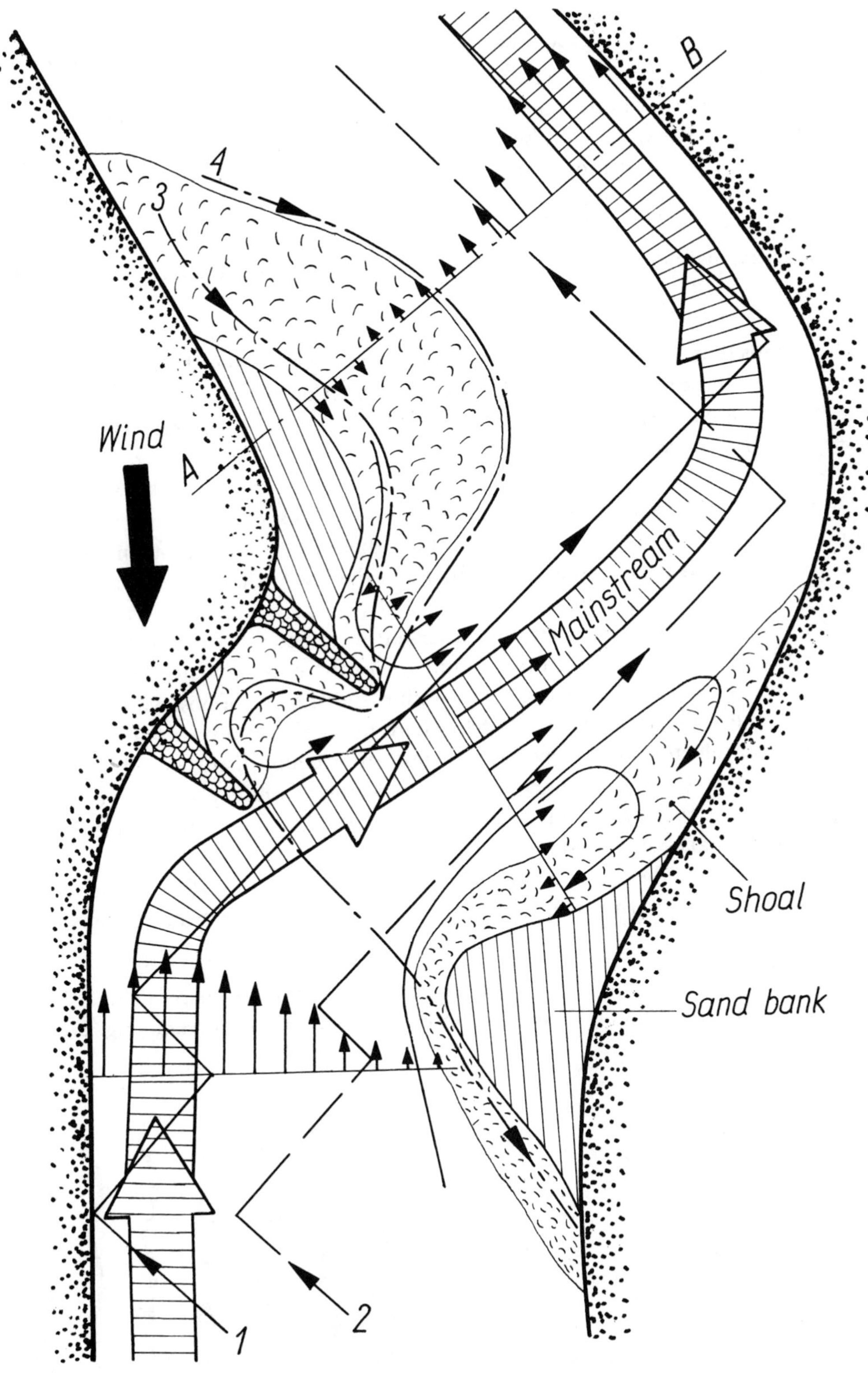
B
A
3
Wind
A
Mainstream
Shoal
Sand bank
1
2

For example, taking some simplifying assumption, yachts 1 and 2 (in Fig. 275) are sailing to windward, and one helmsman can identify the main stream and attempts to set his course accordingly, while the other sails on with no regard for the varying velocity of the current. If in similar conditions, but with no current, the boat's own speed v_s is 4.5 ft./sec., then yacht 1, by sailing in the stream in deep water, where the current moves at $v_c = 3$ ft./sec., has a resultant speed of:

$$v_{R1} = v_s + v_c = 4.5 + 3.0 = 7.5 \text{ ft./sec.}$$

Yacht 2, meanwhile, sailing in a current averaging 1.2 ft./sec. has a resultant speed

$$v_{R2} = v_s + v_c = 4.5 + 1.2 = 5.7 \text{ ft./sec.}$$

This means that the speed of yacht 1 will be 30 per cent higher than that of yacht 2, and if the wind drops so that the speed of the boat on her own, v_s, is only 3 ft./sec., then the advantage held by yacht 1 will increase to 40 per cent. If $v_s = 1.5$ ft./sec., it will increase to 60 per cent.

When sailing upriver, one should avoid the main stream, and steer where the currents are weakest, especially where there is slack or dead (reversed flow) water, as in course 3 in Fig. 275, or else along the edge of a shoal, as in course 4. Proper use of shoals is particularly helpful when the level of the water is normal or low.

River sailing would be considerably easier if it were possible to identify the main stream without difficulty, but, in fact, finding it in the moving water and forecasting its eventual course calls for a special routine and the gift of observation. There are certain indications to help one decide where the main stream is. The surface of a river is not uniform. Some portions are constantly being disturbed while others seem to be at rest. In one place waves are formed, while elsewhere is calm. The nature of the surface reveals whether the river is flowing swiftly or lazily, yet it is possible to make very serious mistakes.

To judge correctly the speed of the current by studying the surface of the water one has to consider first the effect the wind has on it. There are two extreme cases of wind effect:

(a) When the direction of the wind is the same as that of the current (Fig. 276a)
(b) When the direction of the wind is opposite to that of the current (Fig. 276b).

Fig. 276

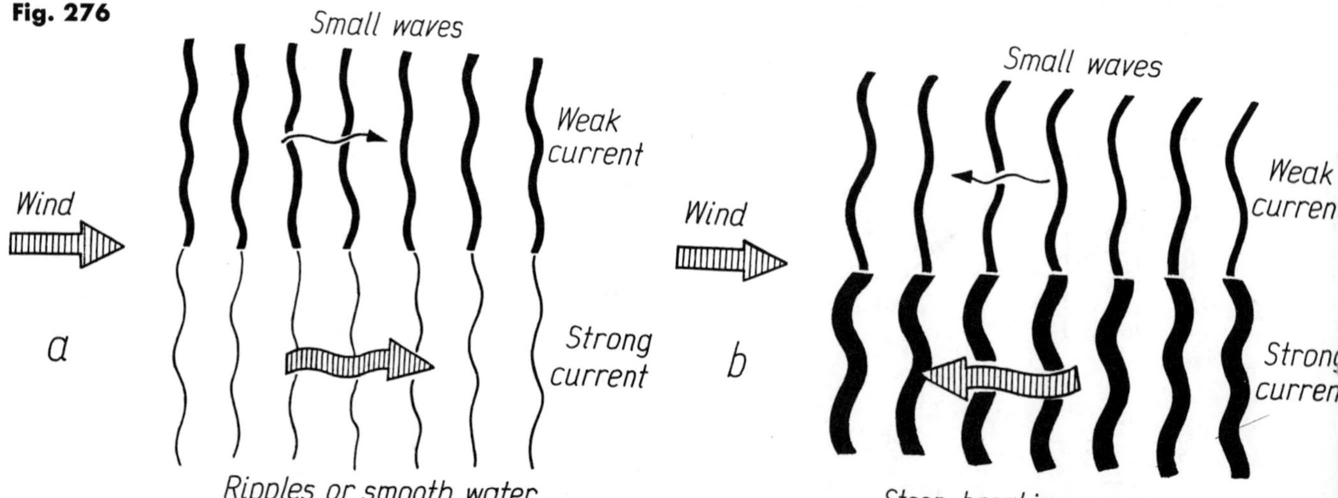

In case a the speed of the wind, which acts upon the water surface and generates waves, is relatively lower over the main stream than in places where the current is weaker. Therefore, higher and steeper waves will appear in places where the current velocity is small. The main stream meanwhile will have small waves or ripples, and may even have none at all. When sailing close-hauled up a river one should select a course among the biggest waves for only there will the opposing currents be weak. Conversely, when sailing down the river, before the wind, the route should lead one through the smallest waves, since they indicate the whereabouts of the strongest advantageous current.

In case b, where the wind is against the current, the main stream will be indicated by steep, perhaps breaking, waves because the speed of the wind, relative to the moving water, will be highest there. The weaker currents are marked by small waves, because there the resultant of wind and current is lowest. In this case, when sailing downriver to windward, one should aim to keep among the steep waves, while when running upriver one should seek the smooth water.

(e) Sailing in Shallow Water

The conditions that obtain in shallow water can have tremendous influence on the wave pattern generated by sailing craft, and thus on their wave-making resistance and so on their performance. Sometimes the increased resistance due to the shallowness of the water is large enough to cancel out any gain that had been expected from "getting out of the tide," that is, sailing close inshore, hoping to sail faster in slack but shallow water.

Figure 277 gives the qualitative variation of the hydrodynamic resistance of yacht B, sailing in shallow water, whose depth is slightly greater than her draft, and

Fig. 277

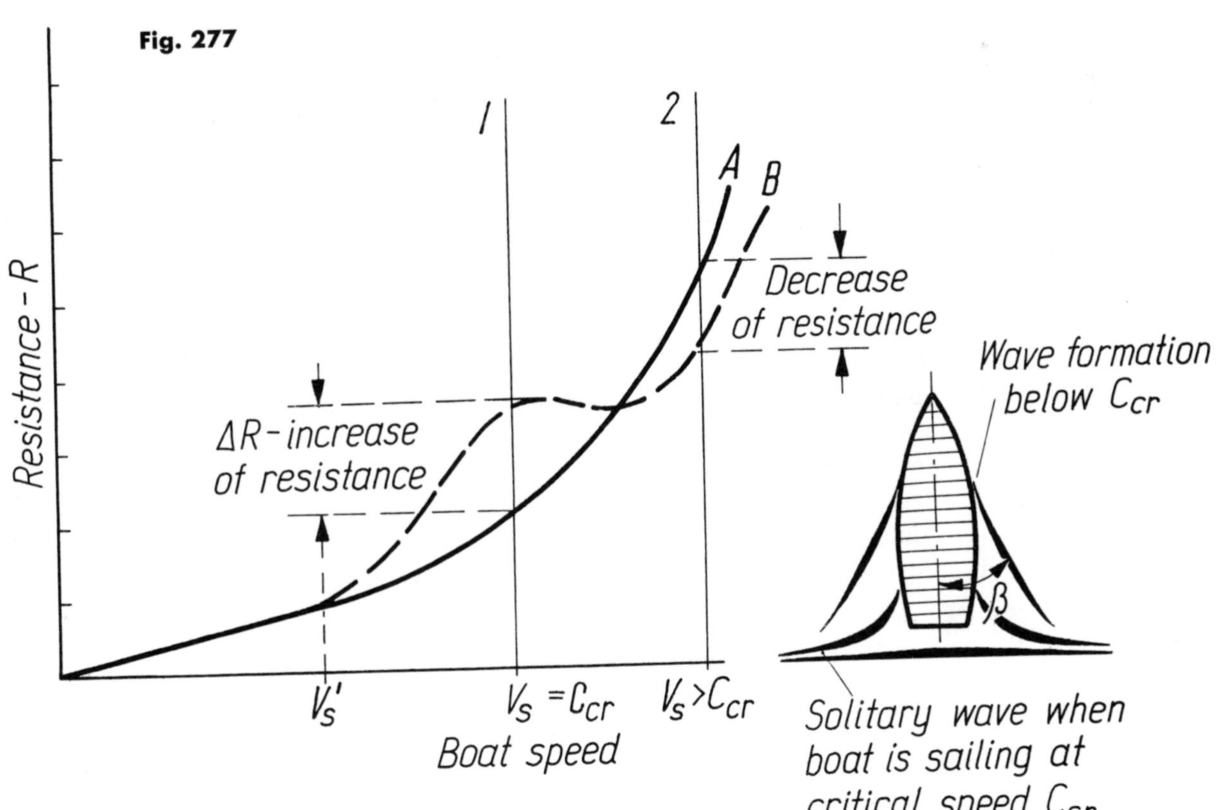

of yacht A, sailing in water of unrestricted depth. At low sailing speeds, below v'_s, where the influence of wave-making resistance is very small, and the yachts are basically only overcoming friction resistance, the resistance curve for hull A is similar to that for B. At speeds above v'_s, where wave-making resistance becomes an important factor, the shallower water conditions have a marked effect on yacht B's resistance curve.

The problem is, to what degree is the hydrodynamic resistance increased at different ratios of water depth to draft of hull, and how far is it worth risking grounding the boat to cheat the tide?

Figure 258 already showed that wave propagation is the result of the orbital motion of the water particles. If the water is sufficiently deep, these orbits are circular. Therefore, if the water depth is limited to, say, half the length of the wave, the sea bed will deform this orbital movement, limiting the velocity (c) of the waves. There is a definite maximum, usually called the critical wave velocity c_{cr} for any given depth of water h, which will equal:

$$c_{cr} = \sqrt{gh} = 5.7\sqrt{h}$$

where c_{cr} represents the velocity in ft./sec.
g represents acceleration due to gravity (32.3 ft./sec.^{2})
h represents depth in ft.

This means that the waves produced by the yacht cannot be propagated faster than the critical value c_{cr} which corresponds to water depth. In other words, wave velocity is completely defined by the water depth and not by the boat's speed, v_s, with which the waves are usually traveling on water of unrestricted depth. If the speed of a sailing vessel, v_s, is approaching the critical wave velocity, c_{cr}, the wave pattern generated by the hull changes very radically compared with its normal V shape (cf. Fig. 153).

At first the angle β between the line of the crests of the divergent waves is increased from its normal 20° to the hull centerline to nearly 90°, and the divergent and transverse waves combine into one large steep transverse wave called a solitary wave (see Fig. 277). As the wave pattern around the hull changes, the hydrodynamic resistance rises rapidly above its value in deep water. The maximum increase of resistance ΔR is reached when the solitary wave attains its greatest dimension, that is, when the boat's speed $v_s \cong c_{cr}$. This is marked on Fig. 277 by the vertical line 1 intersecting the resistance curves. At a speed v_s greater than c_{cr}, however, the resistance of yacht B sailing in the shallows decreases again, and may become smaller than that on unrestricted depth, as shown by the intersection of curves A and B by the vertical line.

The moment at which the resistance to motion due to the solitary wave increases is readily felt by the crew. The yacht slows down so suddenly that it feels as though she were dragging over the shoal and the effect of the human body inertia can actually be felt. This phenomenon appears when the yacht enters a shallow area at great speed, and may serve as a warning to the crew if the water is muddy or the depth cannot otherwise be determined.

When $v_s > c_{cr} = 5.67\sqrt{h}$, the solitary wave cannot keep up with the sailing craft, and is left behind, so that the hydrodynamic resistance decreases. The water surface around the hull becomes smooth, and this means a reduction in the wave-making resistance. The motion energy of a yacht dissipated in the generation of waves can now be used to increase the speed and overcome friction resistance.

Small overcanvassed planing dinghies, if there is enough power in the wind to drive the boat to exceed the critical value c_{cr} of $5.7\sqrt{h}$, may take advantage of the solitary wave. On the other hand, heavy-keel yachts are unable to do so, and therefore they have to be more careful when selecting a course which will exploit slack but shallow water.

The extra resistance encountered on entering a shallow water zone is shown in the curves drawn in Fig. 278. The table below includes suitable values of C_{cr} for various depths of water.

Depth of water in ft.	3	4	6	8	10	15	20	25	30	40
Critical velocity c_{cr} in ft./sec.	9.9	11.4	14.0	16.1	18.0	22.1	25.5	28.5	31.2	36.0
in knots	5.8	6.7	8.3	9.5	10.6	13.0	15.0	16.8	18.4	21.2

Fig. 278

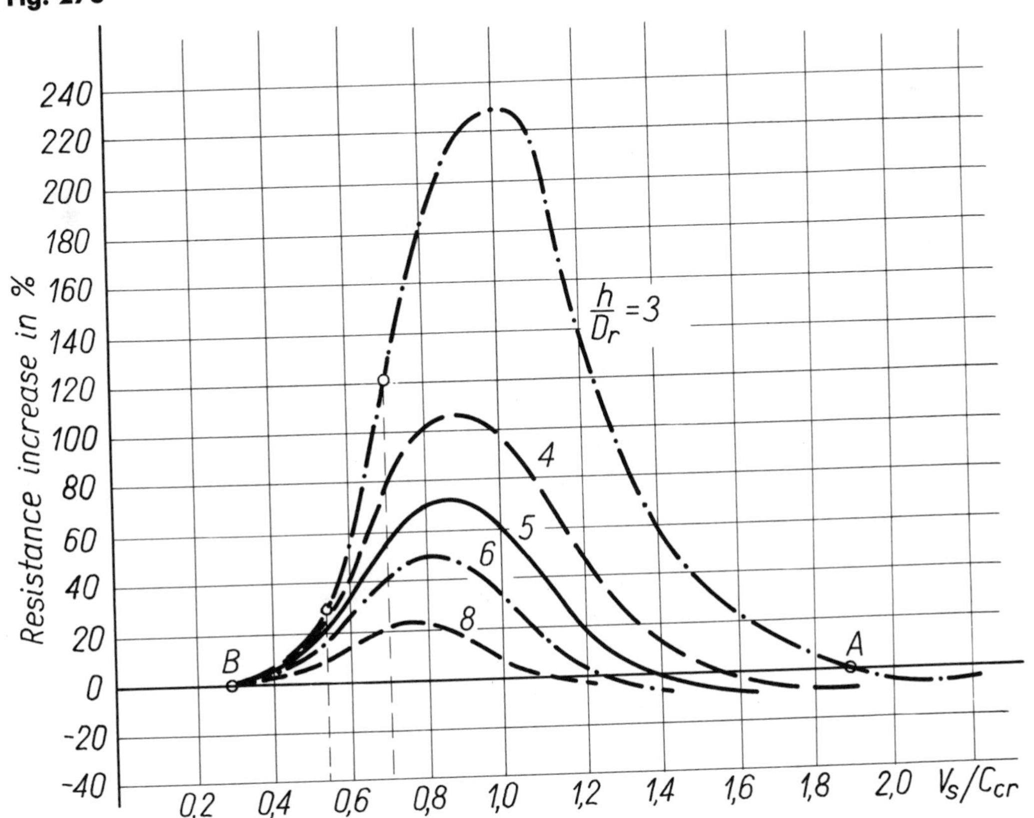

The method of using the curves and the table is best understood from an example. The results will be rather of qualitative values than accurate. If the average draft of a hull, Dr, is 5 ft., and a helmsman sailing with a speed v_s of 7 knots enters shallow water whose depth is 15 ft. then the ratio $h/Dr = 15/5 = 3$, and the critical velocity $c_{cr} = 13$ knots, so that the ratio $v_s/c_{cr} = 7/13 \cong 0.54$. The corresponding hydrodynamic resistance increase, taken from the graphs in Fig. 278 will be 30 per cent compared with the resistance in deep water. If the yacht's speed had been 9 knots instead of 7 knots then $v_s/c_{cr} = 9/13 \cong 0.7$ and the extra resistance due to the shallow water would have been about 120 per cent.

A study of the curves in Fig. 278 makes it clear that the loss in speed when sailing under restricted water depth conditions is greater the smaller is the ratio h/Dr. When a boat has only a few inches of water under her keel the increase in resistance may be several times greater compared with unrestricted water resistance. If we return to the example where the curve of $h/Dr = 3$, we can see that a decrease of the resistance to motion, due to leaving the solitary wave behind the stern cannot be reached until v_s exceeds 1.9 C_{cr}, i.e., 1.9×13, or 24.7 knots (see point A on the graph).

Shallow water has no influence on the wave pattern when the boat's speed v_s is below 0.3 c_{cr}, i.e., 0.3×13, or 3.9 knots (see point B on the graph). The conclusion to be drawn is that it can pay to sail in shallow water to cheat the tide, but only in light winds, when the boat's speed is relatively low. In a strong wind producing a higher boat speed, it is not always an advantage to avoid the current and the deeper water, and a compromise must be made between contradictory requirements. In any case, observation of the wave pattern around the hull can supply valuable information.

APPENDIX

(a) Characteristics of Force and Motion

It can easily be proved that if a body is moving at a given speed and in a given direction, its motion is the result of certain forces applied to it. Of course, in ordinary life we are all aware of forces weak and strong, but to forecast the effect of a force its special characteristics must be known, so it is customary to treat it as a measurable quantity.

A force can be represented graphically as in Fig. A-1. Here the line AB represents a force of about 5 lb., the length of the line showing its magnitude and the arrow at B its direction, while A at the other end of the line is the point at which it is applied.

A force then has three characteristics:

(a) Magnitude
(b) Direction
(c) Point of application

Fig. A-1

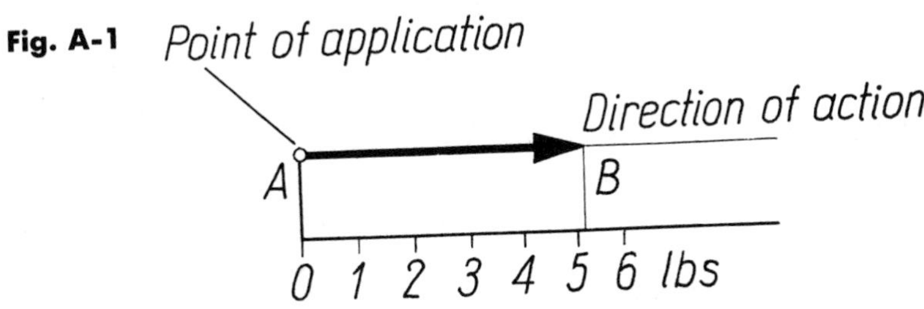

These are also characteristics of such quantities as velocity, acceleration, and pressure; any quantity which fulfills the requirements a, b, and c above is known as a vector, and can be represented graphically in a similar way to the force in Fig. A-1. The weight of a body, for example, although actually distributed with its mass, can be drawn as a single vector, applied at the point which is called the center of gravity (CG). With a simple geometrical shape, such as a ball, the CG is at its center, but the CG of a yacht is more difficult to find.

A very important characteristic of the CG is that a body suspended or supported at the CG will remain in equilibrium; in other words, if a body is turned about its CG to a new position, it will remain there. An iron ball again is the classical example of this rule. Because of this vectors representing graphically forces due to gravity will have their point of application at the CG of a body.

The action of a force may produce several effects, such as setting in motion a body which until then had been at rest or changing the existing velocity or direction of motion of a body already moving. It is difficult to find an example in which only one force is applied, since normally at least two forces act simultaneously. Even in such a simple case as a stone falling through the air under the force of gravity, there is also a force of air friction which acts upward, reducing its velocity.

The elementary mechanics of motion were formulated by Sir Isaac Newton (1643–1727) in four laws, but for our purpose it is sufficient to consider two only:

1. *The Principle of Inertia:* Every body remains at rest or in uniform motion in a straight line when acted on by a system of forces whose resultant force is zero.

2. *The Independence of Forces:* Every external force acting on a body produces acceleration of that body in the direction of the acting force. This acceleration is directly proportional to the magnitude of the force and inversely proportional to the mass of the body:

$$a = \frac{F}{m}$$

where a = acceleration ft./sec.^{2}
F = force, in lb.
m = mass, in slugs

$$\left(1 \text{ slug} = \frac{1}{32.2}\frac{\text{lb./sec.}^2}{\text{ft.}}\right)$$

A floating boat being hauled along by a rope (as in Fig. A-2) provides a better illustration of the relations between forces and motion. For the boat to move at a uniform velocity the water resistance R must be neutralized by a force F, the two being equal in magnitude but acting in opposite directions. If the pulling force F is suddenly stopped, the boat will continue to move ahead (due to inertia), but at a gradually lessening speed (retardation) until she comes to rest.

There are still other forces acting which do not contribute to the motion of the boat: its weight W and the vertical upward pressure of the water on the immersed hull Δ, the two again being equal and opposite.

Fig. A-2

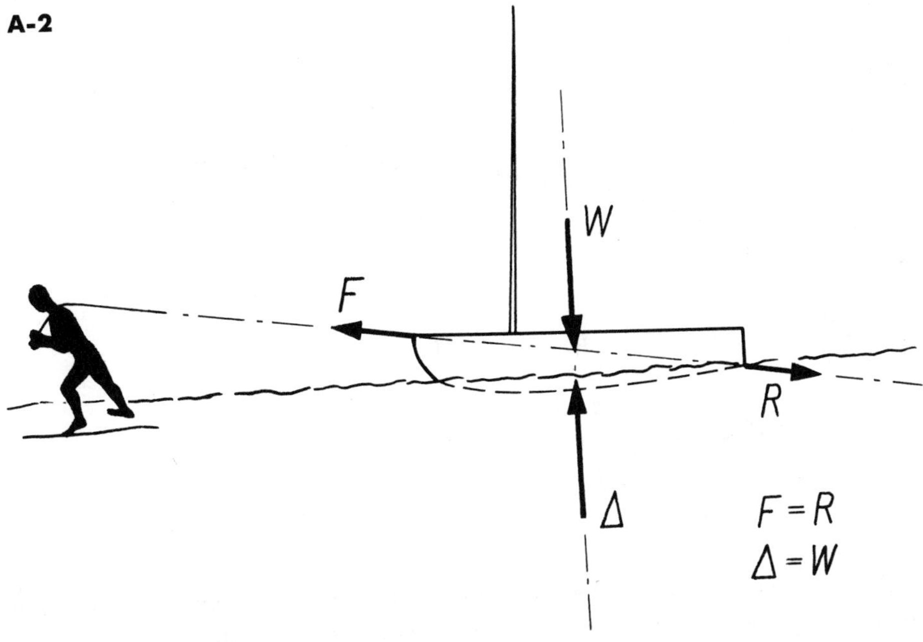

While the boat is in steady motion the distance covered increases in proportion to the time elapsed. This may be stated symbolically

$$S = v \times t$$

where S denotes the distance in feet
v denotes velocity in ft./sec.
t denotes time in seconds

This relationship between distance, velocity, and time is expressed graphically, as a straight line, in Fig. A-3.

When the boat of Fig. A-2 is on the point of being hauled from her position at rest, the velocity is zero. When the force F is first applied, the velocity will not be uniform, but will be increasing, and the distance covered by the boat can be calculated from the equation:

$$S = \tfrac{1}{2} at^2$$

where S denotes the distance in feet
a denotes acceleration in ft./sec.^{2}
t denotes time in seconds

Fig. A-3

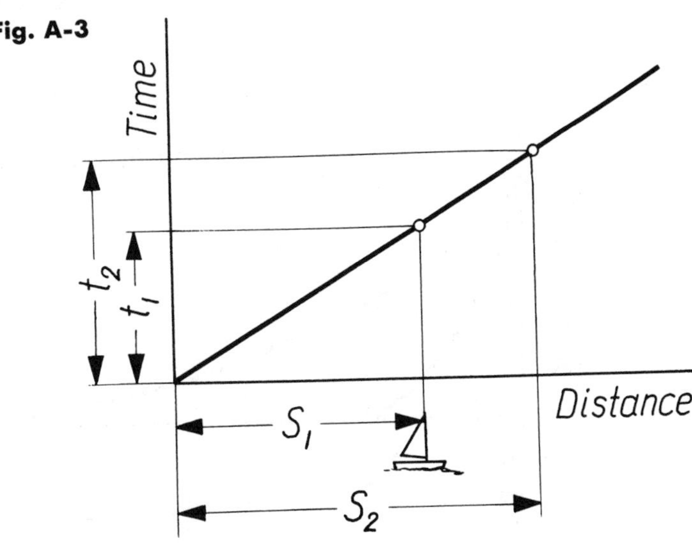

Fig. A-4

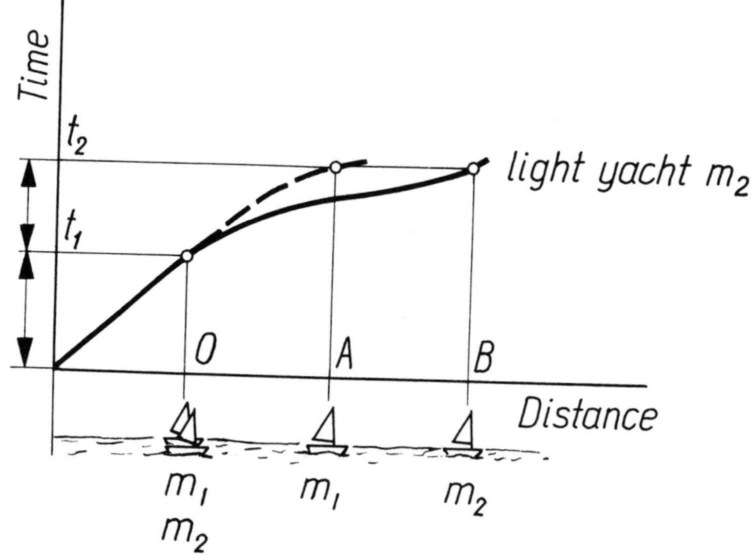

After a certain time t, when the applied force F has become equal to the resistance of the water R, the velocity will be constant, and the equation for uniform velocity ($S = v \times t$) will apply. The acceleration of the boat in the initial stage depends on the tension of the rope, and is greater when force F is greater.

The equation $a = F/m$ also shows that the magnitude of the acceleration depends on the boat's mass. If the force F is the same, it will be greater for the lighter boat. Figure A-4 shows the distance sailed by two yachts with similar rigging but of different displacement (or mass) during a short squall. Let us assume that at the time they encountered the squall both were at the same position O and sailing at the same velocity; that the mass (m_1) of yacht No. 1 is greater than the mass (m_2) of yacht No. 2. If we also assume that during a squall lasting t_2-t_1 seconds, both yachts were sailing under an increased force F, then the acceleration of the lighter yacht $a_2 = F/m_2$ is greater than the acceleration of the heavier one, $a_1 = F/m_1$, and so yacht No. 2 will cover a longer distance (OB) than yacht No. 1 (OA).

The product of mass and velocity, $m \times v$, is called momentum. A heavy yacht must drop her sails some distance before reaching her mooring, so that her momentum can be dissipated by the resistance of the water, R, during a period of time t: $m \times v = R \times t$. The graph in Fig. A-5 shows the braking time for two yachts of different displacements (mass) entering a port at the same speed. It shows that for the heavier yacht it is not only more difficult to gather speed, but also to stop. The heavier yacht, of course, will also be less sensitive to the influence of the waves.

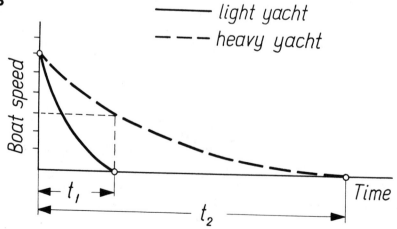

Fig. A-5

light yacht
heavy yacht
Boat speed
Time
t_1
t_2

Fig. A-6

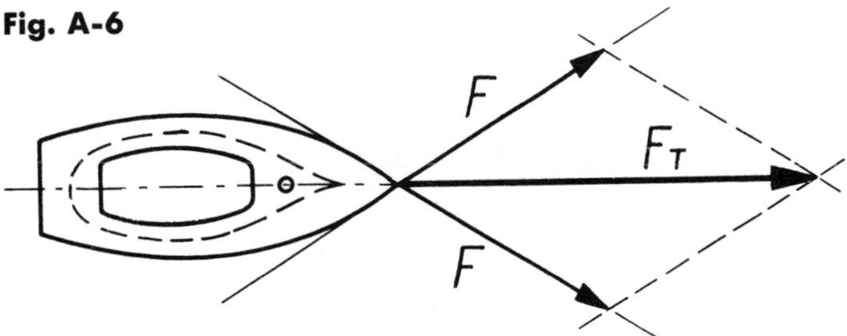

(b) The Parallelogram of Forces and Velocities

Newton's second law states that each force acting on a body produces acceleration in the direction of its action. If a body receives several accelerations simultaneously, an observer will detect only their combined effect, that is, that the body is affected in one direction only.

Figure A-6 shows a boat hauled by two ropes, spaced symmetrically, the tension on each rope being F. Under the action of these two forces, the boat will move in the direction midway between the ropes, as though instead of two forces there were only the one resultant force F_T. The direction and the magnitude of this F_T can be found graphically by constructing a "parallelogram of forces." Two adjacent sides represent the direction and size of the two forces F, and the diagonal drawn across the complete parallelogram from the point at which the forces are applied gives the direction and magnitude of the resultant force. Moreover, the construction of the parallelogram, which makes it possible to replace two forces by one force, also works the other way, so that one force can be replaced by two forces, a process which is known as the resolution of a force.

This method is useful in practice, for when studying the motion of a yacht it is often easier to treat the action of the force by resolving it into convenient directions. In this case the vector representing a total force must be treated as the diagonal of a chosen parallelogram. For instance, it is sometimes convenient to resolve the aerodynamic force F_T on the sail (see Fig. A-7) into forces acting in two directions, one F_R along the centerline of the hull, and the other F_H perpendicular to it. Velocities, and indeed vectors of any kind, can be treated in the same way, adding and resolving them by using the parallelogram of forces.

Suppose a yacht (as in Fig. A-8) is sailing at a velocity v_s, heading toward a marker buoy M which the helmsman wishes to round to port. At the point A she meets a strong current of velocity, v_c. Obviously the yacht will tend to drift to starboard, since the resultant velocity v_R and course sailed are not in the direction of the buoy (see Fig. A-8a). Now by resolving v_R into its forward-motion component v_F and its drift component v_D (as in Fig. A-8b) the basic velocity in the direction of the buoy and the drift velocity can be obtained. If an inexperienced helmsman keeps his boat always heading toward the buoy, the boat will follow the course shown by the curve ABCD. Eventually he might even be compelled to tack before he could round the buoy. To avoid this and reach the buoy by the shortest course

Fig. A-7

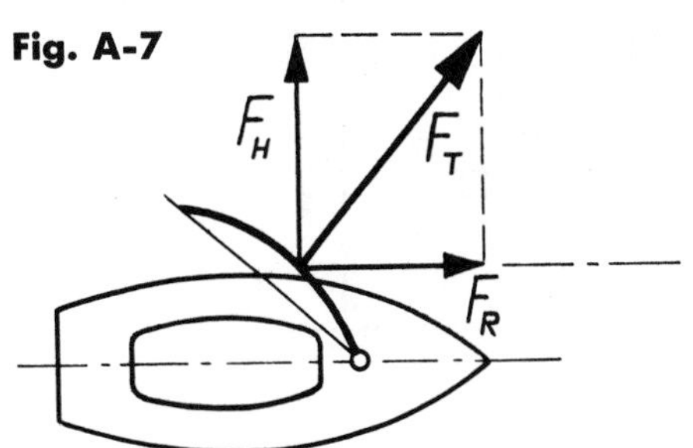

Fig. A-8

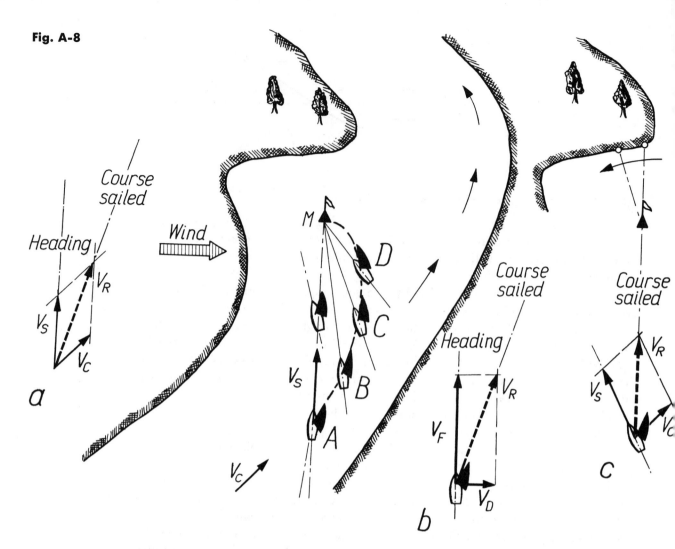

in the shortest time, the helmsman should choose his course so that the boat velocity v_s combined with the current velocity v_c will produce a resultant velocity v_R in the direction of the buoy (Fig. A-8c). In practice this means selecting some object, such as a tree on the horizon, behind the buoy and steering so that it remains fixed relative to the buoy.

(c) Floating

Floating is a fundamental characteristic of any yacht and is due to hydrostatic pressure on the immersed portion of the hull. This pressure acts perpendicularly to the wetted surface and increases with its depth (see Fig. A-9). The resultant up-

Fig. A-9

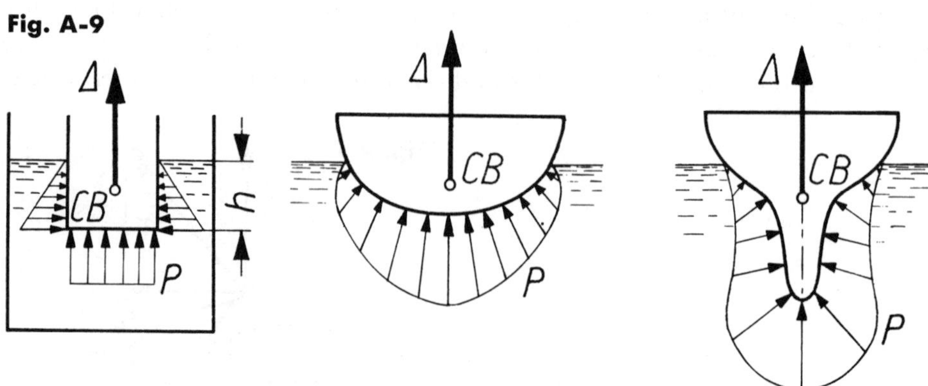

Fig. A-10

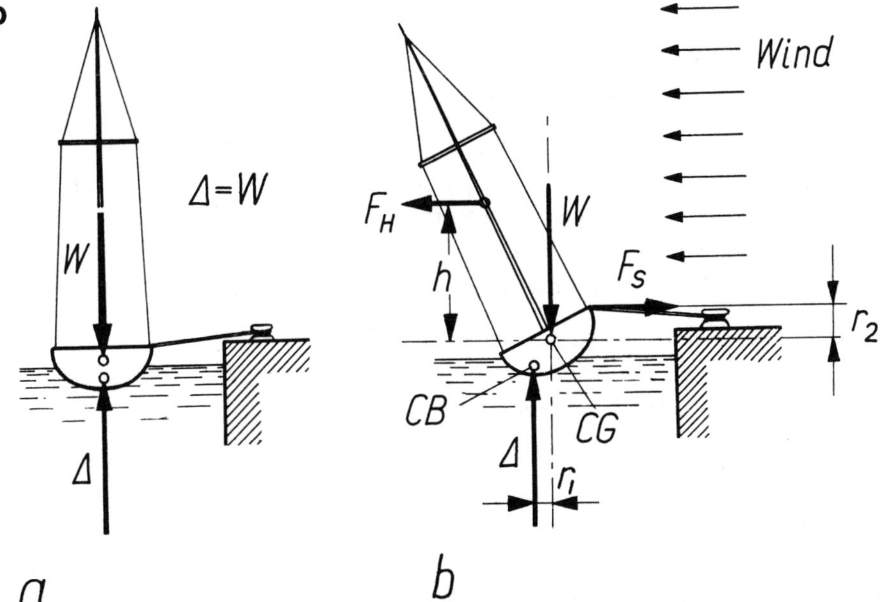

ward pressure, or buoyancy Δ, can be treated as the sum of all the partial pressures p, and is equivalent to the static displacement of the boat. The line of action of this force (buoyant lift) passes through the "center of buoyancy" CB, which is at the center of gravity of the "boat-shaped" mass of water displaced by the hull. On smooth water the force is exerted vertically.

Archimedes discovered that the weight of the water displaced was the same as the weight of the body floating in it. However, a boat traveling at a considerable speed may develop dynamic lift, which makes the hull rise and skim over the surface of the water. A specially designed hull may even produce dynamic lift so great that it equals the weight of the boat.

Since a boat may be supported in the water not only by its buoyancy but also by dynamic lift, modern yacht designers are compelled to take into consideration factors that in the past could be disregarded. The classic law of hydrostatic displacement, or buoyancy, discovered by Archimedes cannot fully explain the phenomena that develop during high-speed sailing. This first became obvious during modern experiments with fast motorboats and hydrofoils. New tendencies which exploit dynamic lift are now apparent in the designs of light-displacement racing boats and are producing speedy craft with improved performance, especially on the reach, which could never be obtained on the basis of the traditional approach.

(d) Conditions of Equilibrium

If a yacht without sails is made fast to a pier, in no wind (as in Fig. A-10a), then according to the principles of mechanics the yacht will be in equilibrium if the weight of the yacht, W, is equal to her displacement, Δ. In other words, the sum of the vertical forces must be zero.

When a strong wind is blowing (as in Fig. A-10b), the mast and stays will be affected by the wind force F_H, and the yacht will heel to leeward away from the pier. The mooring rope will be under tension of force F_S, opposing the action of the wind force F_H. The weight of the yacht, W, will remain as before, working through the center of gravity CG, but the center of buoyancy, CB, with the displacement force Δ will be shifted to the left. (For simplicity, it is assumed that all the forces are working in one lateral plane.)

Three conditions must now be satisfied for the yacht to be in equilibrium:

1. The sum of the vertical forces must be zero.
2. The sum of the horizontal forces must be zero.
3. The sum of the moments must be zero.

For the vertical forces, having due regard to their direction, we have: $W - \Delta = 0$ (or, $\Delta - W = 0$); and similarly, for the horizontal forces: $F_H - F_S = 0$ (or $F_S - F_H = 0$).

The list of the yacht, however, is caused by the turning effect or moment of the forces applied. By definition (Fig. A-11), the moment M of a force about a given point is the product of the force F and the perpendicular r drawn from the given point to the line of action of the force: $M = F \times r$.

Conventionally, moments producing clockwise turning effects are considered as positive, and those producing anticlockwise effects negative.

Therefore, taking all the moments about CB (or any other point), we have:

$$-F_H \times h + \Delta \times r_1 + F_S \times r_2 + W \times O = 0$$

where $-F_H \times h$ is an anticlockwise moment due to the action of the heeling force F_H on the heeling arm h

$\Delta \times r_1$ is a righting moment due to the displacement of the yacht acting in a clockwise direction on the righting arm r_1. It is the natural result of the shifting of the center of buoyancy CB in relation to CG

$F_S \times r_2$ is also the righting moment of the rope tension F_S, acting in a clockwise direction on the arm r_2

and the term $W \times O$ expresses the fact that the weight of the yacht has no turning effect about the CG.

In this example the forces were treated in a simplified way by assuming that they would all act in one plane. On a real sailing boat a more complex system of forces acts, including:

(a) Forces of gravity
(b) Aerodynamic forces
(c) Hydrodynamic forces

distributed in space and demanding three-dimensional treatment.

Fig. A-11

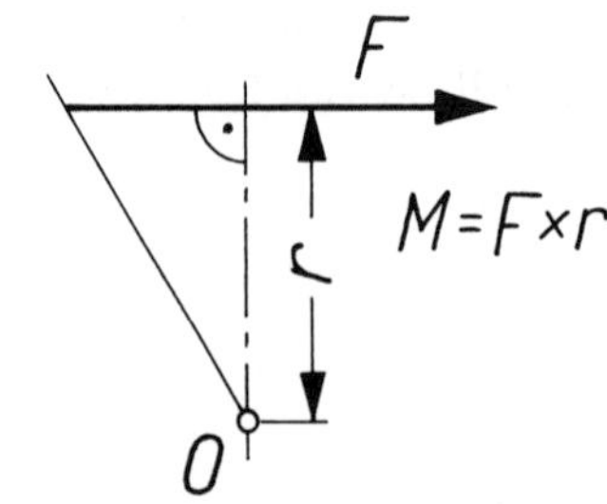

(e) Conversion Factors

	Multiply	*by*	*to obtain*
A. *Length*	inches	2.54	centimeters
	feet	0.3048	meters
	miles	5280	feet
	miles	1.609	kilometers
	miles	0.8684	nautical miles
	nautical miles	6080	feet
B. *Area*	sq. inches	6.45	sq. centimeters
	sq. feet	0.093	sq. meters
	sq. feet	144	sq. inches
C. *Volume*	cubic feet	0.0283	cubic meters
	cubic feet	1728	cubic inches
D. *Velocity (speed)*	ft./sec.	0.592	knots
	ft./sec.	0.682	miles
	ft./sec.	1.097	kilometers/hour
	ft./sec.	0.305	meters/sec.
	knot	1.69	ft./sec.
	meter/sec.	3.28	ft./sec.
	meter/sec.	3.6	kilometers
	kilometer/hour	0.911	feet/sec.
	kilometer/hour	0.539	knots
	kilometer/hour	0.278	meters/sec.
E. *Weight*	tons (short)	2000	pounds
	tons (short)	907.18	kilograms
	tons (short)	0.907	tons (metric)
	tons (long)	2240	pounds
	tons (long)	1016	kilograms
	tons (metric)	1000	kilograms
	tons (metric)	2205	pounds
	kilogram	2.205	pounds
	pounds	0.454	kilogram
F. *Pressure*	Atmospheres	76.0	centimeters of mercury
	Atmospheres	29.92	inches of mercury
	Atmospheres	1.033	kilograms/sq. centimeters
	Atmospheres	14.7	pounds/sq. inch
	Atmospheres	2116.2	pounds/sq. foot
	inches of water	5.198	pounds/sq. foot
	inches of water	25.38	kilograms/sq. meter
	kilogram/sq. meter	0.2048	pounds/sq. foot

(f) Beaufort Scale of Wind Speed

Beaufort No.	Seaman's description of wind	Terms used in U.S. Weather Bureau forecasts	Wind speed		Approximate pressure in pounds per ft.^{2}
			in knots	in m./sec.	
0	Calm	Light	Less than 1	Less than 0.3	Less than 0.01
1	Light air		1–3	0.3–1.5	0.01–0.06
2	Light breeze		4–6	1.6–3.3	0.06–0.2
3	Gentle breeze	Gentle	7–10	3.4–5.4	0.2–0.4
4	Moderate breeze	Moderate	11–16	5.5–8.0	0.4–1.0
5	Fresh breeze	Fresh	17–21	8.1–10.7	1.0–2.0
6	Strong breeze	Strong	22–27	10.8–13.8	2.0–3.0
7	Moderate gale (high wind)		28–33	13.9–17.1	3.0–4.0
8	Fresh gale	Gale	34–40	17.2–20.7	4.0–6.0
9	Strong gale		41–47	20.8–24.4	6.0–9.0
10	Whole gale (heavy gale)	Whole gale	48–55	24.5–28.3	9.0–12.0
11	Storm		56–65	28.4–33.5	12.0–16.0
12	Hurricane	Hurricane	Above 65	Above 33.6	Above 16.0

* From *Yachting Magazine,* U.S.A.

Description of sea	Approximate effect on racing dinghy	Psychological scale*
Sea like a mirror		
Ripples, no foam crests	Crew sit on leeward side of boat or on centerline.	Boredom
Small wavelets, crests have a glassy appearance and do not break	Crew sit on windward side of boat	Mild pleasure
Large wavelets, crests begin to break. Perhaps scattered white caps	Crew ballasting on weather gunwale. Racing machines like 5-0-5, FD may plane	Pleasure
Small waves becoming longer. Fairly frequent white caps	Crew ballasting out hard over weather gunwale. Most dinghies will plane	Great pleasure
Moderate waves, taking a more pronounced long form. Many white caps, some spray	Light dinghies have to ease sheets in heavier gusts	Delight
Large waves begin to form. Extensive white caps everywhere, some spray	Start reefing main sails small jibs	Delight tinged with anxiety
Sea heaps up and white foam from breaking waves begins to be blown in well-marked streaks along the direction of the wind.		Anxiety tinged with fear
Moderately high waves of greater length. Edges of crests break into spindrift. The foam is blown in well-marked streaks along the direction of wind	Very difficult to sail, even under jib only	Fear tinged with terror
High waves. Dense streaks of foam along the direction of the wind. Spray may affect visibility. Sea begins to roll		Great terror
Very high waves with long overhanging crests. The surface of the sea takes on a white appearance. The rolling of the sea becomes heavy and shocklike. Visibility is affected		Panic
Exceptionally high waves. The sea is completely covered with long white patches of foam. Visibility is affected. Small- and medium-sized ships are lost to view for long periods		I want my Mummy
The air is filled with foam and spray. Sea completely white with driving spray. Visibility very seriously affected		Yes, Mr. Jones

PORTSMOUTH YARDSTICK TABLE

1961 Figures

Started in 1951 the Portsmouth Scheme is not a handicapping system, but is the means whereby any boat that has been given a handicap under any system can be given an equivalent handicap under any other system when it sails in a regatta or other inter-club event. The scheme is based on the Portsmouth Standard Yardstick Table, which is a list of one-design and restricted classes rated in terms of Portsmouth Association Numbers, defined as "times over a common but unspecified distance." As an example, the Portsmouth Number of the International 14ft is 89 and that the National Firefly is 103, because it has been established that, on the average, a Firefly will take 103 minutes to cover a distance which can be covered, over the same course and in the same race, in 89 minutes by an International 14ft.

Numbers in parentheses refer to Terylene/Dacron sails. It will be seen that information on many classes now using Terylene/Dacron is lacking, so handicappers must use their judgment, and will have to take a firm line with those competitors who try to make the omissions of this Table an excuse for racing with Terylene/Dacron sails on cotton handicaps.

PRIMARY YARDSTICKS

Class	Terylene/Dacron	Number
National 14ft Merlin Rocket	(91)	96
Royal Dart 16½ft O.D.		96
Teign Corinthian 16½ft O.D.		96
Teign Corinthian 16ft		97
X Class O.D.		100
Essex O.D.		100
Thames Estuary O.D.		100
National Redwing 14ft Dinghy	(98)	101
National 12ft Dinghy	(98)	103
National Enterprise (racing rig)	(98)	103
National Firefly 12ft O.D.	(100)	103
Wildcat		103
Benfleet O.D.		107
14ft Jewel O.D.	(111)	113
R.N. 14ft Dinghy		115
Hamble Star O.D.	(112)	115

SECONDARY YARDSTICKS

Class	Terylene/Dacron	Number
Thai Catamaran (racing)	(65)	
Thai Catamaran (cruising)	(66)	
Freedom Catamaran	(66)	
Cougar Mk. III	(69)	
Cougar Mks. I and II	(70)	
Flying Streak	(70)	
Shearwater Catamaran	(73)	
Jumpahead (racing) Catamaran	(76)	
Flying Cat III	(79)	
Hurricane Catamaran	(82)	
16ft Kittiwake Catamaran	(82)	
International Star		83
International 10 sq m Canoe		83
Norfolk Punt		83
Malibu Outrigger (U.S.A.)		83
Cheetah Cat II	(83)	
International Flying Dutchman		84
International 5.0.5		84
18ft Jollyboat (trapeze)		85
30 sq m "Windfall"		85
Thistle (U.S.A.)		85
C Scow (U.S.A.)		85
Highlander (US.A.)		85
18ft Jollyboat		86
Raven (U.S.A.)		86
North Norfolk 16ft		86
International 110		87
Osprey Mks. I and II	(87)	
International 14ft Dinghy		89
National Hornet		89
22 sq m		89
Pembroke Dinghy		89
International Dragon		90
National Flying Fifteen		90
Daring	(90)	
International 12 sq m Sharpie		91
International Finn		91
National 18ft Dinghy		91
Caneton (restricted)		91
National Swallow		91
Solent Sunbeam		91
International Tornado		91
Gurnard G		91
Flattie (U.S.A.)		91
Great Yarmouth O.D.		92
Interlake (U.S.A.)		92
14ft Mercury O.D.	(92)	
15½ft Kestrel		93
19ft Lightning (U.S.A.)		93
Y-Flyer (U.S.A.)		93
National Swordfish O.D.		94
Broads O.D.		94
Waveney O.D.		94
Horning Rebel O.D.		94
Yare & Bure O.D.		94
Comet (U.S.A.)		94
Jet 14 (U.S.A.)		94
Swift O.D. Catamaran	(94)	
Pegasus 14ft O.D. (Genoa)	(94)	
Scorpion 14ft O.D.	(94)	
Folkboat (stripped)		95
Tumlare (small)		95
Atalanta		95
Mercury (U.S.A.)		95
Chichester Harbour 18ft Dinghy		96
Liverpool Bay Falcon O.D.		96
Pegasus 14ft O.D.	(96)	
Turkeyfoot (U.S.A.)		97
Rebel (U.S.A.)		97
16ft Wayfarer	(97)	
15ft Albacore	(95)	98
Lymington Slipway 5 ton		98
U.S. National O.D. (U.S.A.)		98
Indian (U.S.A.)		98
4 m O.K.	(98)	
U.K. Cherub 12ft Restricted	(99)	
International Olympic (1936) Monotype		100
River Cat	(100)	
Starcross Viking		101
Blakeney 16ft O.D.		102
Oulton Gull		102
Y.W. People's Boat		102
Wineglass Restricted	(98)	103
Irish Dinghy Racing Association 14ft O.D.		103
Y.W. Solo		103
Hardway Seabird 14ft O.D.		103
Victory O.D.		103
Norfolk O.D. Dinghy		103
Sandpiper		104
Hardway Wind 14ft Restricted		104
Worthing O.D.		104
Montague O.D. Sharpie		104
Viking 16½ft (bermudan)		105
Y.M. 16ft Sharpie (bermudan)		105
Poole Hawk		106
Y.W. G.P. Fourteen	(103)	106
Belouga		106
C.I.R.C. (Guernsey)		106
North Devon Y.C. O.D.		106
Mayfly O.D.	(105)	107
C.I.R.C. (Jersey)		107
Y.M. Junior 13½ft		107
Solent Seagull 18ft Mk. III O.D.		107
Royal Harwich O.D.		107
St. Mawes O.D.		107
Slipway 18ft		107
Coronation		107
Weymouth Falcon O.D.		107
Sprog O.D.		107
Emsworth O.D. (bermudan)		107
Graduate (83½ sq ft)	(105)	107
Nipper (U.S.A.)		107
Loch Long O.D.		107
Poole Dolphin O.D.		108
National Enterprise (cruising)		108
Firecrest		108
Pleiad O.D.		108
Wivenhoe O.D.		108
Eastbourne Seabird		109
14ft Dabchick O.D.		109
Fox Wizard		110
Chichester Harbour Z		110
Solent Seagull 16ft Mk. II		110
Seabird Half-Rater		110
Oxey Bird O.D.		111
Hurst O.D.		111
Menai Straits O.D.		111
Y.W. Dayboat	(108)	112
Pintail 18ft		112
Stokes Bay Nicholson O.D.		112
Y.W. Vagabond	(112)	
Fleetwind O.D.	(111)	113
Hamworthy O.D. Snipe		113
Christchurch Coot O.D.		113
East Cowes Sharpie O.D.		113
Tod Fibreglass 12ft		113
International Penguin 11½ft		113
Island 14ft O.D.		114
Dart 12½ft O.D.		114
Lymington 14ft Pram		114
Portsmouth Stormalong		114
Sprite 14ft O.D.		114
Port Dinorwic 16ft Restricted		114
11ft Gull		116
Axe 12ft O.D.		116
Felixstowe Ferry O.D.		116
West Kirby 16ft Star		116
Silhouette II	(116)	
Flying Moth		118
British Moth		118
Skippy 12ft		118
Beetle Cat (U.S.A.)		118
Eleven Plus	(114)	119
Wakeman (bermudan)		119
12ft bermudan Wright Dinghy		120
East Cowes 12ft O.D.		121
12ft Walker Dinghy		122
Y.W. Heron	(120)	125
Wakeman (gunter)		125
Portchester Duck O.D.		128
Lymington Scow		128
West Wight Scow		129
International Cadet		132
Duckling		132

LIST OF SYMBOLS

A	wetted area of the hull, also lateral area of the fin keel or rudder
AR	aspect ratio
a	unbalanced arm
B	beam of the hull
c	wave velocity
C_D	aerodynamic drag coefficient
C_L	aerodynamic cross wind force coefficient
C_H	aerodynamic heeling force coefficient
C_R	aerodynamic driving force coefficient
C_T	aerodynamic total force coefficient
C_f	coefficient (air)
C_{fr}	friction coefficient (water)
C_s	side force coefficient (water)
CB	center of buoyancy
CG	center of gravity
CE	center of effort
CLR	center of lateral resistance
D	aerodynamic drag
D_r	draft of the hull
DWL	designed water-line
F_H	heeling force (air)
F_R	driving force (air)
F_V	vertical (downward) component of sail force
F_T	total aerodynamic force
F_s	side force (water)
F_{lat}	horizontal component of the heeling force
g	acceleration due to gravity 32.2 ft./sec^2.
H_w	height of the wave
I	height of the fore-triangle
i	angle of incidence of the rudder
J	base of the fore-triangle
L	length of the hull and also cross wind force
L_w	length of the wave (sea wave)
l	chord of the sail profile (camber)

LOA	length over all
LWL	load water-line
M_R	righting moment
M_H	heeling moment
p	static pressure
q	dynamic pressure $= \frac{\rho v^2}{2}$
R	total hydrodynamic resistance of the hull
R_f	hydrodynamic skin friction
R_i	hydrodynamic resistance due to leeway
R_h	hydrodynamic resistance due to heel
R_T	total hydrodynamic force on a hull
R_w	wave-making resistance
R_e	Reynolds number
RA	righting arm
R_r	hydrodynamic resistance of the rudder
S_A	sail area
v_A	apparent wind velocity
v_S	boat's velocity
v_T	true wind velocity
v_{mg}	speed made good to windward
u_{orb}	orbital velocity of surface particles in a sea wave
W	weight of the yacht
Δ	displacement in long tons or pounds
∇	immersed volume in cu. ft. corresponding to the displacement
α (alpha)	angle of incidence of the sail
α_F	angle of incidence of the foresail
α_M	angle of incidence of the mainsail
β (beta)	apparent course
$(\beta - \lambda)$	heading
γ (gamma)	true course
ε_A (epsilon)	aerodynamic drag angle
ε_W	hydrodynamic drag angle
δ_F (delta)	angle of trim of the foresail
δ_M	angle of trim of the mainsail
Θ (theta)	angle of heel
λ (lambda)	angle of leeway
ν (nu)	kinematic viscosity: air 1.57×10^{-4} ft.^{2}/sec. water 1.23×10^{-5} ft.^{2}/sec.
ρ_A (rho)	mass density of air: 0.00238 lb. sec.^{2}/ft.^{4}
ρ_W	mass density of water: fresh — 1.94 lb. sec.^{2}/ft.^{4} salt — 1.99 lb. sec.^{2}/ft.^{4}
τ (tau)	longitudinal trim of the hull

REFERENCES

1. "The Aerodynamics of Yacht Sail," E. P. Warner, S. Ober, Trans. of the Society of N.A.M.E., 1925.
2. "Beiträge zur Theorie des Segelns," H. Croseck, Springer, Berlin, 1925.
3. "The Forces on a Yacht's Sail," T. Tanner, Journal Royal Aero. Soc., 1930.
4. "Regatta Segeln. Die aerodynamic der Segel," M. Curry, 1949.
5. "Sailing Aerodynamics," J. Morwood, 1954.
6. "The Geometry of Sailing to Windward," T. Tanner, R.I.N.A. Trans., 1960.
7. "Full Scale Tank Tests of an International 10 sq. Metre Class Canoe," T. Tanner, R.I.N.A. Trans., 1960.
8. "Performance Trials on the 5.5 Metre Yacht *Yeoman,* Y.R.C. Report, No. 1.
9. "Some Experimental Studies of the Sailing Yacht," K. S. M. Davidson, Trans. S.N.A.M.E., 1936.
10. "A Preliminary Report on a Comparison between Theory and Experiment in Relation to the Effects of Aspect Ratio on the Side Force and Induced Drag of Keels," T. Tanner, A.C.Y.R., 1960.
11. "Wind Tunnel Test of a ⅓rd Scale Model of an X-One Design Yacht's Sails," C. A. Marchaj A.C.Y.R., 1962.
12. "An Investigation into the Performance of a Dragon Class Yacht," J. R. Flewitt, N. Bromfield, W. Crago, (Saunders-Roe), 1960 Rep.
13. "An Analysis of Data Obtained from Tank Tests on a Model Dragon Class Yacht," W. A. Crago, (Saunders-Roe), 1960 Rep.
14. "An Investigation to Determine the Effects of Changes of Displacement and Trim on the Performance of a Dragon Class Yacht," Y.R.C. Report, No. 2., 1956.
15. Some unpublished reports, Yacht Wind Tunnel, Hayes, Mddx., England, M. S. Hooper.
16. "The Pitching of Sailing Ships Close-hauled in a Head Sea," A.C.Y.R., 1960.
17. "The Behaviour of the Sailing Yacht," H. M. Barkla, R.I.N.A., 1960.
18. A Note on Problems Associated with Sail Force Measurements, T. Tanner, A. Chapleo, C. Marchaj, B. Thwaites, A.C.Y.R., 1961.
19. "Preliminary Note on Results of Rigid Sail Tests in the Unheeled Position," C. A. Marchaj, A. Q. Chapleo, A.C.Y.R., 1961.
20. "Visual observations of the Flow round the sails of a model Yacht," C. A. Marchaj, A. Q. Chapleo, A.C.Y.R., 1961.
21. Papers presented at the conference on Yacht Design and Research, A.C.Y.R., 1962.
22. "High Speed Sailing," H. M. Barkla, Trans. R.I.N.A., 1951.
23. "Basic Naval Architecture," K. C. Barnaby, 1954.
24. Series of articles entitled "Sailing Yacht Performance" by J. C. Sainsbury, "Ship & Boatbuilder," August 1961 to June 1962.

25. "The Wind Tunnel Balances in the Large Low Speed Tunnel at Southampton University," P. O. A. L. Davies, R. W. Dyke, C. A. Marchaj, A.A.S.U. Rep. No. 208, 1962.
26. "Yacht Testing," Allan, Doust, Ware, R.I.N.A., 1956.
27. "Some Problems of Yacht Measurement," D. Phillips-Birt, R.I.N.A., 1958.
28. An article by K. S. M. Davidson, edited by Batchelor and Davies, "Surveys in Mechanics," Cambridge, 1956.
29. Technical Memoranda published by Stevens Institute of Technology, Hoboken, New Jersey, nos. 10, 16, 17, 55, 85, 87, 108, 129, 133.
30. "Model Tests with Sailboat Hulls," Prof. Ata Nutku, Publications of the Turkish Shipbuilding Research Institute, Technical University, Istanbul, 1957.
31. Some publications ed. by Amateur Yacht Research Society.
32. "Faster Sailing," Robert Bavier, Jr., 1954.
33. "Scientific Sailboat Racing," Ted Wells, 1950.
34. "Sailing to Win," Robert Bavier, Jr., 1956.
35. "An Eye for a Yacht," D. Phillips-Birt, 1955.
36. "Sailing Boats," Uffa Fox, 1959.
37. "Sceptre," Hugh Somerville, 1958.
38. "Offshore," I. H. Illingworth, 1955.
39. "Where Seconds Count," I. H. Illingworth, 1958.
40. "Sailing Wind and Current," Ian Proctor, 1953.
41. "Hydrodynamics in Ship Design," Harold E. Saunders, 1958.
42. Series of articles by F. E. M. Ducker, published in "Yachting Monthly," 1943–44.
43. "The Following Sea, Broaching and Surging," Peter du Cane, G. J. Goodrich, R.I.N.A., 1962.
44. "Fluid-Dynamic Drag," S. F. Hoerner, 1958.
45. "High-Speed Small Craft," Peter du Cane, 1956.
46. "Cruising Yachts," T. Harrison Butler, 1958.
47. Yachting Magazines: "Yachting World," "Yachts and Yachting," "Yachting Monthly," "Yachting," "Sea-Spray."

INDEX